CW00695851

ANGLICAN EDITION

HYMNS OLD & NEW

ANGLICAN EDITION

Compiled by
Patrick Appleford, Kevin Mayhew, Susan Sayers

Revised impression 1988

First published in Great Britain in 1986 by
KEVIN MAYHEW LTD,
Rattlesden,
Bury St Edmunds, Suffolk IP30 0SZ

ISBN 0 86209 071 7

Printed in Great Britain
at the University Printing House, Oxford

ABBA, FATHER, LET ME BE YOURS

1

Words: D. Bilborough
Music: D. Bilborough, arranged by Roland Fudge

2

ABIDE WITH ME

('Eventide' 10 10.10 10.)

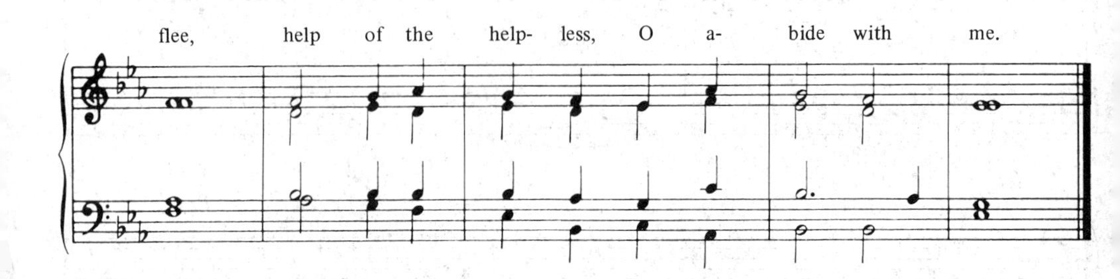

2. Swift to its close
 ebbs out life's little day;
earth's joys grow dim,
 its glories pass away;
change and decay
 in all around I see;
O thou who changest not,
 abide with me.

3. I need thy presence
 every passing hour;
what but thy grace
 can foil the tempter's power?
Who like thyself
 my guide and stay can be?
Through cloud and sunshine,
 O abide with me.

4. I fear no foe
 with thee at hand to bless;
ills have no weight,
 and tears no bitterness.
Where is death's sting?
 Where, grave, thy victory?
I triumph still,
 if thou abide with me.

5. Hold thou thy Cross
 before my closing eyes;
shine through the gloom,
 and point me to the skies;
heaven's morning breaks,
 and earth's vain shadows flee;
in life, in death,
 O Lord, abide with me!

Words: H. F. Lyte (1793-1847)
Music: W. H. Monk (1823-89)

A GREAT AND MIGHTY WONDER

('Es is ein Ros' entsprungen' 76.76.676.)

[HARMONY]

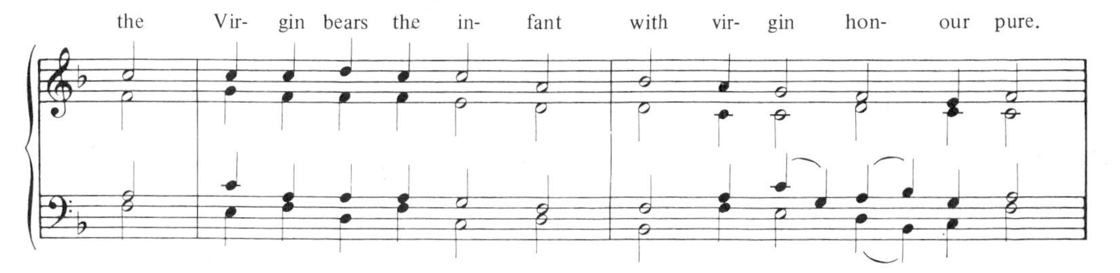

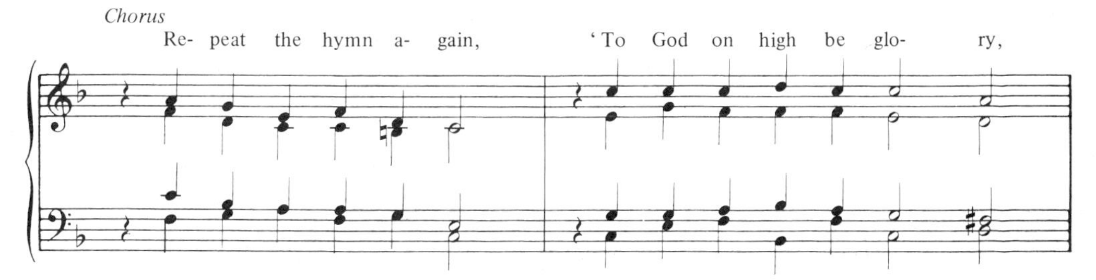

2. The word becomes incarnate,
   and yet remains on high;
   and cherubim sing anthems
   to shepherds from the sky.

3. While thus they sing your Monarch,
   those bright angelic bands,
   rejoice, ye vales and mountains,
   ye oceans, clap your hands.

4. Since all he comes to ransom,
   by all to be adored,
   the infant born in Beth'lem,
   the Saviour and the Lord.

Words: St Germanus (c. 634-732), tr. J. M. Neale
Music: German Melody, harmonised by Michael Praetorius (1571-1621)

ALL CREATION BLESS THE LORD

('Benedicite' 77.75.D.)

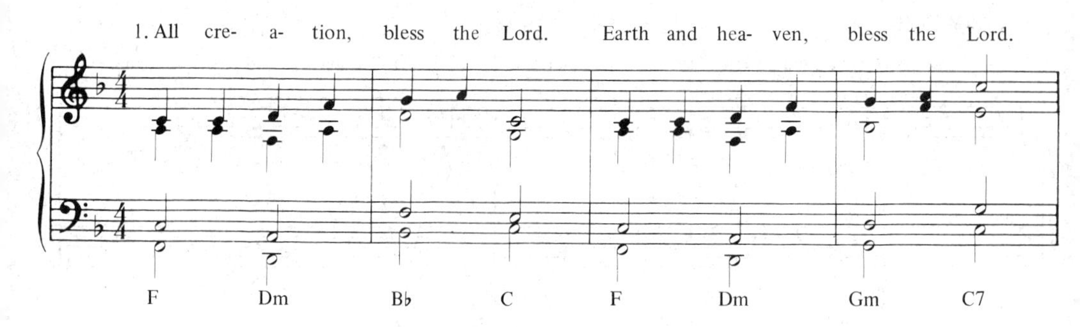

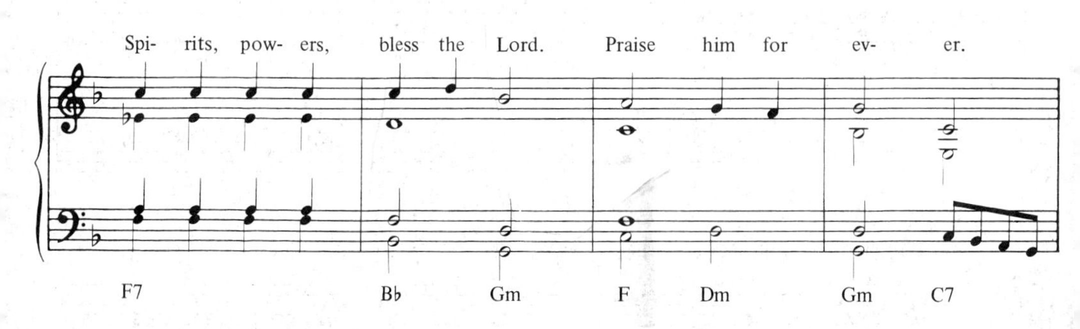

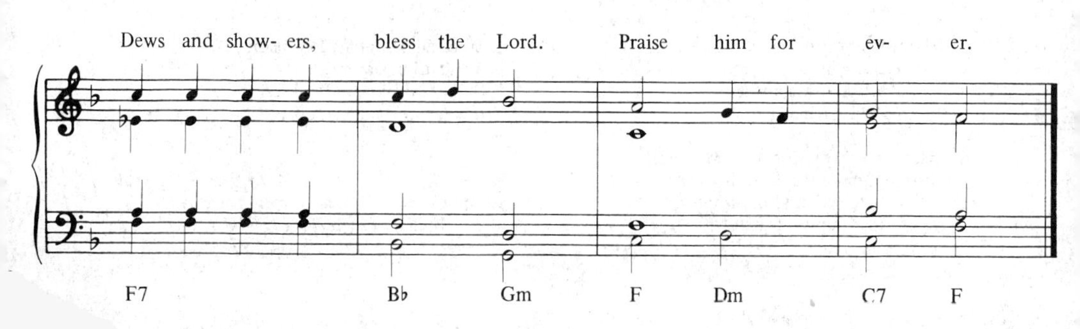

2. Winds and breezes, bless the Lord.
Spring and autumn, bless the Lord.
Winter, summer, bless the Lord.
Praise him for ever.
Fire and heat, bless the Lord.
Frost and cold, bless the Lord.
Ice and snow, bless the Lord.
Praise him for ever.

3. Night and daytime, bless the Lord.
Light and darkness, bless the Lord.
Clouds and lightning, bless the Lord.
Praise him for ever.
All the earth, bless the Lord.
Hills and mountains, bless the Lord.
Trees and flowers, bless the Lord.
Praise him for ever.

4. Springs and rivers, bless the Lord,
Seas and oceans, bless the Lord.
Whales and fishes, bless the Lord.
Praise him for ever.
Birds and insects, bless the Lord.
Beasts and cattle, bless the Lord.
Let all creatures bless the Lord.
Praise him for ever.

5. Let God's people bless the Lord.
Men and women, bless the Lord.
All creation, bless the Lord.
Praise him for ever.
Let God's people bless the Lord.
Men and women, bless the Lord.
All creation, bless the Lord.
Praise him for ever.

Words and Music: Hayward Osborne

5

ALL CREATURES OF OUR GOD AND KING

('Lasst uns erfreuen' 88.44.88. & Alleluias)

2. Thou rushing wind that art so strong,
ye clouds that sail in heaven along,
O praise him, alleluia!
Thou rising morn, in praise rejoice,
ye lights of evening, find a voice:

3. Thou flowing water, pure and clear,
make music for thy Lord to hear,
alleluia, alleluia!
Thou fire so masterful and bright,
that givest man both warmth and light:

4. Dear mother earth, who day by day
unfoldest blessings on our way,
O praise him, alleluia!
The flowers and fruits that in thee grow
let them his glory also show:

5. And all ye men of tender heart,
forgiving others, take your part,
O sing ye, alleluia!
Ye who long pain and sorrow bear,
praise God and on him cast your care:

6. And thou, most kind and gentle death,
waiting to hush our latest breath,
O praise him, alleluia!
Thou leadest home the child of God,
and Christ our Lord the way hath trod:

7. Let all things their creator bless,
and worship him in humbleness,
O praise him, alleluia!
Praise, praise the Father, praise the Son,
and praise the Spirit, Three in One.

Words: W.H. Draper (1855-1933),
based on the 'Cantico di Frate Sole'
of St Francis of Assisi (1182-1226)
Music: Melody from 'Geistliche Kirchengesang' (1623),
arranged by R. Vaughan Williams

ALLELUIA (× 8)

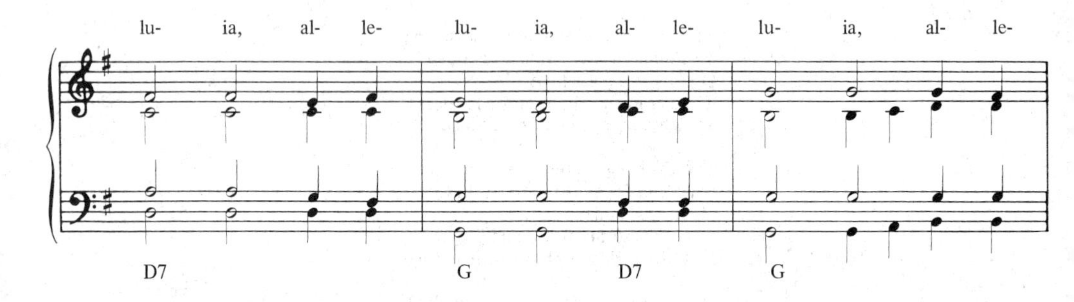

2. Jesus is Lord . . .

3. And I love him . . .

4. Christ is risen . . .

Additional verses may be composed to suit the occasion. For example:

5. Send your Spirit . . .

6. Abba, Father . . .

7. Come, Lord Jesus . . .

Words and Music: Unknown, arranged by John Rombaut
Additional Words: Sandra Joan Billington

ALLELUIA, LORD JESUS, YOU ARE RISEN FROM THE DEAD

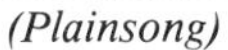

Verse: Cantor

1. *For Easter*

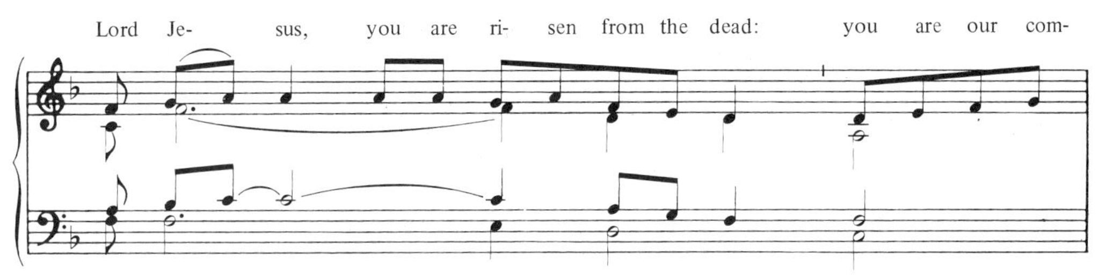

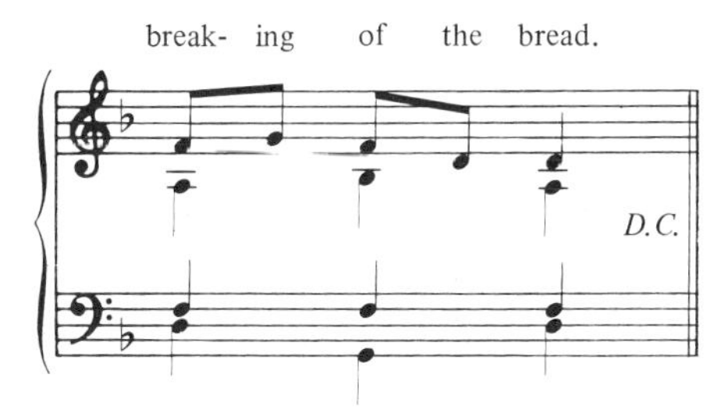

2. *For Advent and Christmas*

Lord Jesus, Word of God made man for us,
you reveal your glory to our broken world,
and we worship you. Come again in glory!

3. *For Passiontide*

Lord Jesus, obedient to the Father's will,
you became a slave, enduring death for us.
Now you reign as Lord. Come again in glory!

4. *For Pentecost*

Lord Jesus, you are at the Father's side:
you have sent your Spirit to renew our joy,
and we praise you. Come again in glory!

Words: Damian Lundy
Music: adapted from Plainsong

ALLELUIA, BY YOUR SPIRIT (Alleluia for forgiveness)

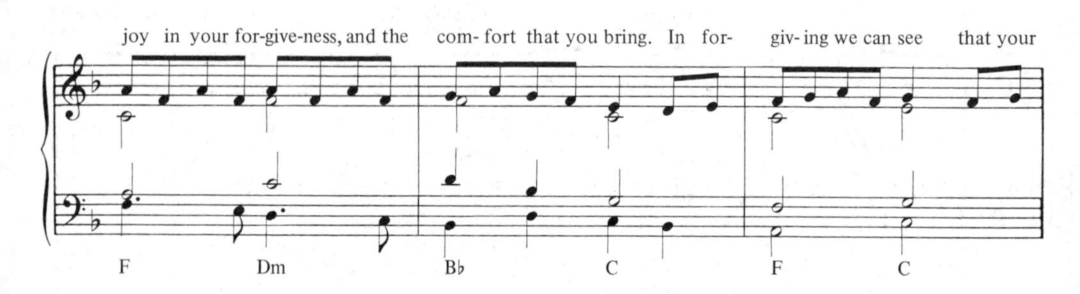

2. Alleluia, alleluia!
By your Spirit we will pray
that the flame of your forgiveness
may be bright in us today,
so your Kingdom may increase
till we all possess your peace.
Alleluia, sing hosanna to the King!

3. Alleluia, alleluia!
By your Spirit we will live
in the light of resurrection
and the promise that you give
to be with us every day
as we journey on our way.
Alleluia, sing hosanna to the King!

Words and Music: Susan Sayers,
arranged by Frances M. Kelly

ALLELUIA, GIVE THANKS (**Alleluia No. 1**)

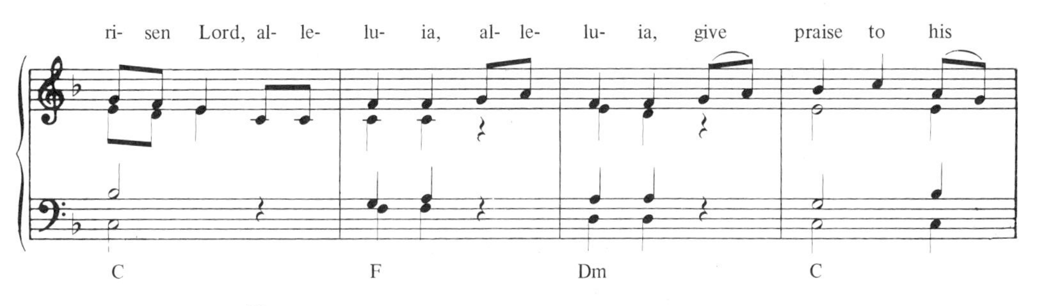

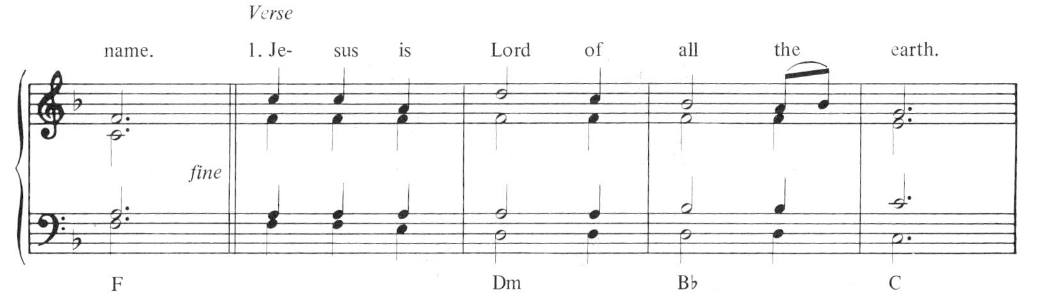

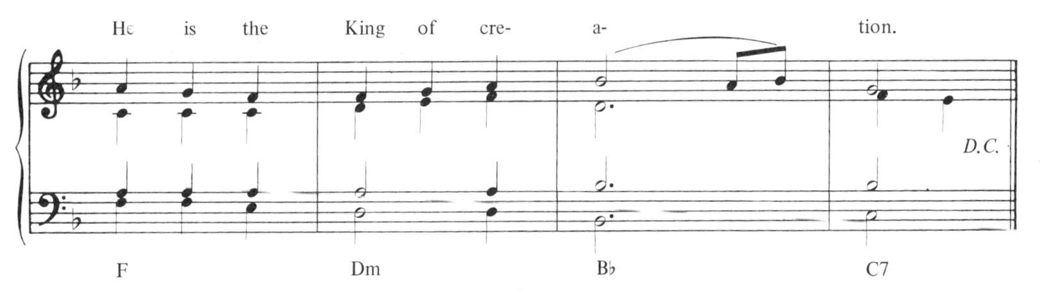

2. Spread the good news o'er all the earth.
Jesus has died and is risen.

3. We have been crucified with Christ.
Now we shall live for ever.

4. God has proclaimed the just reward:
life for all men, alleluia.

5. Come, let us praise the living God,
joyfully sing to our Saviour.

Words and Music: Donald Fishel

ALLELUIA, HEARTS TO HEAV'N AND VOICES RAISE
('Lux Eoi' 87.87.D.)

2. Christ is risen, Christ the first-fruits
of the holy harvest field,
which will all its full abundance
at his second coming yield;
then the golden ears of harvest
will their heads before him wave,
ripened by his glorious sunshine,
from the furrows of the grave.

3. Christ is risen, we are risen;
shed upon us heavenly grace,
rain, and dew, and gleams of glory
from the brightness of thy face;
that we, with our hearts in heaven,
here on earth may fruitful be,
and by angel-hands be gathered,
and be ever, Lord, with thee.

4. Alleluia, alleluia,
glory be to God on high;
alleluia to the Saviour,
who has gained the victory;
alleluia to the Spirit,
fount of love and sanctity;
alleluia, alleluia,
to the Triune Majesty.

Words: Christopher Wordsworth (1807-85)
Music: Arthur Sullivan (1842-1900)

11

ALLELUIA, SING TO JESUS
('Hyfrydol' 87.87.D.)

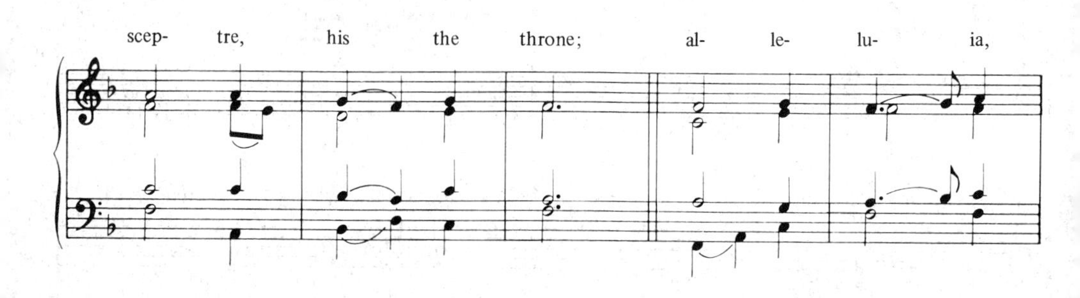

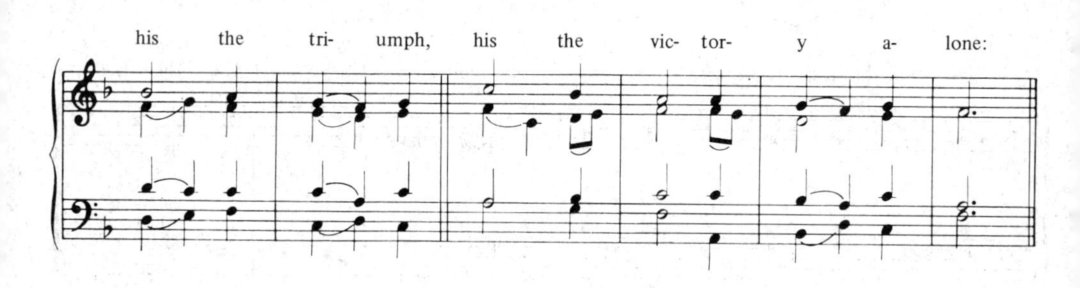

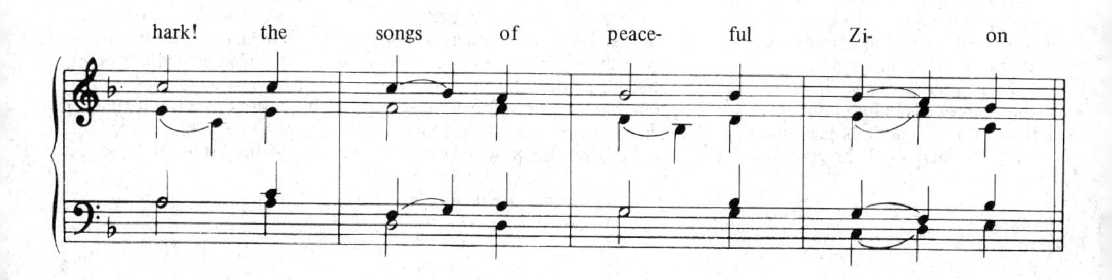

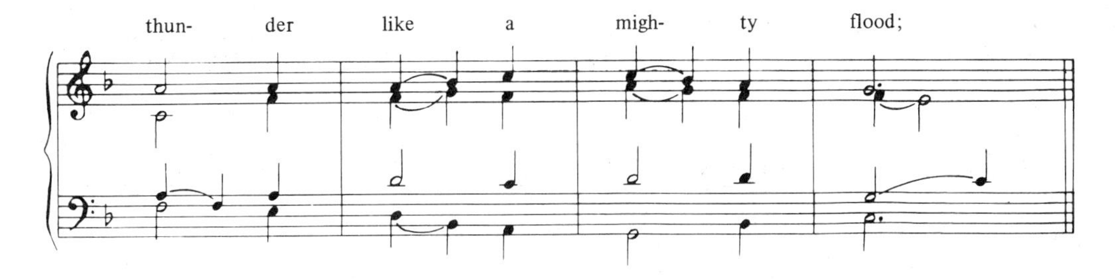

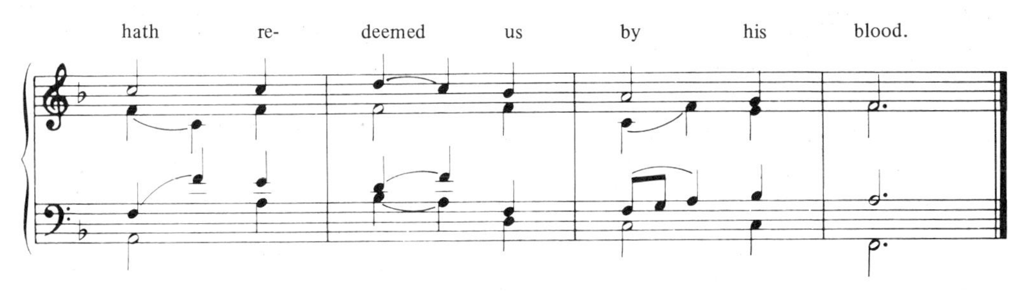

A different harmonisation of this tune may be found at Hymn 251

2. Alleluia, not as orphans
are we left in sorrow now;
alleluia, he is near us,
faith believes, nor questions how;
though the cloud from sight received him
when the forty days were o'er,
shall our hearts forget his promise,
'I am with you evermore'?

3. Alleluia, Bread of Angels,
thou on earth our food, our stay;
alleluia, here the sinful
flee to thee from day to day;
intercessor, friend of sinners,
earth's Redeemer, plead for me,
where the songs of all the sinless
sweep across the crystal sea.

4. Alleluia, King eternal,
thee the Lord of lords we own;
alleluia, born of Mary,
earth thy footstool, heaven thy throne;
thou within the veil hast entered
robed in flesh, our great High Priest;
thou on earth both priest and victim
in the Eucharistic Feast.

Words: W. Chatterton Dix (1837-98)
Music: R. H. Prichard (1811-87)

12 ALL GLORY, LAUD AND HONOUR

[HARMONY]

('St Theodulph' 76.76.D.)

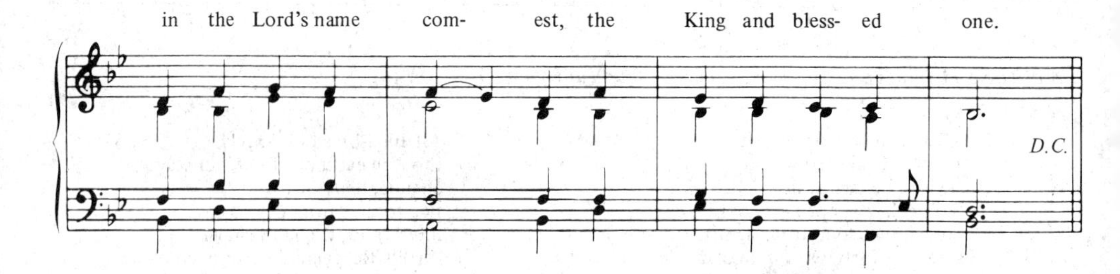

2. The company of angels
are praising thee on high,
and mortal men and all things
created make reply.

3. The people of the Hebrews
with palms before thee went:
our praise and prayer and anthems
before thee we present.

4. To thee before thy passion
they sang their hymns of praise:
to thee now high exalted
our melody we raise.

5. Thou didst accept their praises,
accept the prayers we bring,
who in all good delightest,
thou good and gracious King.

Words: Theodulph of Orleans (821),
tr. J. M. Neale (1818-66)
Music: Melchior Teschner (1584-1635)

ALL HAIL, THE POWER OF JESUS' NAME

('Miles Lane' C.M.)

13

2. Crown him, ye martyrs of your God,
who from his altar call;
praise him whose way of pain ye trod,
and crown him Lord of all.

3. Ye prophets who our freedom won,
ye searchers, great and small,
by whom the work of truth is done,
now crown him Lord of all.

4. Sinners, whose love can ne'er forget
the wormwood and the gall,
go spread your trophies at his feet,
and crown him Lord of all.

5. Let every tribe and every tongue
to him their hearts enthrall:
lift high the universal song,
and crown him Lord of all.

Words: Edward Perronet (1726-92)
Music: William Shrubsole (1760-1806)

ALL MY HOPE ON GOD IS FOUNDED
('Michael' 87.87.67.)

2. Pride of man and earthly glory,
sword and crown betray God's trust;
what with lavish care man buildeth,
tower and temple, fall to dust.
But God's power, hour by hour,
is my temple and my tower.

3. God's great goodness ay endureth,
deep his wisdom, passing thought:
splendour, light and life attend him,
beauty springeth out of nought.
Evermore, from his store,
new-born worlds rise and adore.

4. Still from man to God eternal
sacrifice of praise be done,
high above all praises praising
for the gift of Christ his Son.
Christ doth call one and all:
ye who follow shall not fall.

Words: J. Neander (1650-80),
paraphrased by Robert Bridges
Music: Herbert Howells (1892-1983)

15

ALL OVER THE WORLD

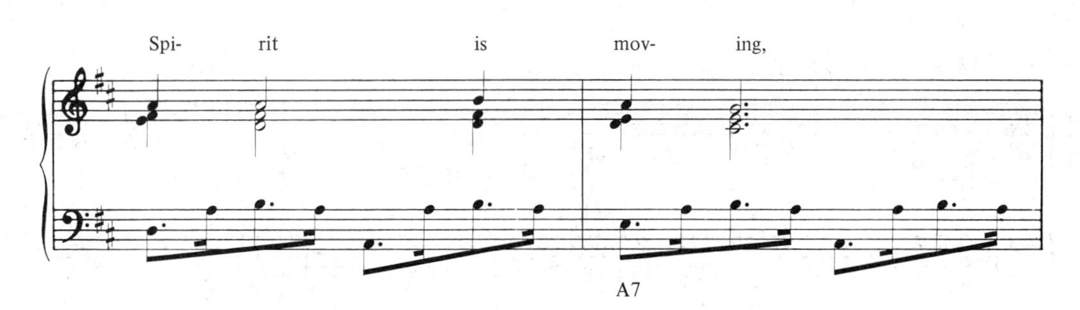

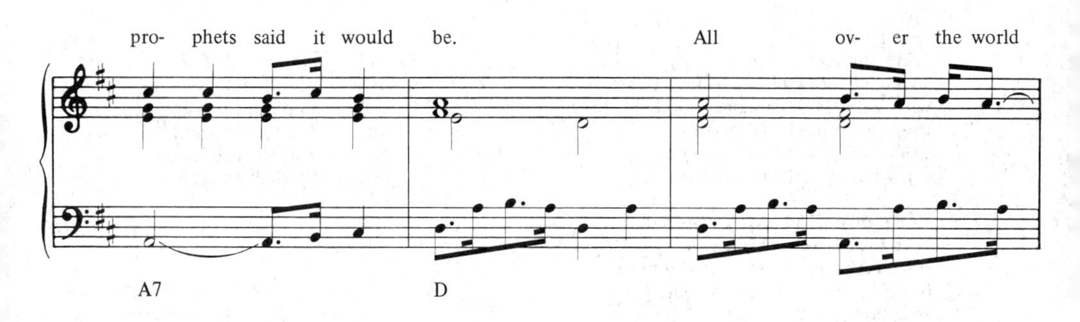

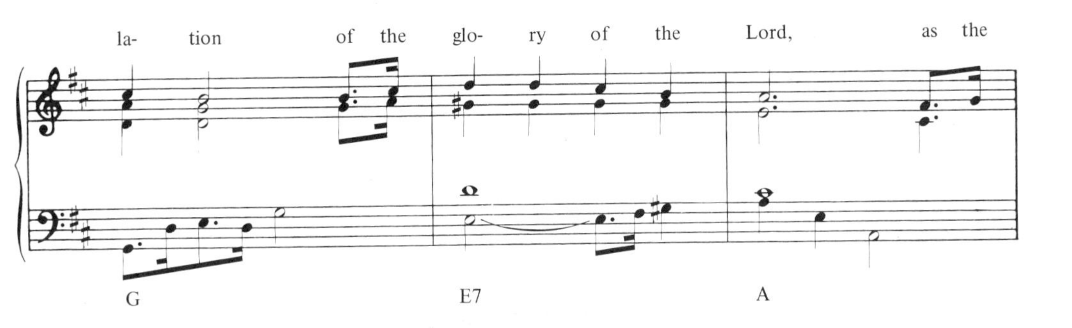

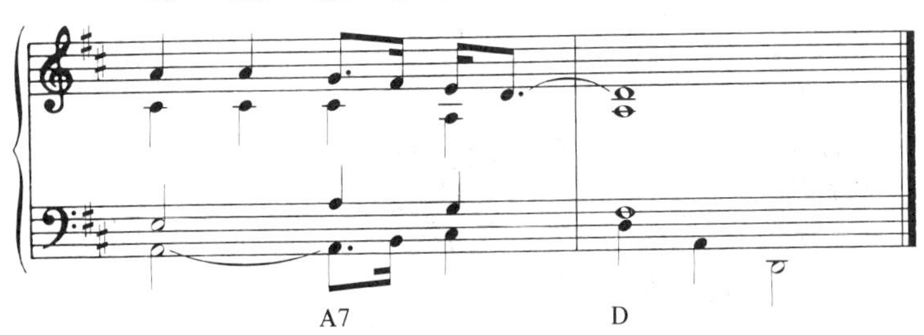

2. All over this land . . .

3. All over the church . . .

4. All over us all . . .

5. Deep down in my heart . . .

Words and Music: Roy Turner,
arranged by Michael Irwin

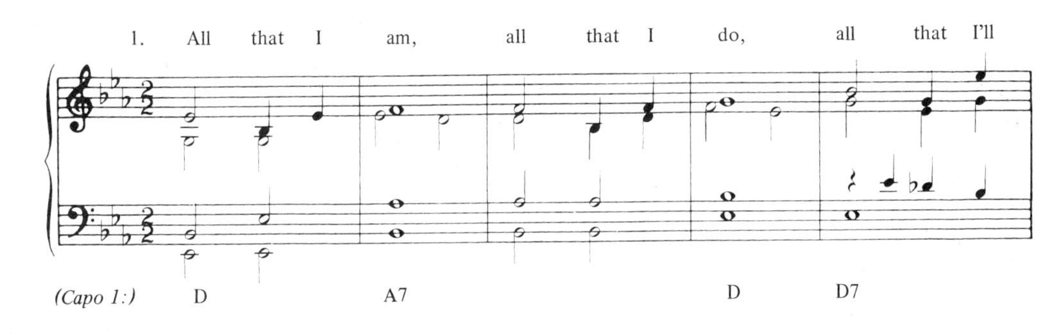
1. All that I am, all that I do, all that I'll
(Capo 1:) D A7 D D7

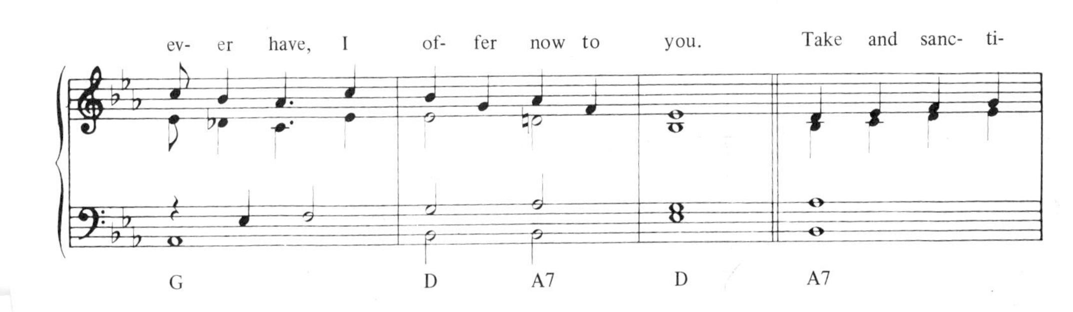
ev- er have, I of- fer now to you. Take and sanc- ti-
G D A7 D A7

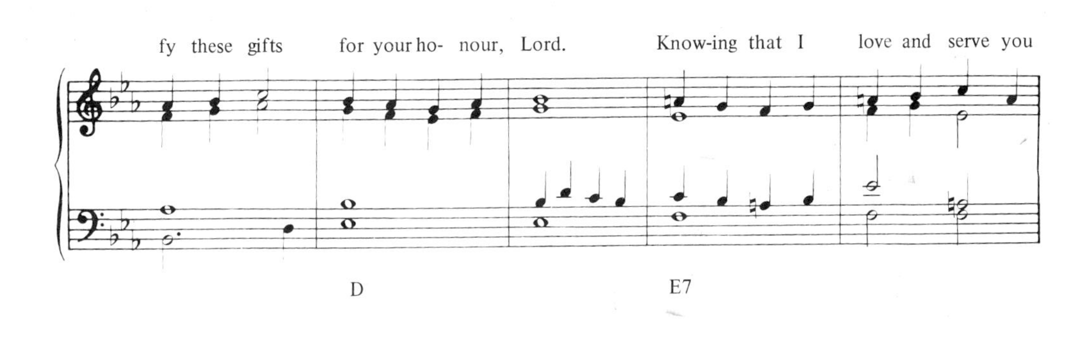
fy these gifts for your ho- nour, Lord. Know-ing that I love and serve you
D E7

is e- nough re- ward. All that I am, all that I
A7 D A7

ALL PEOPLE THAT ON EARTH DO DWELL

('Old 100th' L.M.)

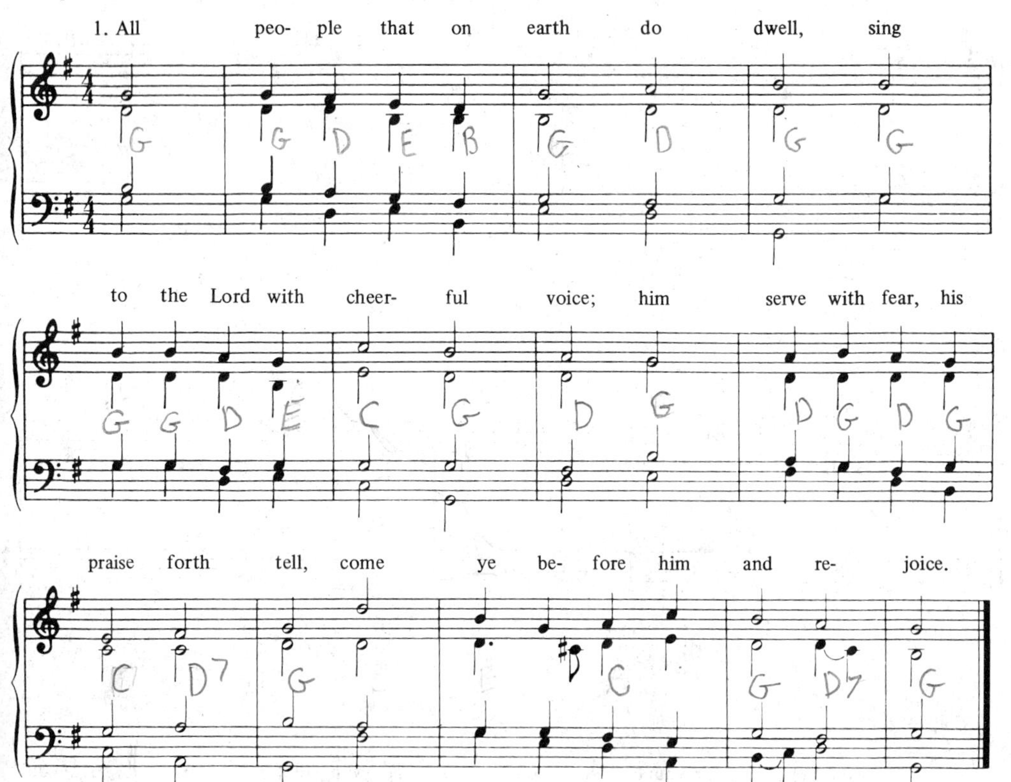

2. The Lord, ye know, is God indeed,
without our aid he did us make;
we are his folk, he doth us feed
and for his sheep he doth us take.

3. O enter then his gates with praise,
approach with joy his courts unto;
praise, laud, and bless his name always,
for it is seemly so to do.

4. For why? the Lord our God is good:
his mercy is for ever sure;
his truth at all times firmly stood,
and shall from age to age endure.

5. To Father, Son and Holy Ghost,
the God whom heaven and earth adore,
from men and from the angel-host
be praise and glory evermore.

Words, based on Psalm 100: William Kethe 'Day's Psalter' (1560)
Music: 'Genevan Psalter' (c. 1551)

2. All that I dream, all that I pray,
all that I'll ever make,
I give to you today.
Take and sanctify these gifts
for your honour, Lord.
Knowing that I love and serve you
is enough reward.
All that I am, all that I do,
all that I'll ever have
I offer now to you.

Words and Music: Sebastian Temple

Chorus
All the earth pro- claim the Lord; all you na- tions
F Dm B♭ Csus4 C B♭ Gm

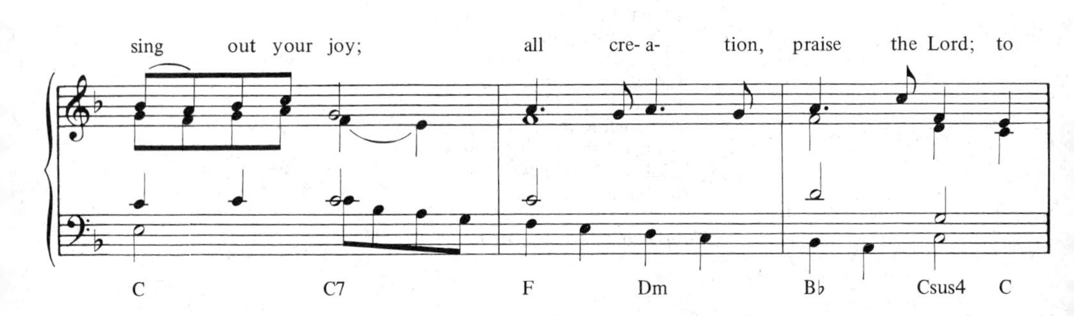
sing out your joy; all cre- a- tion, praise the Lord; to
C C7 F Dm B♭ Csus4 C

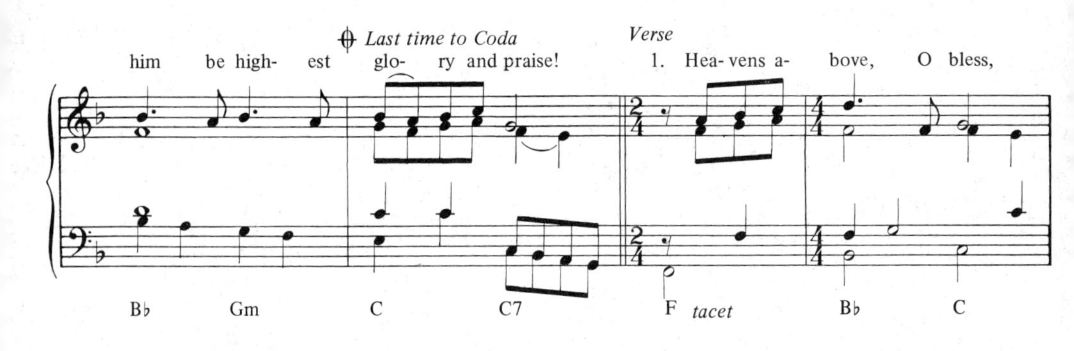
Last time to Coda
Verse
him be high- est glo- ry and praise! 1. Hea- vens a- bove, O bless,
B♭ Gm C C7 F tacet B♭ C

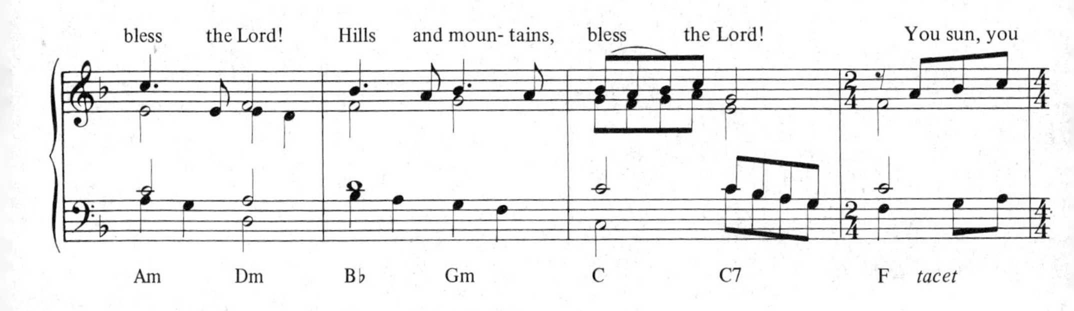
bless the Lord! Hills and moun- tains, bless the Lord! You sun, you
Am Dm B♭ Gm C C7 F tacet

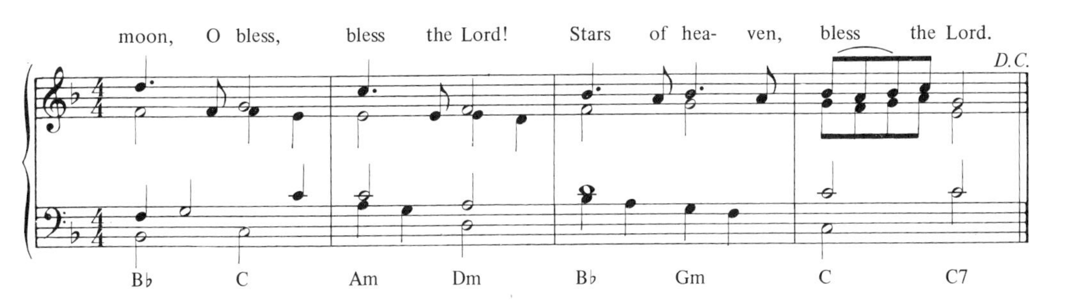

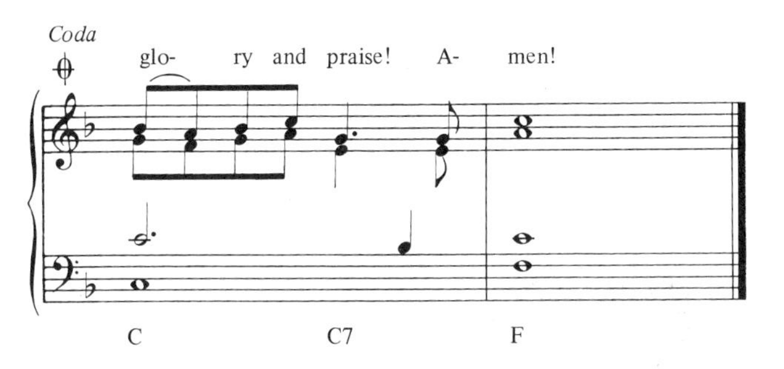

2. Waters and seas, O bless, bless the Lord!
 Plants and earth, now bless the Lord!
 Wild beast and tame, O bless, bless the Lord!
 All you creatures, bless the Lord!

3. Humble of heart, O bless, bless the Lord!
 All you just, now bless the Lord!
 Fountains and springs, O bless, bless the Lord!
 Night and day, now bless the Lord!

4. Sing now to God, O bless, bless the Lord!
 God, our Father: bless the Lord!
 For Christ, his Son, O bless, bless the Lord!
 Spirit Holy: bless the Lord!

Words and Music: Alfred Camilleri,
arranged by Frances M. Kelly

ALL THE NATIONS OF THE EARTH

2. Snow capped mountains, praise the Lord.
Alleluia.
Rolling hills, praise the Lord.
Alleluia.

3. Deep sea water, praise the Lord.
Alleluia.
Gentle rain, praise the Lord.
Alleluia.

4. Roaring lion, praise the Lord.
Alleluia.
Singing birds, praise the Lord.
Alleluia.

5. Kings and princes, praise the Lord.
Alleluia.
Young and old, praise the Lord.
Alleluia.

Words, based on Psalm 148: Michael Cockett
Music: Kevin Mayhew

20 ALL THE RICHES OF HIS GRACE

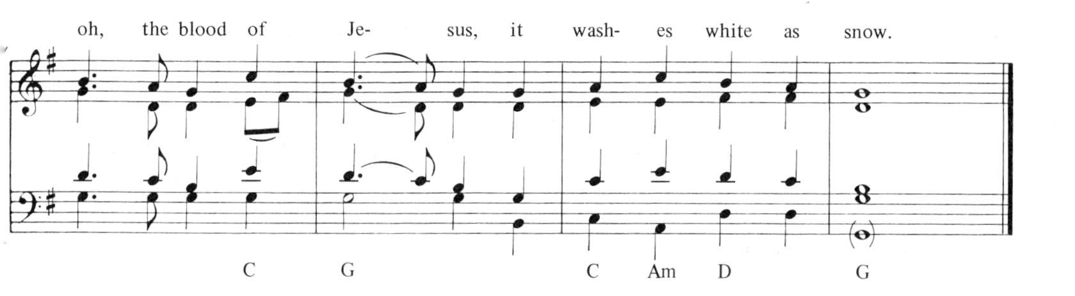

2. Oh, the word of Jesus, *(x3)*
   it cleanses white as snow.

3. Oh, the love of Jesus, *(x3)*
   it makes his body whole.

Part **1** *and Part* **2** *can be sung against each other (in which case use the accompaniment and chords for Part* **1** *).*

Words and Music: Part 1 - Jan Harrington
Part 2 - Anonymous, arranged by Betty Pulkingham

ALL THINGS BRIGHT AND BEAUTIFUL

(First tune: 'Royal Oak' 76.76. & Chorus)

Chorus

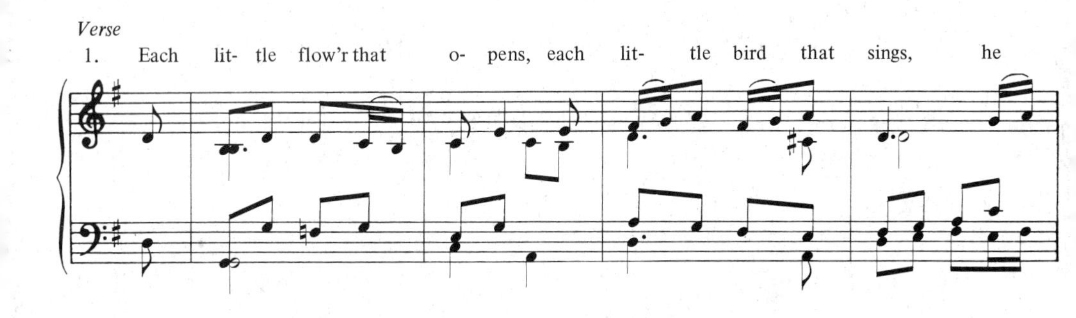

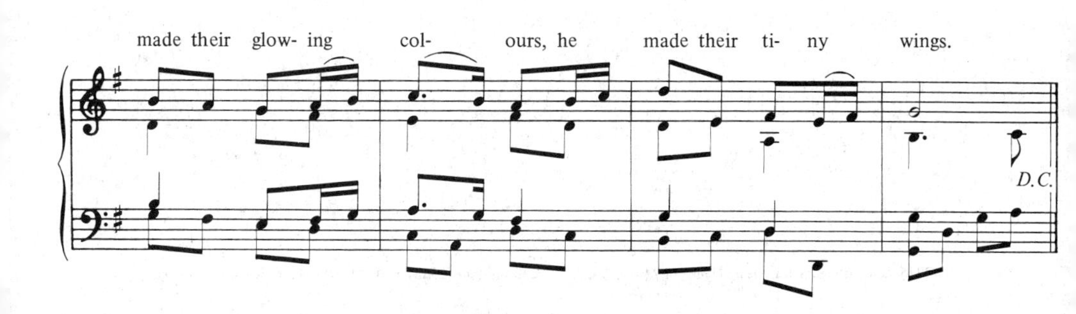

2. The purple-headed mountain,
the river running by,
the sunset and the morning,
that brightens up the sky.

3. The cold wind in the winter,
the pleasant summer sun,
the ripe fruits in the garden,
he made them every one.

4. The tall trees in the greenwood,
the meadows for our play,
the rushes by the water,
to gather every day.

5. He gave us eyes to see them,
and lips that we may tell
how great is God almighty,
who has made all things well.

Words: Cecil Frances Alexander (1818-95)
Music: First tune - Traditional English melody, adapted by Martin Shaw

Second tune overleaf

ALL THINGS BRIGHT AND BEAUTIFUL

(Second tune: 'All things bright and beautiful' 76.76. & Chorus)

[HARMONY]

2. The purple-headed mountain,
   the river running by,
   the sunset and the morning,
   that brightens up the sky.

3. The cold wind in the winter,
   the pleasant summer sun,
   the ripe fruits in the garden,
   he made them every one.

4. The tall trees in the greenwood,
   the meadows for our play,
   the rushes by the water,
   to gather every day.

5. He gave us eyes to see them,
   and lips that we may tell
   how great is God almighty,
   who has made all things well.

Words: Cecil Frances Alexander (1818-95)
Music: Second tune - W.H. Monk (1823-89)

ALL TO JESUS I SURRENDER
('I surrender all' 87.87. & Chorus)
[HARMONY]

2. All to Jesus I surrender,
humbly at his feet I bow,
worldly pleasures all forsaken,
take me, Jesus, take me now.

3. All to Jesus I surrender,
make me, Saviour, wholly thine,
let me feel thy Holy Spirit,
truly know that thou art mine.

4. All to Jesus I surrender,
Lord, I give myself to thee;
fill me with thy love and power,
let thy blessing fall on me.

5. All to Jesus I surrender,
now I feel the sacred flame;
oh, the joy of full salvation!
Glory, glory to his name!

Words: J.W. Van Deventer
Music: W.S. Weeden, arranged by Roland Fudge

ALL YE WHO SEEK A COMFORT SURE

('St Bernard' C.M.)

[HARMONY]

1. All ye who seek a com- fort sure in trou- ble and dis- tress

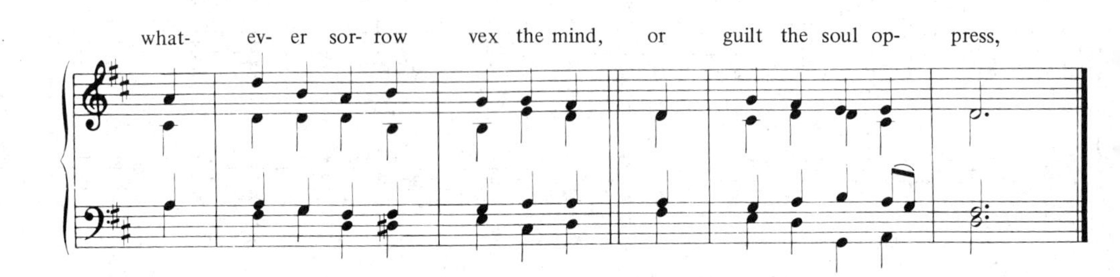

2. Jesus, who gave himself for you
   upon the cross to die,
   opens to you his sacred heart;
   oh, to that heart draw nigh.

3. Ye hear how kindly he invites;
   ye hear his words so blest:
   'All ye that labour, come to me,
   and I will give you rest.'

4. O Jesus, joy of saints on high,
   thou hope of sinners here,
   attracted by those loving words
   to thee I lift my prayer.

5. Wash thou my wounds in that dear blood
   which forth from thee doth flow;
   new grace, new hope inspire a new
   and better heart bestow.

Words: 'Quicumque certum quaeritis' (18th century),
tr. E. Caswall
Music: H. Lindenborn (1741),
adapted by J. Richardson (1851)

A MAN THERE LIVED IN GALILEE
('Tyrol' D.C.M.)

2. A man there died on Calvary
above all others brave;
his fellow-men he saved and blessed,
himself he scorned to save.
No thought can gauge the weight of woe
on him, the sinless, laid;
we only know that with his blood
our ransom price was paid.

3. A man there reigns in glory now,
divine, yet human still,
that human which is all divine
death sought in vain to kill.
All power is his; supreme he rules
the realms of time and space;
yet still our human cares and needs
find in his heart a place.

Words: Somerset Corry Lowry (1855-1932)
Music: Tyrolean Melody

✓ AND CAN IT BE THAT I SHOULD GAIN
('Sagina' 88.88.88.)

[HARMONY]

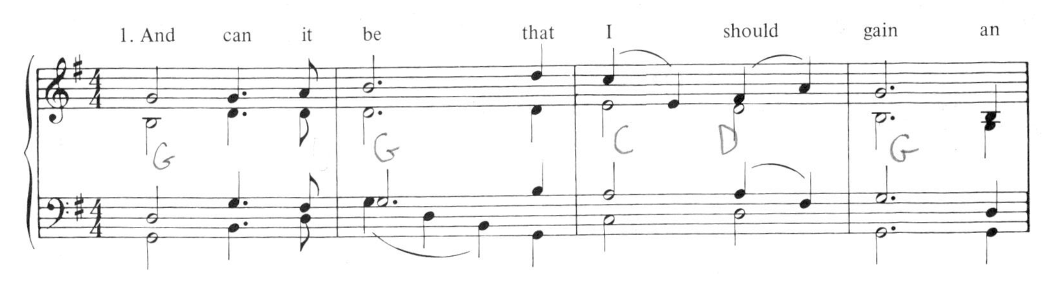

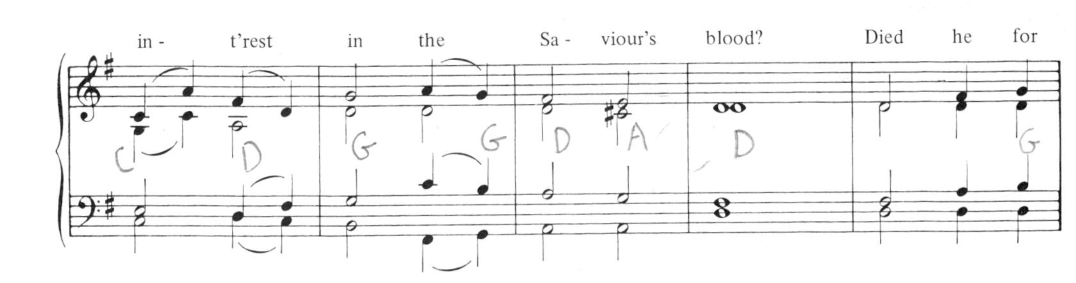

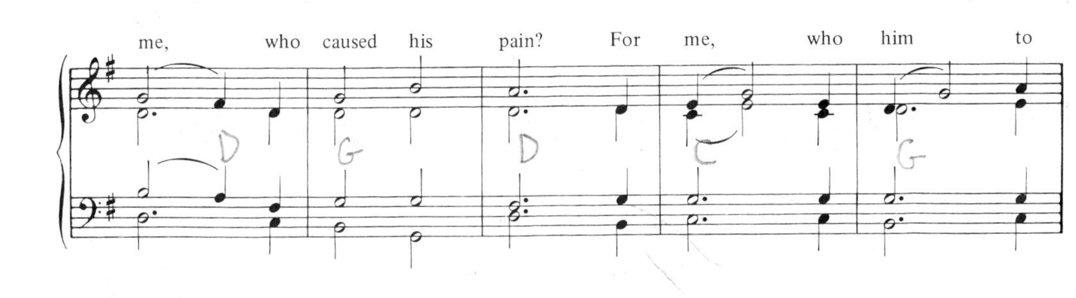

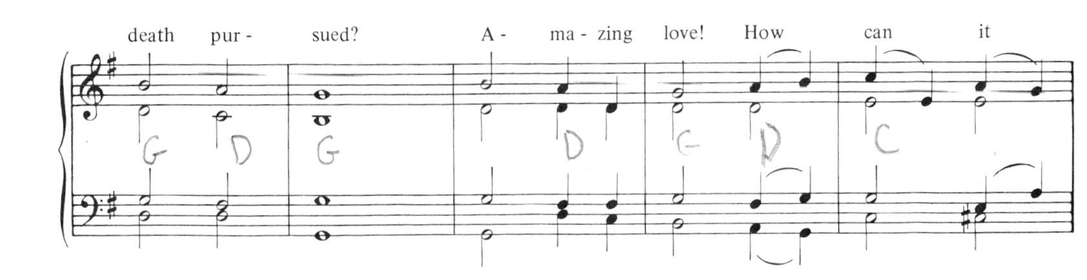

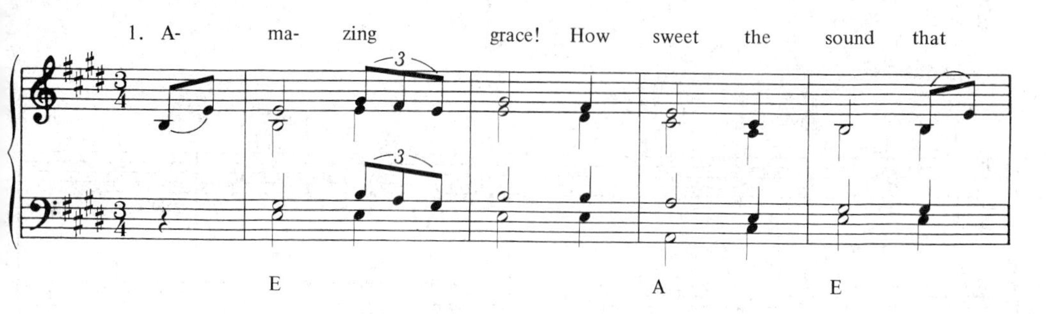

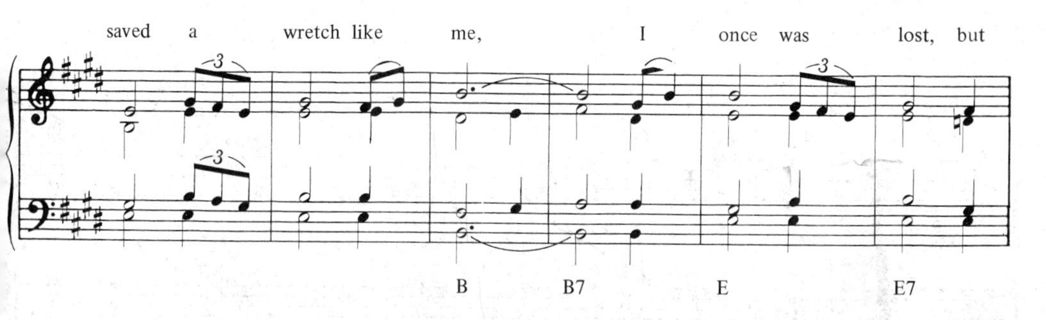

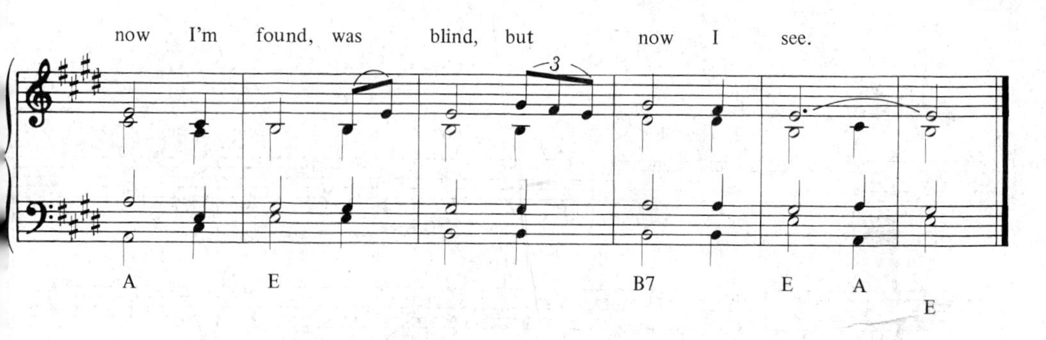

2. 'Twas grace that taught my heart to fear,
and grace my fears relieved.
How precious did that grace appear
the hour I first believed!

3. Through many dangers, toils and snares
I have already come.
'Tis grace hath brought me safe thus far,
and grace will lead me home.

4. The Lord has promised good to me;
his word my hope secures.
He will my shield and portion be
as long as life endures.

Words: John Newton (1725-1807)
Music: American folk melody,
arranged by John Rombaut

27
AND DID THOSE FEET IN ANCIENT TIME
('Jerusalem' D.L.M.)
Slow, but with animation
1. And did those feet in ancient time walk upon England's mountains green? And was the holy Lamb of God on England's pleasant pastures seen? And did the

2. 'Tis mystery all! The Immortal dies:
who can explore his strange design?
In vain the first-born seraph tries
to sound the depths of love divine.
'Tis mercy all! Let earth adore,
let angel minds inquire no more.

3. He left his Father's throne above -
so free, so infinite his grace -
emptied himself of all but love,
and bled for Adam's helpless race.
'Tis mercy all, immense and free;
for, O my God, it found out me!

4. Long my imprisoned spirit lay
fast bound in sin and nature's night;
thine eye diffused a quickening ray -
I woke, the dungeon flamed with light;
my chains fell off, my heart was free.
I rose, went forth, and followed thee.

5. No condemnation now I dread;
Jesus, and all in him, is mine!
Alive in him, my living Head,
and clothed in righteousness divine,
bold I approach the eternal throne,
and claim the crown, through Christ, my own.

Words, based on Scripture: Charles Wesley (1707-88)
Music: Thomas Campbell (1825-76)

poco cresc.
coun- ten- ance di- vine shine forth up- on our cloud- ed
poco cresc.

f
poco rit.
hills? And was Je- ru- sa- lem build- ed here a- mong those
f
poco rit.

dark sa- ta- nic mills?
f a tempo
ff

mf
2. Bring me my bow of burn- ing gold! Bring me my
mf

ar- rows of de- sire! Bring me my spear! O clouds un-

fold! Bring me my cha- ri- ot of fire! I will not
p
p

Words: William Blake (1757-1827)
Music: C.H.H. Parry (1848-1918)

28

AND NOW, O FATHER, MINDFUL OF THE LOVE

(First tune: 'Song 1' 10 10.10 10.10 10.)

pure, im- mor- tal sac- ri- fice.

2. Look, Father, look on his anointed face,
and only look on us as found in him;
look not on our misusings of thy grace,
our prayer so languid, and our faith so dim:
for lo, between our sins and their reward
we set the passion of thy Son our Lord.

3. And then for those, our dearest and our best,
by this prevailing presence we appeal:
O fold them closer to thy mercy's breast,
O do thine utmost for their soul's true weal;
from tainting mischief keep them white and clear,
and crown thy gifts with strength to persevere.

4. And so we come: O draw us to thy feet,
most patient Saviour, who canst love us still;
and by this food, so aweful and so sweet,
deliver us from every touch of ill:
in thine own service make us glad and free,
and grant us never more to part with thee.

Words: William Bright (1824-1901)
Music: First tune - Orlando Gibbons (1583-1625)
Second tune overleaf

AND NOW, O FATHER, MINDFUL OF THE LOVE
(Second tune: 'Unde et memores' 10 10.10 10.10 10.)

2. Look, Father, look on his anointed face,
and only look on us as found in him;
look not on our misusings of thy grace,
our prayer so languid, and our faith so dim:
for lo, between our sins and their reward
we set the passion of thy Son our Lord.

3. And then for those, our dearest and our best,
by this prevailing presence we appeal:
O fold them closer to thy mercy's breast,
O do thine utmost for their soul's true weal;
from tainting mischief keep them white and clear,
and crown thy gifts with strength to persevere.

4. And so we come: O draw us to thy feet,
most patient Saviour, who canst love us still;
and by this food, so aweful and so sweet,
deliver us from every touch of ill:
in thine own service make us glad and free,
and grant us never more to part with thee.

Words: William Bright (1824-1901)
Music: Second tune - W.H. Monk (1823-89)

A NEW COMMANDMENT I GIVE UNTO YOU

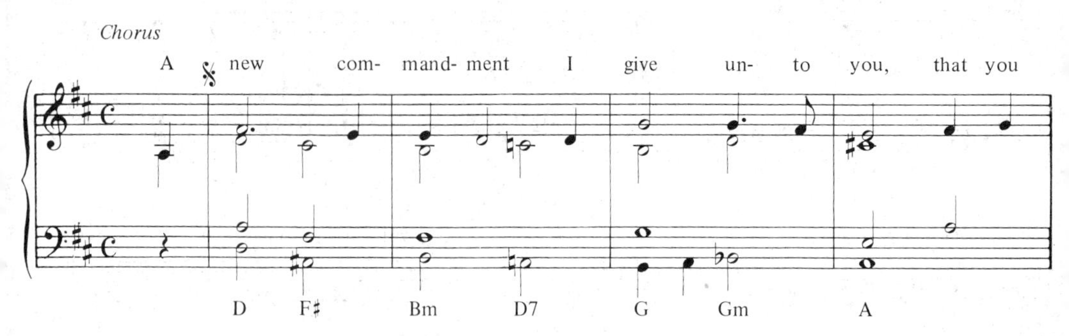

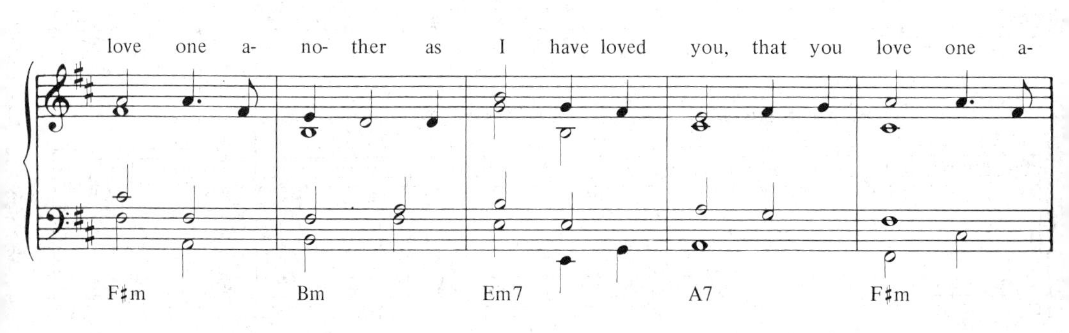

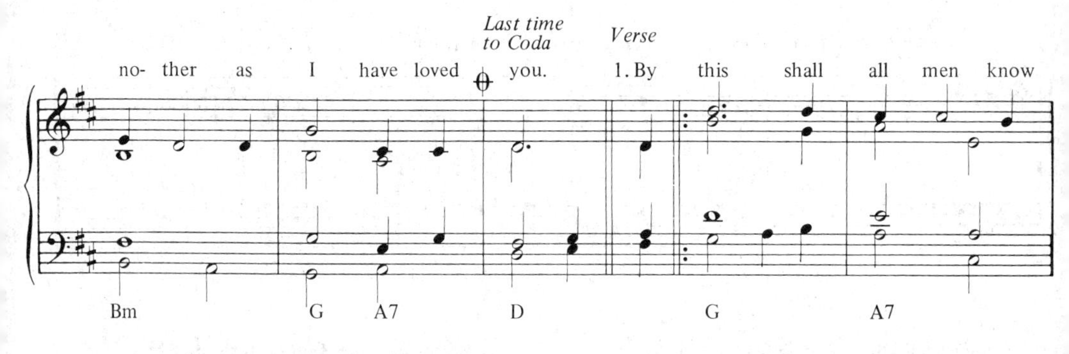

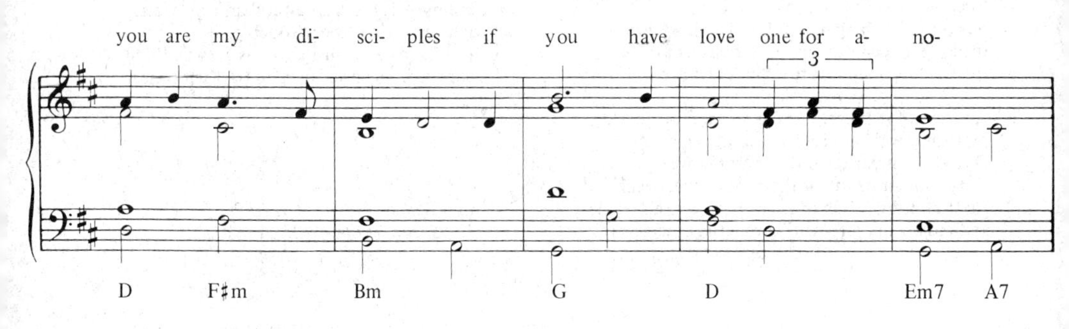

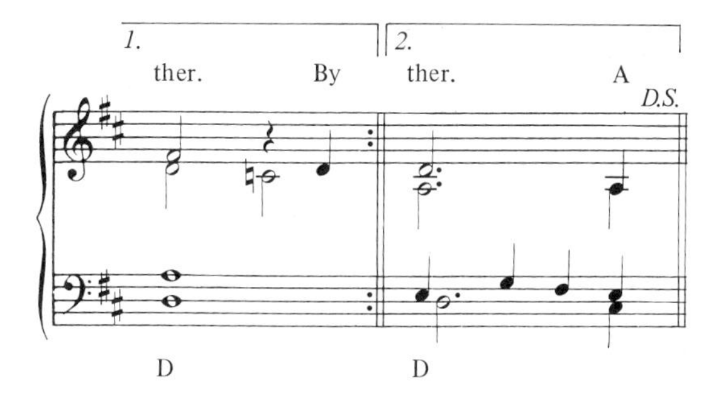

2. You are my friends if you do what I command you.
   Without my help you can do nothing.
   You are my friends if you do what I command you.
   Without my help you can do nothing.

3. I am the true vine, my Father is the gard'ner.
   Abide in me: I will be with you.
   I am the true vine, my Father is the gard'ner.
   Abide in me: I will be with you.

4. True love is patient, not arrogant nor boastful;
   love bears all things, love is eternal.
   True love is patient, not arrogant nor boastful;
   love bears all things, love is eternal.

Refrain and Verse 1 Words and Music: Unknown, arranged by Aniceto Nazareth
Verses 2 - 4, based on John 15 & 1 Cor. 13, and Music: Aniceto Nazareth
This arrangement: Frances M. Kelly

An alternative accompaniment can be found in SONGS OF NEW LIFE, No. 34.

ANGELS FROM THE REALMS OF GLORY
('Iris' 87.87. & Chorus)

2. Shepherds, in the fields abiding,
   watching o'er your flocks by night,
   God with man is now residing,
   yonder shines the infant Light:

3. Sages, leave your contemplations;
   brighter visions beam afar:
   Seek the great Desire of Nations;
   ye have seen his natal star:

4. Saints before the altar bending,
   watching long in hope and fear,
   suddenly the Lord, descending,
   in his temple shall appear:

5. Though an infant now we view him,
   he shall fill his Father's throne,
   gather all the nations to him;
   every knee shall then bow down:

Words: James Montgomery (1771-1854)
Music: Flemish melody,
harmonised by Charles Wood (1866-1926)

ANGEL-VOICES EVER SINGING

('Angel-voices' 85.85.84.3.)

31

[HARMONY]

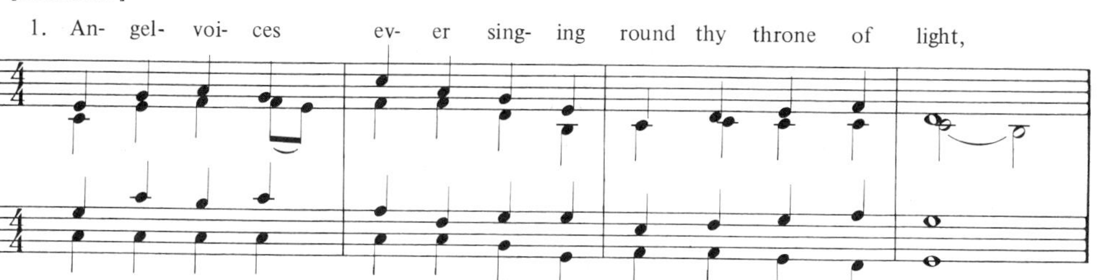

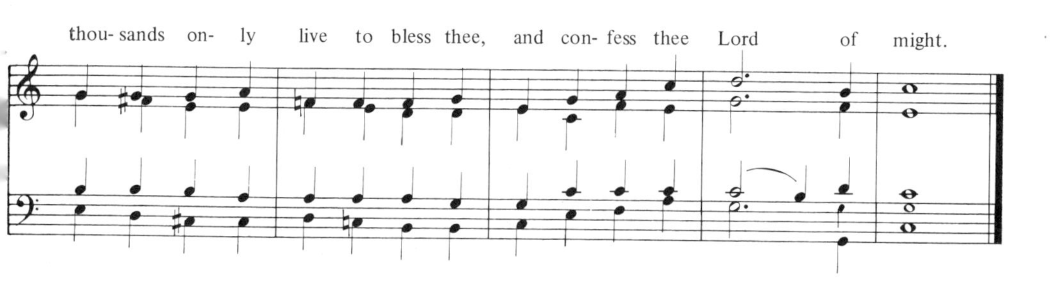

2. Thou who art beyond the farthest
mortal eye can scan,
can it be that thou regardest
songs of sinful man?
Can we know that thou art near us
and wilt hear us?
Yes, we can.

3. Yes, we know that thou rejoicest
o'er each work of thine;
thou didst ears and hands and voices
for thy praise design;
craftsman's art and music's measure
for thy pleasure
all combine.

4. In thy house, great God, we offer
of thine own to thee;
and for thine acceptance proffer
all unworthily,
hearts and minds and hands and voices
in our choicest
psalmody.

5. Honour, glory, might, and merit
thine shall ever be,
Father, Son and Holy Spirit,
Blessed Trinity.
Of the best that thou hast given
earth and heaven
render thee.

Words: Francis Pott (1832-1909)
Music: Edwin George Monk (1819-1900)

32

A SAFE STRONGHOLD OUR GOD IS STILL

('Ein' feste Burg' 87.87.66.667.)

2. With force of arms we nothing can,
 full soon were we down-ridden;
 but for us fights the proper Man,
 whom God himself hath bidden.
 Ask ye, Who is this same?
 Christ Jesus is his name,
 the Lord Sabaoth's Son;
 he, and no other one,
 shall conquer in the battle.

3. And were this world all devils o'er,
 and watching to devour us,
 we lay it not to heart so sore;
 not they can overpower us.
 And let the prince of ill
 look grim as e'er he will,
 he harms us not a whit;
 for why? his doom is writ;
 a word shall quickly slay him.

4. God's word, for all their craft and force,
 one moment will not linger,
 but, spite of hell, shall have its course;
 'tis written by his finger.
 And though they take our life,
 goods, honour, children, wife,
 yet is their profit small;
 these things shall vanish all:
 the City of God remaineth.

Words, based on Romans 8: 35-38:
Martin Luther (1483-1546)
translated by Thomas Carlyle
Music: Martin Luther (1483-1546)

AS EARTH THAT IS DRY (Come to the waters)

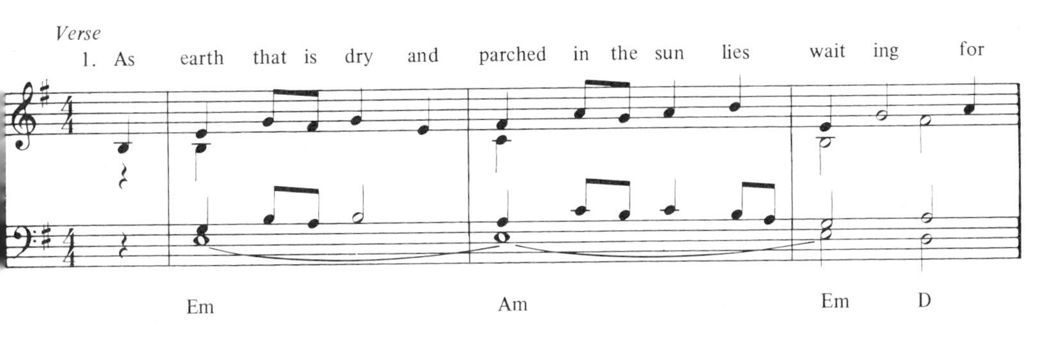

2. Though you have no money,
come, buy my corn
and drink my red wine.
Why spend precious gold
on what will not last?
Hear me, and your soul will live.

3. As one on a journey
strays from the road
and falls in the dark,
my mind is a wanderer,
choosing wrong paths,
and longing to find a star.

4. The Lord is your light,
the Lord is your strength;
turn back to him now.
For his ways are not
the ways you would choose,
and his thoughts are always new.

5. As rain from the mountains
falls on the land
and brings forth the seed,
the Word of the Lord
sinks deep in our hearts,
creating the flower of truth.

Words, based on Isaiah 55, and Music: Anne Conway, arranged by Frances M. Kelly

As we are ga- thered, Je- sus is here,
G G (B bass) C Am7 D C (E bass) D (F♯bass) G
one with each oth- er, Je- sus is here,
G G (B bass) C Am7 D C (E bass) D (F♯bass) G
joined by the Spi- rit, washed in the blood,
C Am7 D G Em
part of the Bo- dy, the Church of God.
C G (B bass) A7 D C (E bass) D (F♯bass)

Words: John Daniels
Music: John Daniels, arranged by Roland Fudge

35

AS WITH GLADNESS MEN OF OLD

('Dix' 77.77.77.)

[HARMONY]

2. As with joyful steps they sped
to that lowly manger-bed,
there to bend the knee before
him whom heaven and earth adore,
so may we with willing feet
ever seek thy mercy seat.

3. As they offered gifts most rare
at that manger rude and bare,
so may we with holy joy,
pure, and free from sin's alloy,
all our costliest treasures bring,
Christ to thee our heavenly King.

4. Holy Jesu, every day
keep us in the narrow way;
and, when earthly things are past,
bring our ransomed souls at last
where they need no star to guide,
where no clouds thy glory hide.

5. In the heavenly country bright
need they no created light,
thou its Light, its Joy, its Crown,
thou its Sun which goes not down;
there for ever may we sing
alleluias to our King.

Words, based on Matthew 2: William Chatterton Dix (1837-98)
Music: Conrad Kocher (1786-1872)

AT THE LAMB'S HIGH FEAST WE SING

('Salzburg' 77.77.D.)

[HARMONY]

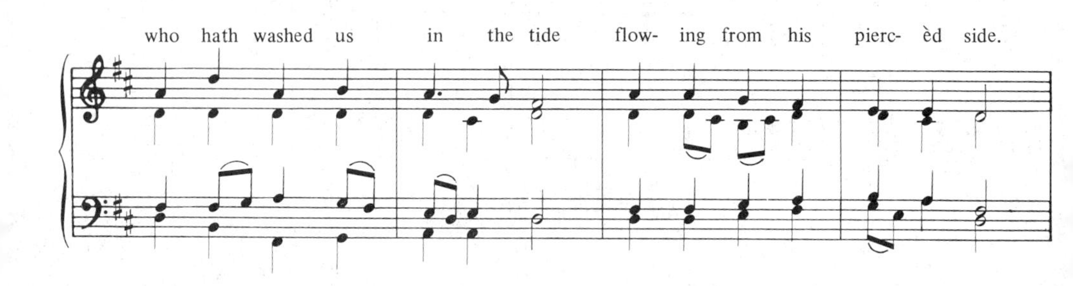

2. Where the paschal blood is poured,
death's dark angel sheathes his sword;
Israel's hosts triumphant go
through the wave that drowns the foe.
Christ the Lamb, whose blood was shed,
paschal victim, paschal bread;
with sincerity and love
eat we manna from above.

3. Mighty victim from the sky
powers of hell beneath thee lie;
death is broken in the fight;
thou hast brought us life and light,
now thy banner thou dost wave;
conquering Satan and the grave;
see the prince of darkness quelled;
heaven's bright gates are open held.

4. Paschal triumph, paschal joy,
only sin can this destroy;
from sin's death do thou set free
souls re-born, dear Lord, in thee.
Hymns of glory, songs of praise,
Father unto thee we raise.
Risen Lord, all praise to thee,
ever with the Spirit be.

Words: Seventh century,
tr. Robert Campbell (1814-68)
Music: Melody by J. Hintze (1622-1702)
harmonised by J. S. Bach

37

AT THE NAME OF JESUS
(First tune: 'Evelyns' 65.65.D.)

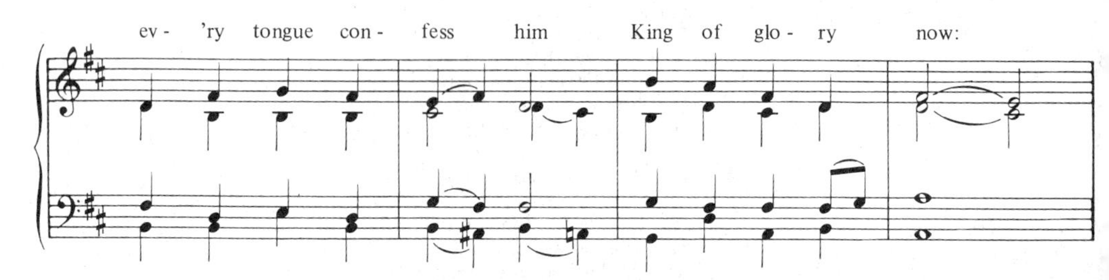

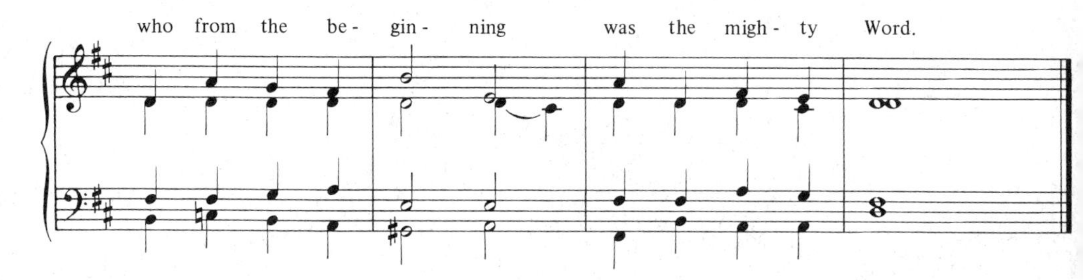

AT THE NAME OF JESUS
(Second tune: 'Camberwell' 65.65.D.)

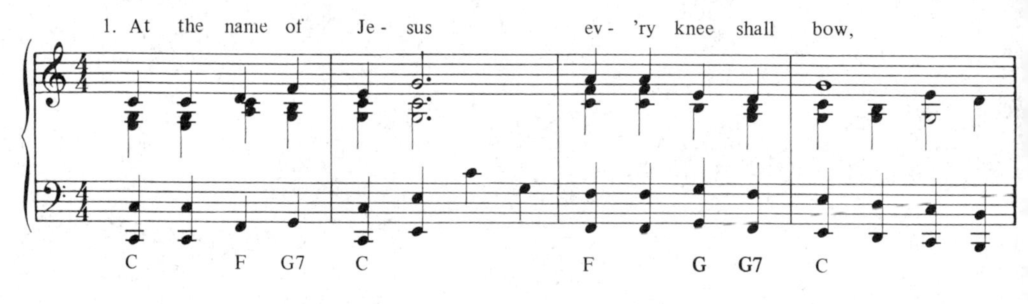

2. At his voice creation sprang at once to sight,
all the angel faces, all the hosts of light,
thrones and dominations, stars upon their way,
all the heavenly orders, in their great array.

3. Humbled for a season, to receive a name
from the lips of sinners unto whom he came,
faithfully he bore it spotless to the last,
brought it back victorious when from death he passed.

4. Bore it up triumphant, with its human light,
through all ranks of creatures to the central height,
to the throne of Godhead, to the Father's breast,
filled it with the glory of that perfect rest.

5. Name him, brothers, name him, with love as strong as death.
but with awe and wonder, and with bated breath.
He is God the Saviour, he is Christ the Lord,
ever to be worshipped, trusted and adored.

6. In your hearts enthrone him; there let him subdue
all that is not holy, all that is not true;
crown him as your captain; in temptation's hour
let his will enfold you in its light and power.

7. Brothers, this Lord Jesus shall return again,
with his Father's glory, with his angel train,
for all wreaths of empire meet upon his brow,
and our hearts confess him King of glory now.

Words, based on Philippians 2:6ff.: Caroline Maria Noel (1817-77)
Music: First tune - W.H. Monk (1823-89) Second tune - Michael Brierley

38

AWAKE, AWAKE: FLING OFF THE NIGHT
('Deus tuorum militum' L.M.)

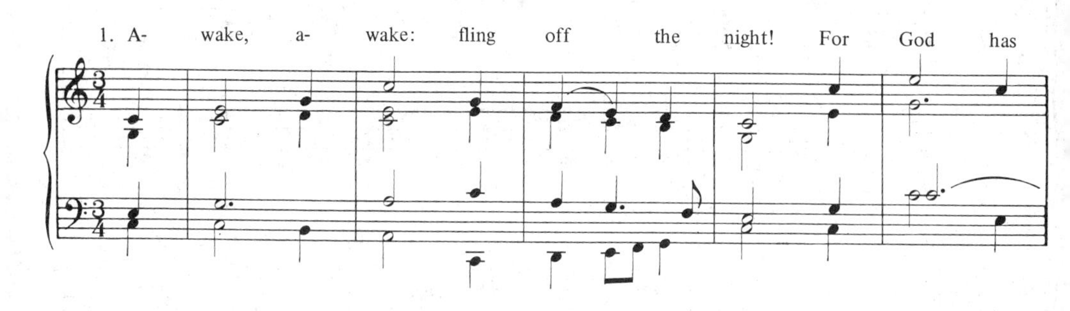

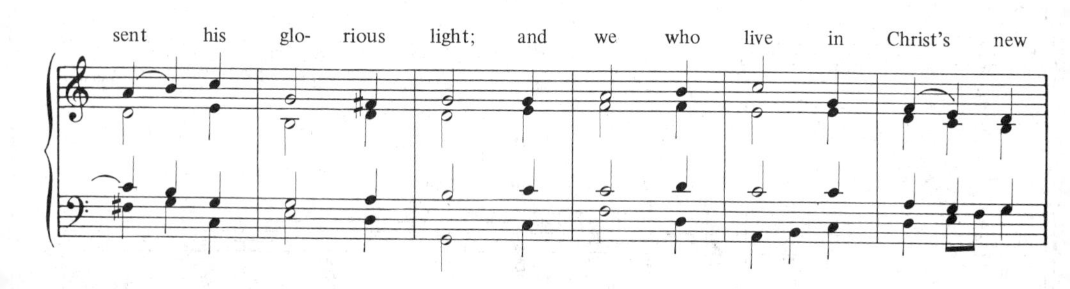

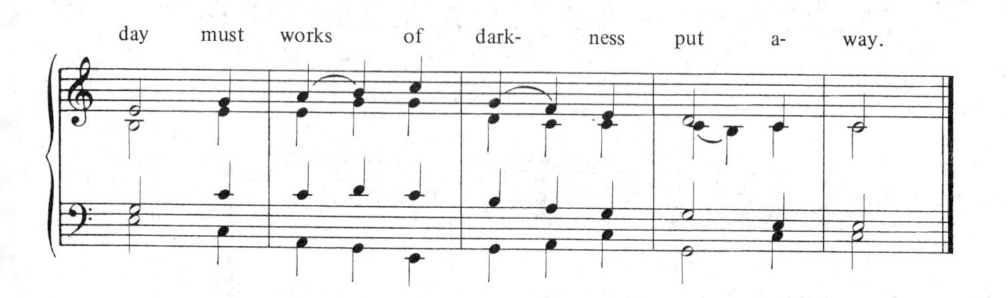

2. Awake and rise, like men renewed,
men with the Spirit's power endued.
The light of life in us must glow,
and fruits of truth and goodness show.

3. Let in the light; all sin expose
to Christ, whose life no darkness knows.
Before his cross for guidance kneel;
his light will judge and judging, heal.

4. Awake, and rise up from the dead,
and Christ his light on you will shed.
Its power will wrong desires destroy,
and your whole nature fill with joy.

5. Then sing for joy, and use each day;
give thanks for everything alway.
Lift up your hearts; with one accord
praise God through Jesus Christ our Lord.

Words, based on Ephesians 5: 6-20: J. R. Peacey (1896-1971)
Music: from the 'Grenoble Antiphoner' (1753 & 1868)

AWAKE, MY SOUL, AND WITH THE SUN
('Morning hymn' L.M.)

[HARMONY]

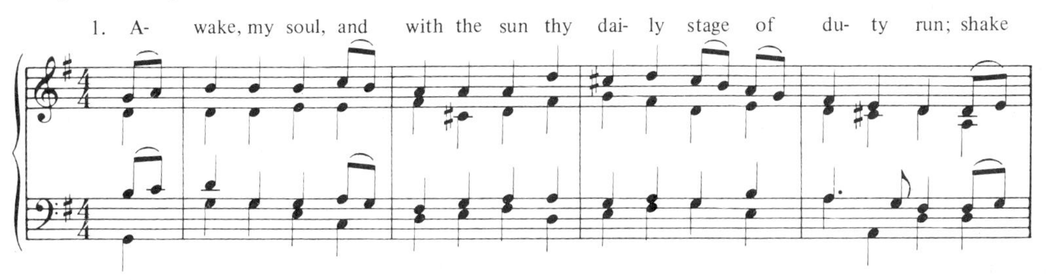

2. Redeem thy mis-spent time that's past,
   and live this day as if thy last;
   improve thy talent with due care;
   for the great day thyself prepare.

3. Let all thy converse be sincere,
   thy conscience as the noon-day clear;
   think how all-seeing God thy ways
   and all thy secret thoughts surveys.

4. Wake, and lift up thyself, my heart,
   and with the angels bear thy part,
   who all night long unwearied sing
   high praise to the eternal King.

Part II

5. Glory to thee, who safe hast kept
   and hast refreshed me whilst I slept;
   grant, Lord, when I from death shall wake,
   I may of endless light partake.

6. Lord, I my vows to thee renew;
   disperse my sins as morning dew;
   guard my first springs of thought and will,
   and with thyself my spirit fill.

7. Direct, control, suggest, this day,
   all I design or do or say;
   that all my powers, with all their might,
   in thy sole glory may unite.

This Doxology is sung after either part

8. Praise God, from whom all blessings flow,
   praise him, all creatures here below,
   praise him above, angelic host,
   praise Father, Son, and Holy Ghost.

Words: Thomas Ken (1637-1711)
Music: F. H. Barthelemon (1741-1808)

AWAY IN A MANGER
('Cradle song' 11 11.11 11.)

2. The cattle are lowing, the baby awakes,
but little Lord Jesus no crying he makes.
I love thee, Lord Jesus! Look down from the sky,
and stay by my side until morning is nigh.

3. Be near me, Lord Jesus; I ask thee to stay
close by me for ever, and love me, I pray.
Bless all the dear children in thy tender care,
and fit us for heaven, to live with thee there.

Words and Music: J. Kirkpatrick (1838-1921)

BEFORE THE ENDING OF THE DAY

('Te Lucis' L.M.)

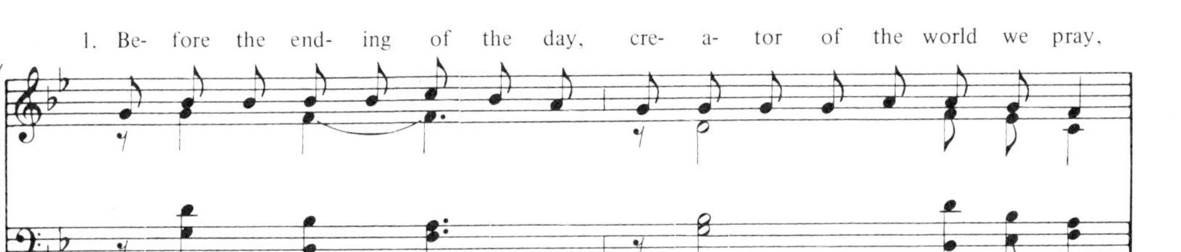

2. From all ill dreams defend our eyes,
from nightly fears and fantasies;
tread under foot our ghostly foe,
that no pollution we may know.

3. O Father, that we ask be done,
through Jesus Christ thine only Son,
who, with the Holy Ghost and thee,
doth live and reign eternally. Amen.

Words: Te lucis ante terminum (pre 8th century), tr. J. M. Neale
Music: Proper Sarum Melody Mode VIII

BE STILL AND KNOW THAT I AM GOD

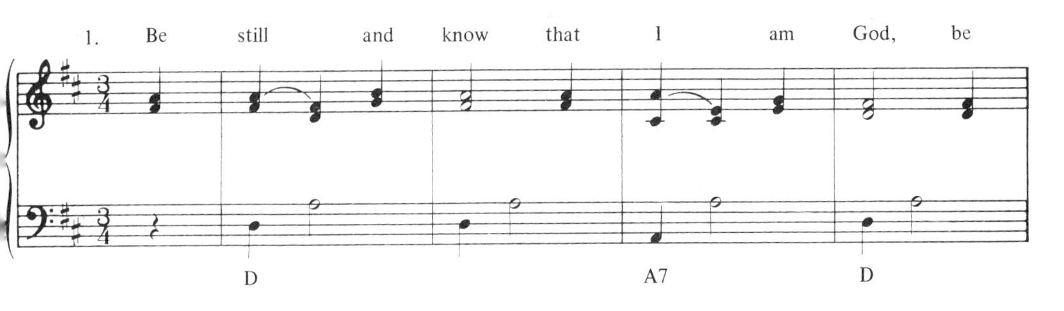

2. I am the Lord that healeth thee . . .

3. In thee, O Lord, I put my trust . . .

Words, based on Psalm 46, and Music: Unknown, arranged by John Rombaut

43

[HARMONY]

BE STILL, MY SOUL
('Finlandia' 10 10.10 10.10 10.)

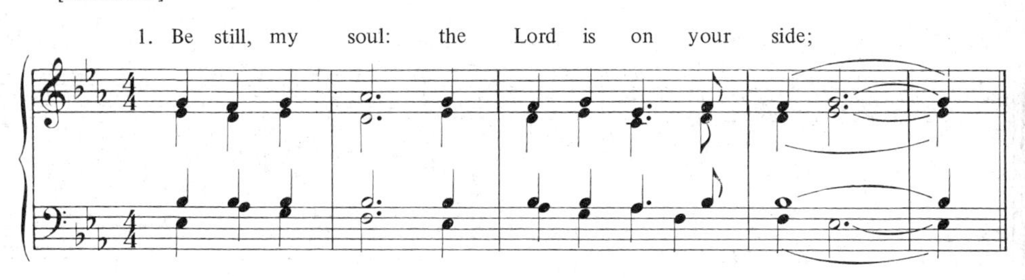

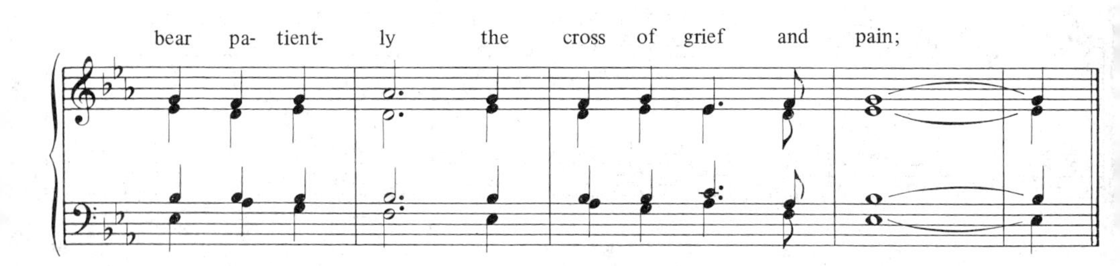

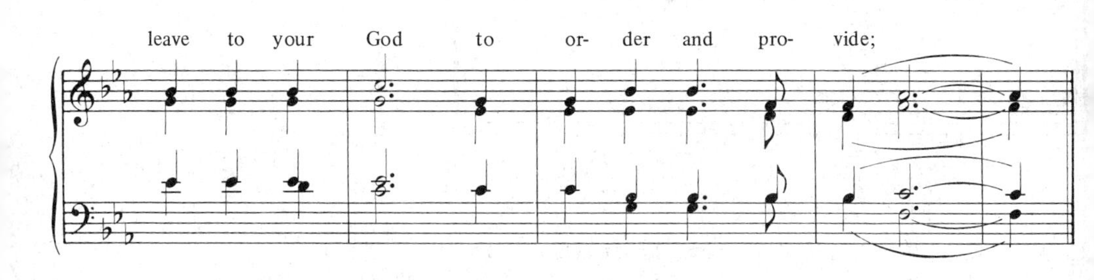

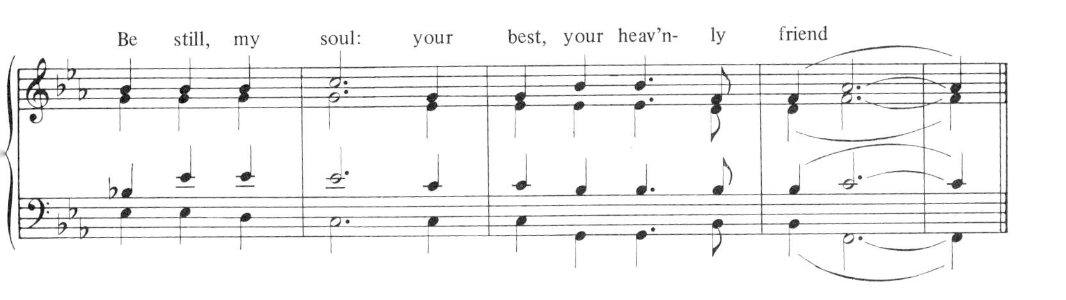

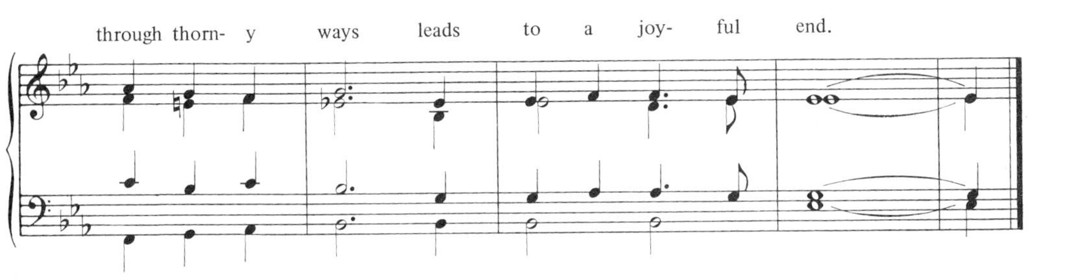

2. Be still, my soul: your God will undertake
to guide the future as he has the past.
Your hope, your confidence let nothing shake,
all now mysterious shall be clear at last.
Be still, my soul: the tempests still obey
his voice, who ruled them once on Galilee.

3. Be still, my soul: the hour is hastening on
when we shall be forever with the Lord,
when disappointment, grief and fear are gone,
sorrow forgotten, love's pure joy restored.
Be still, my soul: when change and tears are past,
all safe and blessed we shall meet at last.

Words: Katharina von Schlegel (1697-?),
translated by J. L. Borthwick
Music: Jean Sibelius (1865-1957)

BETHLEHEM OF NOBLEST CITIES

('Stuttgart' 87.87.)

[HARMONY]

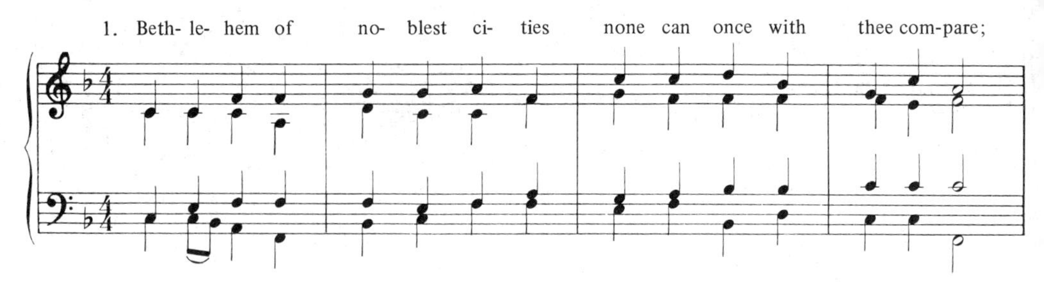

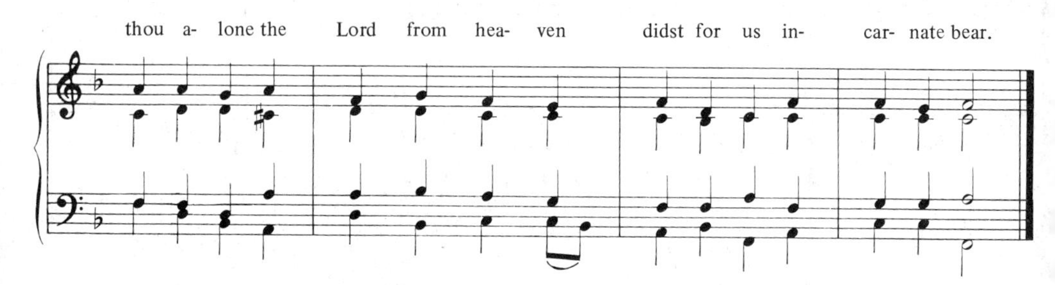

An alternative harmonisation is at Hymn 102

2. Fairer than the sun at morning
   was the star that told his birth,
   to the lands their God announcing,
   hid beneath a form of earth.

3. By its lambent beauty guided,
   see the eastern kings appear;
   see them bend, their gifts to offer -
   gifts of incense, gold and myrrh.

4. Solemn things of mystic meaning!
   Incense doth the God disclose;
   gold a royal child proclaimeth;
   myrrh a royal tomb foreshows.

5. Holy Jesu, in thy brightness
   to the gentile world displayed,
   with the Father and the Spirit,
   endless praise to thee be paid.

Words: *Aurelius Prudentius (348-413),*
translated by Edward Caswall
Music: *German melody,*
arranged by C. F. Witt (c. 1660-1716)

BE THOU MY GUARDIAN AND MY GUIDE

('Abridge' C.M.)

[HARMONY]

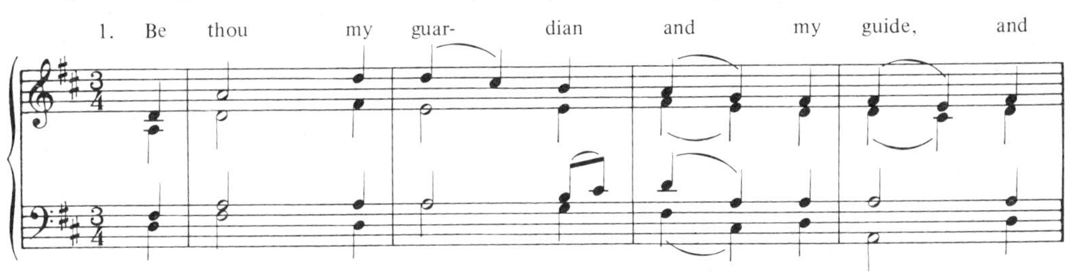

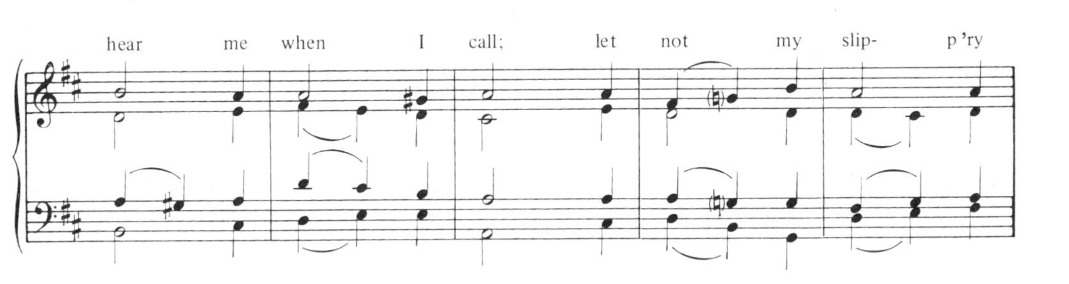

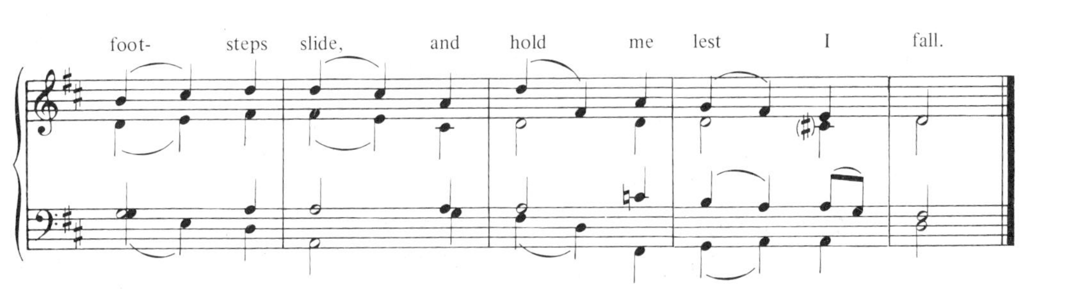

2. The world, the flesh, and Satan dwell
   around the path I tread;
   O save me from the snares of hell,
   thou quickener of the dead.

3. And if I tempted am to sin,
   and outward things are strong,
   do thou, O Lord, keep watch within,
   and save my soul from wrong.

4. Still let me ever watch and pray,
   and feel that I am frail;
   that if the tempter cross my way,
   yet he may not prevail.

Words: Isaac Williams (1802-65)
Music: Isaac Smith (c. 1730-1800)

[HARMONY]

BE THOU MY VISION

('Slane' 10 10.10 10.)

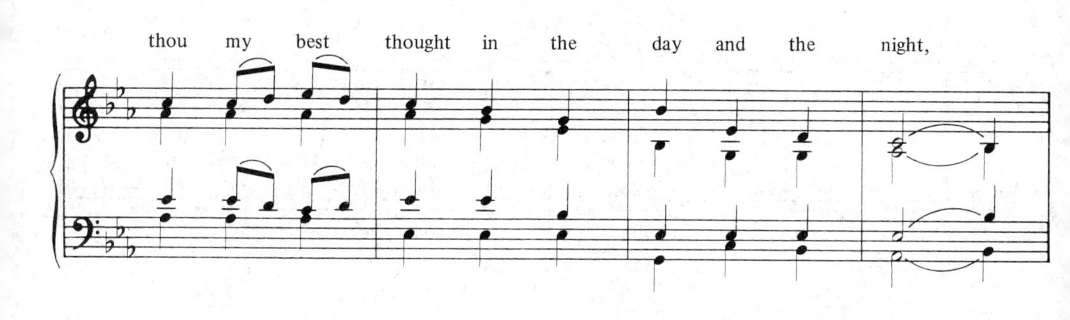

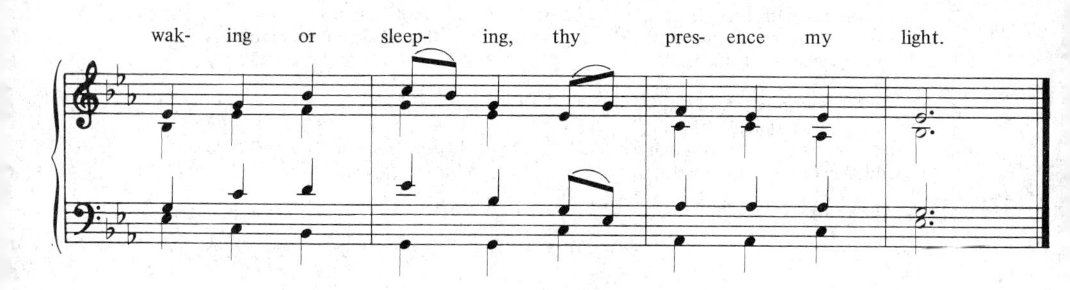

2. Be thou my wisdom, be thou my true word,
I ever with thee and thou with me, Lord;
thou my great Father, and I thy true son;
thou in me dwelling, and I with thee one.

3. Be thou my breast plate, my sword for the fight,
be thou my armour, and be thou my might,
thou my soul's shelter, and thou my high tower,
raise thou me heavenward, O Power of my power.

4. Riches I heed not, nor man's empty praise,
thou mine inheritance through all my days;
thou, and thou only, the first in my heart,
high King of heaven, my treasure thou art!

5. High King of heaven, when battle is done,
grant heaven's joys to me, O bright heaven's sun;
Christ of my own heart, whatever befall,
still be my vision, O Ruler of all.

Words: Irish (8th century), tr. Mary Byrne,
versified by Eleanor Hull
Music: Traditional Irish melody,
harmonised by Martin Shaw (1875-1958)

A different harmonisation of this tune
may be found at Hymn 306

BIND US TOGETHER

2. Made for the glory of God,
   purchased by his precious Son.
   Born with the right to be clean,
   for Jesus the victory has won . . .

3. You are the family of God.
   You are the promise divine.
   You are God's chosen desire.
   You are the glorious new wine . . .

Words and Music: B. Gillman

BLESSED ASSURANCE, JESUS IS MINE
('Blessed assurance' Irregular)

[HARMONY]

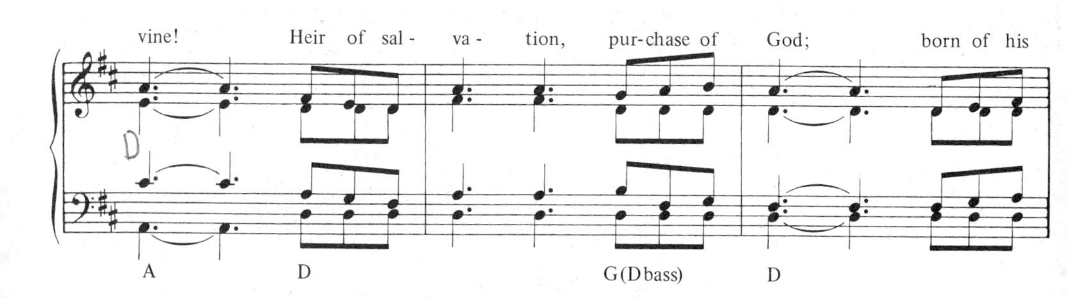

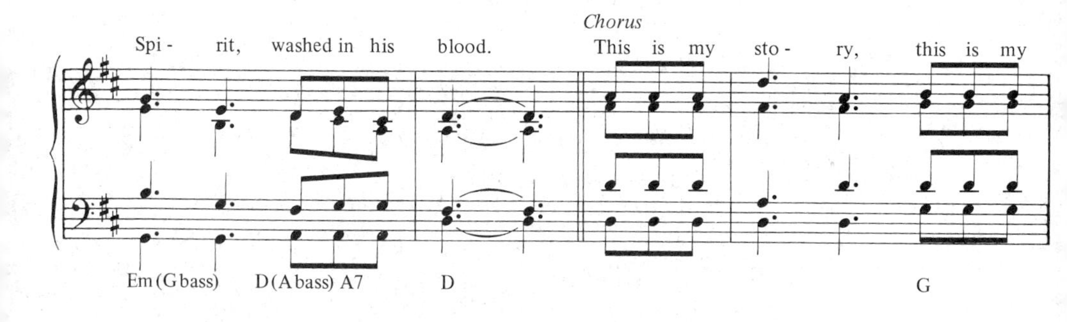

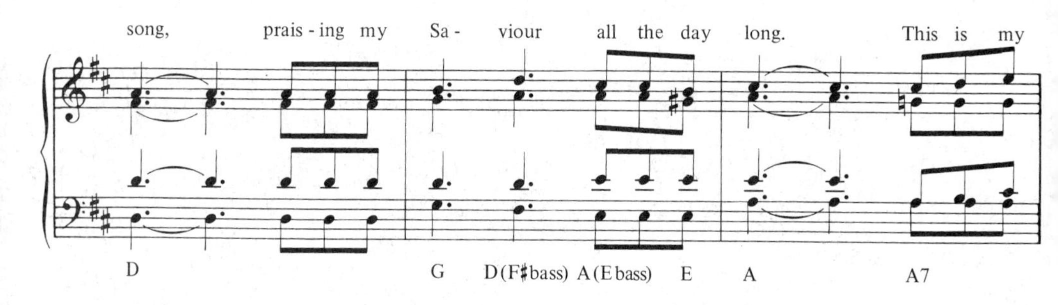

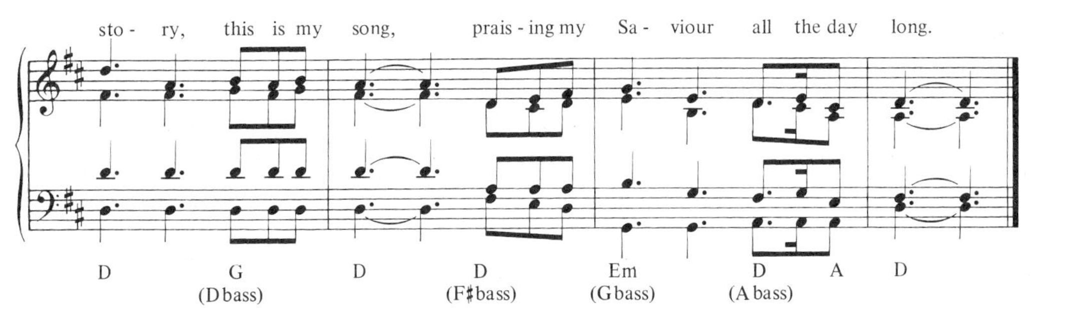

2. Perfect submission, perfect delight,
   visions of rapture burst on my sight;
   angels descending, bring from above
   echoes of mercy, whispers of love.

3. Perfect submission, all is at rest,
   I in my Saviour am happy and blest;
   watching and waiting, looking above,
   filled with his goodness, lost in his love.

Words: Frances van Alstyne (1820-1915)
Music: J.F. Knapp (1839-1908)

BLESSED BE THE NAME

2. Jesus is the name, Jesus is the name, Jesus is the name of the Lord! *(2)*

3. Worthy of all praise, worthy of all praise, worthy of all praise is the Lord! *(2)*

4. Christ has set us free, Christ has set us free, Christ has set us free to be his! *(2)*

5. We are called to live, we are called to live, we are called to live in God's love. *(2)*

Words: Verses 1 & 2 – Unknown; Verses 3–5 – Robert B. Kelly
Music: Unknown, arranged by Frances M. Kelly

BLEST ARE THE PURE IN HEART

('Franconia' S.M.)

[HARMONY]

2. The Lord who left the heavens
   our life and peace to bring,
   to dwell in lowliness with men,
   their pattern and their king.

3. Still to the lowly soul
   he doth himself impart
   and for his dwelling and his throne
   chooseth the pure in heart.

4. Lord, we thy presence seek;
   may ours this blessing be:
   give us a pure and lowly heart,
   a temple meet for thee.

Words: Vv. 1 & 3 - John Keble (1792-1866)
Vv. 2 & 4 - W. J. Hall's 'Psalms and Hymns' (1836)
Music: Traditional melody,
arranged by W. H. Havergal (1793-1870)

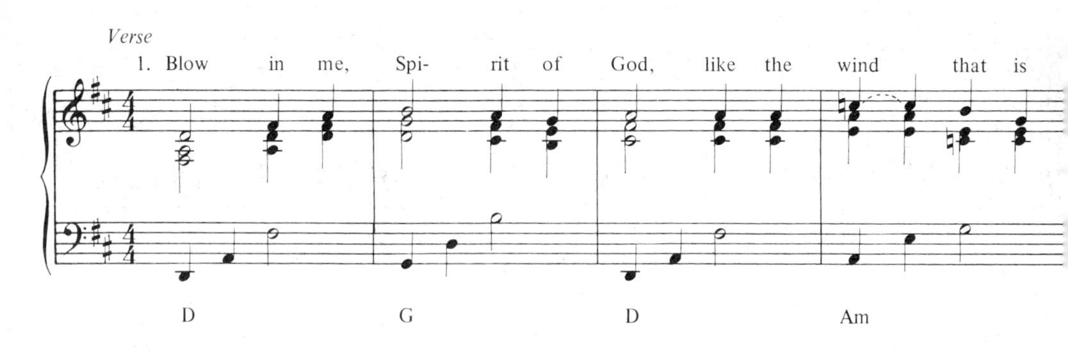
Verse
1. Blow in me, Spi- rit of God, like the wind that is
D
G
D
Am

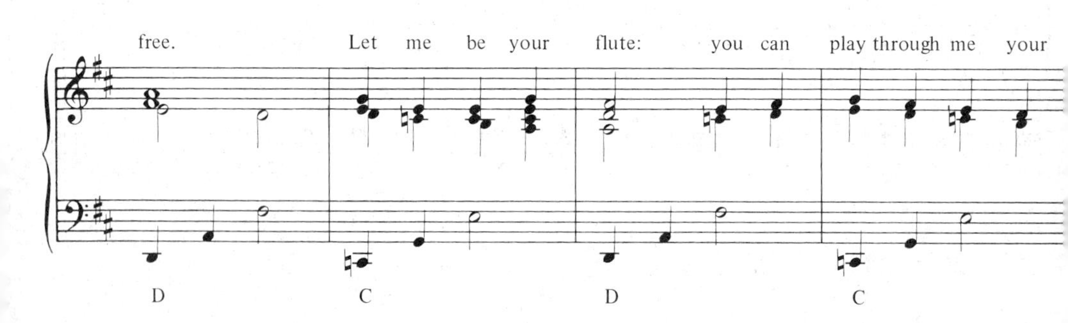
free. Let me be your flute: you can play through me your
D
C
D
C

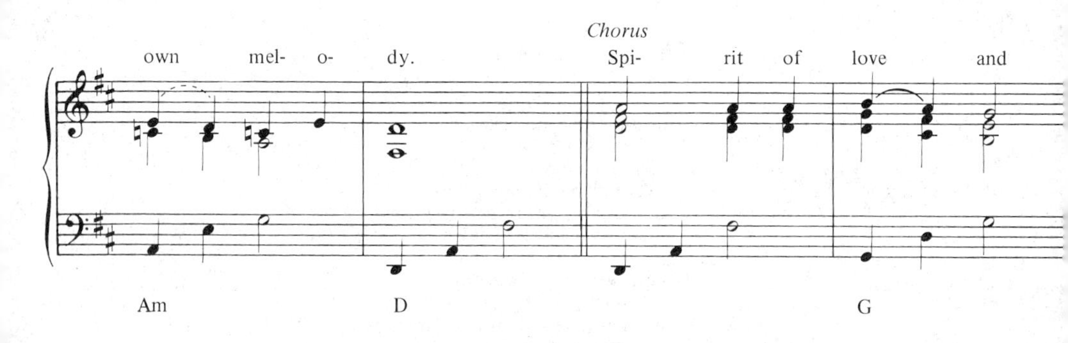
Chorus
own mel- o- dy. Spi- rit of love and
Am
D
G

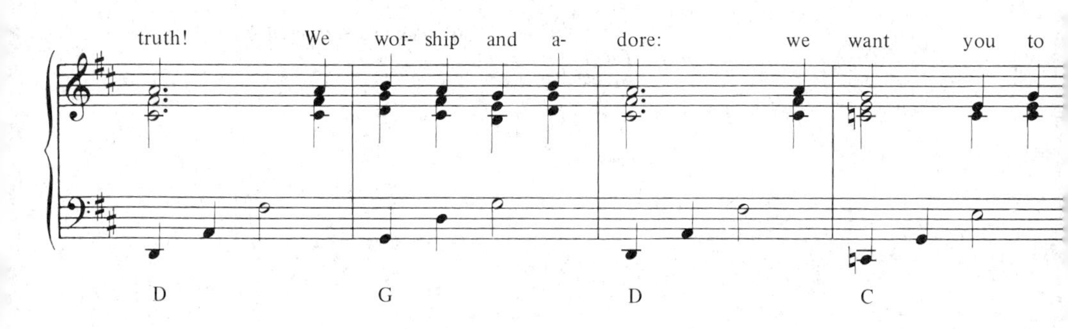
truth! We wor- ship and a- dore: we want you to
D
G
D
C

As a final Coda, repeat the last three bars, over and over again, fading into silence.

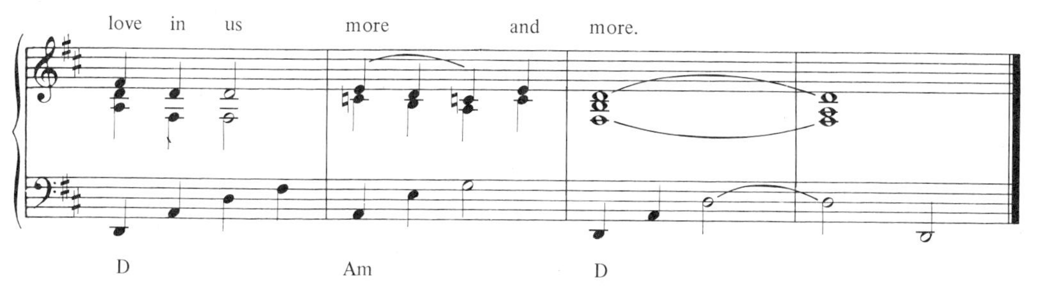

2. Pour in me, Spirit of God,
   like the water that is free.
   Let me be your cup:
   you can fill me full,
   and all can drink of me.

3. Burn in me, Spirit of God,
   like the flame that is free.
   Let me be your lamp:
   you can shine in me
   and bring the blind to see.

4. Fly o'er me, Spirit of God,
   like a bird that is free.
   Let me be your nest:
   you can sing in me
   of love and unity.

Words and Music: Theresa Margaret C.H.N.
arranged by John Rombaut

BREAD OF HEAVEN, ON THEE WE FEED

('Bread of heaven' 77.77.77.)

[HARMONY]

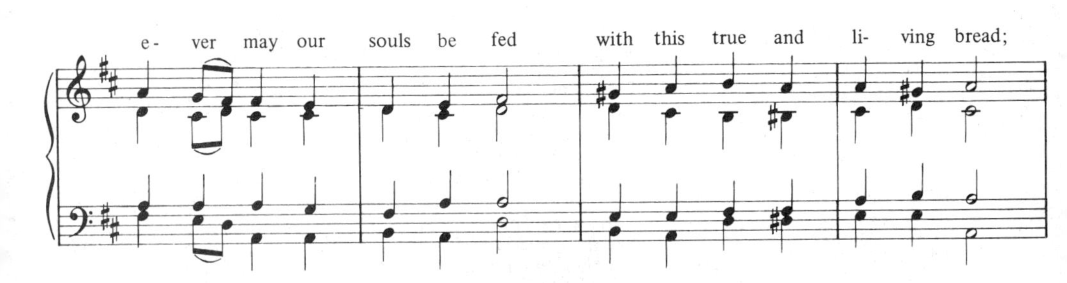

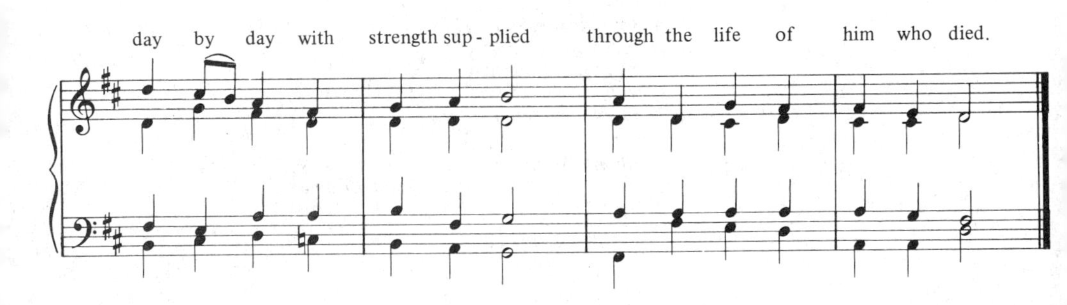

2. Vine of heaven, thy blood supplies
this blest cup of sacrifice;
Lord, thy wounds our healing give,
to thy cross we look and live:
Jesus, may we ever be
grafted, rooted, built in thee.

Words: Josiah Conder (1789-1855)
Music: William Dalrymple Maclagan (1826-1910)

BREAD OF THE WORLD IN MERCY BROKEN

53

(First tune: 'Psalm 118 - Rendez à Dieu' 98.98.D.)

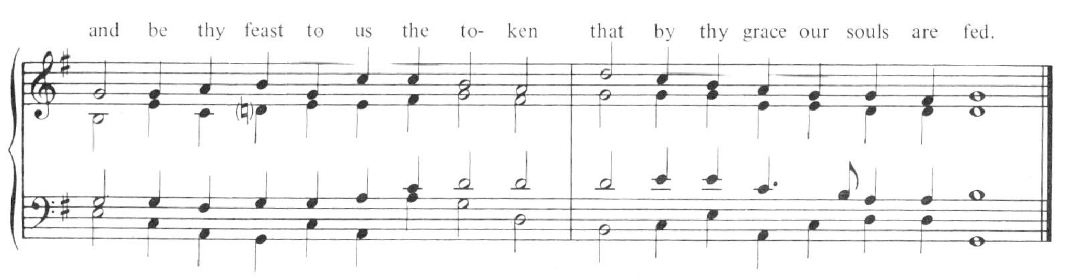

Words: Reginald Heber (1783-1826)
Music: First tune - 'Genevan Psalter' (1543),
composed or arranged by Louis Bourgeois

Second tune overleaf

BREAD OF THE WORLD IN MERCY BROKEN

(Second tune: 'Redstones' 98.98.D.)

2. Look on the heart by sorrows broken,
look on the tears by sinners shed;
and be thy feast to us the token
that by thy grace our souls are fed.

Words: Reginald Heber (1783-1826)
Music: Second tune - Lancelot Hankey

BREATHE ON ME, BREATH OF GOD
('Carlisle' S.M.)

This tune can be found in a different harmonisation at Hymn 428

2. Breathe on me, Breath of God,
   until my heart is pure:
   until with thee I have one will
   to do and to endure.

3. Breathe on me, Breath of God,
   till I am wholly thine,
   until this earthly part of me
   glows with thy fire divine.

4. Breathe on me, Breath of God,
   so shall I never die,
   but live with thee the perfect life
   of thine eternity.

Words: Edwin Hatch (1835-89)
Music: Charles Lockhart (1745-1815)

55

BRIGHT THE VISION THAT DELIGHTED

('Laus Deo' 87.87.)

[HARMONY]

1. Bright the vi- sion that de- ligh- ted once the sight of Ju- dah's seer;

sweet the count- less tongues u- ni- ted to en- trance the pro- phet's ear.

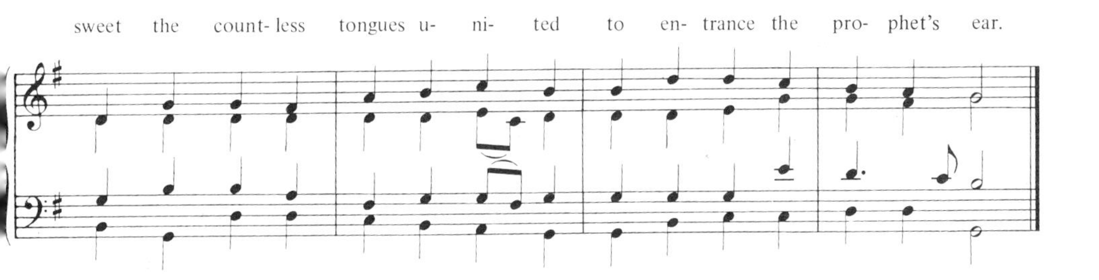

2. Round the Lord in glory seated
cherubim and seraphim
filled his temple, and repeated
each to each the alternate hymn:

3. 'Lord, thy glory fills the heaven;
earth is with its fullness stored;
unto thee be glory given,
holy, holy, holy Lord'.

4. Heaven is still with glory ringing,
earth takes up the angels' cry,
'Holy, holy, holy,' singing,
'Lord of hosts, the Lord most high.'

5. With his seraph train before him,
with his holy Church below,
thus unite we to adore him,
bid we thus our anthem flow:

6. 'Lord, thy glory fills the heaven;
earth is with its fullness stored;
unto thee be glory given,
holy, holy, holy Lord.'

Words, based on Isaiah 6 and Revelation 5: Richard Mant (1776-1848)
Music: Richard Redhead (1820-1901)

Chorus
Bro- ken for me, bro- ken for you;
E G♯m C♯m F♯m B7
Last time to Coda
the bo- dy of Je- sus bro- ken for you.
E G♯m C♯m F♯m B7
Verse
1. He of- fered his bo- dy, he poured out his soul;
2. Come to my ta- ble and with me dine;
3. This is my bo- dy giv- en for you;
4. This is my blood I shed for you,
E F♯m A (B bass) B
Je- sus was bro- ken that we might be whole.
eat of my bread and drink of my wine.
eat it, re- mem- b'ring I died for you.
for your for- give- ness, mak- ing you new.
G♯m F♯m Am (F♯bass) B
D.C.

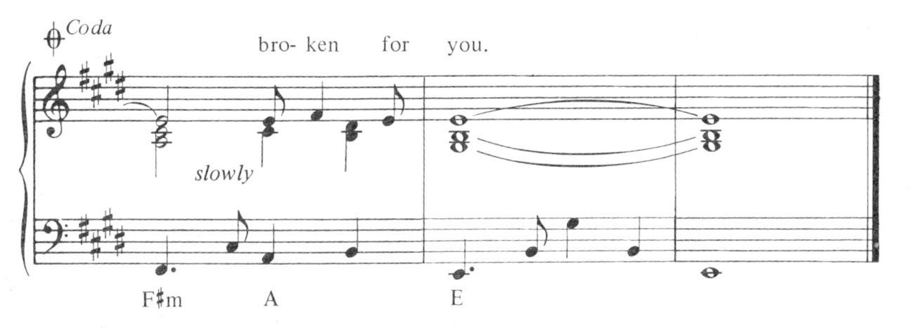

2. Come to my table
   and with me dine;
   eat of my bread
   and drink of my wine.

3. This is my body
   given for you;
   eat it, rememb'ring
   I died for you.

4. This is my blood
   I shed for you,
   for your forgiveness,
   making you new.

Words and Music: Colin and Janet Lunt,
arranged by John Rombaut

BROTHER, LET ME BE YOUR SERVANT **(The servant song)**

[HARMONY]

With warmth, moving along

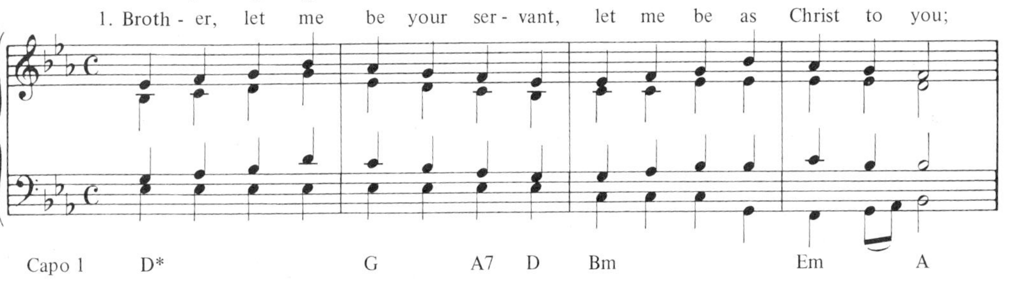

2. We are pilgrims on a journey,
   we are brothers on the road;
   we are here to help each other
   walk the mile and bear the load.

3. I will hold the Christlight for you
   in the night-time of your fear;
   I will hold my hand out to you,
   speak the peace you long to hear.

4. I will weep when you are weeping;
   when you laugh I'll laugh with you.
   I will share your joy and sorrow
   'til we've seen this journey through.

5. When we sing to God in heaven
   we shall find such harmony,
   born of all we've known together
   of Christ's love and agony.

6. Brother, let me be your servant,
   let me be as Christ to you;
   pray that I may have the grace to
   let you be my servant, too.

Words: Richard Gillard
Music: Richard Gillard, arranged by Betty Pulkingham

**Guitar chords and vocal harmonies are not designed to be used together.*

58 BUILD YOUR CHURCH

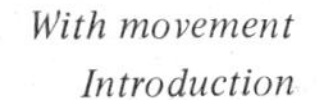

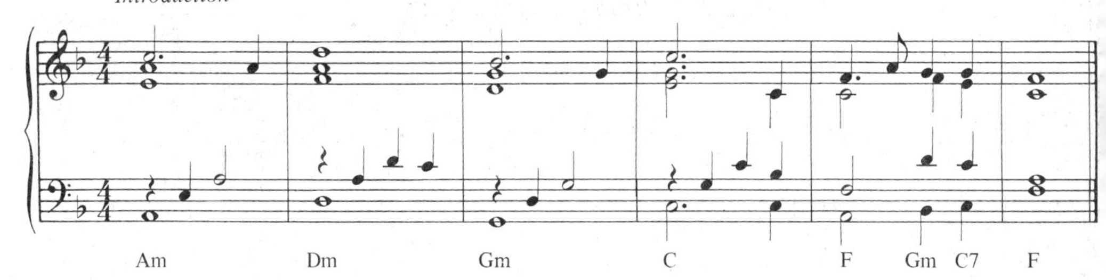

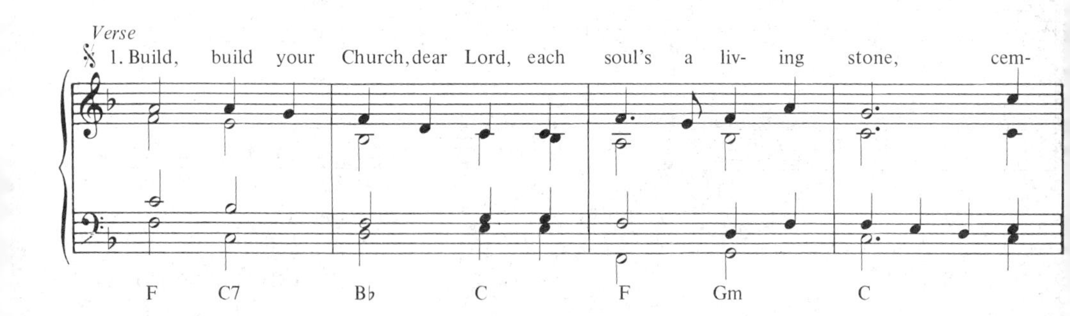

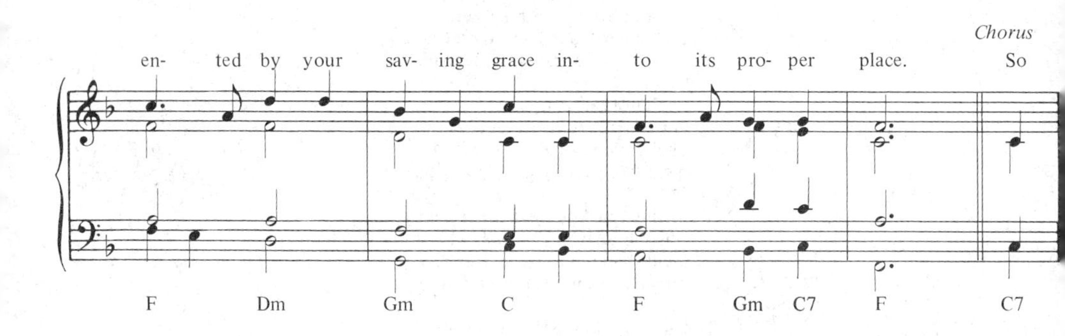

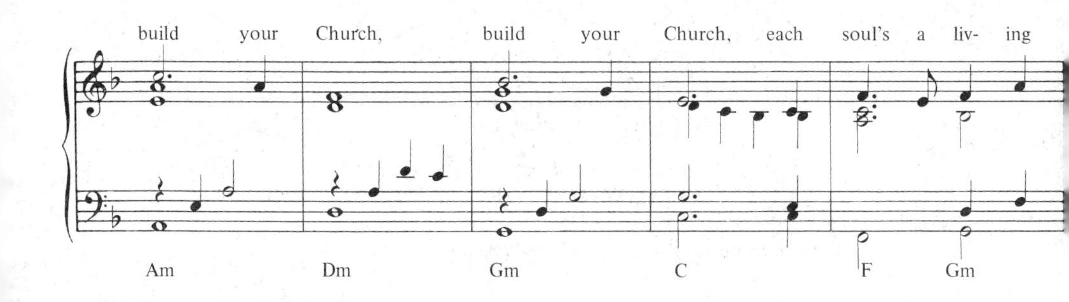

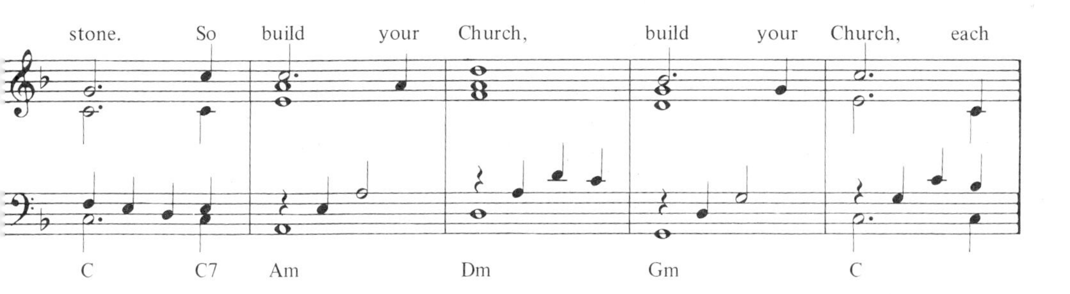

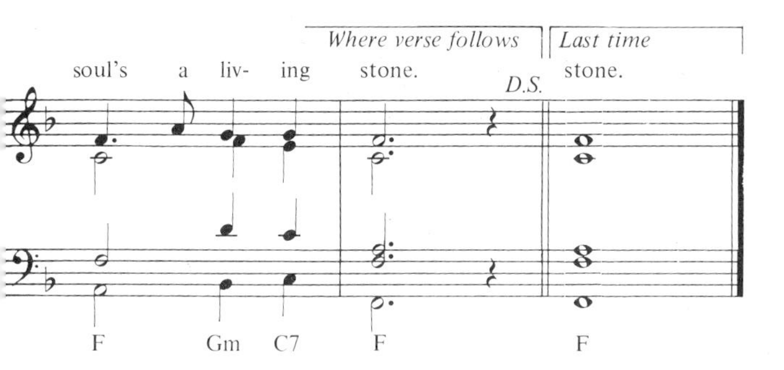

2. Build, build your Church, dear Lord,
you work with nails and wood,
well used to fixing things in place
with carefulness and grace.

3. Build, build your Church, dear Lord;
though stones on earth seem few,
let those whose lives are falling down
be lifted up in you.

4. Build, build your Church, dear Lord;
the door leave open wide,
and all of those who follow Christ
will find their place inside.

Words, based on 1 Peter 2: Graham Jeffery
Music: Kevin Mayhew

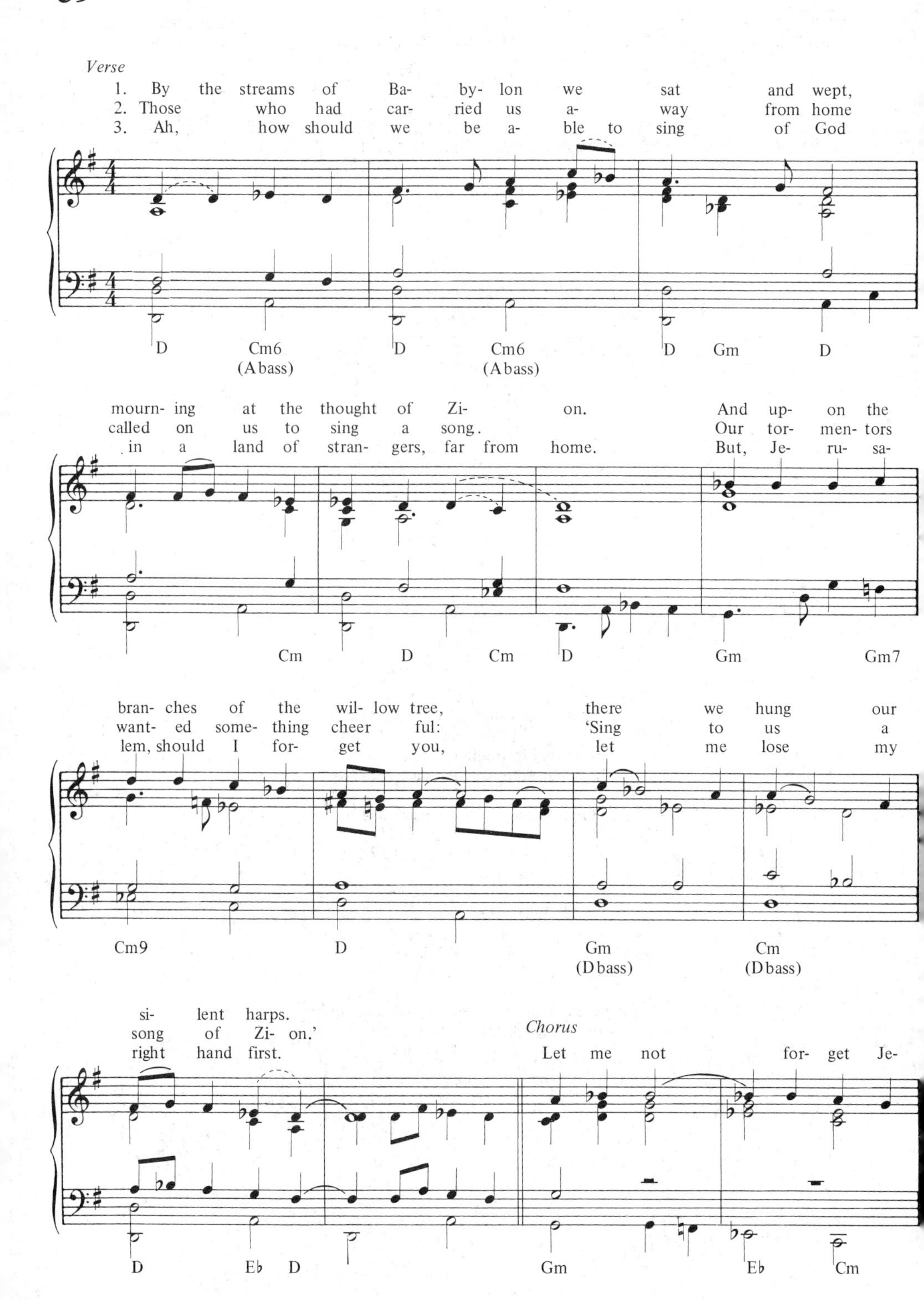

Verse
1. By the streams of Ba- by- lon we sat and wept,
2. Those who had car- ried us a- way from home
3. Ah, how should we be a- ble to sing of God
D Cm6 (A bass) D Cm6 (A bass) D Gm D
mourn- ing at the thought of Zi- on. And up- on the
called on us to sing a song. Our tor- men- tors
in a land of stran- gers, far from home. But, Je- ru- sa-
Cm D Cm D Gm Gm7
bran- ches of the wil- low tree, there we hung our
want- ed some- thing cheer ful: 'Sing to us a
lem, should I for- get you, let me lose my
Cm9 D Gm (D bass) Cm (D bass)
si- lent harps.
song of Zi- on.'
right hand first.
Chorus
Let me not for- get Je-
D E♭ D Gm E♭ Cm

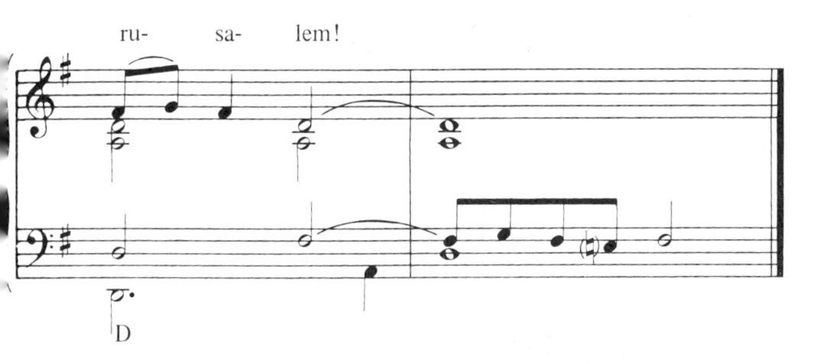

Words, based on Huub Oosterhuis' version of Psalm 137, and Music: Frances M. Kelly

BY THE WATERS OF BABYLON

60

This may be sung as a round. The second voice enters at the fifth bar.

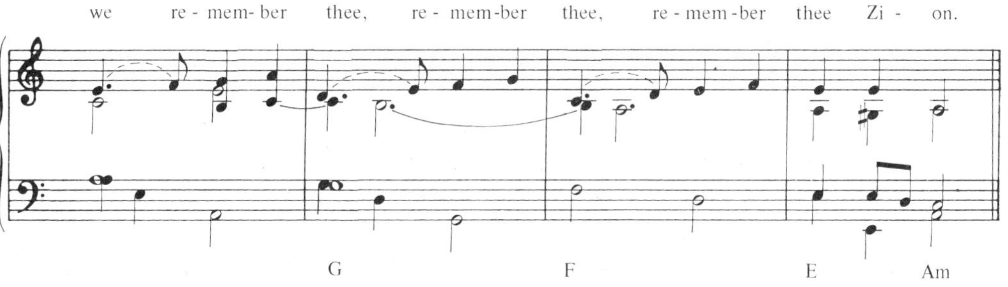

2. On the willows, the willows of Babylon,
   we hung up our harps, for thee Zion;
   how can we sing, can we sing, sing of thee Zion.

3. There our captors, our captors from Babylon,
   tried to make us sing, and sing, of thee Zion;
   but we could not sing, we could not sing, we could not sing Zion.

Words: (based on Psalm 137)
Music: Don McLean and Lee Hays

Introduction

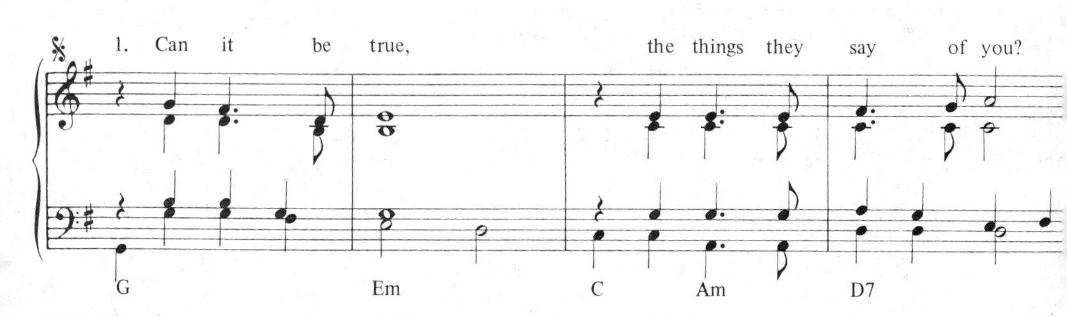

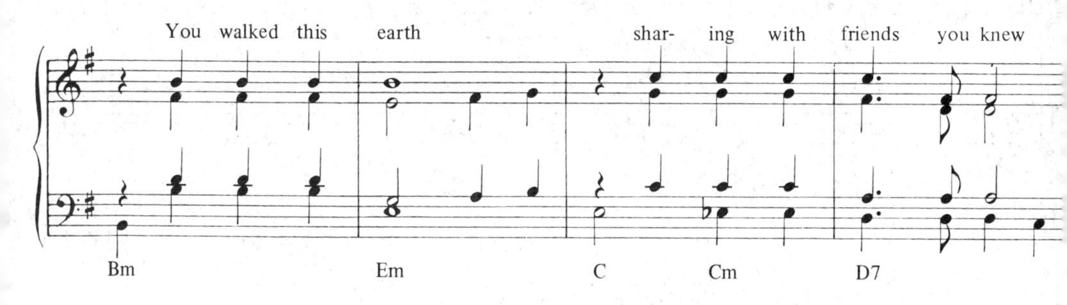

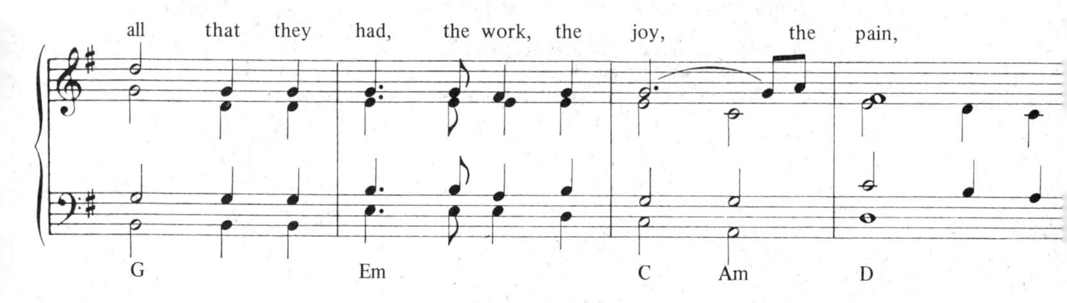

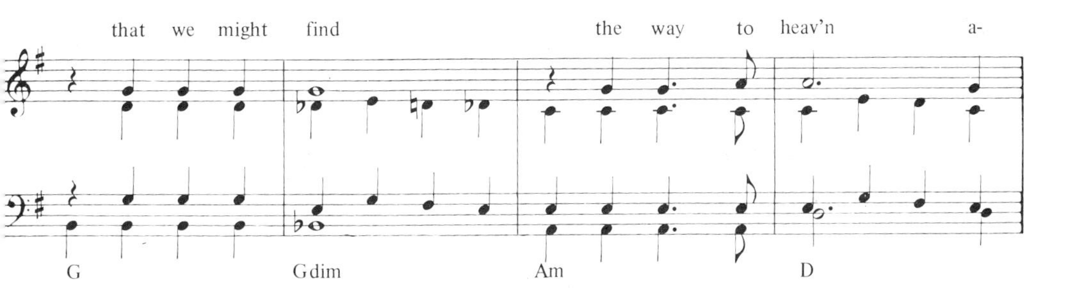

2. And day by day you still return this way;
 but we recall there was a debt to pay:
 out of your love for your own world above,
 you left that holy thing, your endless love to prove.

3. Can it be true, the things they did to you -
 the death, the shame, and were your friends so few?
 yet you returned again alive and free -
 can it be true, my Lord, it had to be.

Words and Music: *Brother William,*
arranged by John Rombaut

62

CHILD IN THE MANGER

('Bunessan' 10 8.10 8.)

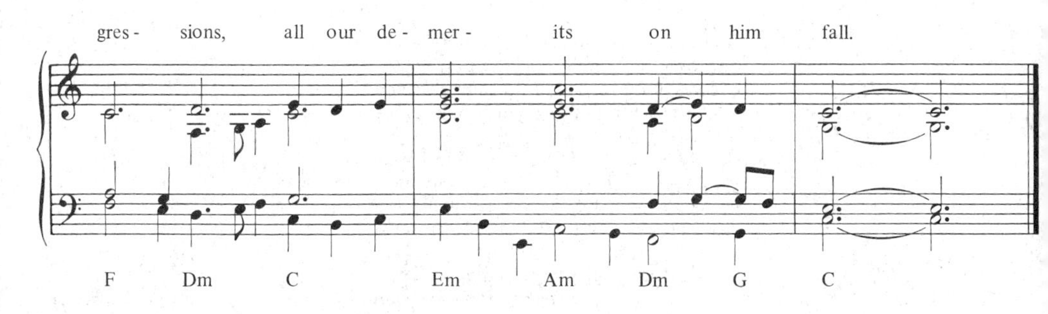

A different arrangement of the tune is at Hymn 326

2. Once the most holy child of salvation
gentle and lowly lived below;
now as our glorious mighty Redeemer,
see him victorious o'er each foe.

3. Prophets foretold him, infant of wonder;
angels behold him on his throne;
worthy our Saviour of all their praises;
happy for ever are his own.

Words: Mary Macdonald (1817-1890),
tr. Lachlan Macbean (1853-1931)
Music: Traditional Gaelic melody,
arranged by Una Macdonald

CHILDREN OF THE HEAVENLY KING

('Melling' 77.77.)

2. We are travelling home to God
in the way the fathers trod;
they are happy now, and we
soon their happiness shall see.

3. Lift your eyes, ye sons of light!
Zion's city is in sight;
there our endless home shall be,
there our Lord we soon shall see.

4. Fear not, brethren! joyful stand
on the borders of your land;
Jesus Christ, your Father's Son,
bids you undismayed go on.

5. Lord, obedient we would go,
gladly leaving all below;
only thou our leader be,
and we still will follow thee.

Words: John Cennick (1718-55)
Music: John Fawcett (1789-1867)
harmonised by John Rombaut

CHRIST BE BESIDE ME

('Bunessan' 55.54.D.)

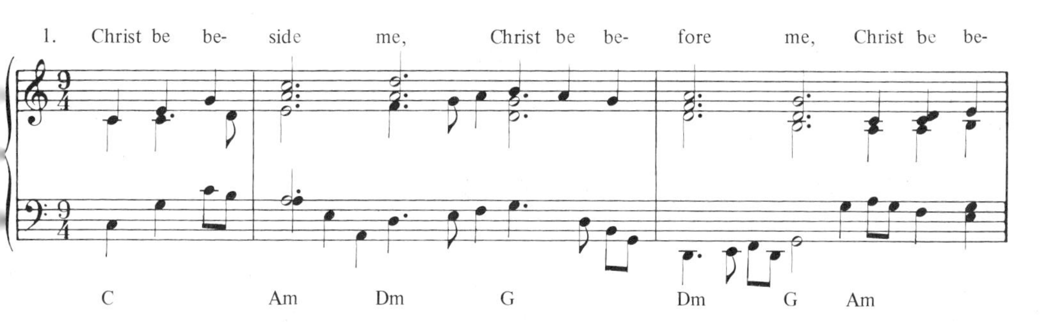

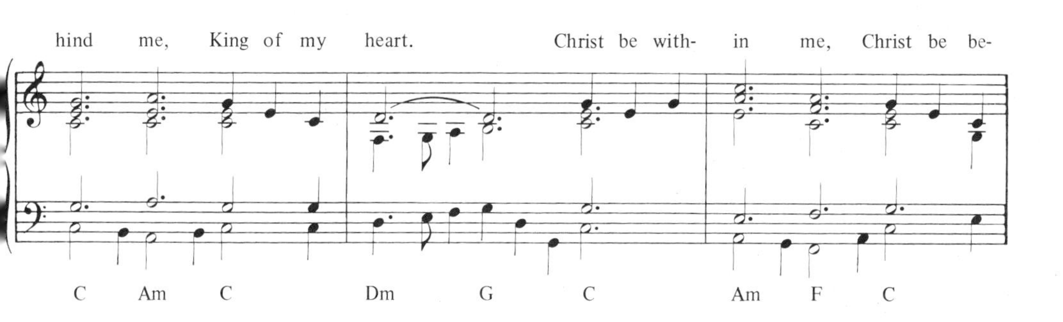

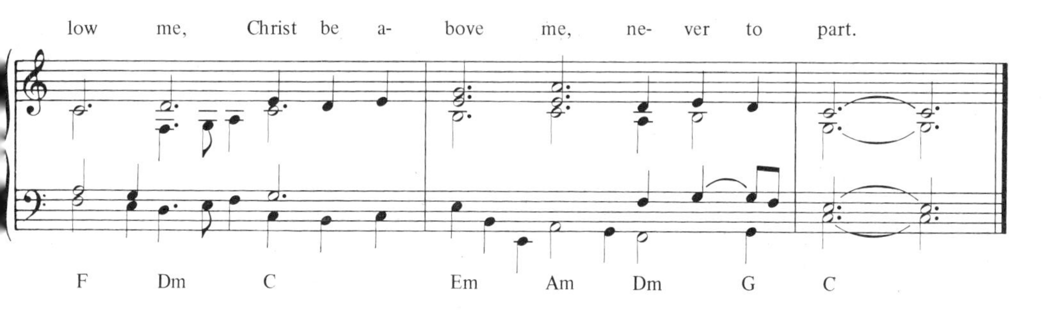

A different arrangement of the tune is at Hymn 326

2. Christ on my right hand,
Christ on my left hand,
Christ all around me,
shield in the strife.
Christ in my sleeping,
Christ in my sitting,
Christ in my rising,
light of my life.

3. Christ be in all hearts
thinking about me.
Christ be on all tongues
telling of me.
Christ be the vision
in eyes that see me,
in ears that hear me,
Christ ever be.

Words: Adapted from 'St Patrick's Breastplate' by James Quinn
Music: Traditional Gaelic melody, arranged by Una MacDonald

CHRISTIANS AWAKE! SALUTE THE HAPPY MORN

('Yorkshire' 10 10.10 10.10 10.)

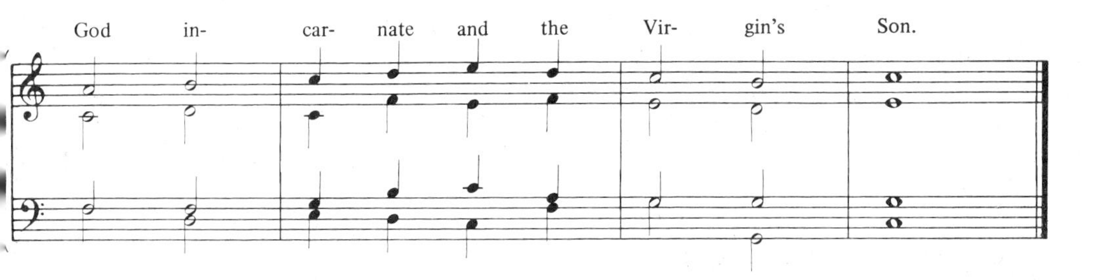

2. Then to the watchful shepherds it was told,
who heard th'angelic herald's voice, 'Behold,
I bring good tidings of a Saviour's birth
to you and all the nations on the earth:
this day hath God fulfilled his promised word,
this day is born a Saviour, Christ the Lord.'

3. He spake; and straightway the celestial choir
in hymns of joy, unknown before, conspire;
the praises of redeeming love they sang,
and heaven's whole orb with alleluias rang:
God's highest glory was their anthem still,
peace upon earth, and unto men good will.

4. To Bethl'hem straight th'enlightened shepherds ran,
to see the wonder God had wrought for man,
and found, with Joseph and the Blessèd Maid,
her son, the Saviour, in a manger laid:
then to their flocks, still praising God, return,
and their glad hearts with holy rapture burn.

5. O may we keep and ponder in our mind
God's wondrous love in saving lost mankind;
trace we the Babe, who hath retrieved our loss,
from his poor manger to his bitter cross;
tread in his steps, assisted by his grace,
till man's first heavenly state again takes place.

6. Then may we hope, th'angelic hosts among,
to sing, redeemed, a glad triumphal song:
he that was born upon this joyful day
around us all his glory shall display;
saved by his love, incessant we shall sing
eternal praise to heaven's almighty King.

Words: John Byrom (1691-1763)
Music: John Wainwright (1723-68),
arranged by W. H. Monk (1823-89)

66 CHRIST IS MADE THE SURE FOUNDATION

[HARMONY]

('Westminster Abbey' 87.87.87.)

2. All that dedicated City,
dearly loved by God on high,
in exultant jubilation
pours perpetual melody:
God the One, and God the Trinal,
singing everlastingly.

3. To this temple, where we call thee
come, O Lord of Hosts, today;
with thy wonted loving kindness
hear thy people as they pray;
and thy fullest benediction
shed within its walls for ay.

4. Here vouchsafe to all thy servants
what they supplicate to gain;
here to have and hold for ever
those good things their prayers obtain,
and hereafter in thy glory
with thy blessed ones to reign.

5. Laud and honour to the Father;
laud and honour to the Son;
laud and honour to the Spirit;
ever Three and ever One:
consubstantial, co-eternal,
while unending ages run.

Words, based on 1 Peter 2: 'Urbs beata Jerusalem' (c. 7th cent.), tr. J. M. Neale
Music: H. Purcell (1659-95), arr. E. Hawkins (1802-68)

CHRIST IS OUR CORNERSTONE

('Harewood' 66.66.88.)

67

[HARMONY]

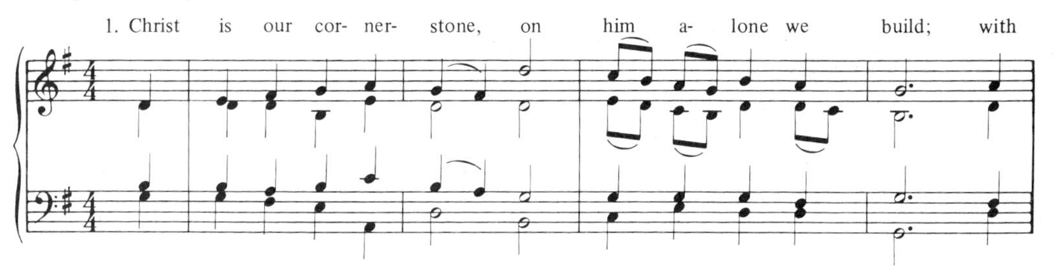

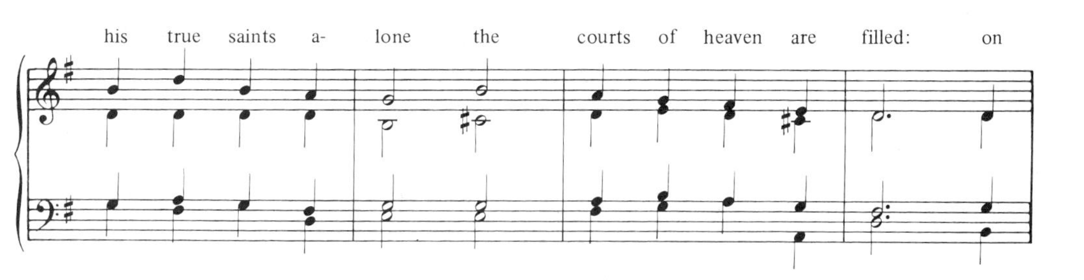

2. O then with hymns of praise
these hallowed courts shall ring;
our voices we will raise
the Three in One to sing;
    and thus proclaim
    in joyful song,
    both loud and long,
    that glorious name.

3. Here, gracious God, do thou
for evermore draw nigh;
accept each faithful vow,
and mark each suppliant sigh;
    in copious shower
    on all who pray
    each holy day
    thy blessings pour.

4. Here may we gain from heaven
the grace which we implore;
and may that grace, once given,
be with us evermore,
    until that day
    when all the blest
    to endless rest
    are called away.

Words, based on 1 Peter 2: from the Latin (7th century),
tr. J. Chandler
Music: Samuel Sebastian Wesley (1810-1876)

68

CHRIST IS THE KING! O FRIENDS REJOICE
('Gelobt sei Gott' 888. & Alleluias)

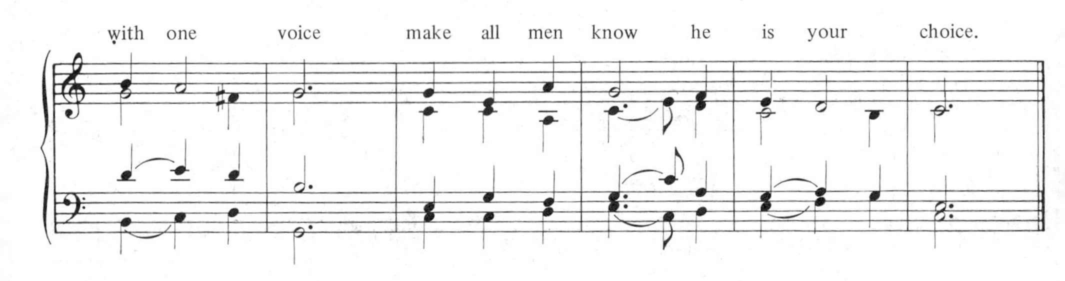

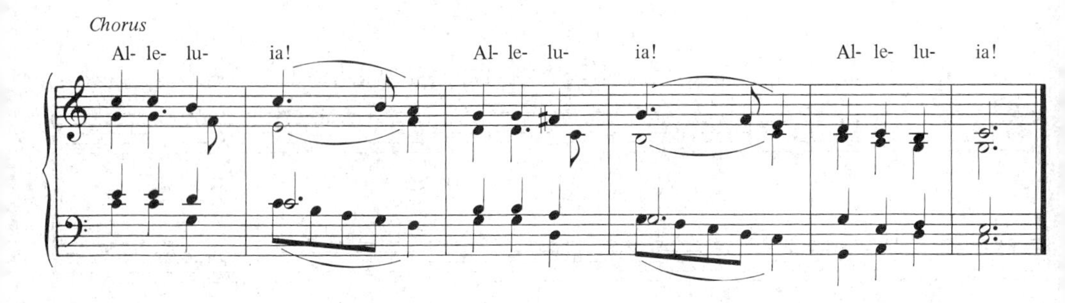

2. O magnify the Lord, and raise
anthems of joy and holy praise
for Christ's brave saints of ancient days.

3. They with a faith for ever new
followed the King, and round him drew
thousands of faithful men and true.

4. O Christian women, Christian men,
all the world over, seek again
the Way disciples followed then.

5. Christ through all ages is the same:
place the same hope in his great name,
with the same faith his Word proclaim.

6. Let Love's unconquerable might
your scattered companies unite
in service to the Lord of light.

7. So shall God's will on earth be done,
new lamps be lit, new tasks begun,
and the whole Church at last be one.

Words: George Kennedy Allen Bell (1883-1958)
Music: from Melchior Vulpius (c. 1560-1616)

CHRIST THE LORD IS RISEN AGAIN
('Wurtemburg' 77.77.4.)

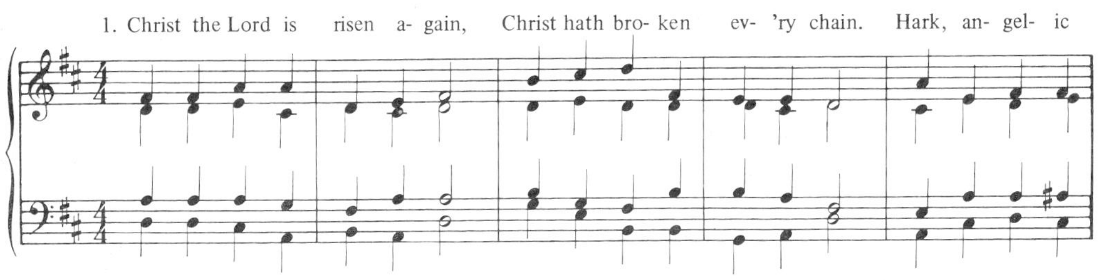

2. He who gave for us his life,
who for us endured the strife,
is our paschal Lamb to-day;
we too sing for joy, and say: Alleluia.

3. He who bore all pain and loss
comfortless upon the cross,
lives in glory now on high,
pleads for us, and hears our cry: Alleluia.

4. He whose path no records tell,
who descended into hell,
who the strong man armed hath bound,
now in highest heaven is crowned. Alleluia.

5. He who slumbered in the grave
is exalted now to save;
now through Christendom it rings
that the Lamb is King of kings. Alleluia.

6. Now he bids us tell abroad
how the lost may be restored,
how the penitent forgiven,
how we too may enter heaven. Alleluia.

7. Thou, our paschal Lamb indeed,
Christ, thy ransomed people feed;
take our sins and guilt away:
let us sing by night and day. Alleluia.

Words: Michael Weisse (c. 1480-1534),
tr. Catherine Winkworth
Music: from 'Hundert Arien' (Dresden, 1694),
perhaps by J. Rosenmuller

70

CHRIST TRIUMPHANT, EVER REIGNING

('Christ triumphant' 85.85. & Chorus)

With triumphant vigour

2. Word incarnate, truth revealing,
   Son of Man on earth!
   Power and majesty concealing
   by your humble birth:

3. Suffering servant, scorned, ill-treated,
   victim crucified!
   Death is through the cross defeated,
   sinners justified:

4. Priestly King, enthroned for ever
   high in heaven above!
   Sin and death and hell shall never
   stifle hymns of love:

5. So, our hearts and voices raising
   through the ages long,
   ceaselessly upon you gazing,
   this shall be our song:

Words: Michael Saward (b. 1932)
Music: Michael Baughen (b. 1930)

CHRIST, WHOSE GLORY FILLS THE SKIES

('Ratisbon' 77.77.77.)

[HARMONY]

2. Dark and cheerless is the morn
unaccompanied by thee;
joyless is the day's return,
till thy mercy's beams I see;
till they inward light impart,
glad my eyes, and warm my heart.

3. Visit then this soul of mine,
pierce the gloom of sin and grief;
fill me, radiancy divine,
scatter all my unbelief;
more and more thyself display,
shining to the perfect day.

Words: Charles Wesley (1707-1788)
Music: from Werner's Choralbuch (Leipzig, 1815)

CITY OF GOD, HOW BROAD AND FAR
('Richmond' C.M.)

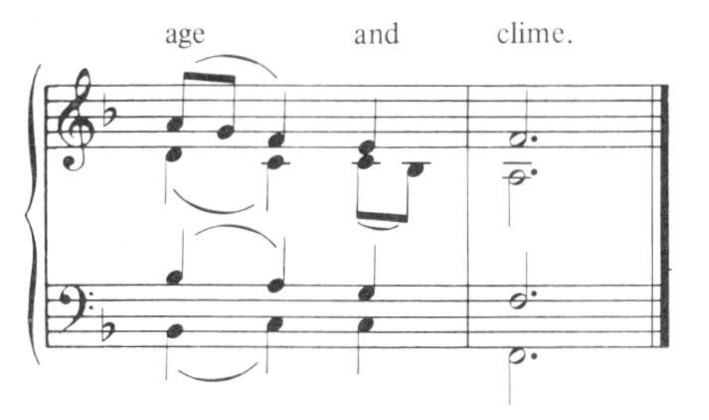

2. One holy Church, one army strong,
   one steadfast, high intent;
   one working band, one harvest song,
   one King omnipotent.

3. How purely hath thy speech come down
   from man's primeval youth!
   How grandly hath thine empire grown
   of freedom, love, and truth!

4. How gleam thy watch-fires through the night
   with never-fainting ray!
   How rise thy towers, serene and bright,
   to meet the dawning day!

5. In vain the surge's angry shock,
   in vain the drifting sands:
   unharmed upon the eternal Rock
   the eternal city stands.

Words: Samuel Johnson (1822-82)
Music: adapted from T. Haweis (1734-1820)

CLEANSE US, O LORD (Sprinkling song)

The guitar chords are a simplification, and should not be used with the keyboard arrangement.

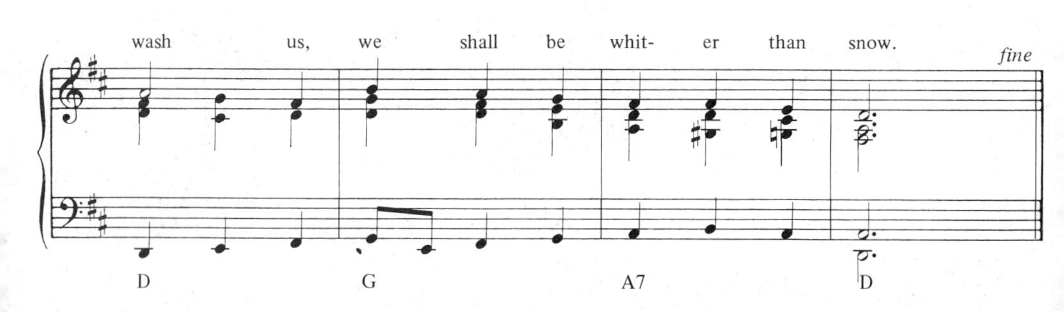

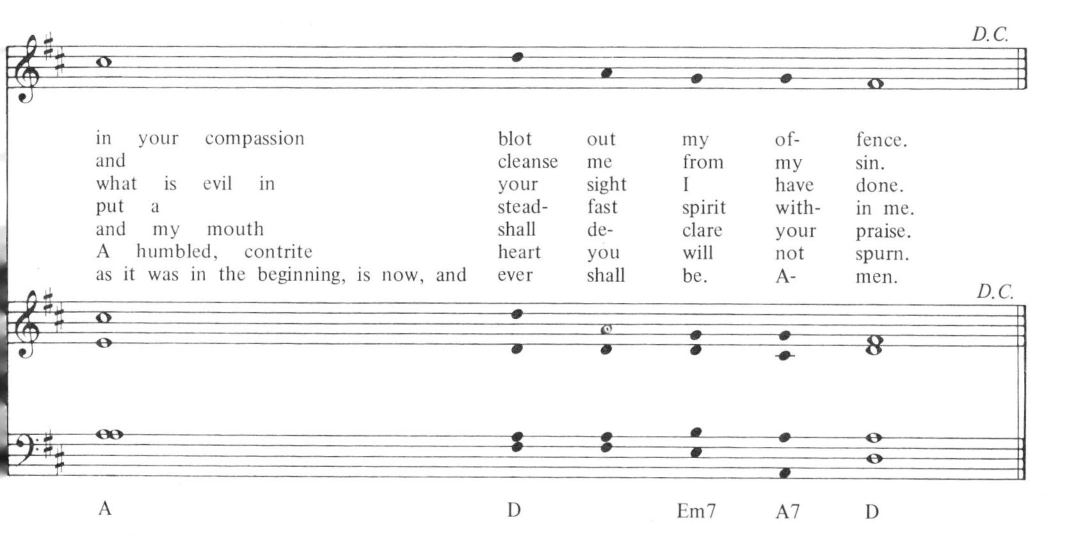

Words: Psalm 51
Music: Response – Peter Sacco
Psalm tone – F.A.G. Ouseley (1825-89)

74 COLOURS OF DAY (Light up the fire

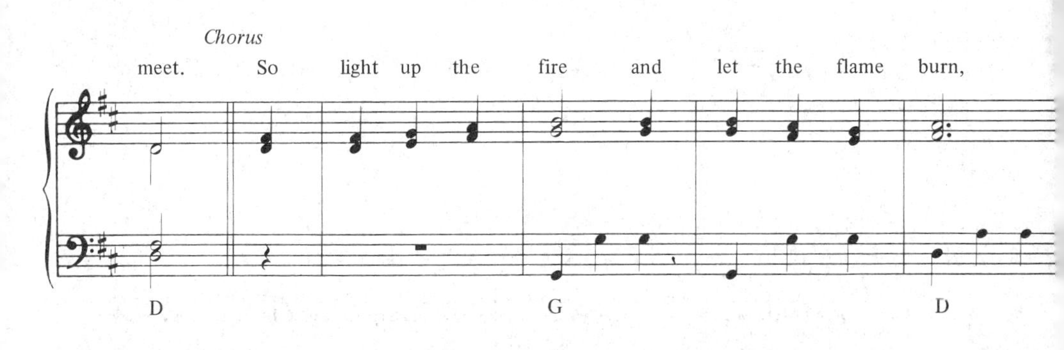

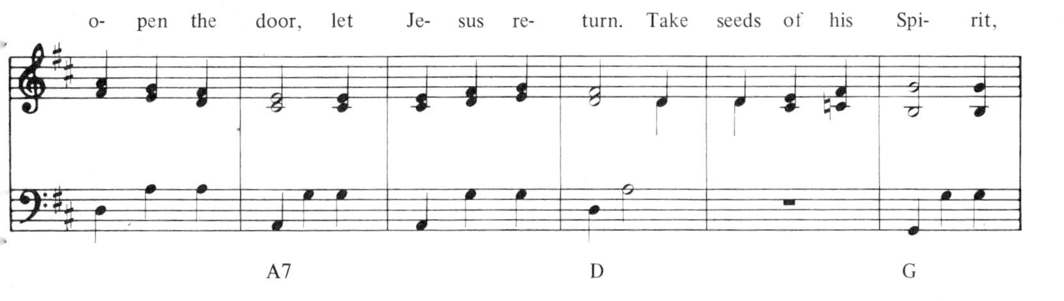

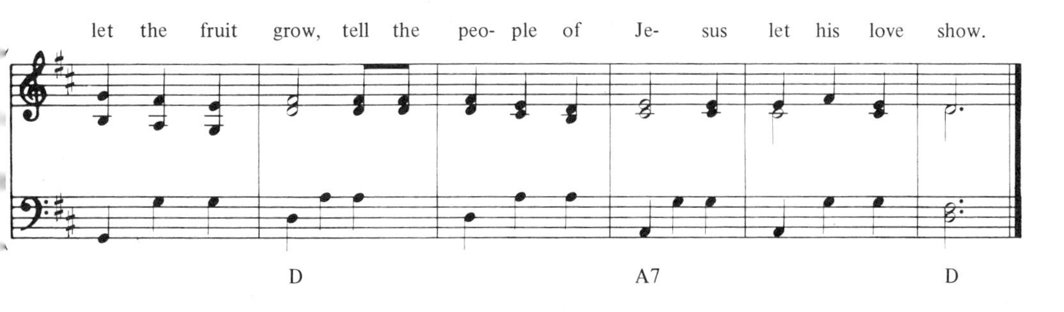

2. Go through the park, on into the town;
the sun still shines on, it never goes down.
The light of the world is risen again;
the people of darkness are needing our friend.

3. Open your eyes, look into the sky,
the darkness has come, the sun came to die.
The evening draws on, the sun disappears,
but Jesus is living, and his Spirit is near.

Words and Music: Sue McClellan, John Pac and Keith Ryecroft.

A simplified guitar accompaniment is given overleaf

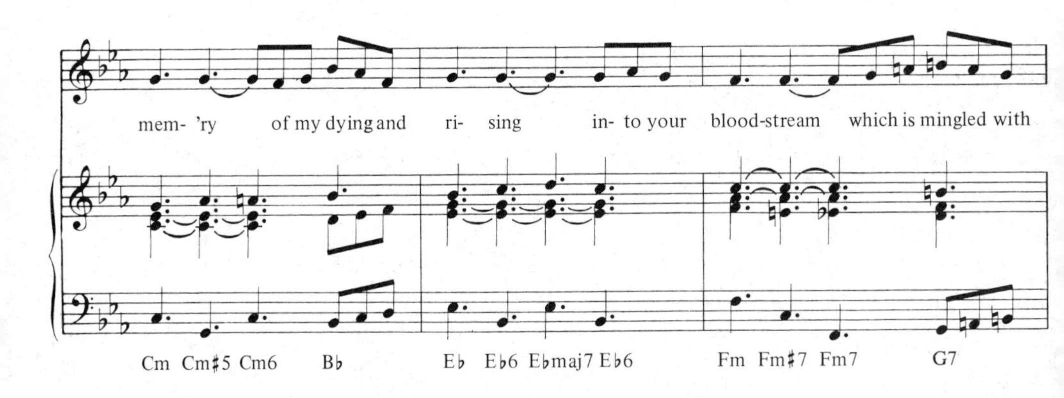

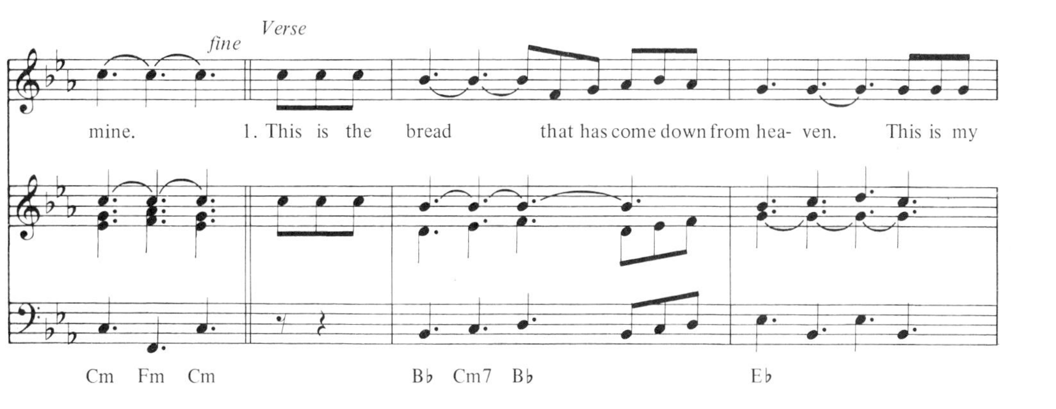

2. He leads us out of the power of darkness,
   and brings us safe to his kingdom of life. *(Col. 1: 13)*

3. No longer I, but now Christ lives within me.
   I live by faith in the Son of our God. *(Gal. 2: 20)*

4. For those in Christ there is no condemnation.
   He sets them free through the Spirit he sends. *(Rom. 8: 1-2)*

5. Thus shall the world know you are my disciples,
   if you can love, and if you can forgive. *(John)*

Words, based on Scripture, and Music: Aniceto Nazareth

See overleaf for a simplified guitar accompaniment

Simplified guitar accompaniment.

3. No longer I, but now Christ lives within me.
I live by faith in the Son of our God. *(Gal 2: 20)*

4. For those in Christ there is no condemnation.
He sets them free through the Spirit he sends. *(Rom 8: 1-2)*

5. Thus shall the world know you are my disciples,
if you can love, and if you can forgive. *(John)*

Words, based on Scripture, and Music: Aniceto Nazareth

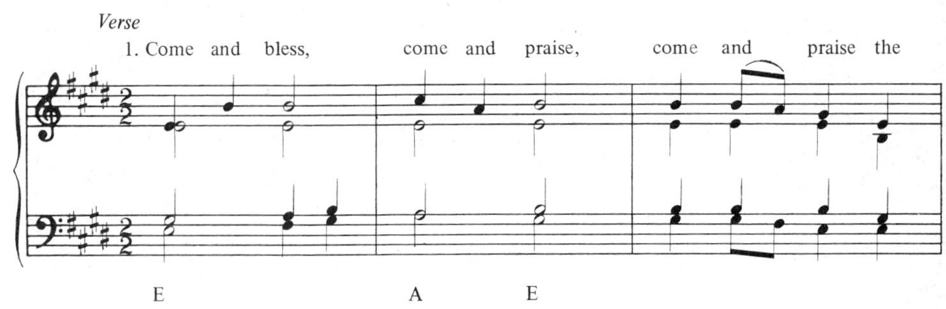
Verse
1. Come and bless, come and praise, come and praise the
E A E

liv- ing God. Al- le- lu, al- le- lu, al- le- lu- ia, Je- sus
B7 E A E B7

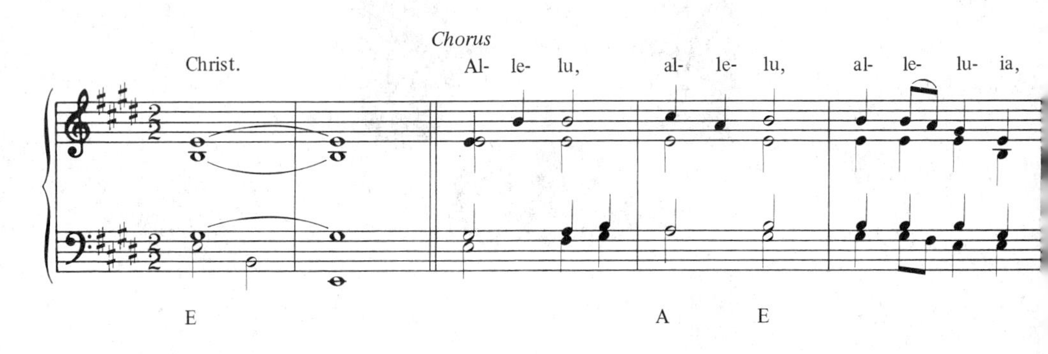
Chorus
Christ. Al- le- lu, al- le- lu, al- le- lu- ia,
E A E

Je- sus Christ. Al- le- lu, al- le- lu,
B7 E A E

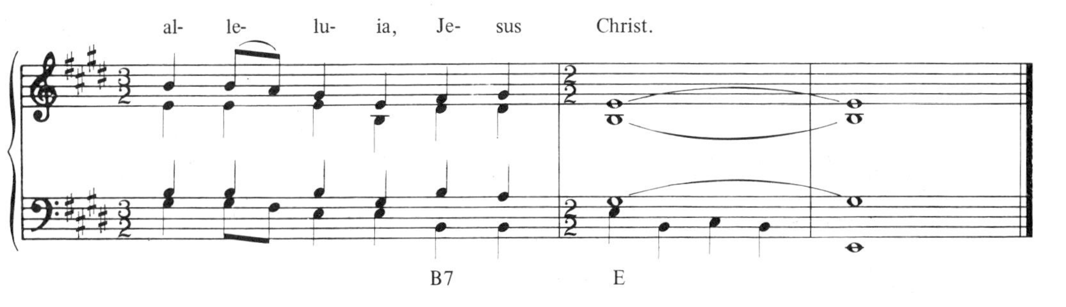

2. Come and seek, come and find,
   come and find the living God.
   Allelu, allelu, alleluia, Jesus Christ.

3. Come and hear, come and know,
   come and know the living God.
   Allelu, allelu, alleluia, Jesus Christ.

4. Come and bless, come and praise,
   come and praise the Word of God.
   Word of God, Word made flesh, alleluia, Jesus Christ.

Seasonal verses

5. Come behold, come and see,
   come and see the new-born babe.
   Allelu, allelu, alleluia, Jesus Christ.

6. Angel choirs sing above,
   'Glory to the Son of God.'
   Shepherd folk sing below, 'Allelu, Emmanuel.'

Words and Music: Mimi Armstrong Farra

COME AND GO WITH ME

2. It's not very far to my Father's house . . .

3. There is room for all in my Father's house . . .

4. Everything is free in my Father's house . . .

5. Jesus is the way to my Father's house . . .

6. Jesus is the light in my Father's house . . .

Other verses may be added spontaneously, such as:

We will clap our hands . . .

There is liberty . . .

We will praise the Lord . . .

etc.

Words and Music: Unknown,
arranged by John Rombaut

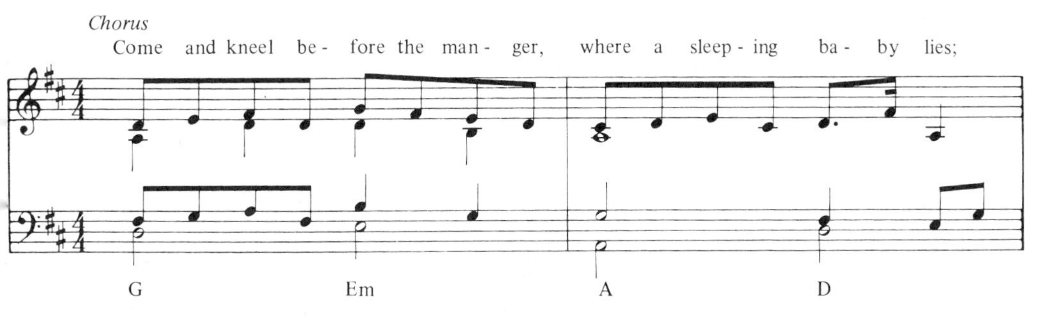

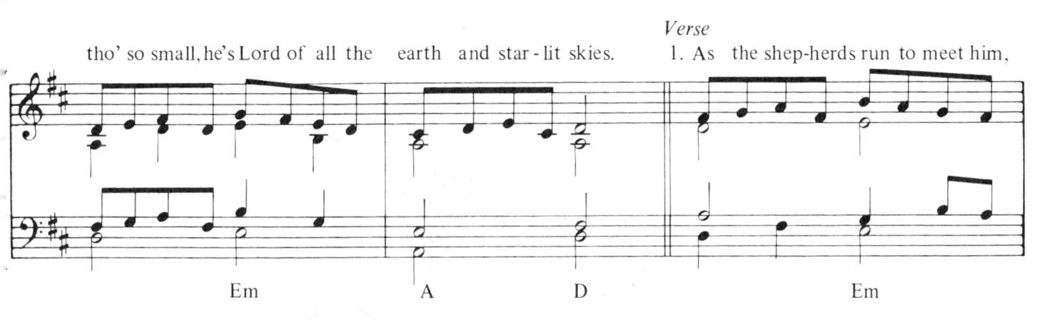

2. Here we lay our lives before him;
we will worship and adore him
as we sing our praises for him –
Jesus Christ is born.

3. Joining with the angel voices
all creation now rejoices
for our God has come to save us –
Jesus Christ is born.

Words and Music: Susan Sayers,
arranged by Frances M. Kelly

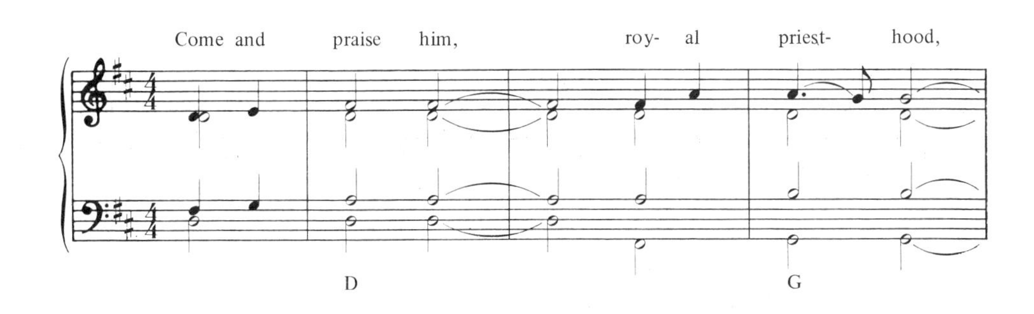

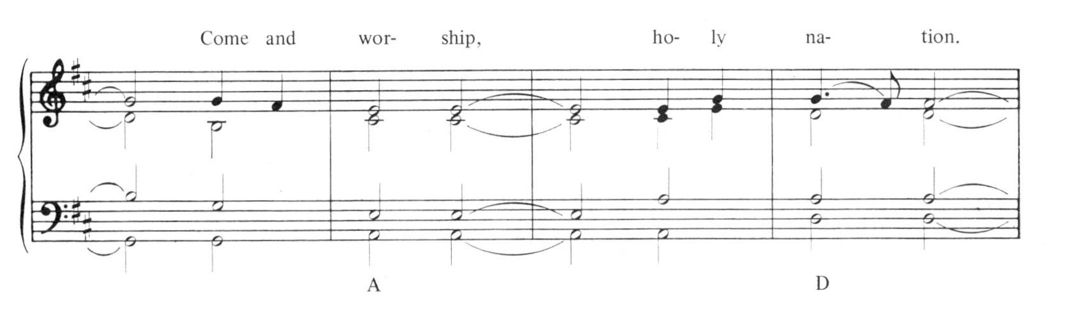

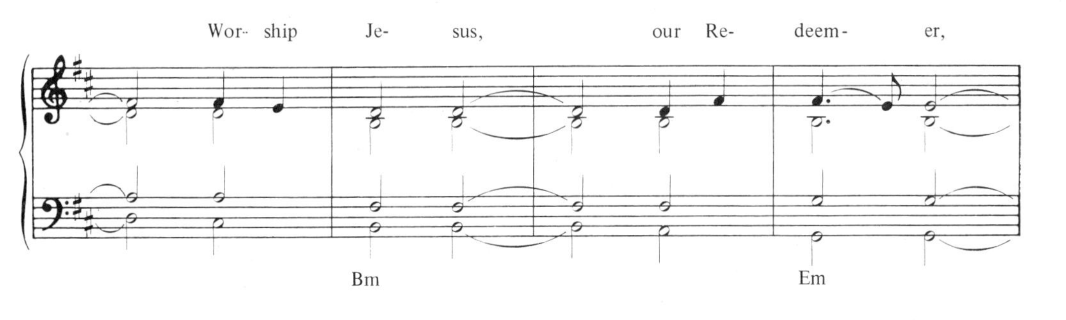

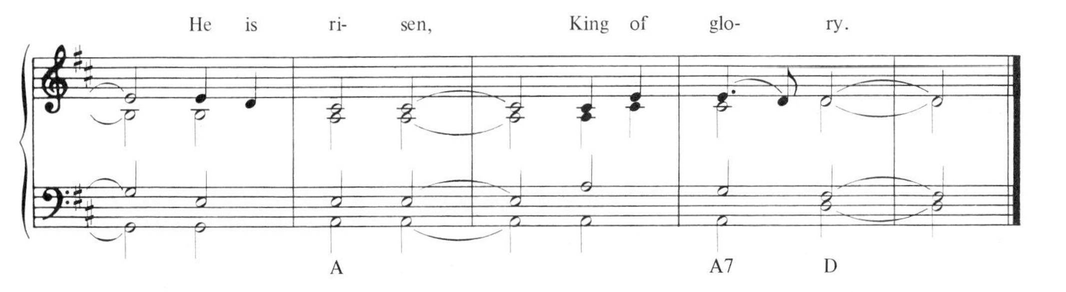

Words and Music: A. Carter, arranged by John Rombaut

COME AND SEE THE SHINING HOPE

('Marching through Georgia')

king- doms of the world become the kingdoms of the Lord: love has the vic- t'ry for ev- er.

2. All the gifts you send us, Lord,
are faithful, good and true;
holiness and righteousness
are shown in all you do:
who can see your greatest Gift
and fail to worship you?
Love has the vict'ry for ever!

3. Power and salvation
all belong to God on high!
So the mighty multitudes
of heaven make their cry,
singing alleluia!
where the echoes never die:
love has the vict'ry for ever!

Words: Christopher Idle (b.1938)
Music: American traditional melody,
arranged by David G. Wilson (b.1940)

The first line may be sung by a cantor or small group, and the second by the congregation. Alternatively, the women could sing the first line, and the men the second.

Words: Psalm 134
Music: Unknown, arranged by Michael Irwin

COME, COME, COME TO THE MANGER

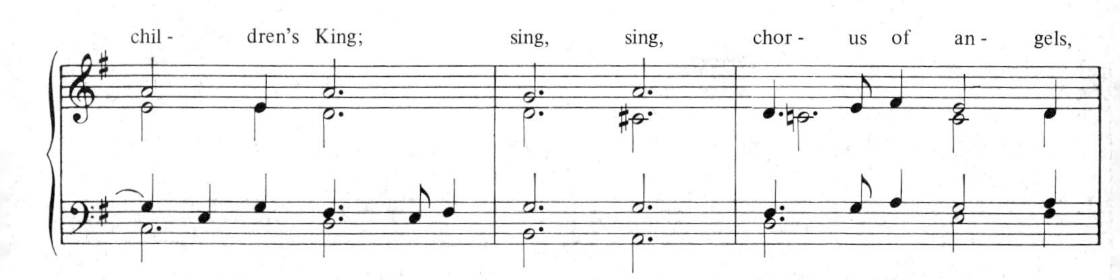

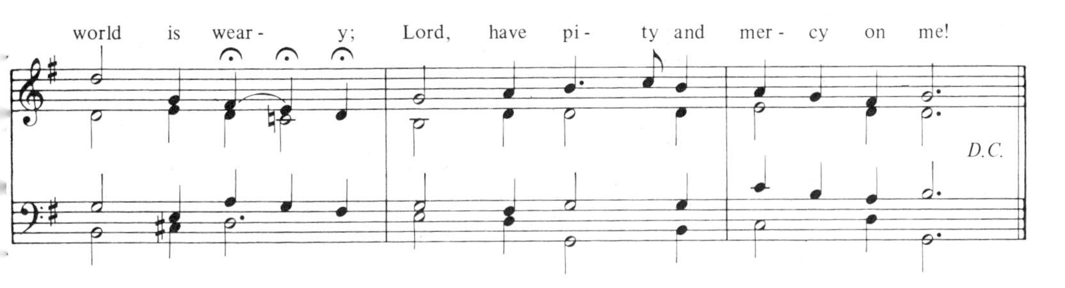

2. He leaves all his glory behind,
 to be born and to die for mankind,
 with grateful beasts his cradle chooses,
 thankless man his love refuses;
 Lord, have pity and mercy on me!

3. To the manger of Bethlehem come,
 to the Saviour Emmanuel's home;
 the heavenly hosts above are singing,
 set the Christmas bells a-ringing;
 Lord, have pity and mercy on me!

Words and Music: F. Gatty

83

COME DOWN, O LOVE DIVINE
('Down Ampney' 66.11.D.)

2. O let it freely burn,
till earthly passions turn
to dust and ashes in its heat consuming,
and let thy glorious light
shine ever on my sight,
and clothe me round, the while my path illuming.

3. Let holy charity
mine outward vesture be,
and lowliness become mine inner clothing:
true lowliness of heart,
which takes the humbler part,
and o'er its own shortcomings weeps with loathing.

4. And so the yearning strong,
with which the soul will long,
shall far outpass the power of human telling
for none can guess its grace,
till he become the place
wherein the Holy Spirit makes his dwelling.

Words: Bianco da Siena (d. 1434),
tr. R. F. Littledale
Music: R. Vaughan Williams (1872-1958)

COME HOLY GHOST, OUR SOULS INSPIRE

('Veni Creator' L.M.)

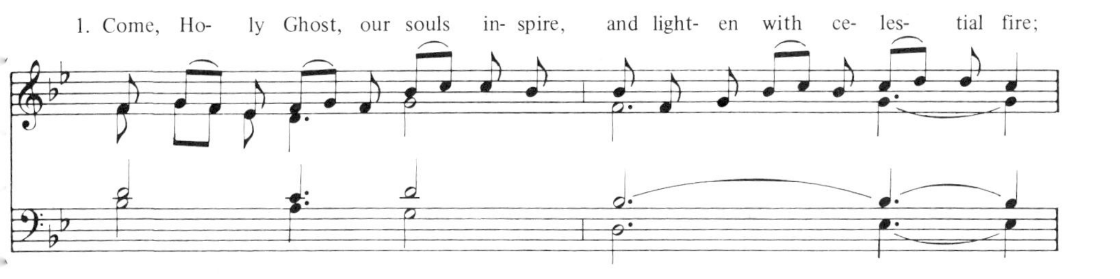

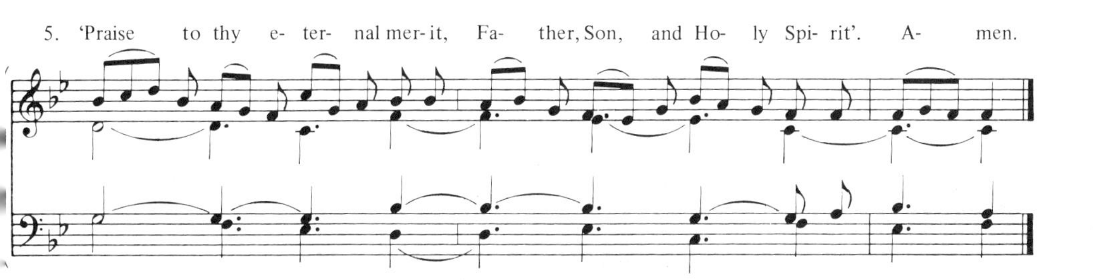

2. Thy blessed unction from above
   is comfort, life, and fire of love;
   enable with perpetual light
   the dullness of our blinded sight.

3. Anoint and cheer our soilèd face
   with the abundance of thy grace:
   keep far our foes, give peace at home;
   where thou art guide no ill can come.

4. Teach us to know the Father, Son,
   and thee, of both, to be but one;
   that through the ages all along
   this may be our endless song,

5. 'Praise to thy eternal merit,
   Father, Son, and Holy Spirit.'
   Amen.

Words: *John Cosin (1594-1672), after Rabanus Maurus (c. 776-856)*
Music: *Proper Sarum melody, harmonised by John Rombaut*

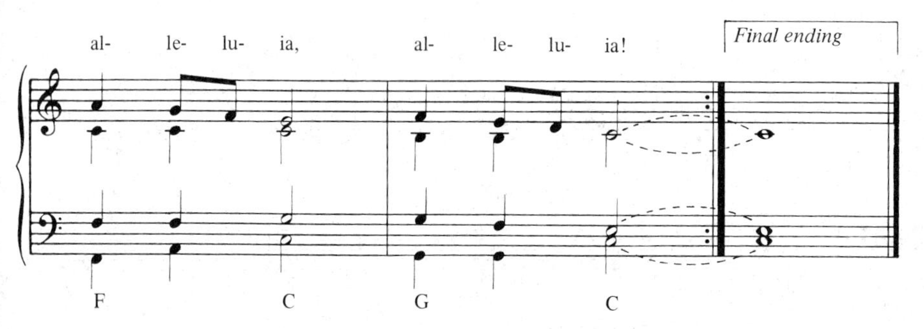

2. Come into his presence, singing:
   Jesus is Lord! *(3)*

3. Come into his presence, singing:
   Worthy the Lamb! *(3)*

4. Come into his presence, singing:
   Glory to God! *(3)*

5. Come into his presence, singing:
   Peace to all men! *(3)*

Words: Verse 1 - unknown;
additional verses - John Ballantine
Music: Unknown,
arranged by John Rombaut

COME, LET US JOIN OUR CHEERFUL SONGS
('Nativity' C.M.)

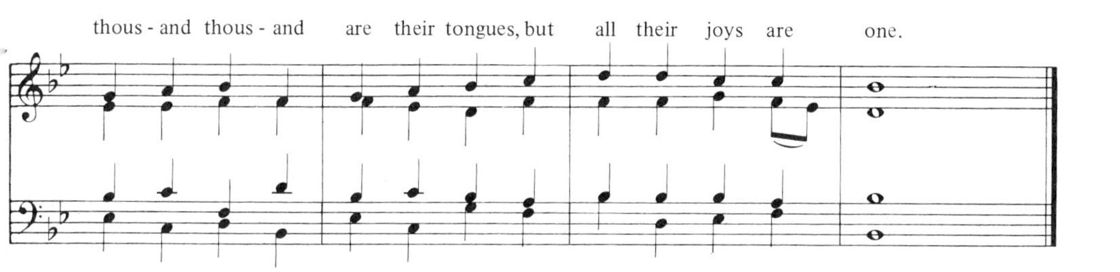

2. 'Worthy the Lamb that died,' they cry,
'to be exalted thus;'
'worthy the Lamb,' our lips reply,
'for he was slain for us.'

3. Jesus is worthy to receive
honour and power divine;
and blessings, more than we can give,
be, Lord, for ever thine.

4. Let all creation join in one
to bless the sacred name
of him that sits upon the throne,
and to adore the Lamb.

Words, based on Revelation 5:11-13: Isaac Watts (1674-1748)
Music: H. Lahee (1826-1912)

COME LET US RAISE A JOYFUL SONG

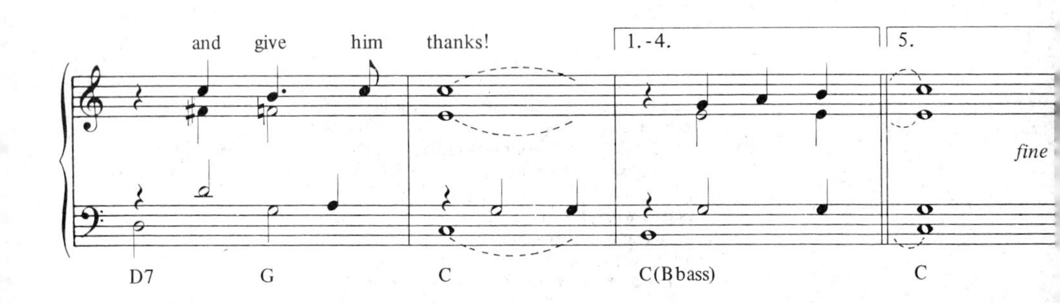

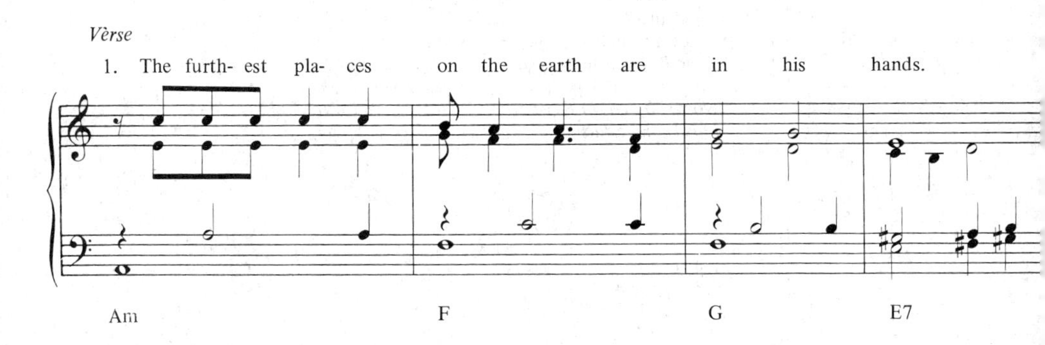

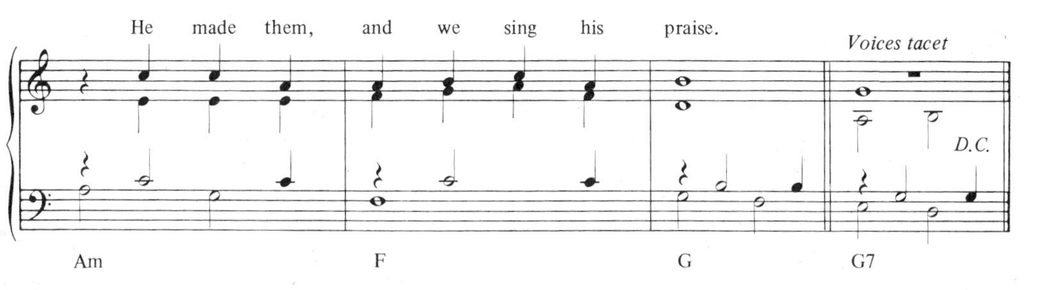

2. The seas and waters on the earth are in his hands.
   He made them, and we sing his praise.

3. The hills and valleys on the earth are in his hands.
   He made them, and we sing his praise.

4. All living creatures on the earth are in his hands.
   He made them, and we sing his praise.

5. And we his people on the earth are in his hands.
   He saved us, and we sing his praise.

Words, based on Psalm 95, and Music: Michael J. Anderson

COME, LORD JESUS, COME

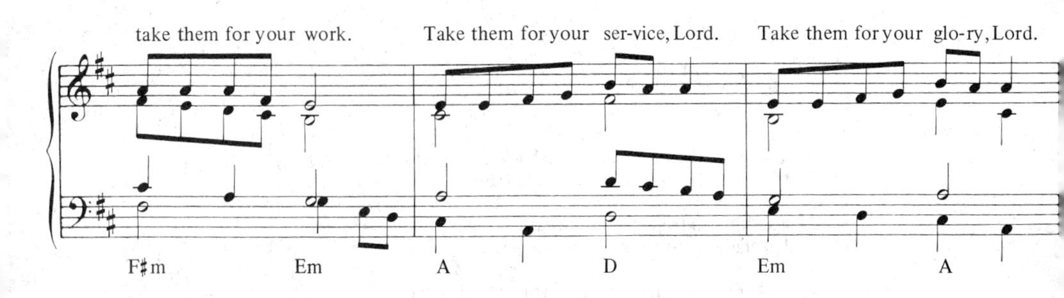

2. Come, Lord Jesus, come.
Come, take my lips,
may they speak your truth.
Take them for your service, Lord.
Take them for your glory, Lord.
Come, Lord Jesus, come.
Come, Lord Jesus, take my lips.

3. Come, Lord Jesus, come.
Come, take my feet,
may they walk your path.
Take them for your service, Lord.
Take them for your glory, Lord.
Come, Lord Jesus, come.
Come, Lord Jesus, take my feet.

4. Come, Lord Jesus, come.
Come, take my heart,
fill it with your love.
Take it for your service, Lord.
Take it for your glory, Lord.
Come, Lord Jesus, come.
Come, Lord Jesus, take my heart.

5. Come, Lord Jesus, come.
Come, take my life,
take it for your own.
Take it for your service, Lord.
Take it for your glory, Lord.
Come, Lord Jesus, come.
Come, Lord Jesus, take my life.

Words and Music: Kevin Mayhew,
arranged by Frances M. Kelly

COME, MY BROTHERS, PRAISE THE LORD

('Michael, row the boat ashore')

2. Come to him with songs of praise,
alleluia,
songs of praise, rejoice in him,
alleluia.

3. For the Lord is a mighty God,
alleluia,
he is King of all the world,
alleluia.

4. In his hands are valleys deep,
alleluia,
in his hands are mountain peaks,
alleluia.

5. In his hands are all the seas,
alleluia,
and the lands which he has made,
alleluia.

6. Praise the Father, praise the Son,
alleluia,
praise the Spirit, the Holy One,
alleluia.

Words and Music: Traditional,
arranged by John Rombaut

90

COME, PRAISE THE LORD THE ALMIGHTY
('Lobe den Herren' 14 14. 4.7.8.)

[HARMONY]

2. Praise to the Father most gracious,
 the Lord of creation!
Praise to his Son, the Redeemer
 who wrought our salvation!
O heav'nly Dove,
praise to thee, fruit of their love,
 Giver of all consolation!

Words, based on Psalm 117: James Quinn
Music: 'Stralsund Gesangbuch' (1665)

COME, THOU HOLY PARACLETE

('Veni, Sancte Spiritus' 777.D.)

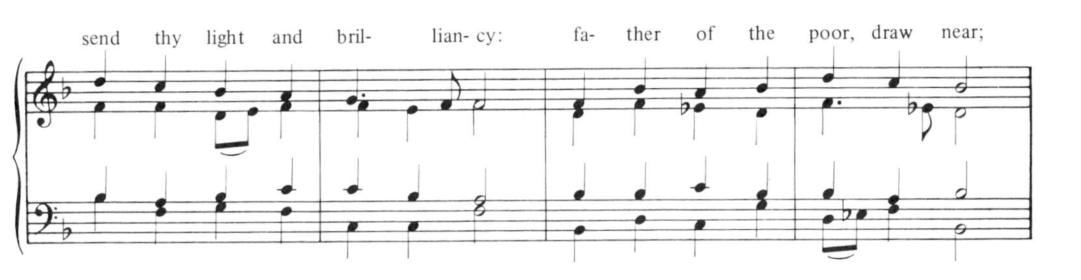

2. Come, of comforters the best,
of the soul the sweetest guest,
come in toil refreshingly:
thou in labour rest most sweet,
thou art shadow from the heat,
comfort in adversity.

3. O thou Light, most pure and blest,
shine within the inmost breast
of thy faithful company.
Where thou art not, man hath nought;
every holy deed and thought
comes from thy divinity.

4. What is soiléd, make thou pure;
what is wounded, work its cure;
what is parchéd, fructify;
what is rigid, gently bend;
what is frozen, warmly tend;
straighten what goes erringly.

5. Fill thy faithful, who confide
in thy power to guard and guide,
with thy sevenfold Mystery.
Here thy grace and virtue send:
grant salvation in the end,
and in heaven felicity.

Words: Stephen Langton (c.1160-1228)
tr. J. M. Neale
Music: Samuel Webbe (1740-1816)

COME, THOU LONG EXPECTED JESUS

('Cross of Jesus' 87.87.)

[HARMONY]

2. Israel's strength and consolation,
hope of all the earth thou art;
dear desire of every nation,
joy of every longing heart.

3. Born thy people to deliver;
born a child and yet a King;
born to reign in us for ever;
now thy gracious Kingdom bring.

4. By thy own eternal Spirit,
rule in all our hearts alone:
by thy all-sufficient merit,
raise us to thy glorious throne.

Words: Charles Wesley (1707-88)
Music: John Stainer (1840-1901)

With a gentle swing
Chorus
a. Come to the wa- ters and I will give you rest. to b.
b. Come to the wa- ters and you will be re-freshed.
final ending
r. h.
D D+4 D A7 D

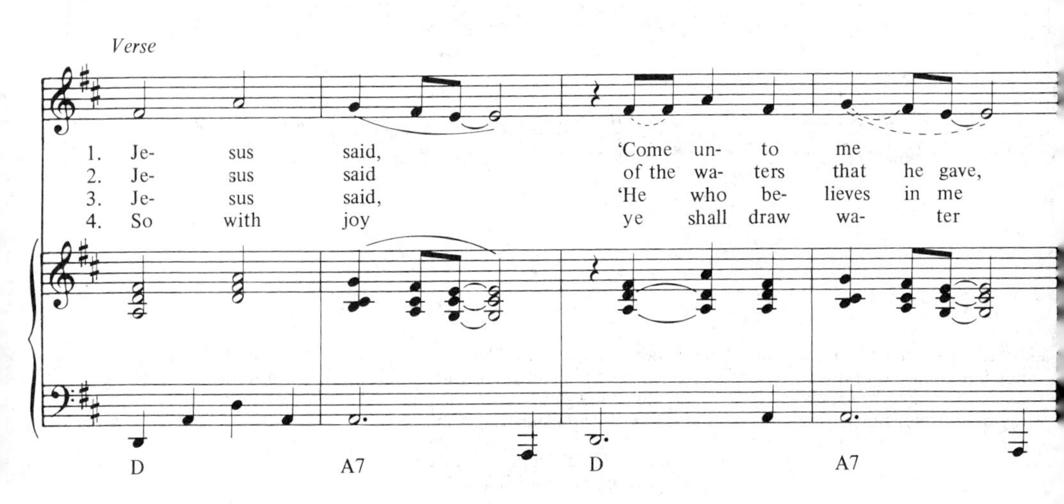
Verse
1. Je- sus said, 'Come un- to me
2. Je- sus said of the wa- ters that he gave,
3. Je- sus said, 'He who be- lieves in me
4. So with joy ye shall draw wa- ter
D A7 D A7

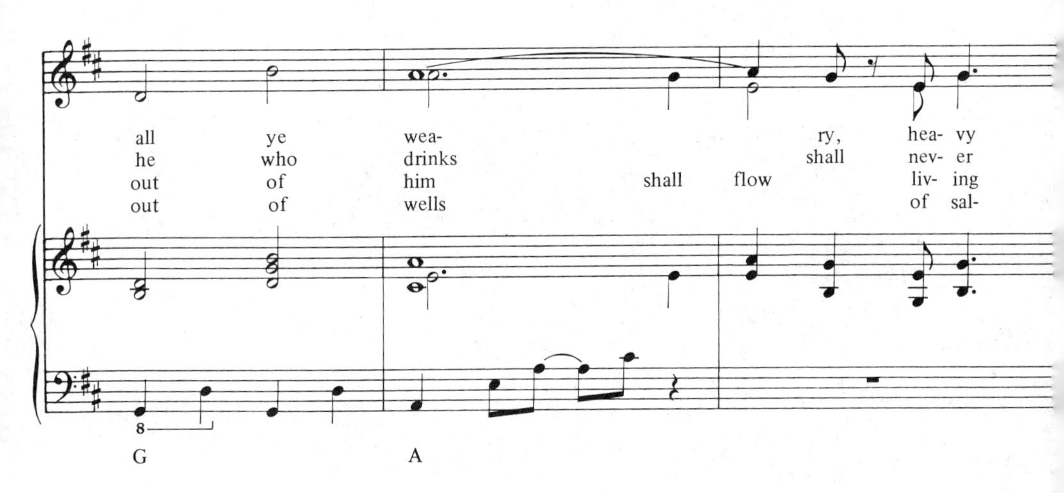
all ye wea- ry, hea- vy
he who drinks shall nev- er
out of him shall flow liv- ing
out of wells of sal-
8
G A

Words, based on Isaiah 55:1-4, and Music: Jodi Page Clark

94 [HARMONY]

COME, YE FAITHFUL, RAISE THE STRAIN

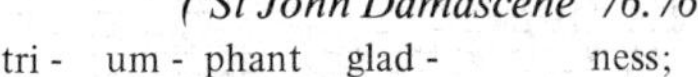
('St John Damascene' 76.76.D.)

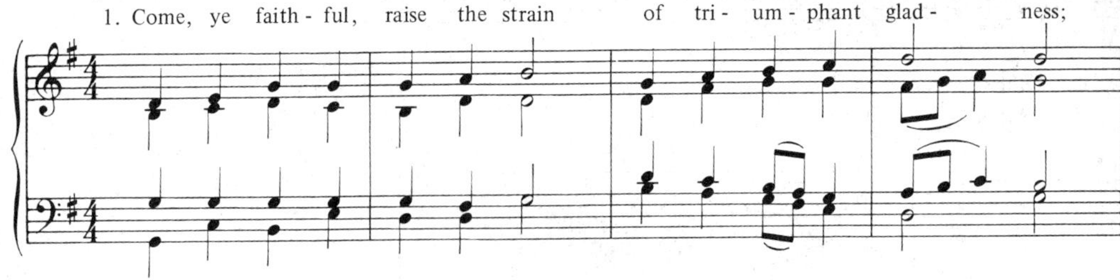

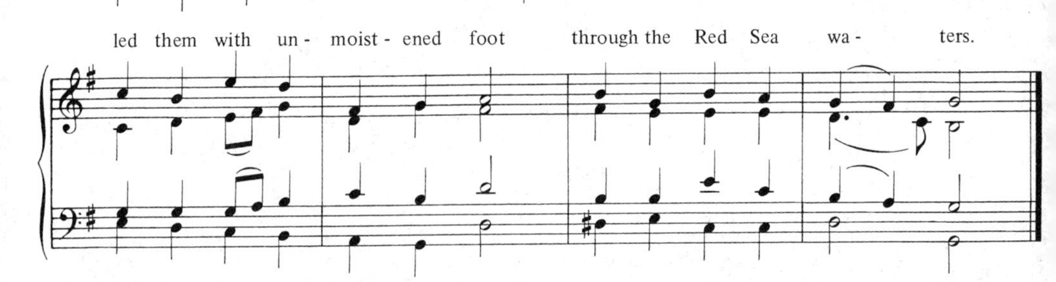

2. 'Tis the spring of souls today;
Christ hath burst his prison,
and from three days' sleep in death
as a sun hath risen;
all the winter of our sins,
long and dark, is flying
from his light, to whom we give
laud and praise undying.

3. Now the queen of seasons bright
with the day of splendour,
with the royal Feast of feasts,
comes its joy to render;
comes to glad Jerusalem,
who with true affection
welcomes in unwearied strains
Jesu's resurrection.

4. Alleluia now we cry
to our King immortal,
who triumphant burst the bars
of the tomb's dark portal;
alleluia, with the Son
God the Father praising;
alleluia yet again
to the Spirit raising.

Words: John Damascene († 754),
tr. J.M. Neale
Music: A.H. Brown (1830-1926)

95

COME, YE THANKFUL PEOPLE COME

('St George's Windsor' 77.77.D.)

[HARMONY]

1. Come, ye thank- ful peo- ple, come, raise the song of har- vest- home!

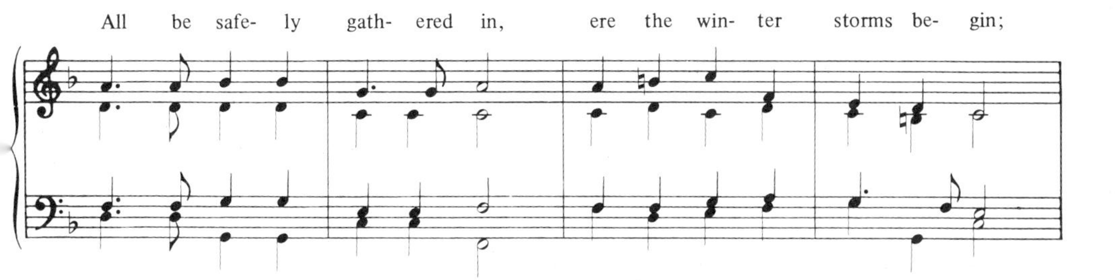

2. We ourselves are God's own field,
fruit unto his praise to yield;
wheat and tares together sown,
unto joy or sorrow grown;
first the blade and then the ear,
then the full corn shall appear:
grant, O harvest Lord, that we
wholesome grain and pure may be.

3. For the Lord our God shall come,
and shall take his harvest home,
from his field shall purge away
all that doth offend, that day,
give his angels charge at last
in the fire the tares to cast,
but the fruitful ears to store
in his garner evermore.

4. Then, thou Church triumphant, come,
raise the song of harvest-home;
all be safely gathered in,
free from sorrow, free from sin,
there for ever purified
in God's garner to abide:
come, ten thousand angels, come,
raise the glorious harvest-home!

Words: Henry Alford (1810-71)
Music: George J. Elvey (1816-93)

COMFORT, COMFORT MY PEOPLE

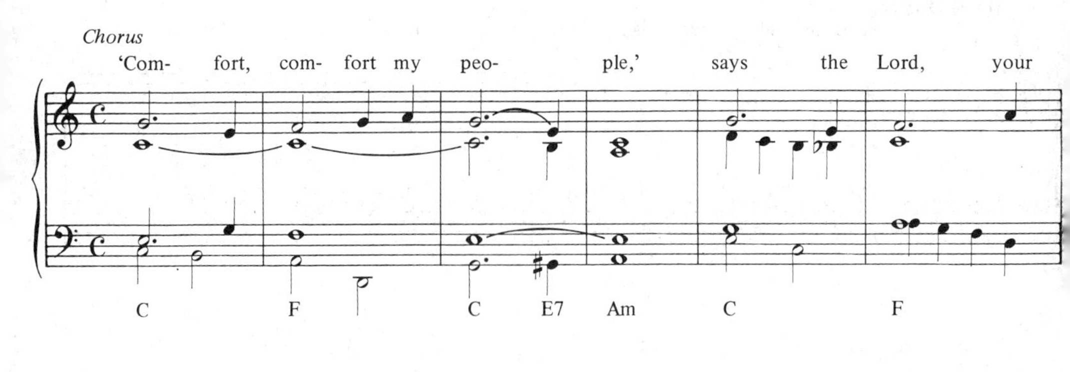

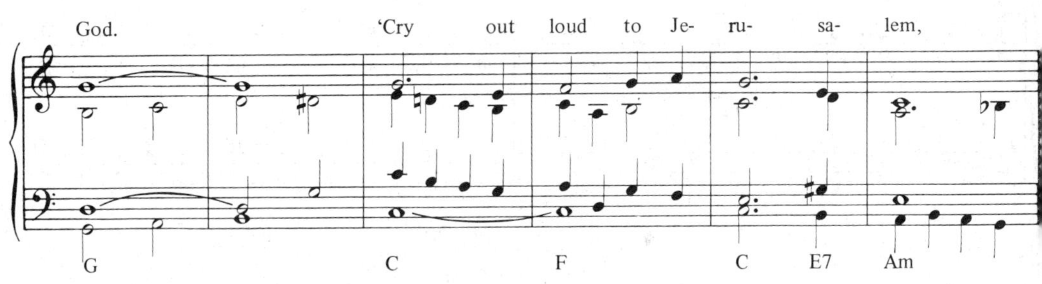

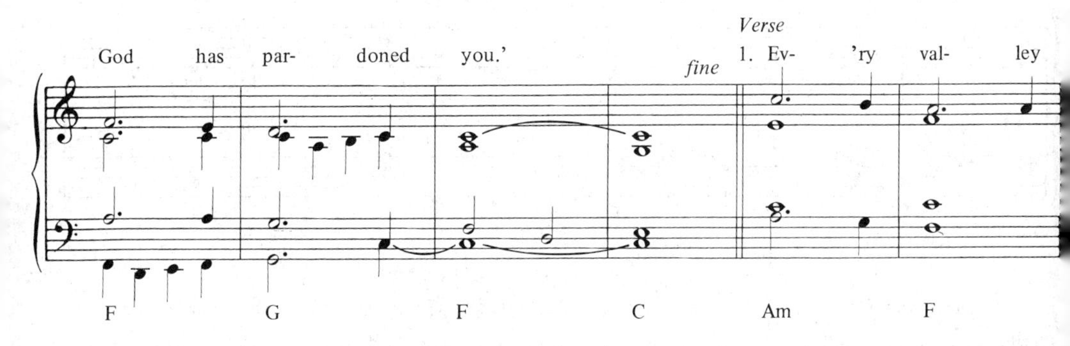

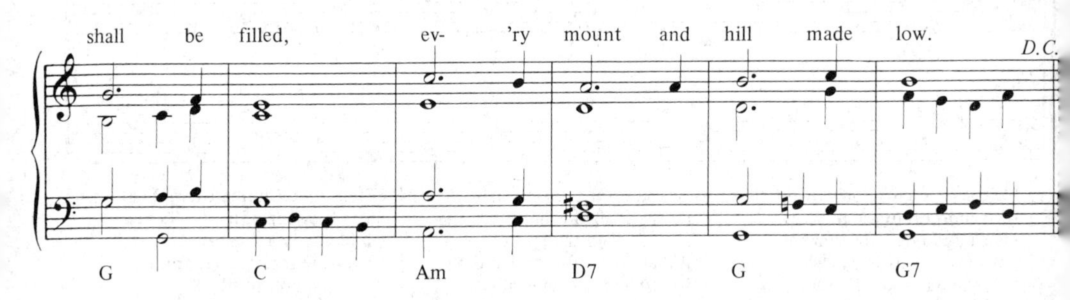

2. In the desert make a path
for the Lord Emmanuel.

3. For the glory of the Lord
soon shall be revealed to me.

Words, based on Isaiah 40, and Music: Anthony D'Souza,
arranged by Aniceto Nazareth

CROWN HIM WITH MANY CROWNS
('Diademata' D.S.M.)

[HARMONY]

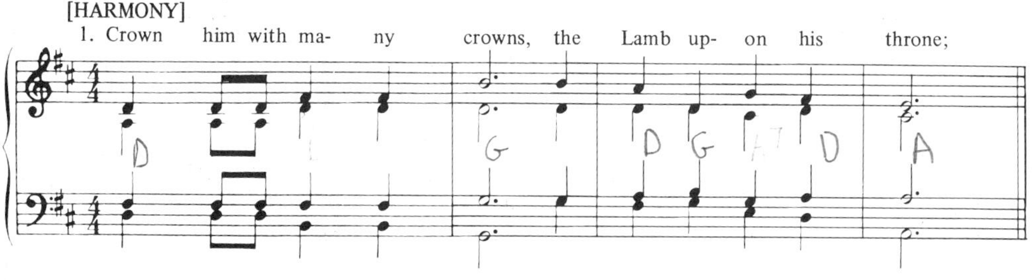

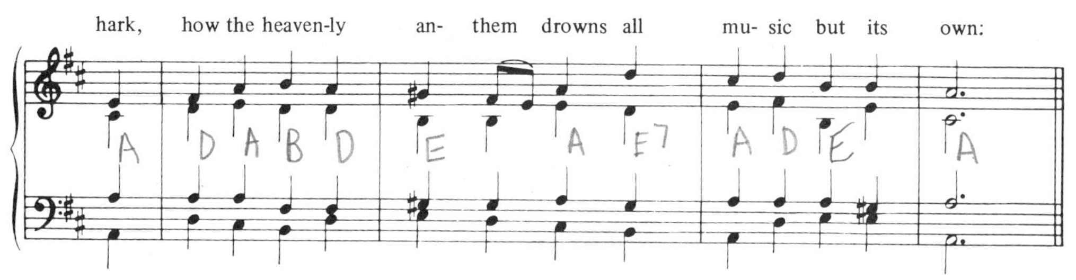

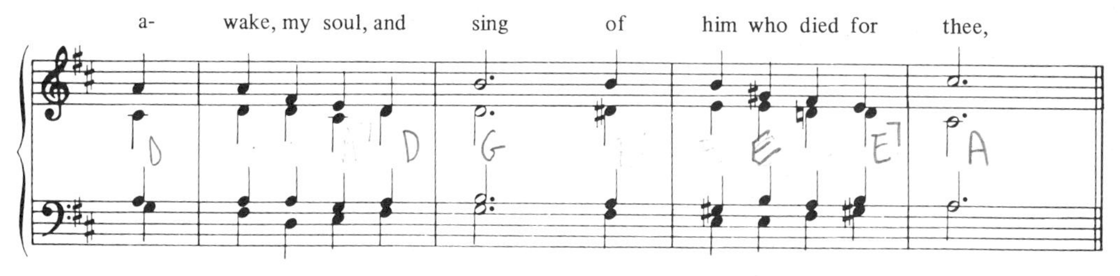

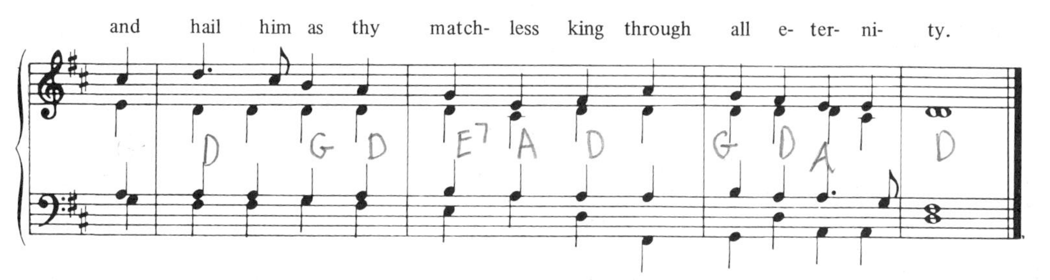

2. Crown him the Virgin's Son,
the God incarnate born,
whose arm those crimson trophies won
which now his brow adorn;
fruit of the mystic rose,
as of that rose the stem,
the root whence mercy ever flows,
the babe of Bethlehem.

3. Crown him the Lord of love;
behold his hands and side
rich wounds, yet visible above
in beauty glorified:
no angel in the sky
can fully bear the sight,
but downward bends his burning eye
at mysteries so bright.

4. Crown him the Lord of peace,
whose power a sceptre sways,
from pole to pole, that wars may cease,
absorbed in prayer and praise:
his reign shall know no end,
and round his piercèd feet
fair flowers of Paradise extend
their fragrance ever sweet.

5. Crown him the Lord of heaven,
one with the Father known,
and the blest Spirit through him given
from yonder triune throne:
all hail, Redeemer, hail,
for thou hast died for me;
thy praise shall never, never fail
throughout eternity.

Words, based on Revelation 19: Matthew Bridges (1800-94)
Music: George J. Elvey (1816-93)

98

DEAR LORD AND FATHER OF MANKIND

('Repton' 86.886.)

2. In simple trust like theirs who heard,
beside the Syrian sea,
the gracious calling of the Lord,
let us, like them, without a word
rise up and follow thee.

3. O Sabbath rest by Galilee!
O calm of hills above,
where Jesus knelt to share with thee
the silence of eternity,
interpreted by love!

4. Drop thy still dews of quietness,
till all our strivings cease;
take from our souls the strain and stress,
and let our ordered lives confess
the beauty of thy peace.

5. Breathe through the heats of our desire
thy coolness and thy balm;
let sense be dumb, let flesh retire;
speak through the earthquake, wind and fire,
O still small voice of calm.

Words: John Greenleaf Whittier (1807-92)
Music: C. Hubert H. Parry (1848-1918)

DING DONG! MERRILY ON HIGH
('Bransle de l'Official' 77.77. & Chorus)

2. E'en so here below, below
let steeple bells be swungen,
and io, io, io,
by priest and people sungen.

3. Pray you dutifully prime,
your matin chime, ye ringers;
may you beautifully rhyme
your evetime song, ye singers.

Words: George Ratcliffe Woodward (1848-1934)
Music: Traditional French melody,
arranged by John Rombaut

2. When the fire is burning all around you,
you will never be consumed by the flames.

3. When the fear of loneliness is looming,
then remember I am at your side.

4. When you dwell in the exile of the stranger,
remember you are precious in my eyes.

5. You are mine, O my child, I am your Father,
and I love you with a perfect love.

Words, based on Isaiah 43: 1-4, and Music: Gerard Markland

DRAW ME, O LORD, TO YOUR HEART OF LOVE

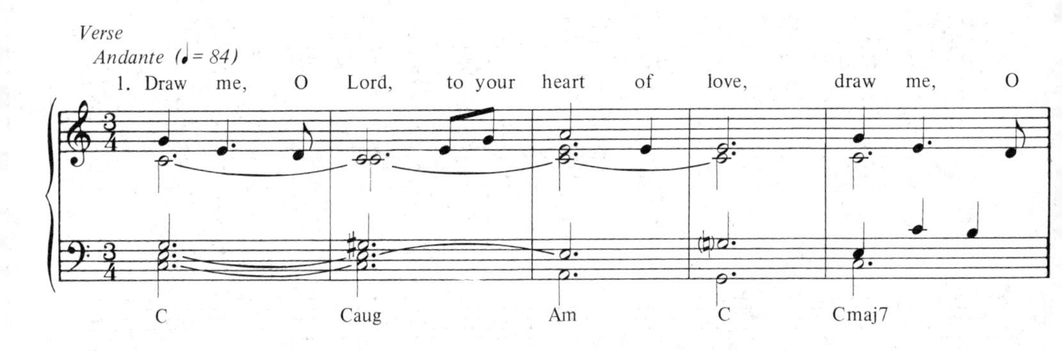

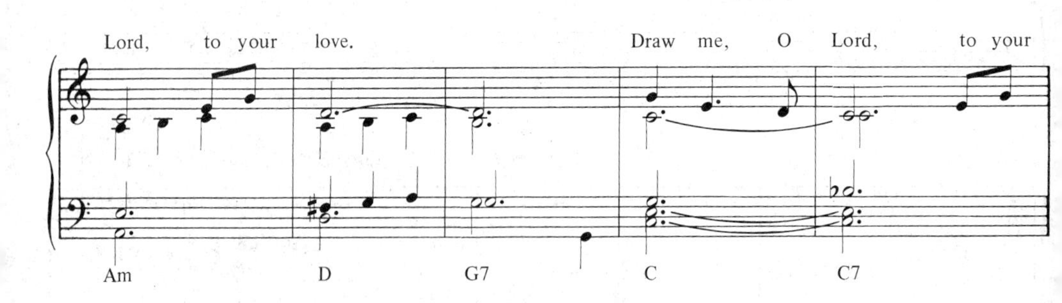

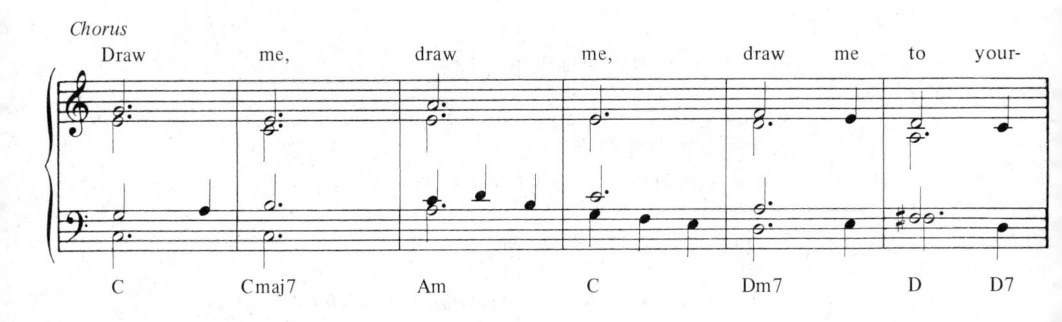

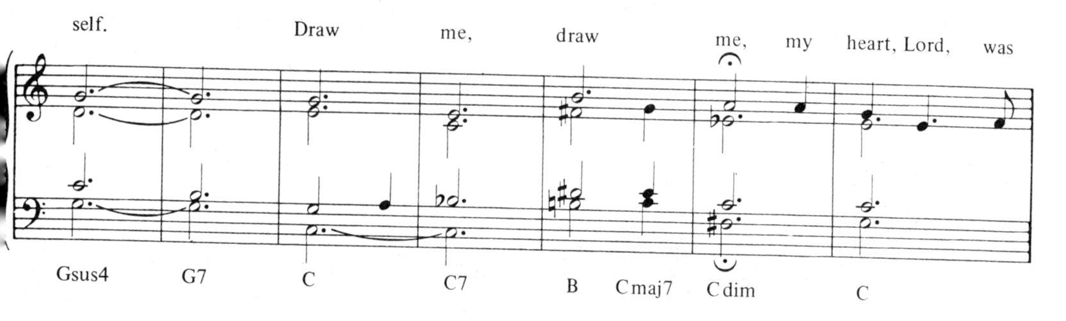

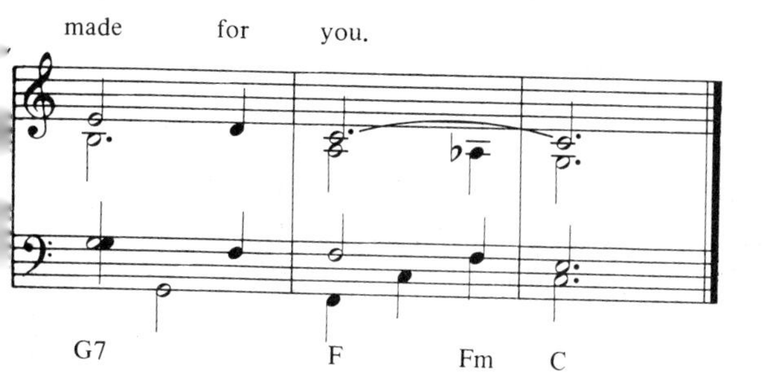

2. You have the words of eternal life,
you are the one sent by God.
Draw me, O Lord, with your words of life,
that I bring Good News to all.

3. You are the Bread that was sent from heav'n,
sent to give life to the world.
Feed me, O Lord, with the Bread of Life,
that I may hunger no more.

4. You are the source of the Spring of Life,
sent to give truth to the world.
Fill me, O Lord, from the Fount of Life,
that I be thirsty no more.

Words and Music: Douglas Rowe,
arranged by Frances M. Kelly

EARTH HAS MANY A NOBLE CITY

('Stuttgart' 87.87.)

[HARMONY]

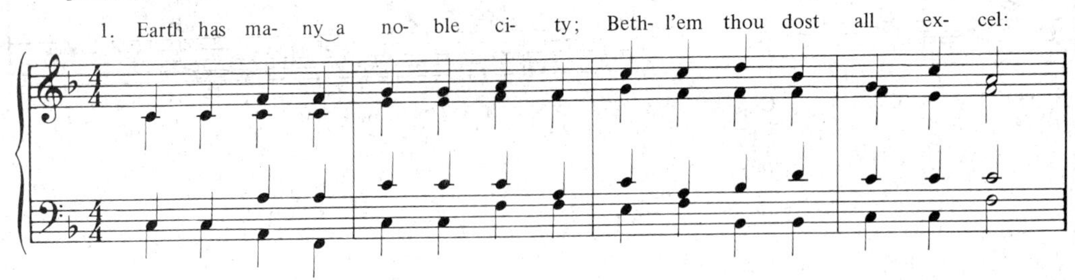

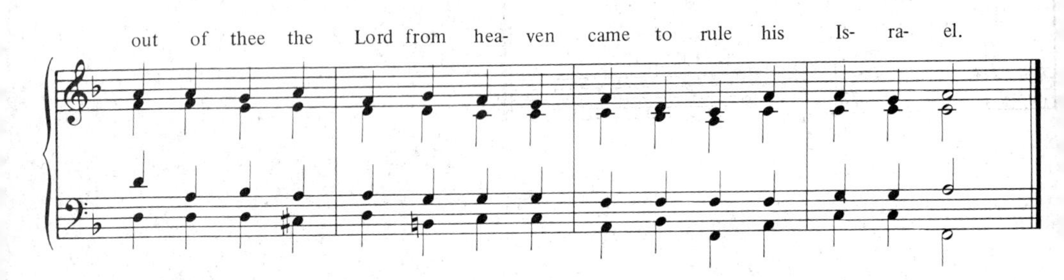

An alternative harmonisation is at Hymn 44

2. Fairer than the sun at morning
   was the star that told his birth,
   to the world its God announcing
   seen in fleshly form on earth.

3. Eastern sages at his cradle
   make oblations rich and rare;
   see them give in deep devotion
   gold and frankincense and myrrh.

4. Sacred gifts of mystic meaning:
   incense doth their God disclose,
   gold the King of kings proclaimeth,
   myrrh his sepulchre foreshows.

5. Jesu, whom the Gentiles worshipped
   at thy glad Epiphany,
   unto thee with God the Father
   and the Spirit glory be.

Words: Aurelius Clemens Prudentius (348-c.413),
tr. E. Caswall
Music: Christian Friedrich Witt (1660-1716)

EARTH IN THE DARK (Glimpses of glory)

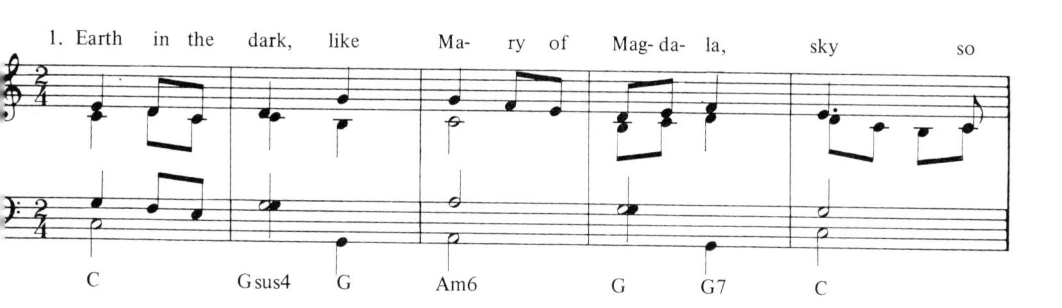

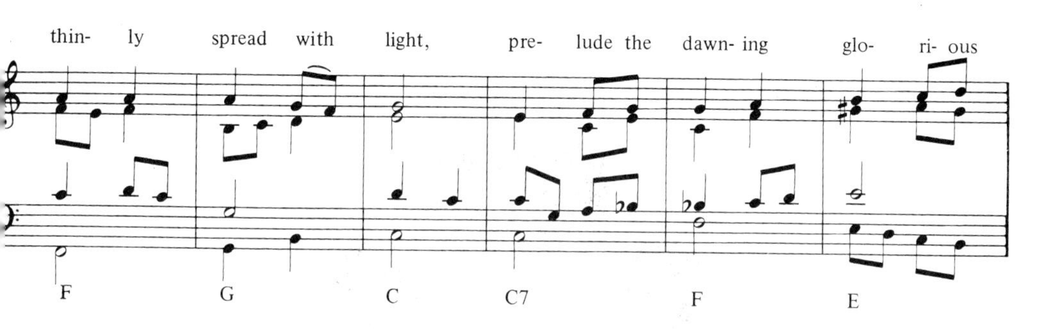

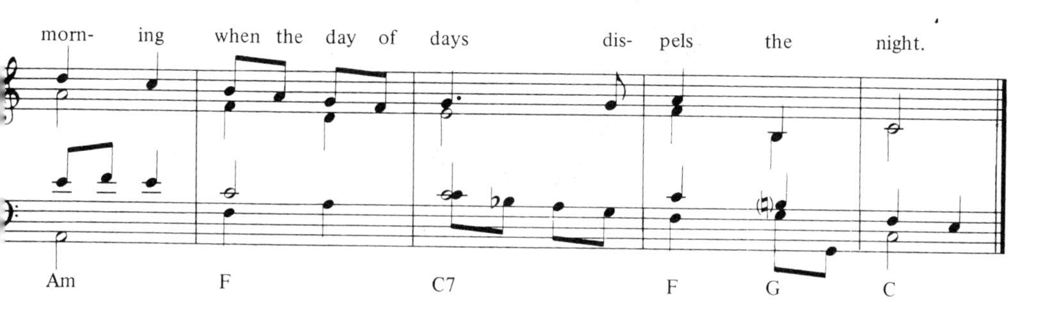

2. Early that morning, Mary of Magdala
rose and sought her buried Lord,
dazzling the whiteness, angelic brightness,
glory Mary glimpsed through tears outpoured.

3. 'Why are you weeping, Mary of Magdala?'
Mary turned herself around.
Mary, still seeking, heard Jesus speaking
'Mary!' 'My Master!' Christ is found.

4. Sing alleluia, Mary of Magdala,
Christ is risen and adored.
Telling the story we glimpse the glory:
seeking we may find our living Lord.

Words, based on John 20, and Music: Patrick Appleford,
arranged by Frances M. Kelly

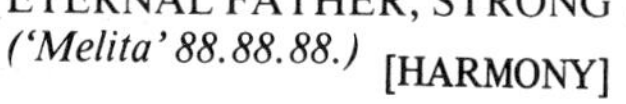

ETERNAL FATHER, STRONG TO SAVE

('Melita' 88.88.88.) [HARMONY]

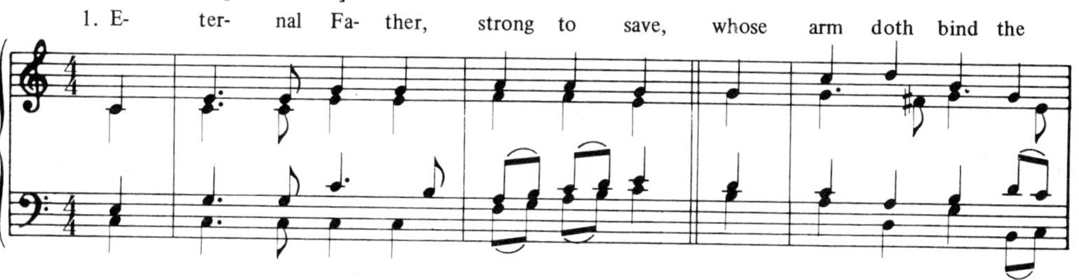

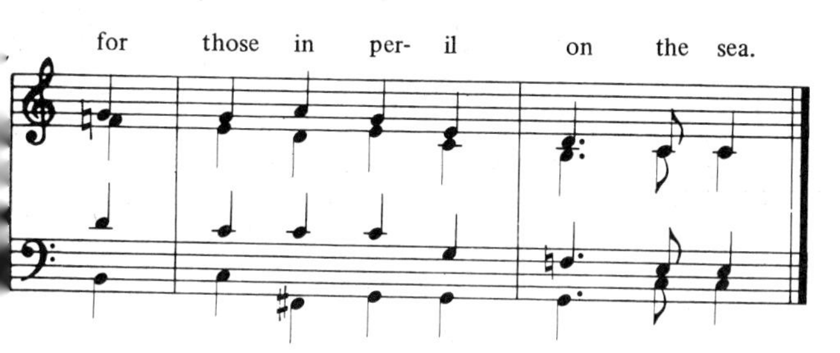

2. O Saviour, whose almighty word
   the winds and waves submissive heard,
   who walkedst on the foaming deep
   and calm amid its rage didst sleep:
   O hear us when we cry to thee
   for those in peril on the sea.

3. O sacred Spirit, who didst brood
   upon the waters dark and rude,
   and bid their angry tumult cease,
   and give, for wild confusion, peace:
   O hear us when we cry to thee
   for those in peril on the sea.

4. O Trinity of love and power,
   our brethren shield in danger's hour.
   From rock and tempest, fire and foe,
   protect them whereso'er they go,
   and ever let there rise to thee
   glad hymns of praise from land and sea.

Words: William Whiting (1825-78)
Music: John B. Dykes (1823-76)

ETERNAL RULER OF THE CEASELESS ROUNI
('Song 1' 10 10.10 10.10 10.,

[HARMONY]

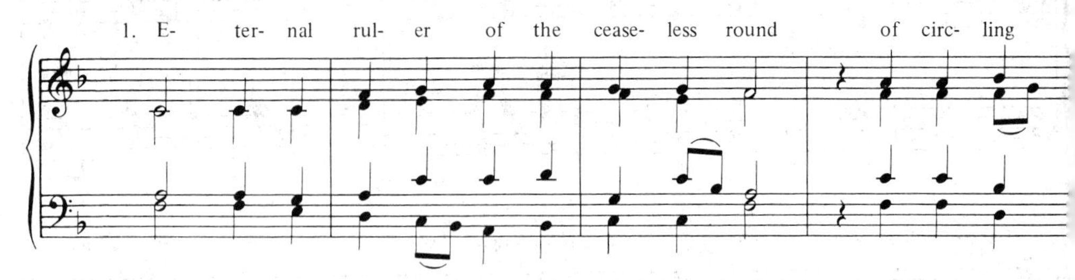

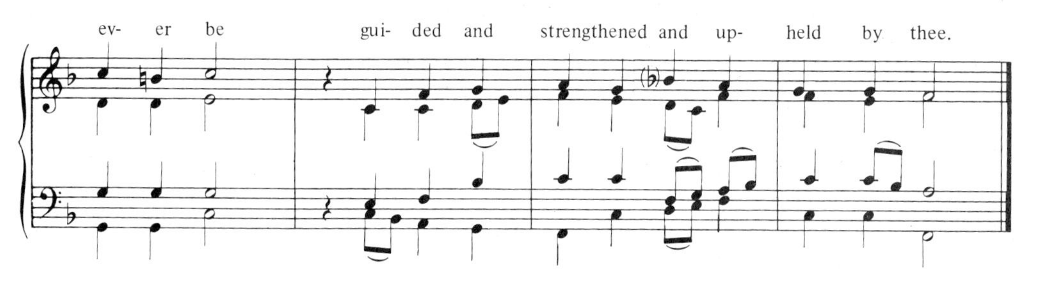

2. We are of thee, the children of thy love,
   the brothers of thy well-belovèd Son;
   descend, O Holy Spirit, like a dove,
   into our hearts, that we may be as one:
   as one with thee, to whom we ever tend;
   as one with him, our Brother and our Friend.

3. We would be one in hatred of all wrong,
   one in our love of all things sweet and fair,
   one with the joy that breaketh into song,
   one with the grief that trembles into prayer,
   one in the power that makes thy children free
   to follow truth, and thus to follow thee.

4. O clothe us with thy heavenly armour, Lord,
   thy trusty shield, thy sword of love divine;
   our inspiration be thy constant word;
   we ask no victories that are not thine:
   give or withhold, let pain or pleasure be;
   enough to know that we are serving thee.

Words: John White Chadwick (1840-1904)
Music: Orlando Gibbons (1583-1625)

FAITHFUL SHEPHERD, FEED ME

('Pastor pastorum' 65.65.)

[HARMONY]

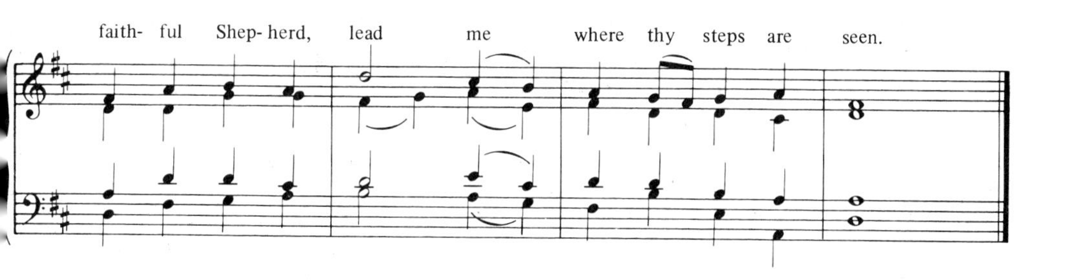

2. Hold me fast, and guide me
   in the narrow way;
   so, with thee beside me,
   I shall never stray.

3. Daily bring me nearer
   to the heavenly shore;
   make my faith grow clearer,
   may I love thee more.

4. Hallow every pleasure,
   every gift and pain;
   be thyself my treasure,
   though none else I gain.

5. Day by day prepare me
   as thou seest best,
   then let angels bear me
   to thy promised rest.

Words: Thomas Benson Pollock (1836-1896)
Music: Philipp Friedrich Silcher (1789-1860)

A simplified guitar accompaniment is given overleaf.

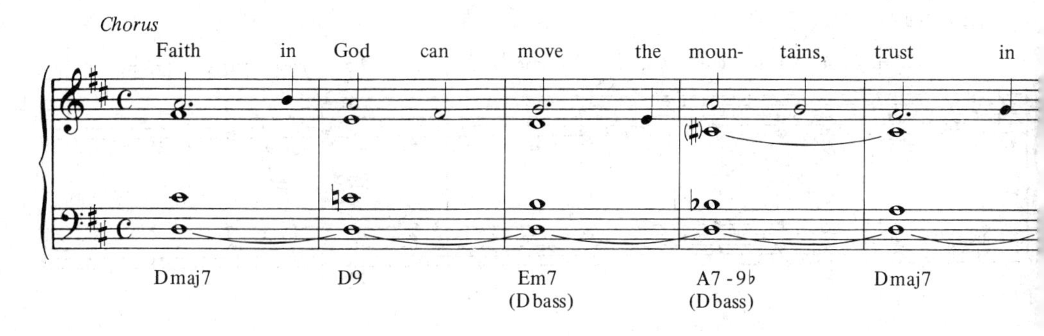

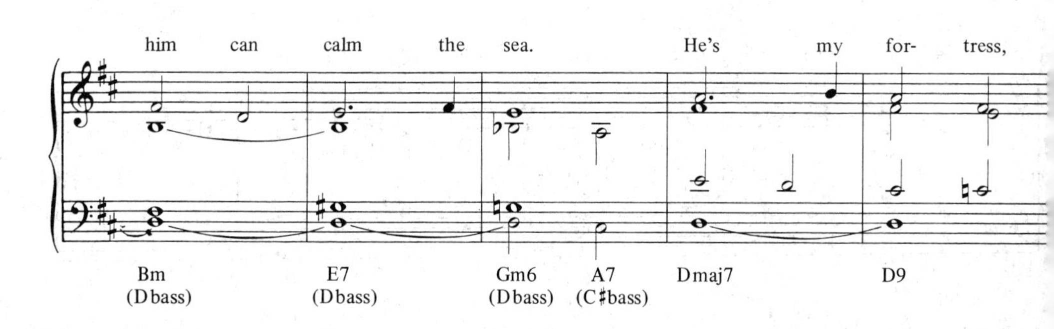

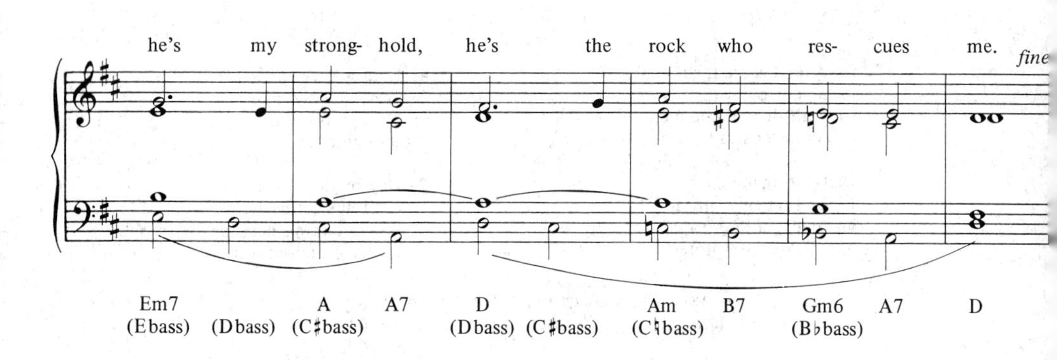

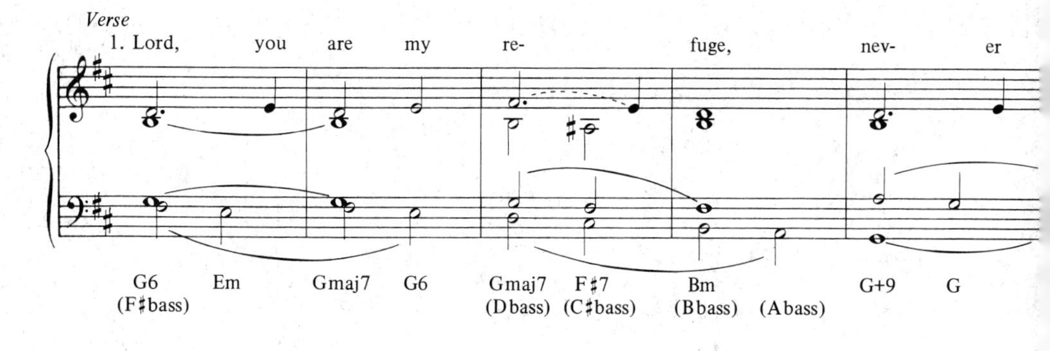

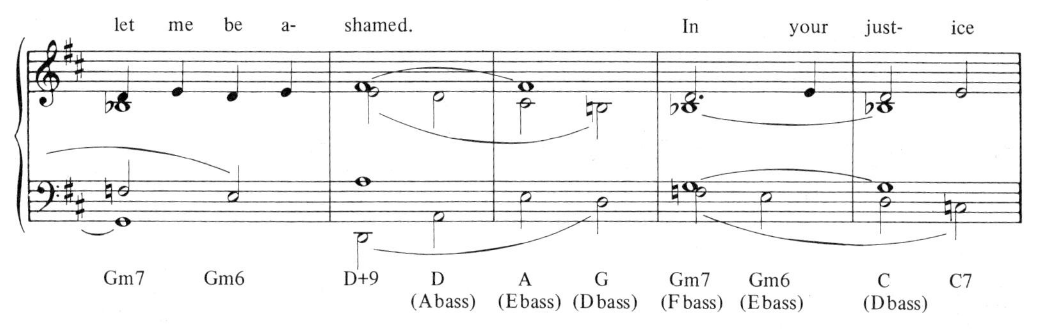

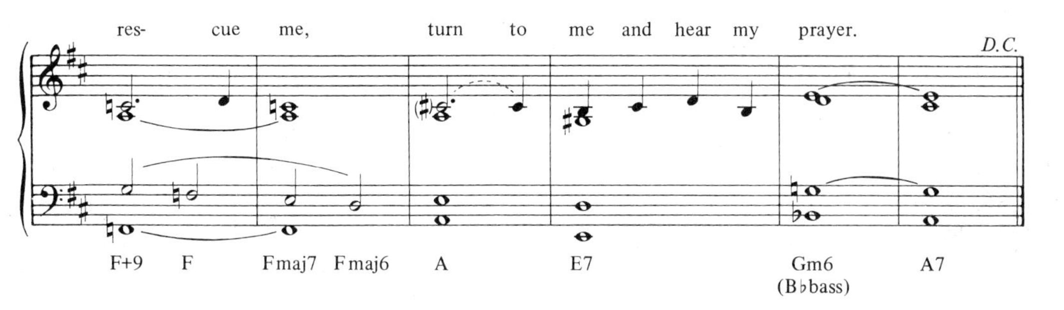

2. You are my salvation,
from oppression set me free.
Ever since my childhood,
you have been my only hope.

3. Bitter troubles burden me,
but you fill me with new life.
From the grave you raise me up,
so my tongue will sing your praise.

Words, based on Psalm 61, and Music: Aniceto Nazareth

Simplified guitar accompaniment

Words, based on Psalm 61, and Music: Aniceto Nazareth

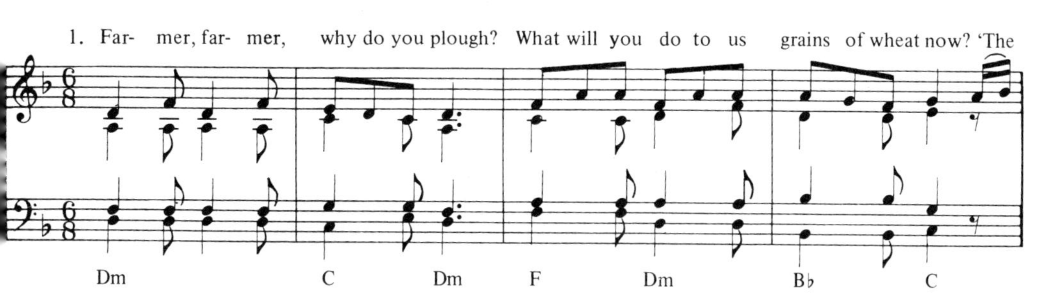

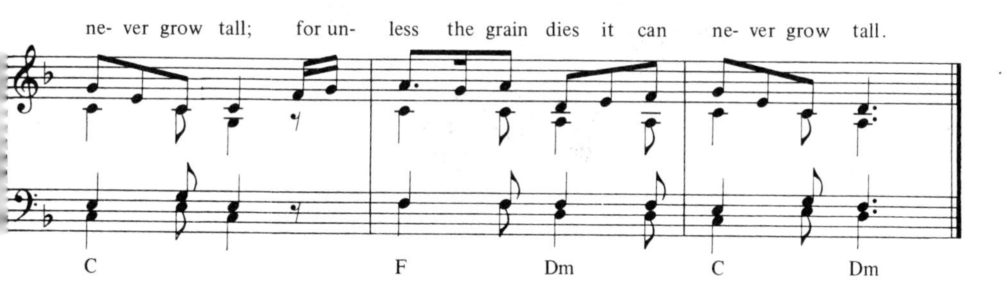

2. Miller, miller, turning your stone,
why must you grind? Can't you leave us alone?
Why must you change us all with your pow'r?
'You can only be bread
if you first become flour;
you can only be bread
if you first become flour.'

3. Baker, baker, kneading the dough,
why do you pound us and pummel us so?
'Unless I work my yeast through you all
I shall find that my bread
is not risen at all;
I shall find that my bread
is not risen at all.'

4. Jesus, Jesus, use us, we pray;
use us to further your glory each day.
'You are my body; you are my bread -
to be broken and shared
that the world may be fed;
to be broken and shared
that the world may be fed.'

Words, based on John 12: 24,
and Music: Susan Sayers,
arranged by John Rombaut

FATHER, HEAR THE PRAYER WE OFFER

(First tune: 'Sussex' 87.87.)

[HARMONY]

FATHER, HEAR THE PRAYER WE OFFER

(Second tune: 'Marching' 87.87.)

[HARMONY]

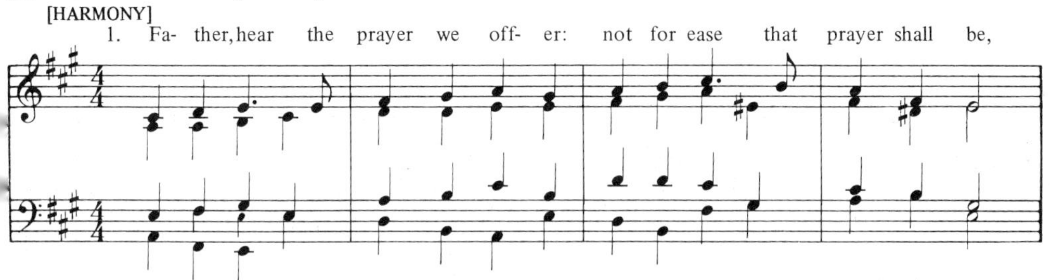

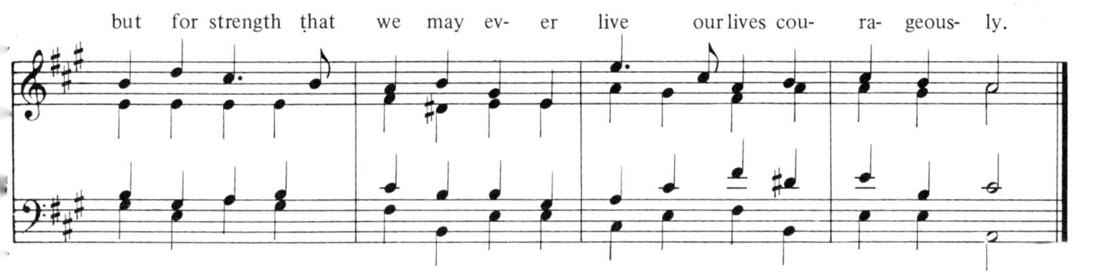

2. Not for ever in green pastures
   do we ask our way to be;
   but the steep and rugged pathway
   may we tread rejoicingly.

3. Not for ever by still waters
   would we idly rest and stay;
   but would smite the living fountains
   from the rocks along our way.

4. Be our strength in hours of weakness,
   in our wanderings be our guide;
   through endeavour, failure, danger,
   Father, be thou at our side.

Words: L. M. Willis (1824-1908)
Music: First tune - English traditional melody, adapted by Ralph Vaughan Williams
Second tune - Martin Shaw (1875-1958)

FATHER, I PLACE INTO YOUR HANDS

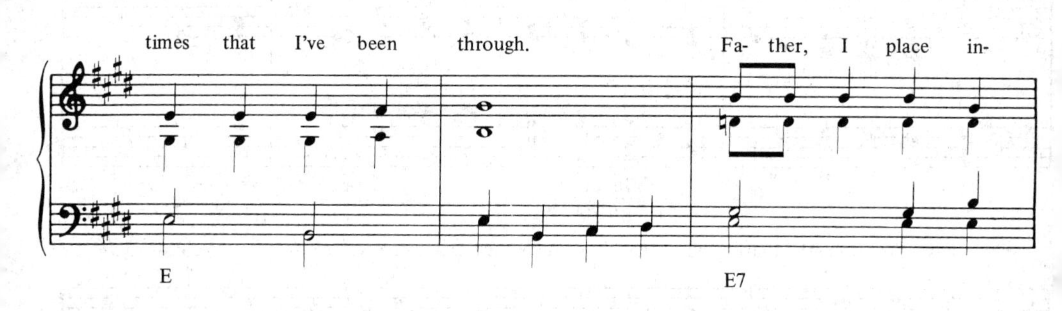

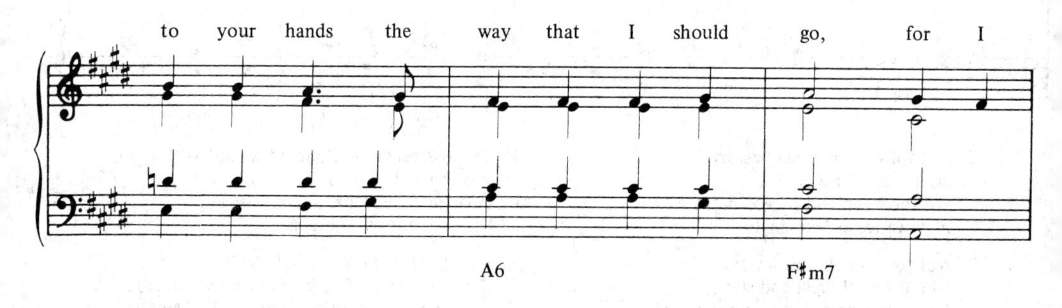

know I al- ways can trust you.

E (B bass) B7 E A E

2. Father, I place into your hands
my friends and family.
Father, I place into your hands
the things that trouble me.
Father, I place into your hands
the person I would be,
for I know I always can trust you.

3. Father, we love to see your face,
we love to hear your voice.
Father, we love to sing your praise,
and in your name rejoice.
Father, we love to walk with you
and in your presence rest,
for we know we always can trust you.

4. Father, I want to be with you
and do the things you do.
Father, I want to speak the words
that you are speaking too.
Father, I want to love the ones
that you will draw to you,
for I know that I am one with you.

Words and Music: J. Hewer

111

FATHER, LORD OF ALL CREATION
('Abbot's Leigh' 87.87.D.)

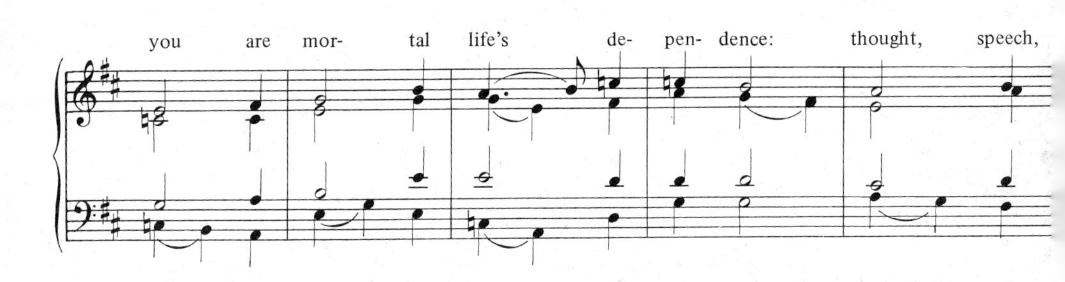

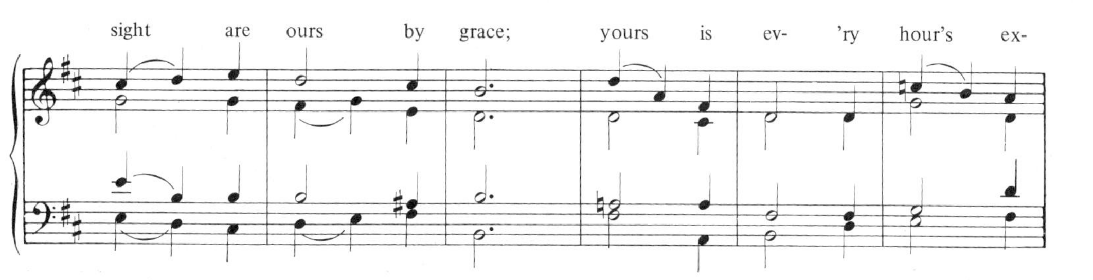

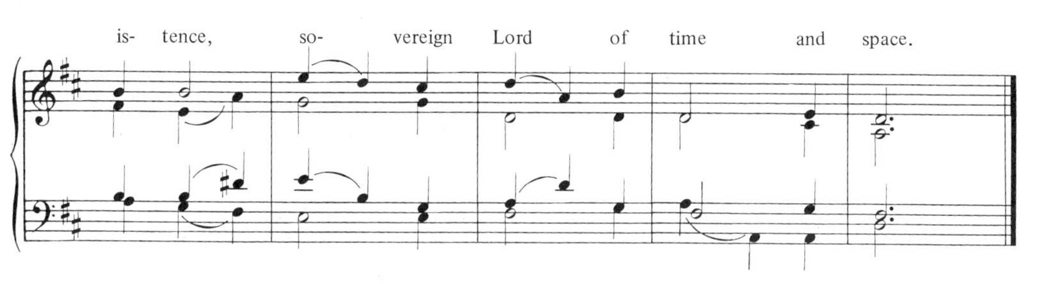

2. Jesus Christ, the man for others,
we, your people, make our prayer:
give us grace to love as brothers
all whose burdens we can share.
Where your name binds us together
you, Lord Christ, will surely be;
where no selfishness can sever
there your love may all men see.

3. Holy Spirit, rushing, burning
wind and flame of Pentecost,
fire our hearts afresh with yearning
to regain what we have lost.
May your love unite our action,
nevermore to speak alone:
God, in us abolish faction,
God, through us your love make known.

Words: Stewart Cross
Music: Cyril V. Taylor (b. 1907)

112

FATHER MOST HOLY, MERCIFUL AND LOVING
('Chartres' 11 11 11.5.)

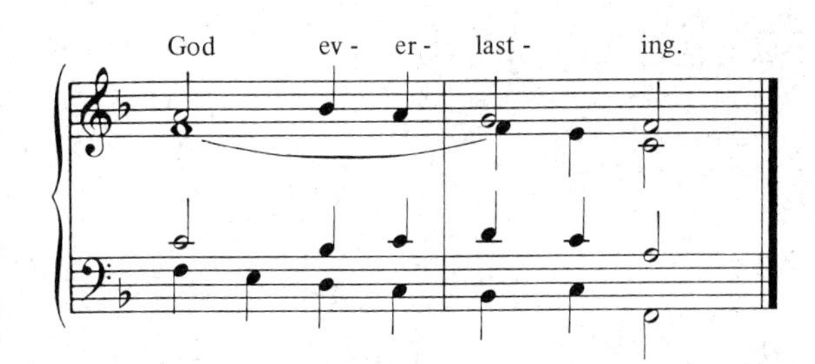

2. Three in a wondrous Unity unbroken,
One perfect Godhead, love that never faileth,
light of the angels, succour of the needy,
hope of all living.

3. All thy creation serveth its Creator,
thee every creature praiseth without ceasing;
we too would sing thee psalms of true devotion:
hear, we beseech thee.

4. Lord God almighty, unto thee be glory,
One in three Persons, over all exalted.
Thine, is as meet, be honour, praise and blessing,
now and for ever.

Words: 'O Pater sancte' (c. 10th century),
tr. Alfred E. Alston
Music: Chartres Antiphoner (1784)

FATHER OF HEAVEN, WHOSE LOVE PROFOUND

113

('Rivaulx' L.M.)

[HARMONY]

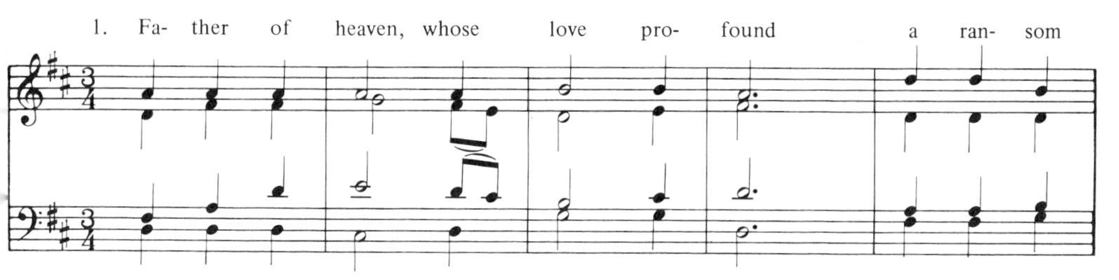

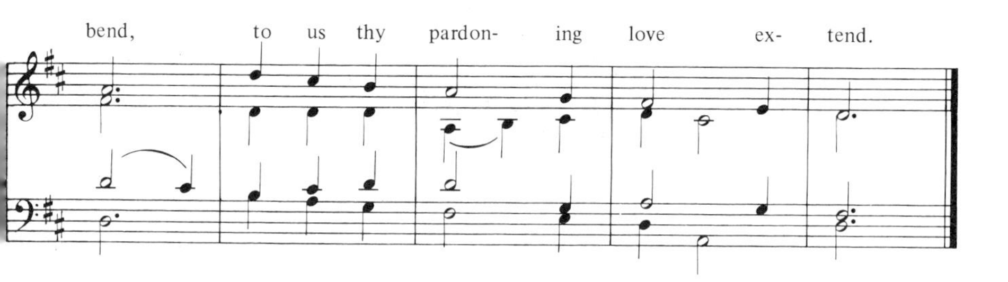

2. Almighty Son, incarnate Word,
our Prophet, Priest, Redeemer, Lord,
before thy throne we sinners bend,
to us thy saving grace extend.

3. Eternal Spirit, by whose breath
the soul is raised from sin and death,
before thy throne we sinners bend,
to us thy quickening power extend.

4. Thrice Holy! Father, Spirit, Son;
mysterious Godhead, Three in One,
before thy throne we sinners bend,
grace, pardon, life to us extend.

Words: Edward Cooper (1770-1833)
Music: John Bacchus Dykes (1823-76)

114

This song may be sung as a round.

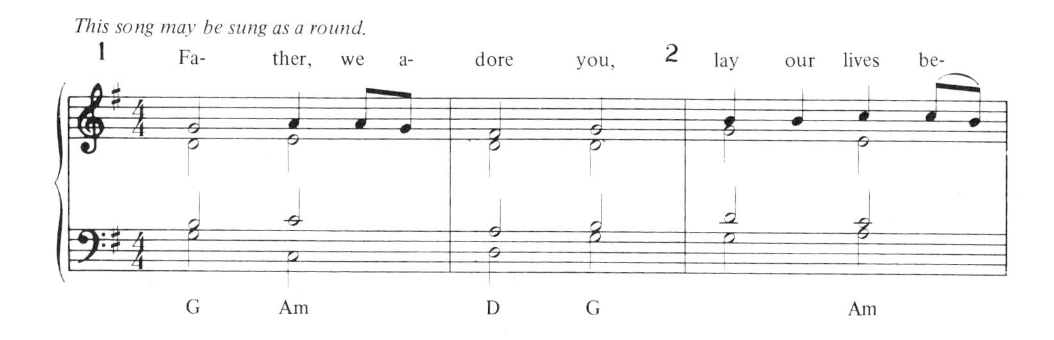

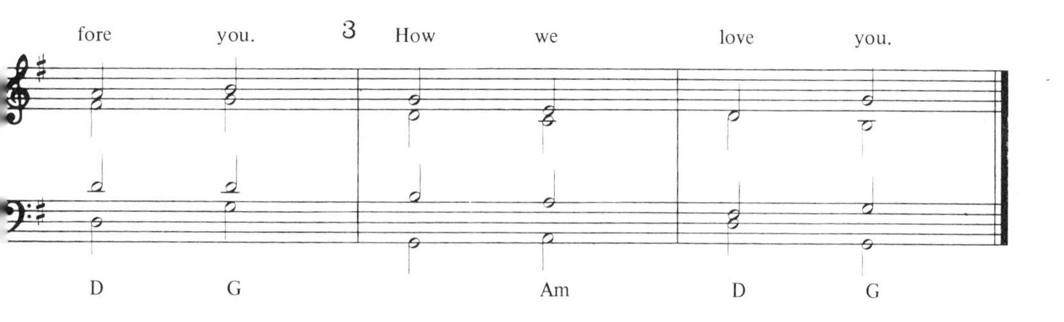

2. Jesus, we adore you . . .

3. Spirit, we adore you . . .

Words and Music: Terrye Coelho

115

FATHER WELCOMES ALL HIS CHILDREN

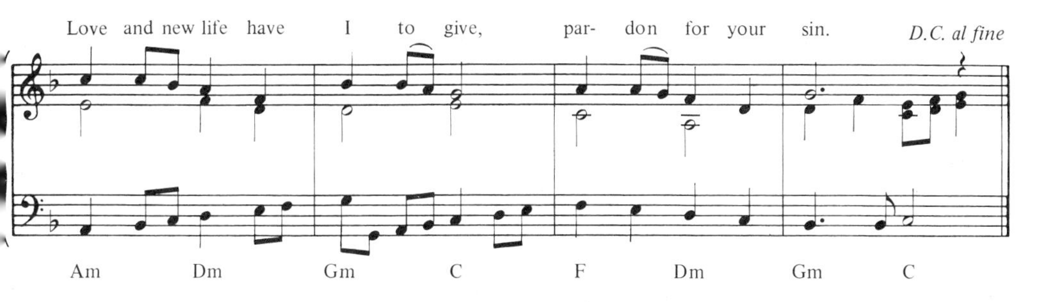

2. In the water, in the Word,
 in his promise, be assured:
 all who believe and are baptised
 shall be born again.

3. Let us daily die to sin;
 let us daily rise with him –
 walk in the love of Christ our Lord,
 live in the peace of God.

Words and Music: Robin Mann,
arranged by Robert B. Kelly

FATHER, WE LOVE YOU

2. Jesus, we love you,
we worship and adore you.

3. Spirit, we love you,
we worship and adore you.

Words and Music: Donna Adkins

FATHER, WHO IN JESUS FOUND US
('Quem pastores laudavere' 88.87.)

[HARMONY]

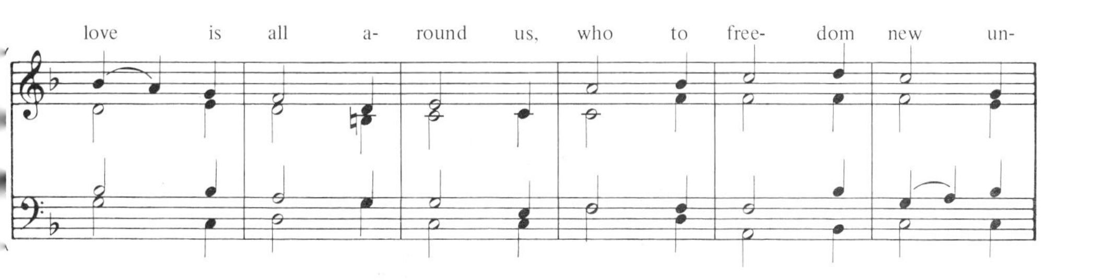

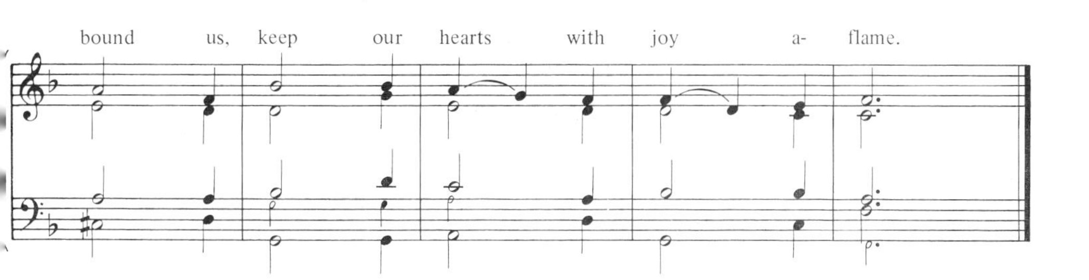

2. For the sacramental breaking,
for the honour of partaking,
for your life our lives remaking,
young and old, we praise your name.

3. From the service of this table
lead us to a life more stable;
for our witness make us able;
blessing on our work we claim.

4. Through our calling closely knitted,
daily to your praise committed,
for a life of service fitted,
let us now your love proclaim.

Words: *Fred Kaan*
Music: *German Carol Melody (14th century), harmonised by Ralph Vaughan Williams (1872-1958)*

FATHER, YOU ARE LIVING **(Keep us, ever living Lord, in you)**

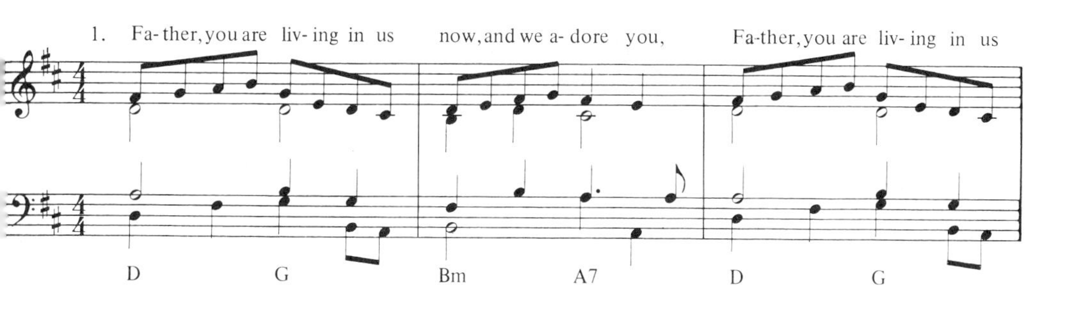

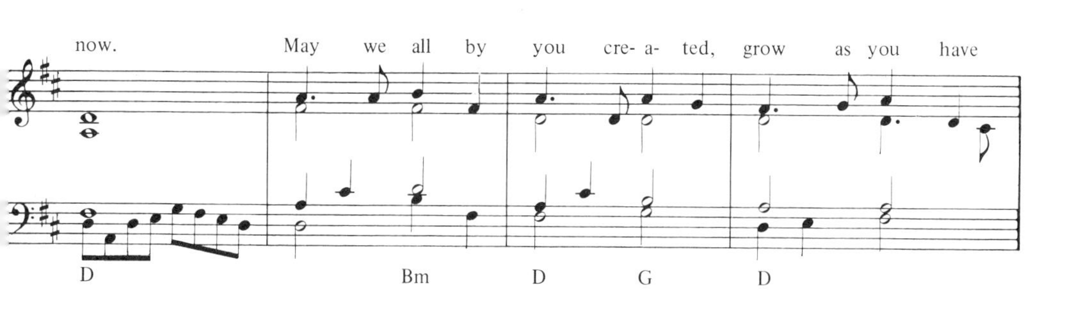

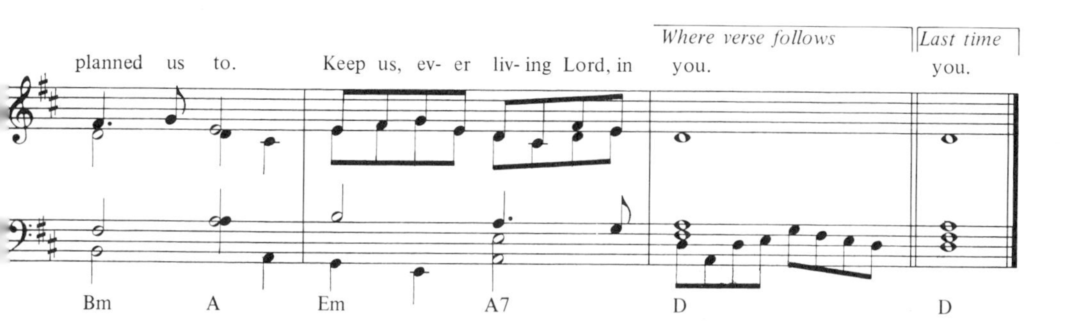

2. Jesus, you are living in us now,
and we adore you,
Jesus, you are living in us now.
May your healing love pervade us,
make us pure and whole and new.
Keep us, ever living Lord, in you.

3. Spirit, you are living in us now,
and we adore you,
Spirit, you are living in us now.
May our light so shine to others
that they're drawn to worship you.
Keep us, ever living Lord, in you.

Words and Music: Susan Sayers,
arranged by Frances M. Kelly

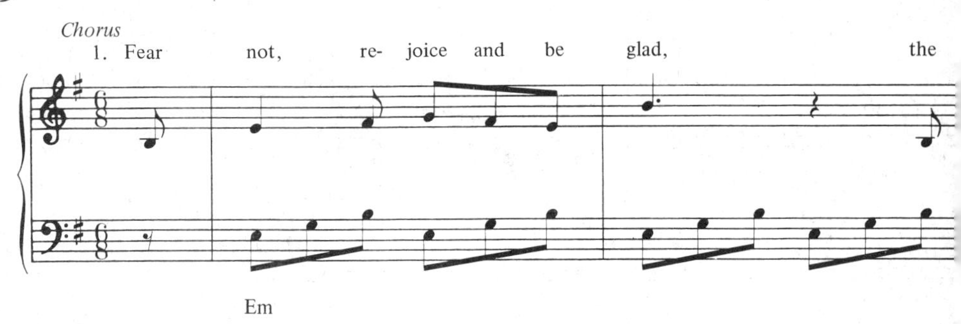
Chorus
1. Fear not, re- joice and be glad, the
Em

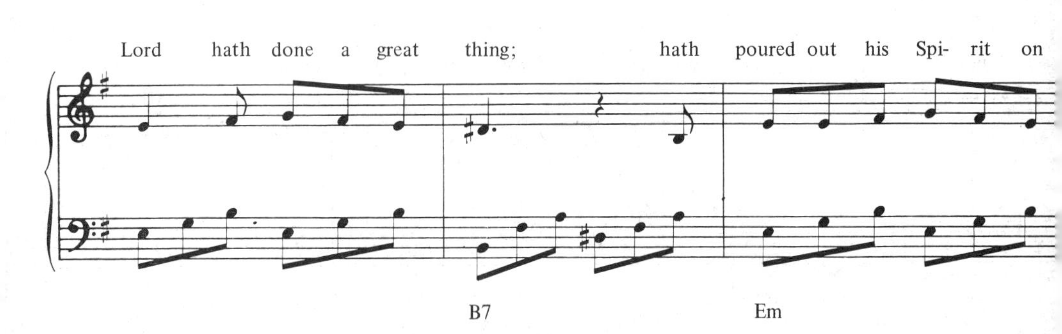
Lord hath done a great thing; hath poured out his Spi- rit on
B7
Em

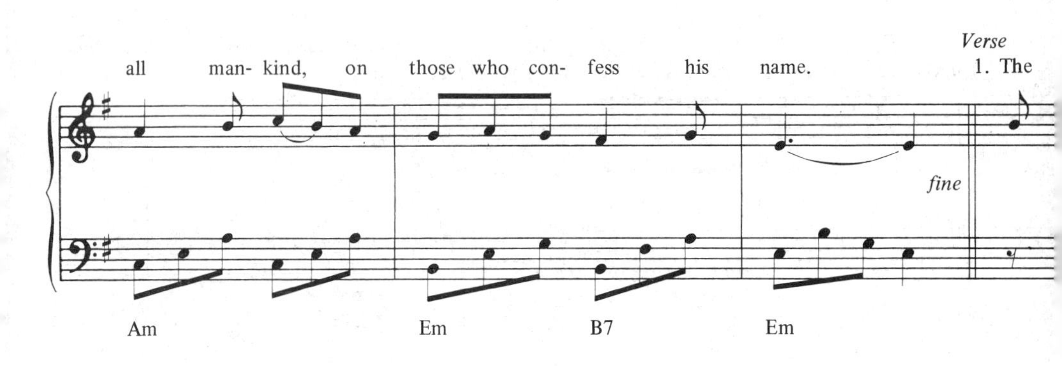
Verse
all man- kind, on those who con- fess his name. 1. The
fine
Am
Em
B7
Em

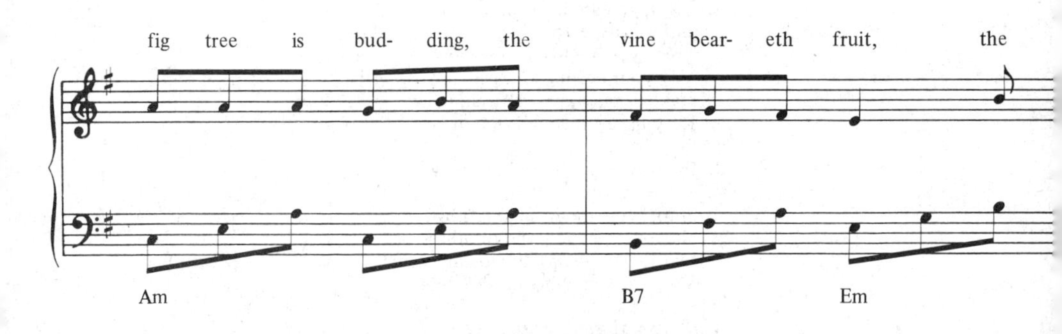
fig tree is bud- ding, the vine bear- eth fruit, the
Am
B7
Em

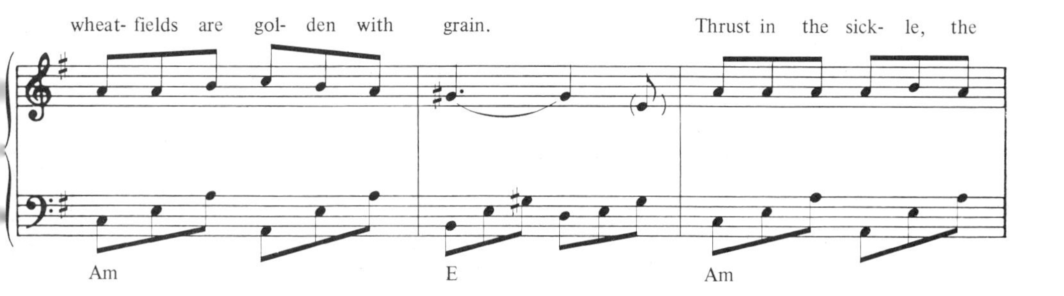

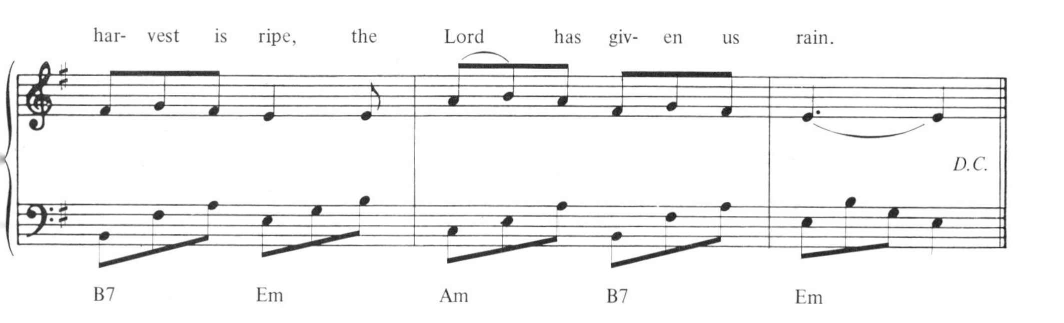

2. Ye shall eat in plenty and be satisfied,
the mountains will drip with sweet wine.
My children shall drink of the fountain of life,
my children will know they are mine.

3. My people shall know that I am the Lord,
their shame I have taken away.
My Spirit will lead them together again,
my Spirit will show them the way.

4. My children shall dwell in a body of love,
a light to the world they will be.
Life shall come forth from the Father above,
my body will set mankind free.

Words, based on Joel 2, 3, 4, and Music: Priscilla Wright

120

FIGHT THE GOOD FIGHT WITH ALL THY MIGHT
(First tune: 'Pentecost' L.M.)

[HARMONY]

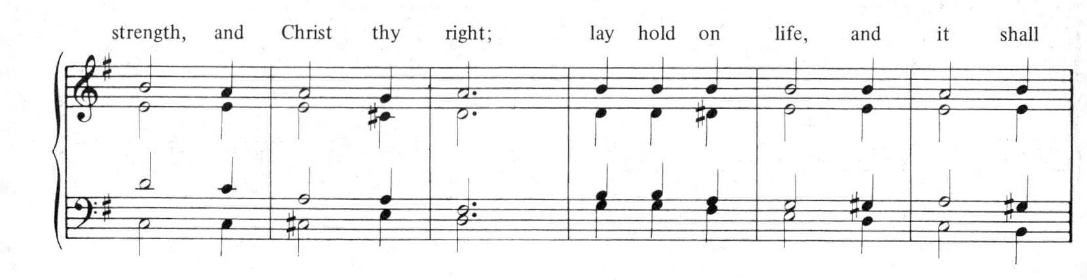

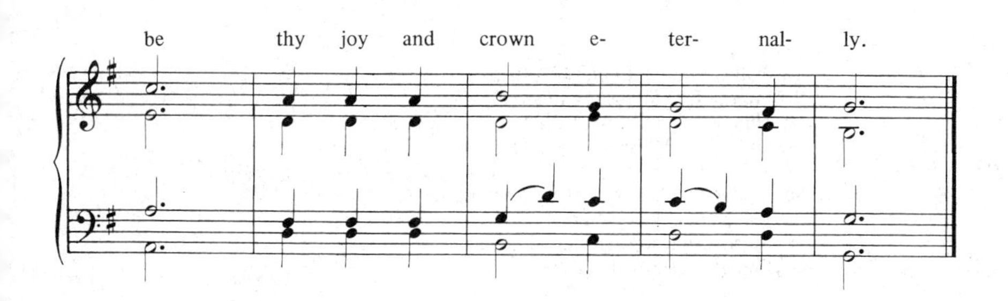

2. Run the straight race
   through God's good grace,
lift up thine eyes
   and seek his face;
life with its way
   before us lies,
Christ is the path,
   and Christ the prize.

3. Cast care aside,
   lean on thy guide;
his boundless mercy
   will provide;
trust, and thy trusting
   soul shall prove
Christ is its life,
   and Christ its love.

4. Faint not nor fear,
   his arms are near,
he changeth not,
   and thou art dear;
only believe,
   and thou shalt see
that Christ is all
   in all to thee.

Words, based on 1 Timothy 6: John Samuel Bewley Monsell (1811-75)
Music: First tune - William Boyd (1847-1928)

FIGHT THE GOOD FIGHT WITH ALL THY MIGHT
(Second tune: 'Duke Street' L.M.)

[HARMONY]

A different harmonisation of this tune may be found at Hymn 413

2. Run the straight race through God's good grace,
lift up thine eyes and seek his face;
life with its way before us lies,
Christ is the path, and Christ the prize.

3. Cast care aside, lean on thy guide;
his boundless mercy will provide;
trust, and thy trusting soul shall prove
Christ is its life, and Christ its love.

4. Faint not nor fear, his arms are near,
he changeth not, and thou art dear;
only believe, and thou shalt see
that Christ is all in all to thee.

Words, based on Timothy 6: John Samuel Bewley Monsell (1811-75)
Music: Second tune - attributed to John Hatton (d. 1793)

FILL THOU MY LIFE
('Richmond' C.M.)

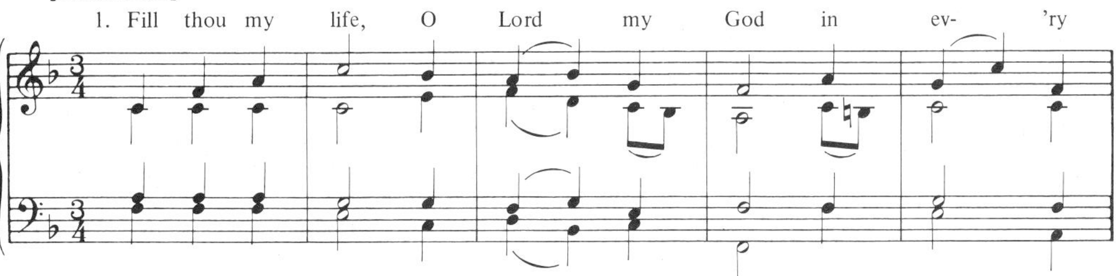

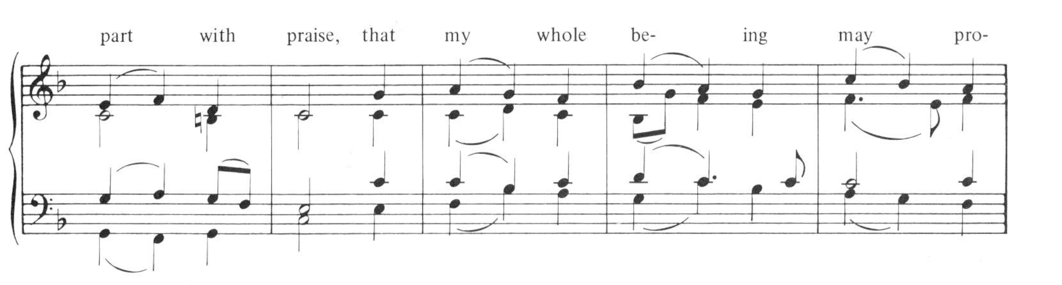

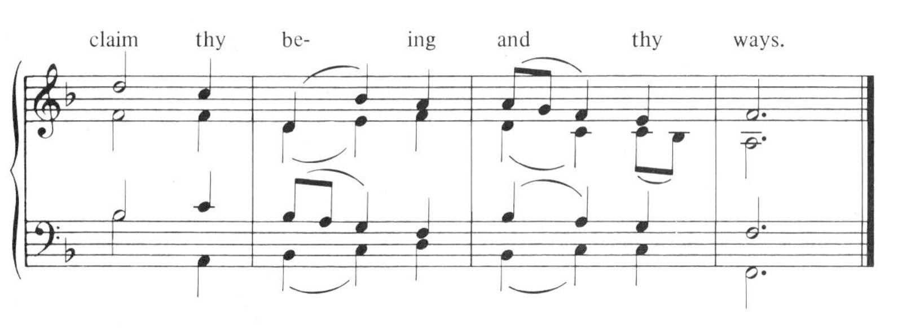

2. Not for the lip of praise alone,
   nor e'en the praising heart,
   I ask, but for a life made up
   of praise in every part:

3. Praise in the common things of life,
   its goings out and in;
   praise in each duty and each deed,
   however small and mean.

4. Fill every part of me with praise:
   let all my being speak
   of thee and of thy love, O Lord,
   poor though I be and weak.

5. So shalt thou, Lord, receive from me
   the praise and glory due;
   and so shall I begin on earth
   the song for ever new.

6. So shall each fear, each fret, each care,
   be turnèd into song;
   and every winding of the way
   the echo shall prolong.

7. So shall no part of day or night
   unblest or common be;
   but all my life, in every step,
   be fellowship with thee.

Words: Horatius Bonar (1808-89)
Music: Thomas Haweis (1734-1820)

122

FILL YOUR HEARTS WITH JOY AND GLADNESS

('Hymn to joy' 87.87.87.)

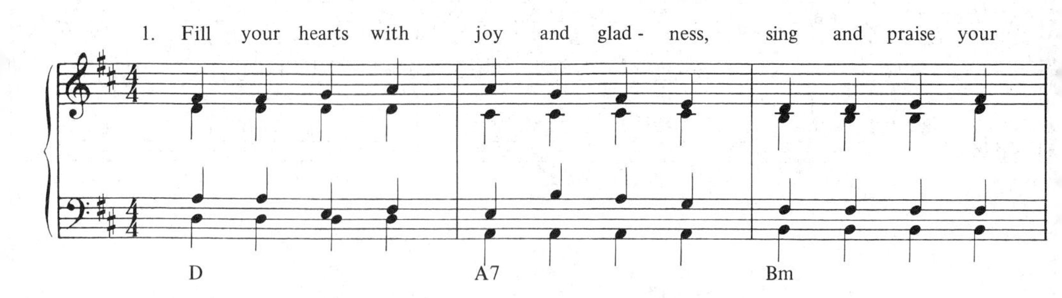

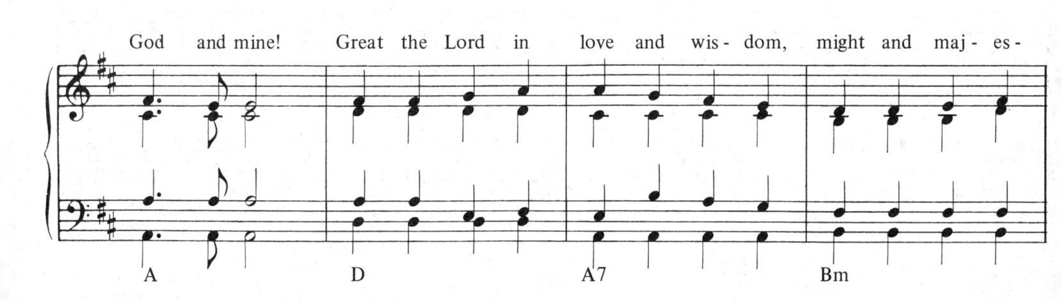

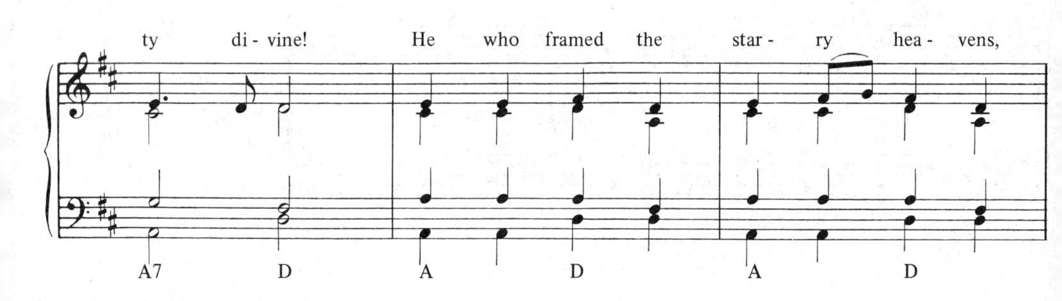

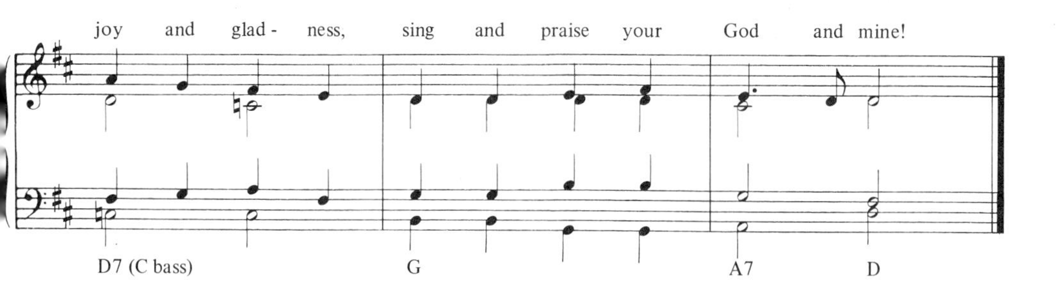

2. Praise the Lord, his people, praise him!
Wounded souls his comfort know.
Those who fear him find his mercies,
peace for pain and joy for woe;
humble hearts are high exalted,
human pride and power laid low.
Praise the Lord, his people, praise him!
Wounded souls his comfort know.

3. Praise the Lord for times and seasons,
cloud and sunshine, wind and rain;
Spring to melt the snows of winter
till the waters flow again;
grass upon the mountain pastures,
golden valleys thick with grain.
Praise the Lord for times and seasons,
cloud and sunshine, wind and rain.

4. Fill your hearts with joy and gladness,
peace and plenty crown your days!
love his laws, declare his judgements,
walk in all his words and ways,
he the Lord and we his children;
praise the Lord, all people, praise!
Fill your hearts with joy and gladness,
peace and plenty crown your days!

Words, based on Psalm 147: Timothy Dudley-Smith (b.1926)
Music: Ludwig van Beethoven, arranged by Michael Irwin

FIRMLY I BELIEVE AND TRULY
(First tune: 'Alton' 87.87.)

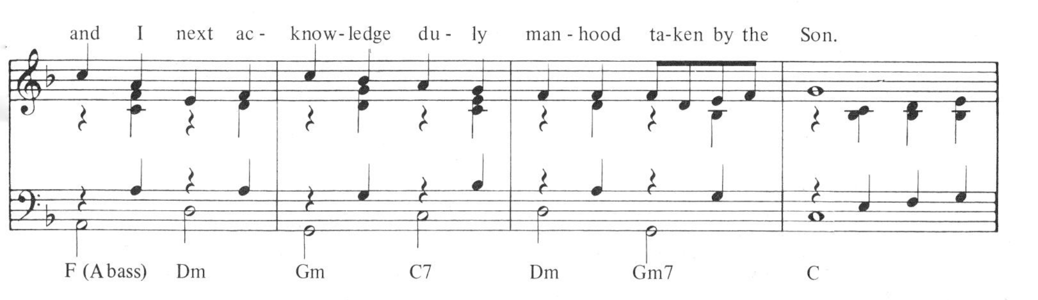

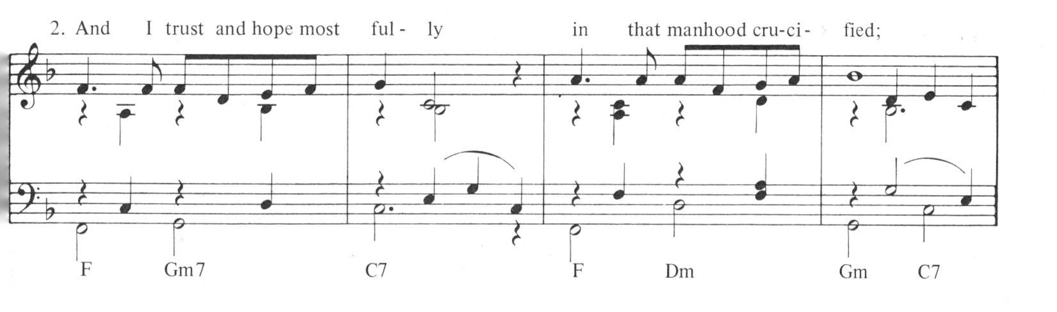

3. Sim- ply to his grace and whol - ly light and life and strength be - long,
C C#o Dm7 G7 Am G (D bass) D7 G
and I love su - preme - ly, sole - ly, him the ho - ly, him the strong.
C C#o Dm7 G7 Am F#o Gm C9 C7
4. And I hold in ven - er - a - tion, for the love of him a - lone,
F Gm7 C7 F Dm Gm C7
ho - ly Church as his cre - a - tion, and her teach - ings as his own.
F (A bass) Dm Gm B♭m6 F (C bass) C9 C7 F
5. A - do - ra - tion ay be giv - en, with and thro' the an - gelic
Dm Gm7 C7 F Dm

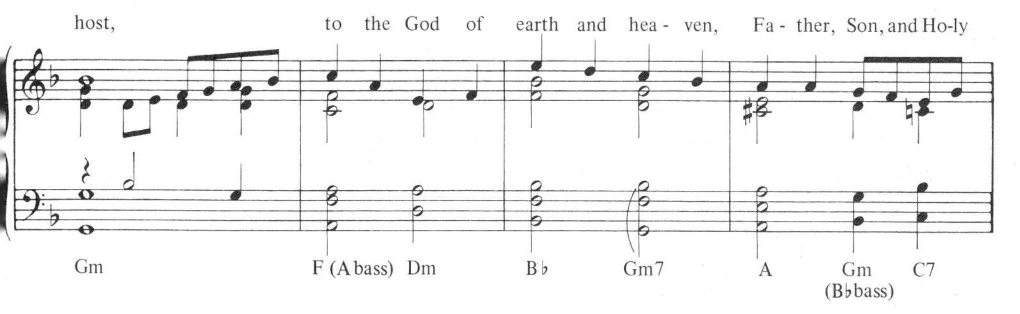

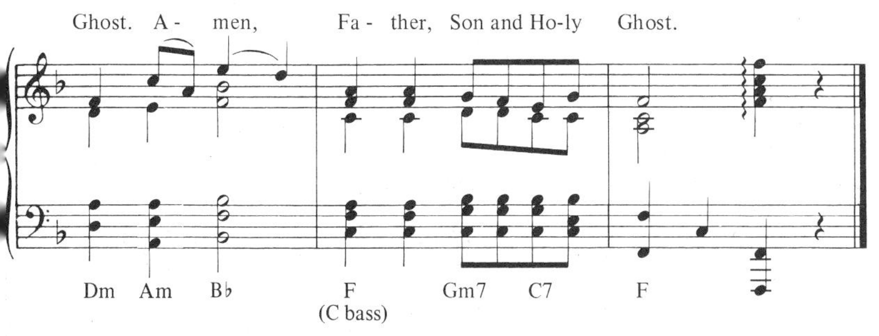

FIRMLY I BELIEVE AND TRULY

(Second tune: 'Shipston' 87.87.)

2. And I trust and hope most fully
   in that Manhood crucified;
   and each thought and deed unruly
   do to death, as he has died.

3. Simply to his grace and wholly
   light and life and strength belong,
   and I love supremely, solely,
   him the holy, him the strong.

4. And I hold in veneration,
   for the love of him alone,
   Holy Church as his creation,
   and her teachings as his own.

5. Adoration ay be given,
   with and through the angelic host,
   to the God of earth and heaven,
   Father, Son, and Holy Ghost.

Words: John Henry Newman (1801-90)
Music: First tune - Patrick Appleford
Second tune - English Traditional melody

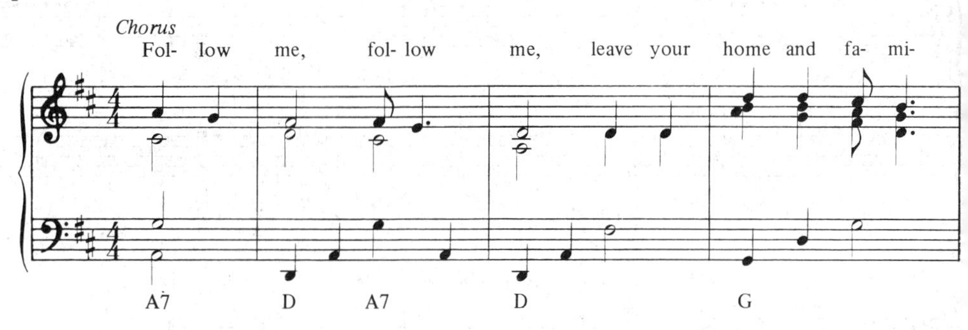
Chorus
Fol- low me, fol- low me, leave your home and fa- mi-
A7 D A7 D G

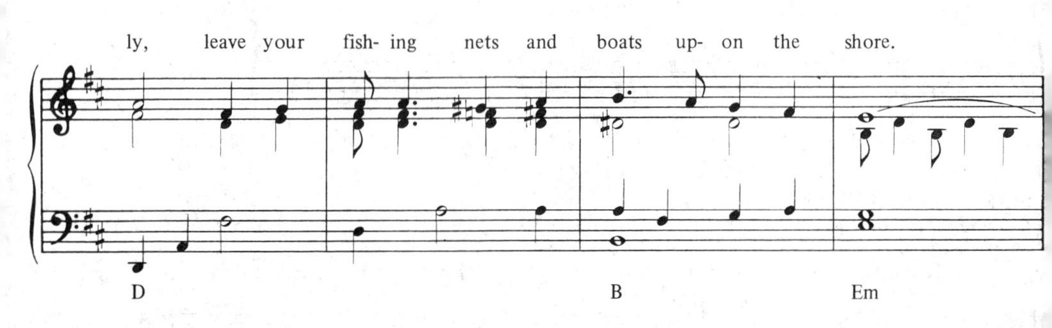
ly, leave your fish- ing nets and boats up- on the shore.
D B Em

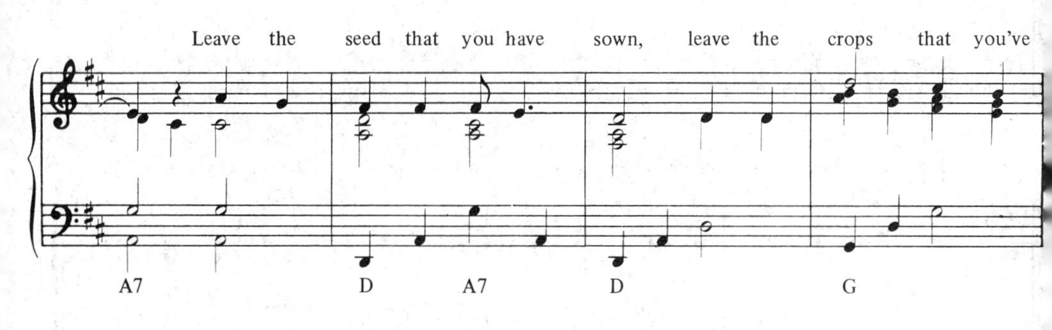
Leave the seed that you have sown, leave the crops that you've
A7 D A7 D G

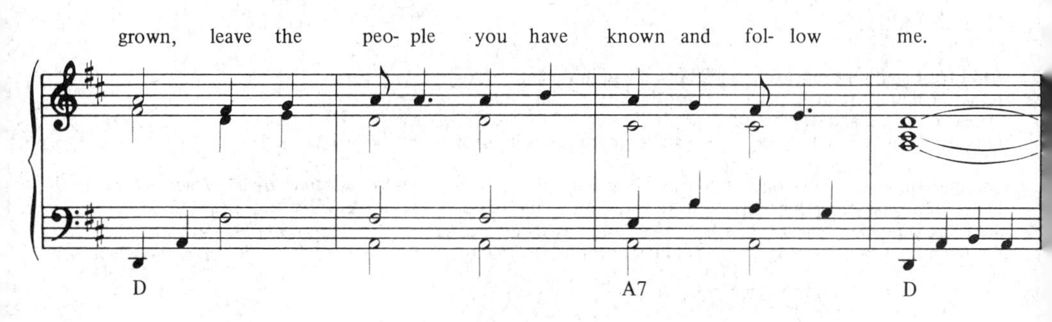
grown, leave the peo- ple you have known and fol- low me.
D A7 D

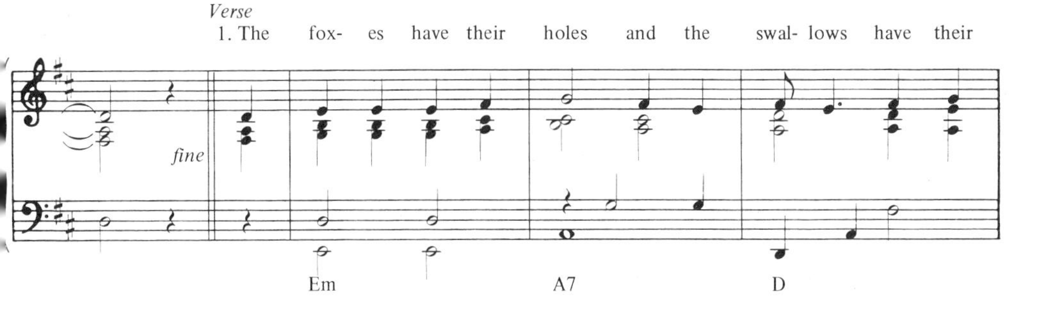

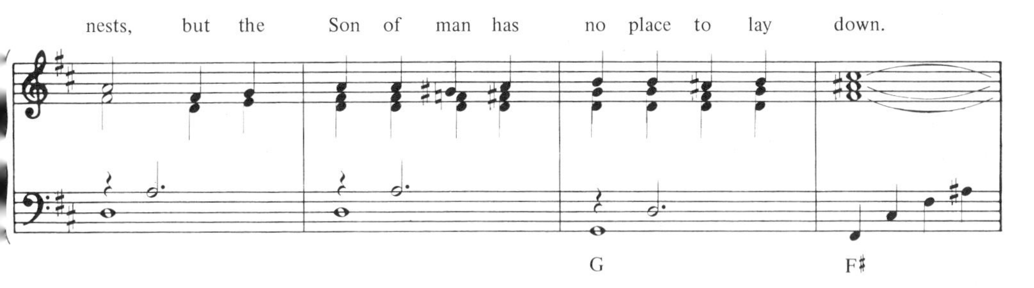

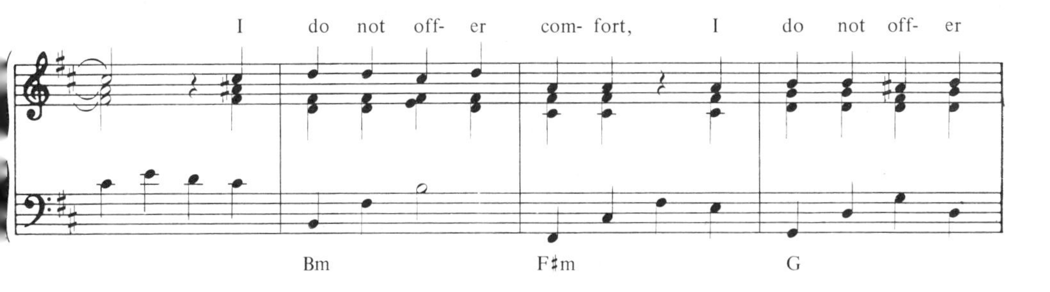

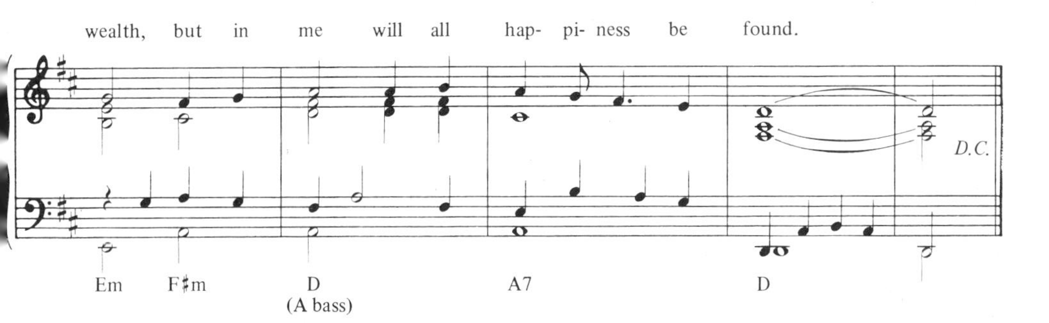

2. If you would follow me,
you must leave old ways behind.
You must take my cross
and follow on my path.
You may be far from loved ones,
you may be far from home,
but my Father will welcome you at last.

3. Although I go away
you will never be alone,
for the Spirit will be
there to comfort you.
Though all of you may scatter,
each follow his own path,
still the Spirit of love will lead you home.

Words, based on Luke 9: Michael Cockett
Music: Madeleine Cuddy

125

FOR ALL THE SAINTS
('Sine Nomine' 10 10.10 4.)

Continues overleaf

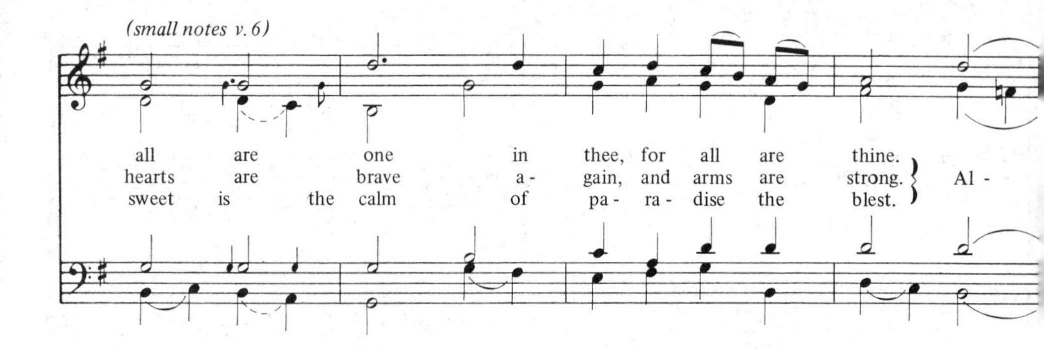

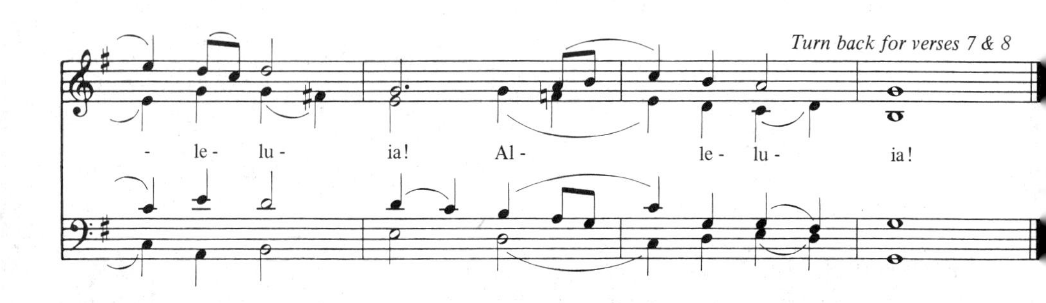

Words: William Washam How (1823-97)
Music: R. Vaughan Williams (1872-1958)

FOR I'M BUILDING A PEOPLE OF POWER

Words and Music: D. Richards

FOR OUR LIFE TOGETHER **(The celebration song)**

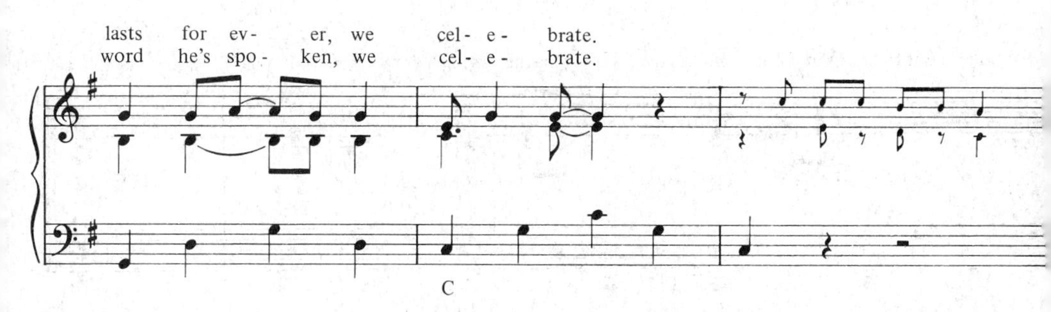

†by his grace
vs. 3
For the joy and for the sor- row, yes- ter- day, to- day,
For the feast- ing at his ta- ble, †
Am
D7
Am
to- mor- row, we cel- e- brate.
we are a- ble to cel- e- brate.
D7
G
2. For your
4. For the
C
G
great cre- a- tion, we cel- e- brate.
Lord a- bove, we cel- e- brate.
C

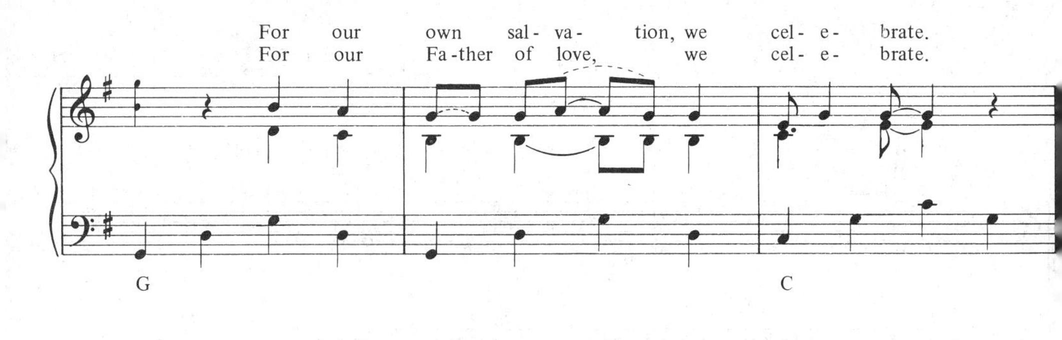
For our own sal- va- tion, we cel- e- brate.
For our Fa-ther of love, we cel- e- brate.
G
C

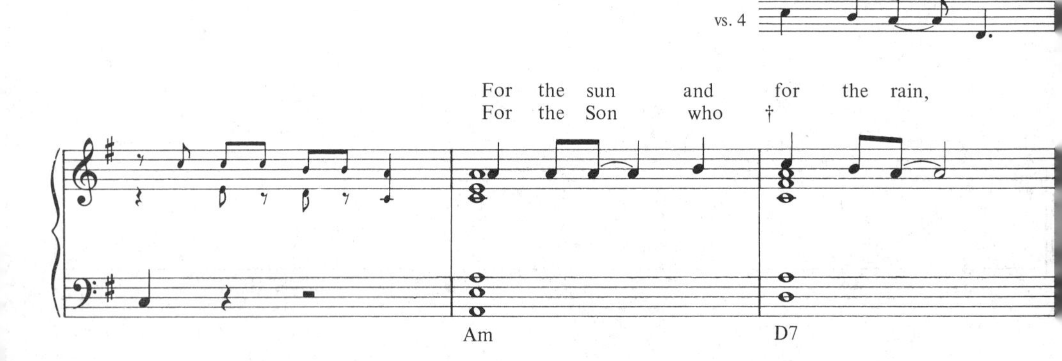
†is our broth- er.
vs. 4
For the sun and for the rain,
For the Son who †
Am
D7

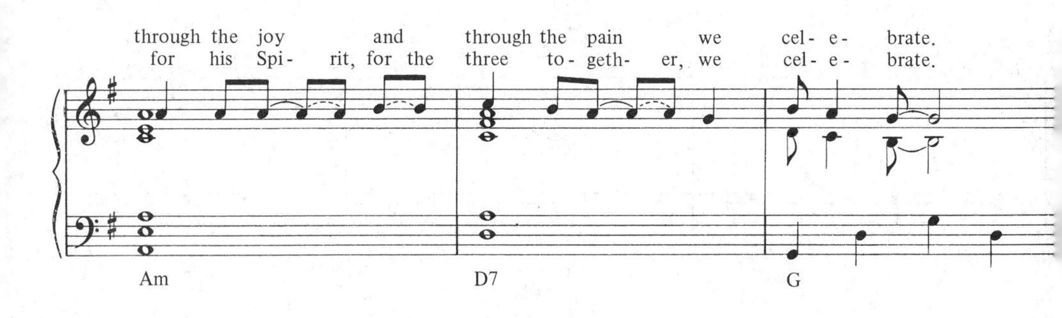
through the joy and through the pain we cel- e- brate.
for his Spi- rit, for the three to- geth- er, we cel- e- brate.
Am
D7
G

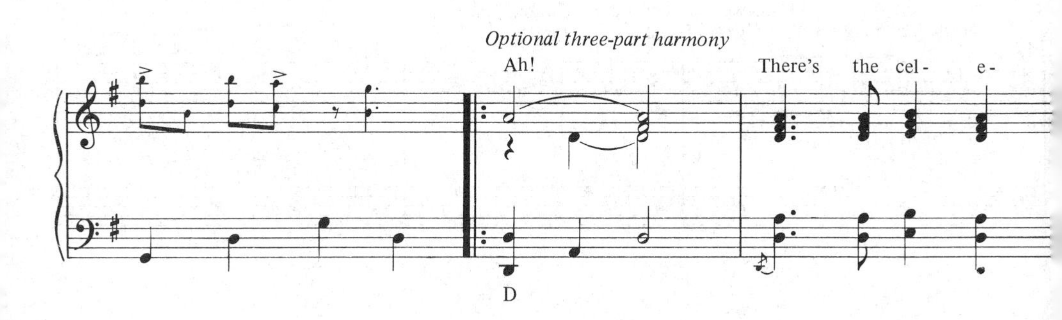
Optional three-part harmony
Ah!
There's the cel- e-
D

Words and Music: Jonathan Asprey and Tim Whipple

128

FOR THE BEAUTY OF THE EARTH
('England's Lane' 77.77.77.)

[HARMONY]

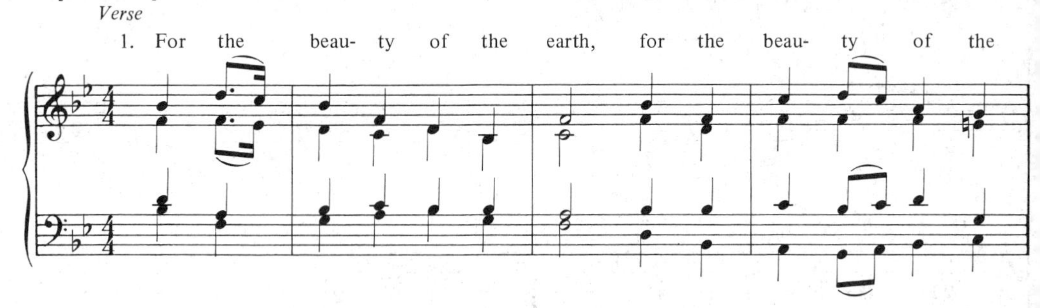

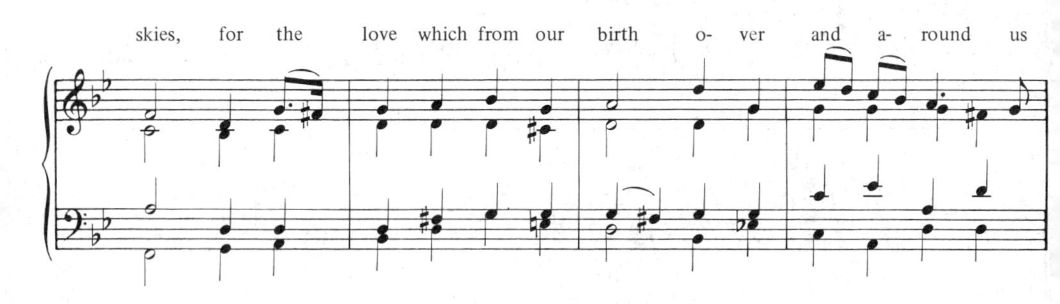

2. For the beauty of each hour,
   of the day and of the night,
   hill and vale and tree and flower,
   sun and moon and stars of light:

3. For the joy of human love,
   brother, sister, parent, child,
   friends on earth, and friends above,
   pleasures pure and undefiled:

4. For each perfect gift of thine,
   to our race so freely given,
   graces human and divine,
   flowers of earth and buds of heaven:

5. For thy Church which evermore
   lifteth holy hands above,
   offering up on every shore
   her pure sacrifice of love,

Words: Folliott Sandford Pierpoint (1835-1917)
Music: Traditional English melody
adapted and harmonised by Geoffrey Shaw (1879-1943)

FOR THE FRUITS OF HIS CREATION

('East Acklam' 84.84.88.84.)

129

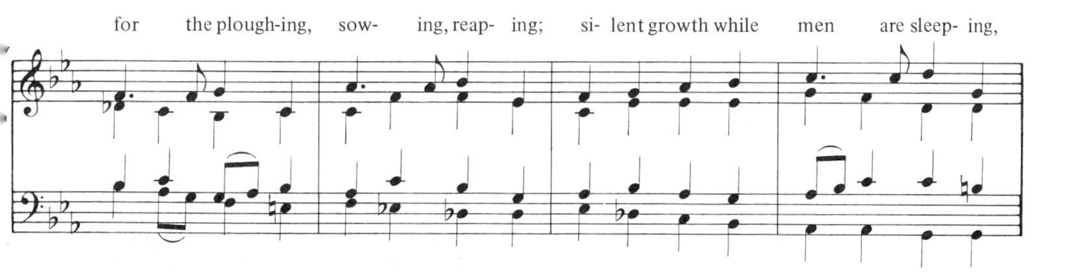

2. In the just reward of labour,
   God's will is done;
   in the help we give our neighbour,
   God's will is done;
   in our world-wide task of caring
   for the hungry and despairing,
   in the harvests men are sharing,
   God's will is done.

3. For the harvests of his Spirit,
   thanks be to God!
   for the good all men inherit,
   thanks be to God;
   for the wonders that astound us,
   for the truths that still confound us,
   most of all, that love has found us,
   thanks be to God.

Words: Fred Pratt Green (b. 1903)
Music: Francis Alan Jackson (b. 1917)

130

FOR THE HEALING OF THE NATIONS

('Alleluia, dulce carmen' 87.87.87.)

[HARMONY]

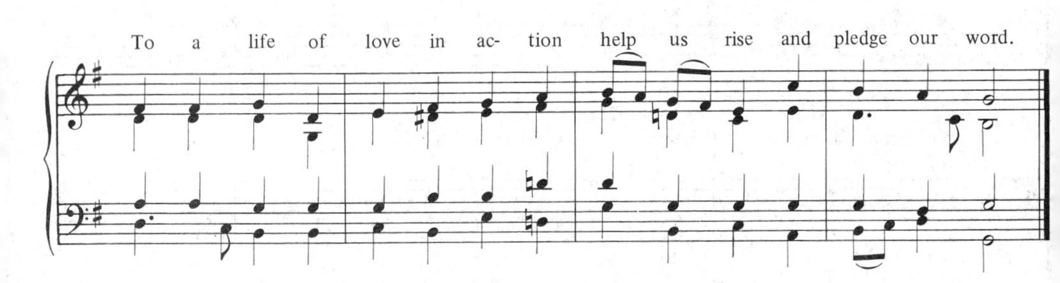

2. Lead us, Father, into freedom,
   from despair your world release;
   that, redeemed from war and hatred,
   men may come and go in peace.
   Show us how through care and goodness
   fear will die and hope increase.

3. All that kills abundant living,
   let it from the earth be banned;
   pride of status, race or schooling,
   dogmas keeping man from man.
   In our common quest for justice
   may we hallow life's brief span.

4. You, creator-God, have written
   your great name on all mankind;
   for our growing in your likeness
   bring the life of Christ to mind;
   that by our response and service
   earth its destiny may find.

Words: Fred Kaan (b. 1929)
Music: 'Essay on the Church Plain Chant' (1782)

FORTH IN THY NAME, O LORD **131**

('Angels' song (Song 34)' L.M.)

[HARMONY]

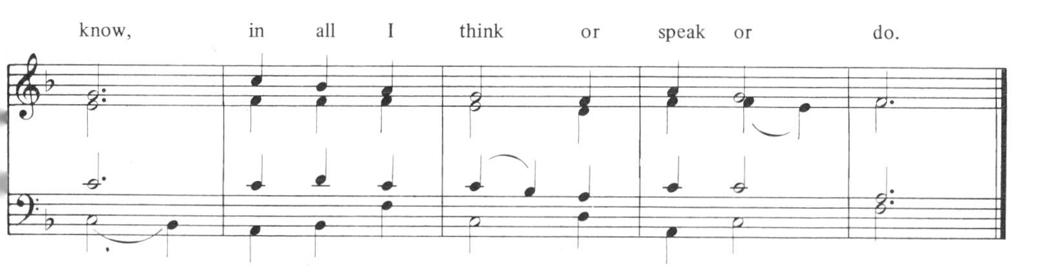

2. The task thy wisdom hath assigned
O let me cheerfully fulfil;
in all my works thy presence find,
and prove thy good and perfect will.

3. Thee may I set at my right hand,
whose eyes my inmost substance see,
and labour on at thy command,
and offer all my works to thee.

4. Give me to bear thy easy yoke,
and every moment watch and pray,
and still to things eternal look,
and hasten to thy glorious day;

5. For thee delightfully employ
whate'er thy bounteous grace hath given,
and run my course with even joy,
and closely walk with thee to heaven.

Words: Charles Wesley (1707-1788)
Music: Orlando Gibbons (1583-1625)

FOR THY MERCY AND THY GRACE

('Culbach' 77.77.)

[HARMONY]

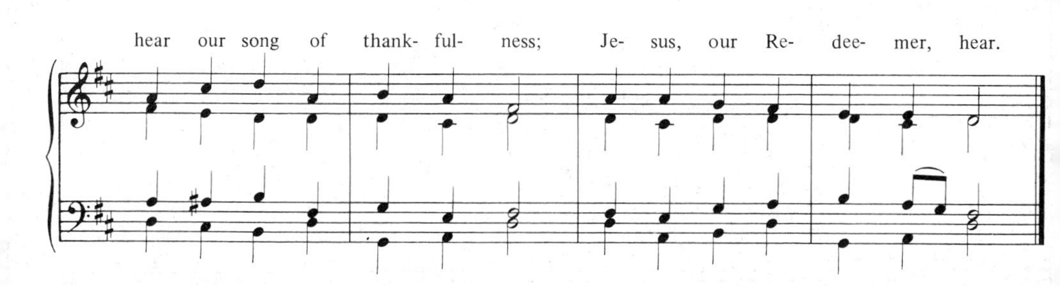

2. In our weakness and distress,
   rock of strength, be thou our stay;
   in the pathless wilderness
   be our true and living Way.

3. Who for us death's awful road
   in the coming year shall tread,
   with thy rod and staff, O God,
   comfort thou his dying bed.

4. Keep us faithful, keep us pure,
   keep us evermore thine own,
   help, O help us to endure,
   fit us for thy promised crown.

5. So within thy palace gate
   we shall praise on golden strings
   thee the only potentate,
   Lord of Lords and King of Kings.

Words: Henry Downton (1818-85)
Music: Johann Scheffler 'Heilige Seelenlust' (1657)

FORTY DAYS AND FORTY NIGHTS
('Heinlein' 77.77.) [HARMONY]

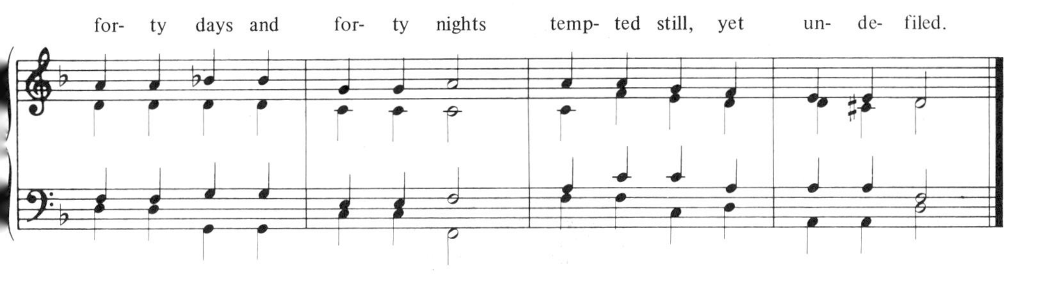

2. Sunbeams scorching all the day,
chilly dew-drops nightly shed,
prowling beasts about thy way,
stones thy pillow, earth thy bed.

3. Let us thy endurance share
and from earthly greed abstain
with thee watching unto prayer,
with thee strong to suffer pain.

4. Then if evil on us press,
flesh or spirit to assail,
victor in the wilderness,
help us not to swerve or fail!

5. So shall peace divine be ours;
holier gladness ours shall be;
come to us angelic powers,
such as ministered to thee.

6. Keep, O keep us, Saviour dear,
ever constant by thy side,
that with thee we may appear
at the eternal Eastertide.

Words: George Hunt Smyttan (1822-70) and others
Music: from 'Nurnbergisches Gesangbuch' (1676)

FOR UNTO US A CHILD IS BORN

Words: Isaiah 9: 6 *Music: Unknown, arranged by Michael Irwin*

Joyfully
Introduction
Capo 1:
D G A D A7 D

Verse
1. For-ward in faith, for-ward in Christ, we are tra- vel- ling on- ward;
D G A D F♯ Bm A

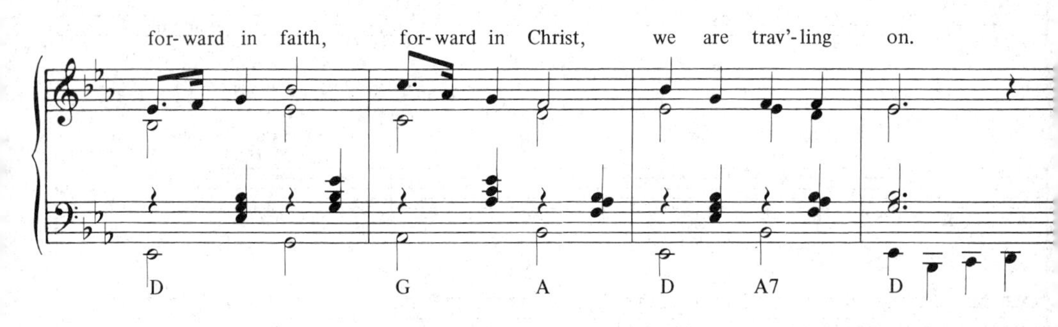
for-ward in faith, for-ward in Christ, we are trav'-ling on.
D G A D A7 D

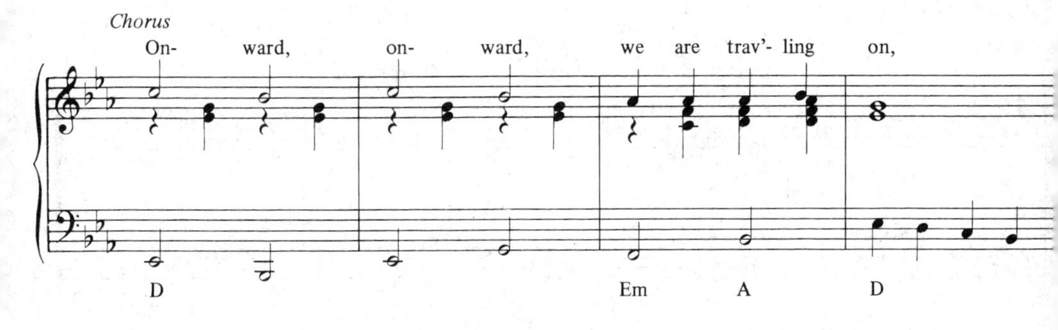
Chorus
On- ward, on- ward, we are trav'- ling on,
D Em A D

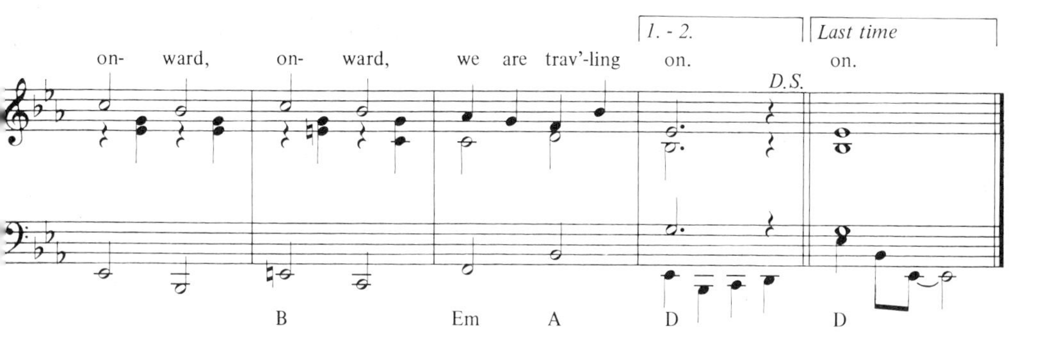

2. Jesus is Lord,
Jesus is Lord,
we are travelling onward;
Jesus is Lord,
Jesus is Lord,
we are trav'ling on.

3. He is our King,
he is our King,
we are travelling onward;
he is our King,
he is our King,
we are trav'ling on.

Words: Graham Jeffery
Music: Kevin Mayhew

136

FROM GLORY TO GLORY ADVANCIN

('Sheen' 14 14.14 1

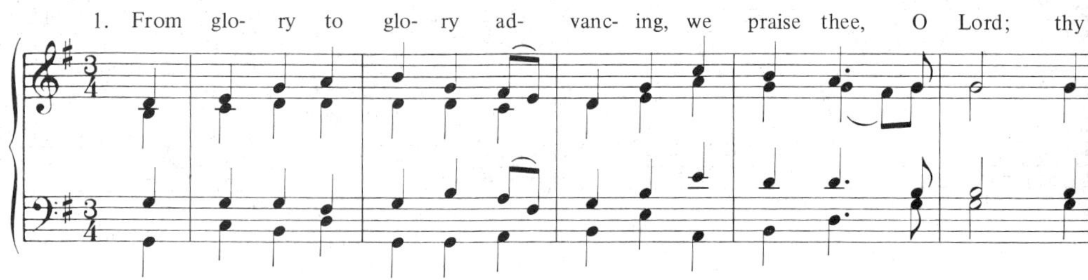

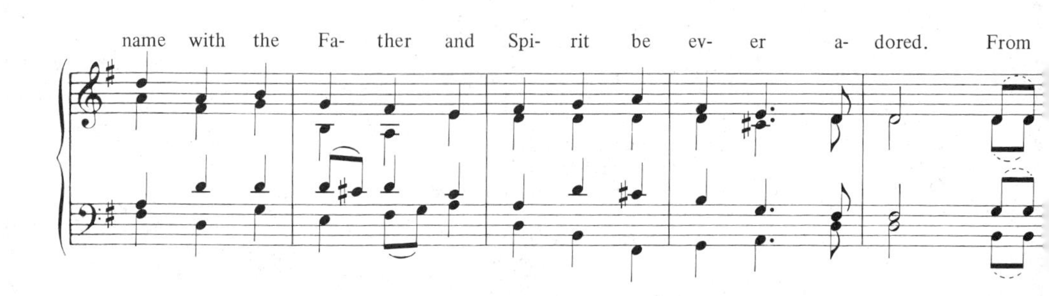

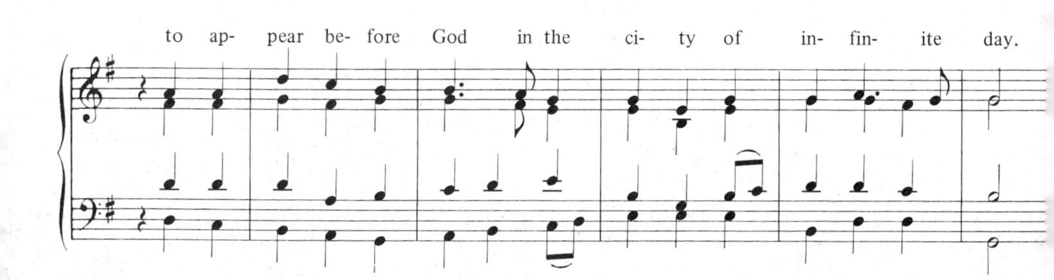

2. Thanksgiving, and glory and worship, and blessing and love,
   one heart and one song have the saints upon earth and above.
   Evermore, O Lord, to thy servants thy presence be nigh;
   ever fit us by service on earth for thy service on high.

Words: from The Liturgy of St James,
tr. C. W. Humphreys
Music: Gustav Holst (1874-1934)

FROM THEE ALL SKILL AND SCIENCE FLOW
('Belgrave' C.M.)

[HARMONY]

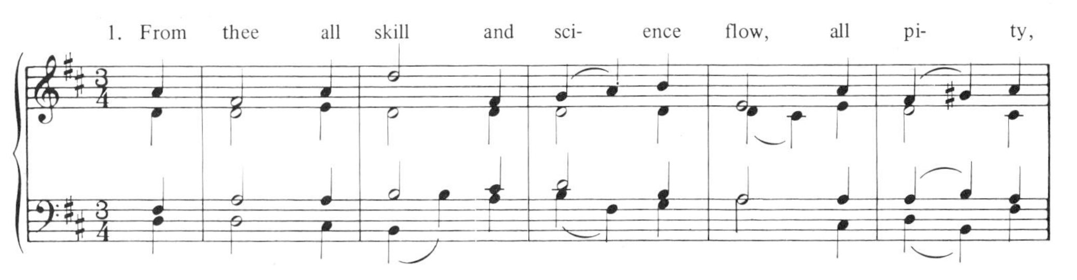

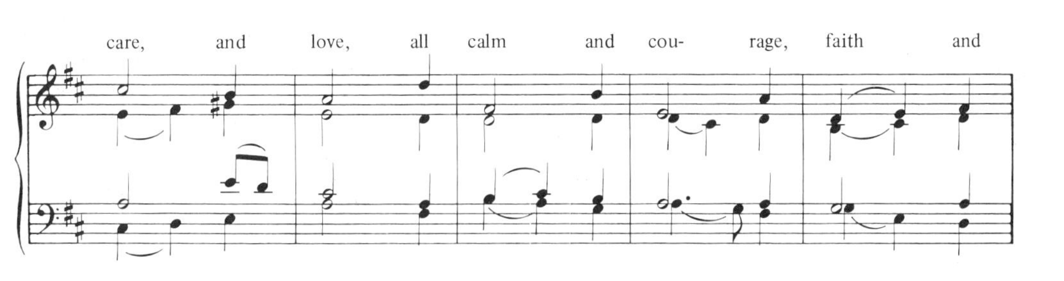

2. And part them, Lord, to each and all,
as each and all shall need,
to rise, like incense, each to thee,
in noble thought and deed.

3. And hasten, Lord, that perfect day
when pain and death shall cease,
and thy just rule shall fill the earth
with health and light and peace;

4. When ever blue the sky shall gleam,
and ever green the sod,
and man's rude work deface no more
the paradise of God.

Words: Charles Kingsley (1819-75)
Music: William Horsley (1774-1858)

For an alternative version of this tune see When All Thy Mercies (574)

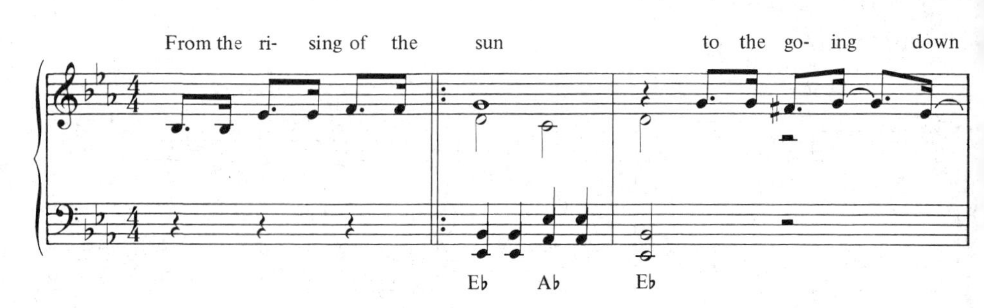
From the ri- sing of the sun to the go- ing down
Eb Ab Eb

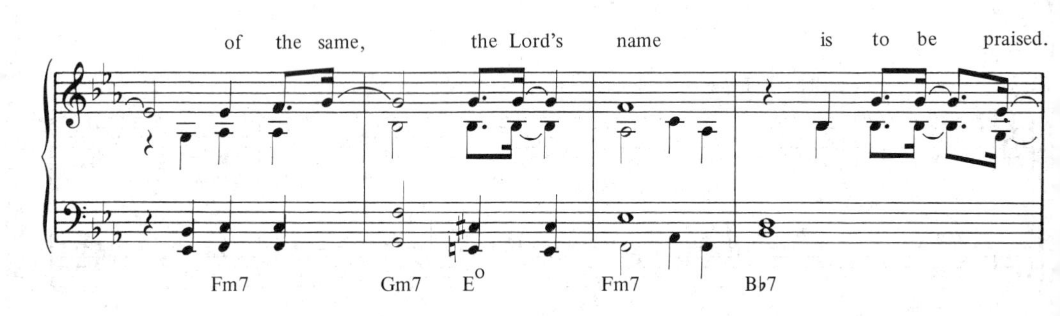
of the same, the Lord's name is to be praised.
Fm7 Gm7 E° Fm7 Bb7

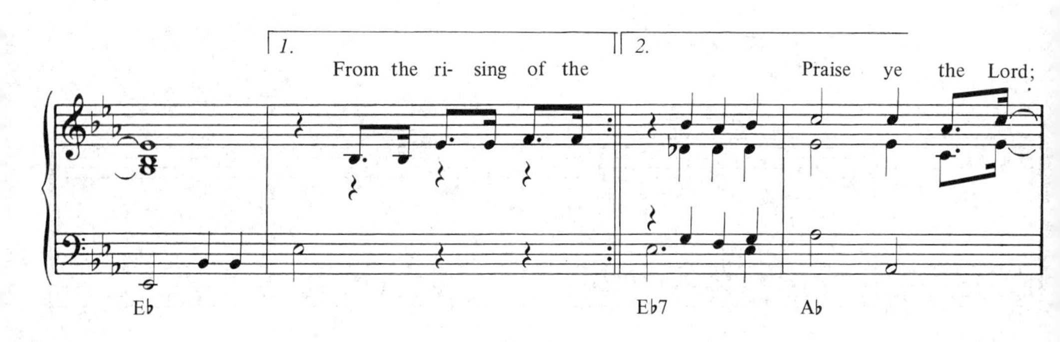
1.
2.
From the ri- sing of the Praise ye the Lord;
Eb Eb7 Ab

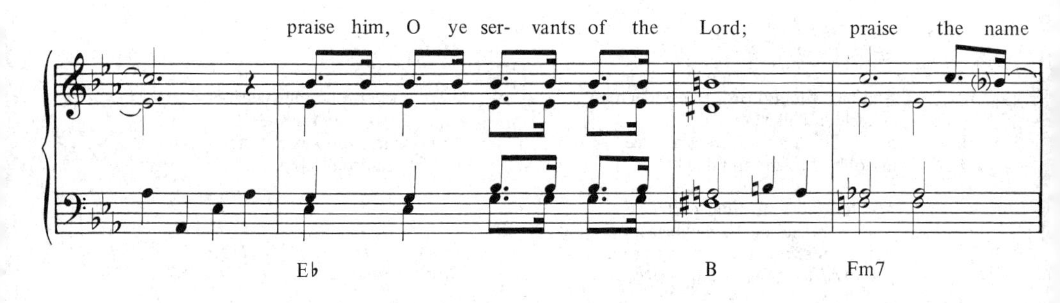
praise him, O ye ser- vants of the Lord; praise the name
Eb B Fm7

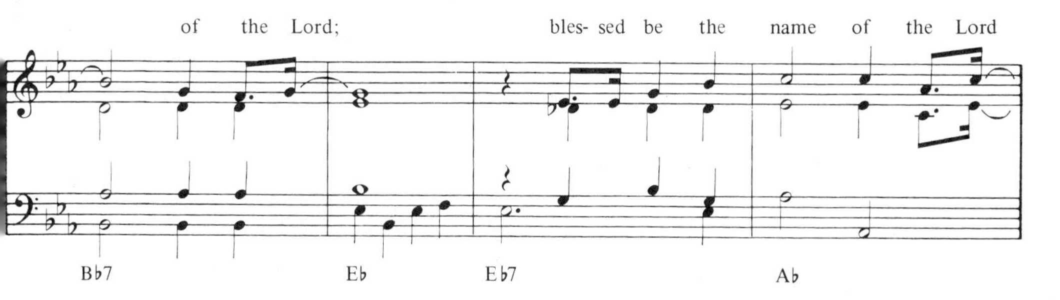

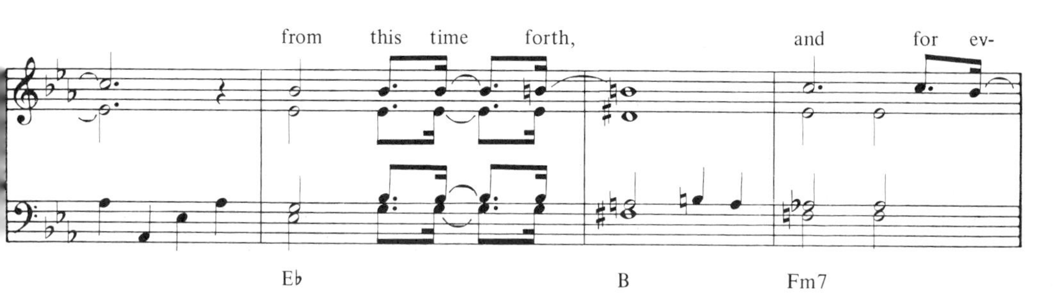

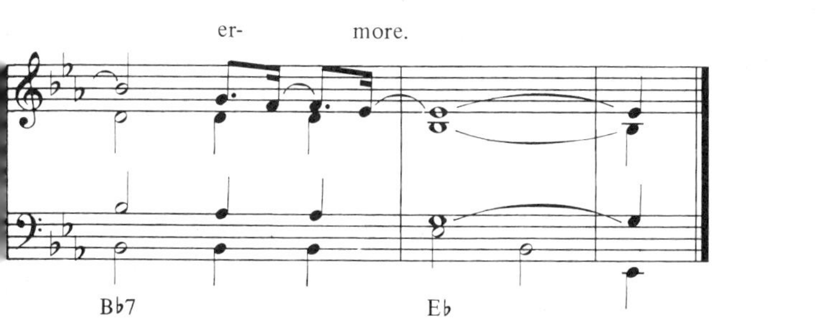

Words, based on Psalm 113, and Music: Paul S. Deming

1. Gifts of bread and wine, gifts we've of- fered,
D Em A G D

fruits of la- bour, fruits of love;
Em A G D

ta- ken, of- fered, sanc- ti- fied, blessed and
Bm G

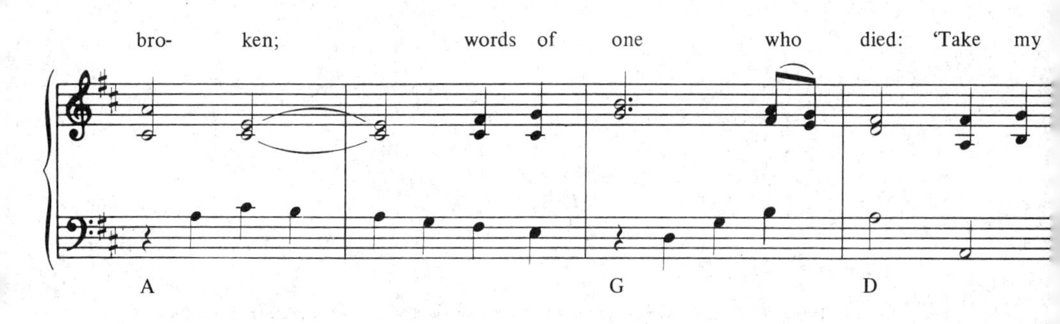
bro- ken; words of one who died: 'Take my
A G D

bo- dy; take my sav- ing blood.' Gifts of

Em A G D

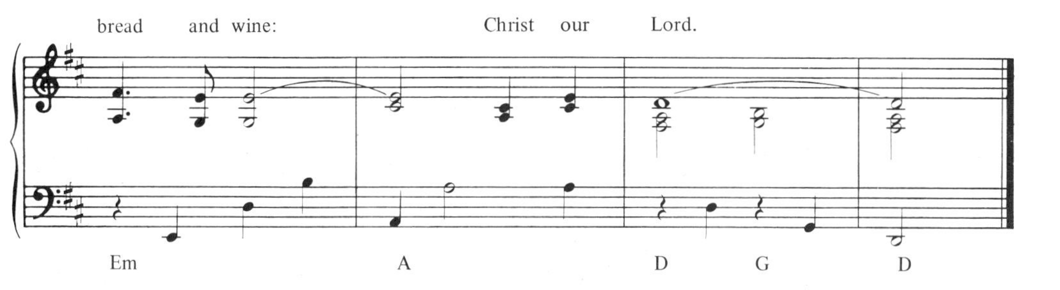

2. Christ our Saviour, living presence here,
as he promised while on earth:
'I am with you for all time,
I am with you in this bread and wine.
Take my body, take my saving blood.'
Gifts of bread and wine: Christ our Lord.

3. Through the Father, with the Spirit,
one in union with the Son,
for God's people, joined in prayer
faith is strengthened by the food we share.
'Take my body, take my saving blood.'
Gifts of bread and wine: Christ our Lord.

Words, based on Mark 14, and Music: Christine McCann

140

GIVE ME JOY IN MY HEART
('Sing Hosanna')

Verse

Chorus

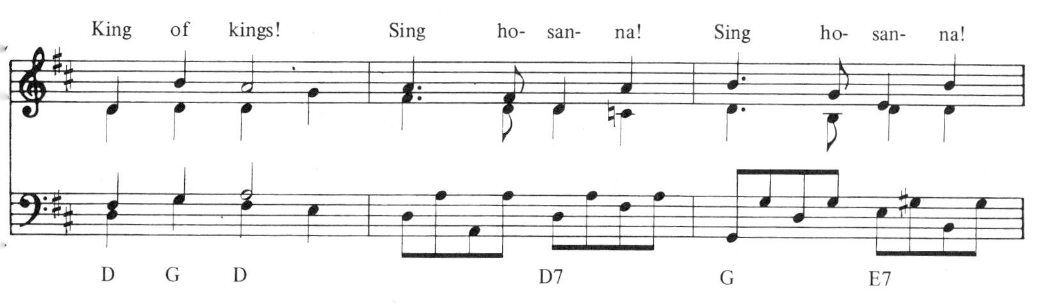

2. Give me peace in my heart, keep me resting . . .

3. Give me love in my heart, keep me serving . . .

4. Give me oil in my lamp, keep me burning,
   give me oil in my lamp, I pray.
   Give me oil in my lamp, keep me burning,
   keep me burning till the break of day.

5. Make me a fisher of men, keep me seeking . . .

Other verses may be added ad lib, e.g.

Give me faith . . . keep me praying . . .

Words and Music: Traditional,
arranged by John Rombaut

GIVE ME PEACE, O LORD, I PRAY

2. Give peace to the world, I pray,
let all quarrels cease today.
May we spread your light and love.
Lord, give us peace.

Words and Music: Estelle White

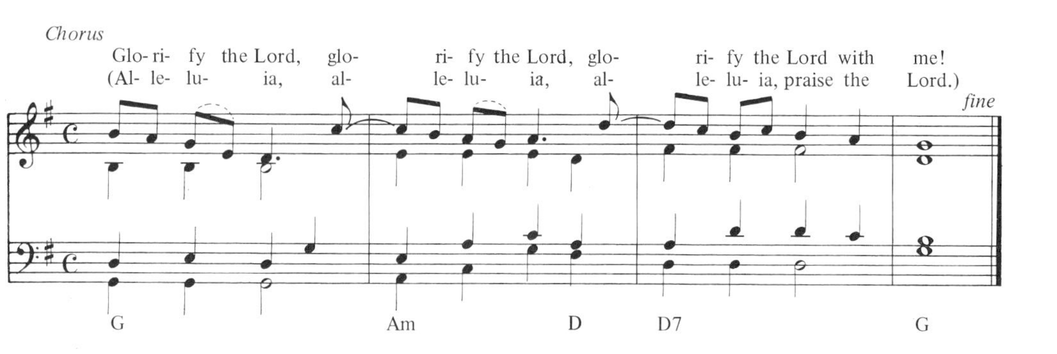

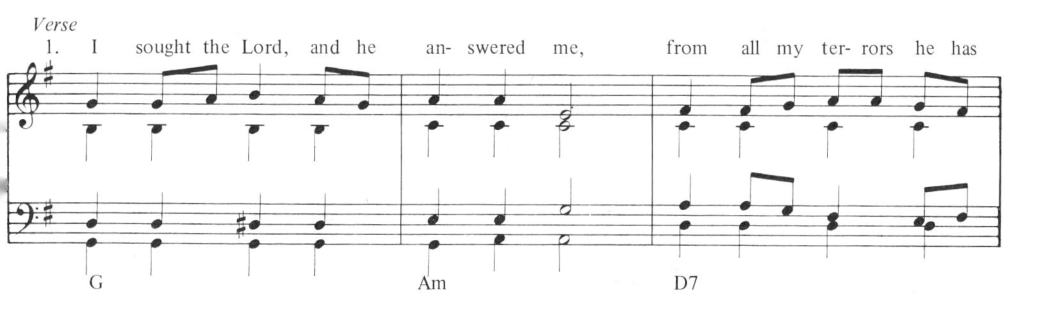

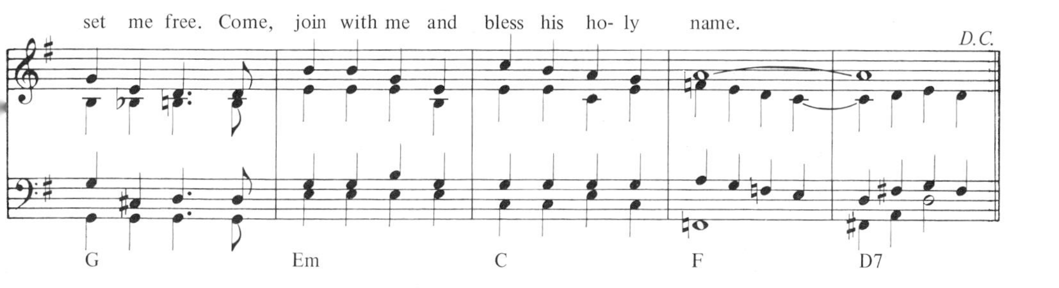

2. Look at the Lord, do not be ashamed,
he will deliver those who call his name.
This poor man called, the Lord has heard his plea.

3. O taste and see that the Lord is good.
Happy are those who put their trust in him.
So fear the Lord and you will know no want.

Words, based on Psalm 34, and Music: Peter Gonsalves, arranged by John Rombaut

143

GLORIOUS THINGS OF THEE ARE SPOKEN

(First tune: 'Austria' 87.87.D.)

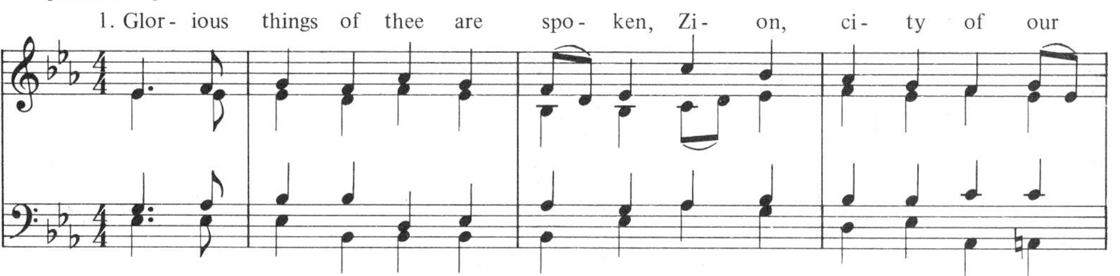

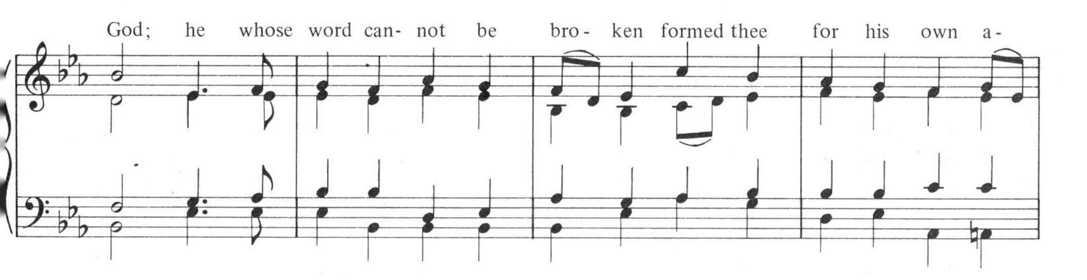

2. See, the streams of living waters,
springing from eternal love,
well supply thy sons and daughters,
and all fear of want remove.
Who can faint while such a river
ever flows their thirst to assuage:
grace which, like the Lord the giver,
never fails from age to age?

3. Round each habitation hovering,
see the cloud and fire appear
for a glory and a covering,
showing that the Lord is near.
Thus they march, the pillar leading,
light by night and shade by day;
daily on the manna feeding
which he gives them when they pray.

4. Saviour, if of Zion's city
I through grace a member am,
let the world deride or pity,
I will glory in thy name.
Fading is the worldling's pleasure,
all his boasted pomp and show;
solid joys and lasting treasure
none but Zion's children know.

Words: John Newton (1725-1807)
Music: First tune – Franz Josef Haydn (1732-1809)
Second tune overleaf

GLORIOUS THINGS OF THEE ARE SPOKEN

(Second tune: 'Abbot's Leigh' 87.87.D.)

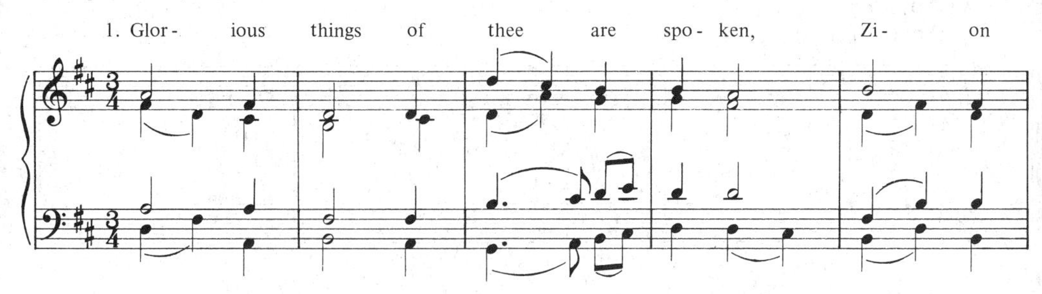

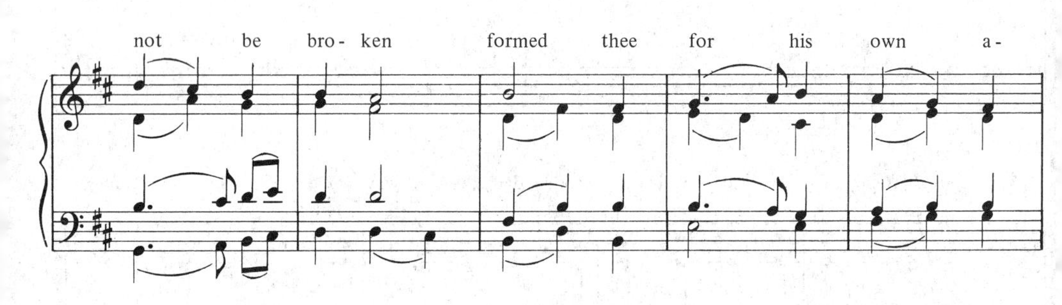

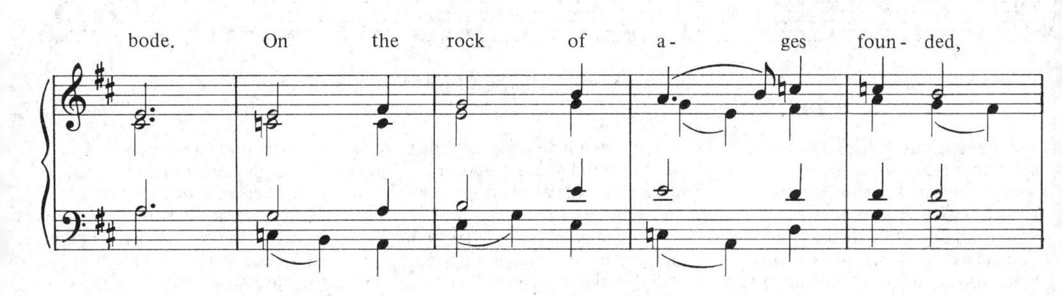

2. See, the streams of living waters,
springing from eternal love,
well supply thy sons and daughters,
and all fear of want remove.
Who can faint while such a river
ever flows their thirst to assuage:
grace which, like the Lord the giver,
never fails from age to age?

3. Round each habitation hovering,
see the cloud and fire appear
for a glory and a covering,
showing that the Lord is near.
Thus they march, the pillar leading,
light by night and shade by day;
daily on the manna feeding
which he gives them when they pray.

4. Saviour, if of Zion's city
I through grace a member am,
let the world deride or pity,
I will glory in thy name.
Fading is the worldling's pleasure,
all his boasted pomp and show;
solid joys and lasting treasure
none but Zion's children know.

Words: John Newton (1725-1807)
Music: Second tune – Cyril V. Taylor (b. 1907)
First tune overleaf

GLORY BE TO JESUS
('Caswall' 65.65.)

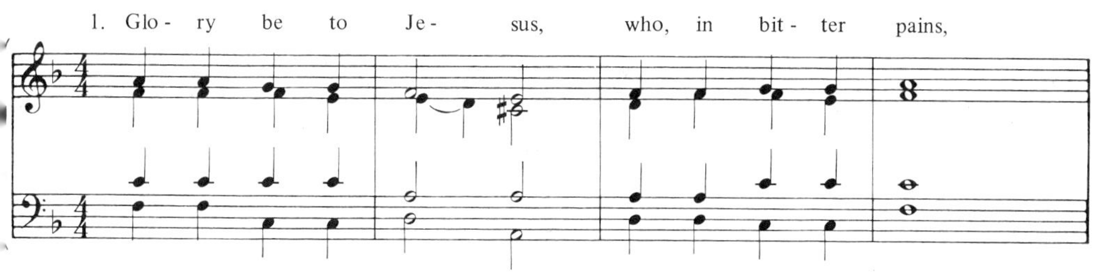

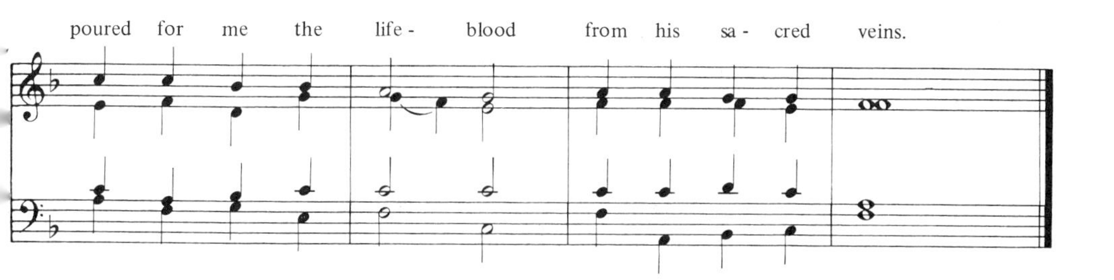

2. Grace and life eternal
in that blood I find:
blest be his compassion,
infinitely kind.

3. Blest through endless ages
be the precious stream,
which from endless torment
doth the world redeem.

4. There the failing spirit
drinks of life her fill;
there as in a fountain
laves herself at will.

5. Abel's blood for vengeance
pleaded to the skies,
but the blood of Jesus
for our pardon cries.

6. Oft as it is sprinkled
on our guilty hearts,
Satan in confusion
terror-struck departs.

7. Oft as earth exulting
wafts its praise on high,
hell with horror trembles;
heaven is filled with joy.

8. Lift ye, then, your voices;
swell the mighty flood;
louder still and louder,
praise the precious blood.

Words: 18th c., tr. Edward Caswall (1814-78)
Music: F. Filitz (1804-76)

145 GLORY BE TO THE SPIRIT OF GOD

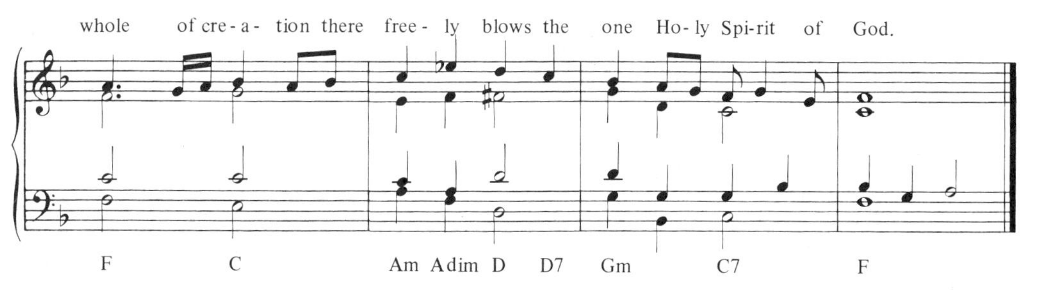

2. Glory be to the Spirit of God,
inspiring all mankind,
for in those very different from
ourselves we find
the same Holy Spirit of God.
May your praises be sung by the old
and the young,
for in everyone who lives
is the breath of the Lord who for ever gives,
the one Holy Spirit of God.

3. Glory be to the Spirit of God,
who fires the Church with grace,
and in such a variety of gifts we trace,
the same Holy Spirit of God.
In our service and care,
in the wisdom we share,
and in everything we do,
may the warmth of your love evermore
break through;
come down, Holy Spirit of God.

Words and Music: Patrick Appleford

GLORY TO GOD **(Peruvian Gloria)**

This song is best sung accompanied only by bongos or a similar percussion instrument. The optional harmony notes give added effect, but those singing the tune should remain on the lower notes.

2. Glory to God, glory to God,
   Son of the Father . . .

3. Glory to God, glory to God,
   glory to the Spirit . . .

Words and Music: Traditional Peruvian,
arranged by Michael Irwin

147

GLORY TO THEE, MY GOD, THIS NIGHT
('Tallis' Canon' L.M.)

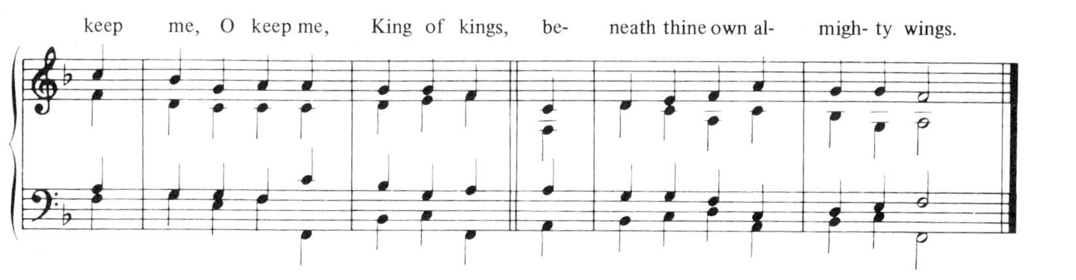

2. Forgive me, Lord, for thy dear Son,
   the ill that I this day have done,
   that with the world, myself and thee,
   I, ere I sleep, at peace may be.

3. Teach me to live, that I may dread
   the grave as little as my bed;
   teach me to die, that so I may
   rise glorious at the awful day.

4. O may my soul on thee repose,
   and with sweet sleep mine eyelids close,
   sleep that may me more vig'rous make
   to serve my God when I awake.

5. Praise God, from whom all blessings flow;
   praise him, all creatures here below;
   praise him above, ye heavenly host;
   praise Father, Son, and Holy Ghost.

Words: Thomas Ken (1637-1711)
Music: Thomas Tallis (c. 1510-85)

148

GLORY TO THEE, O GOD
('Love unknown' 66.66.88.)

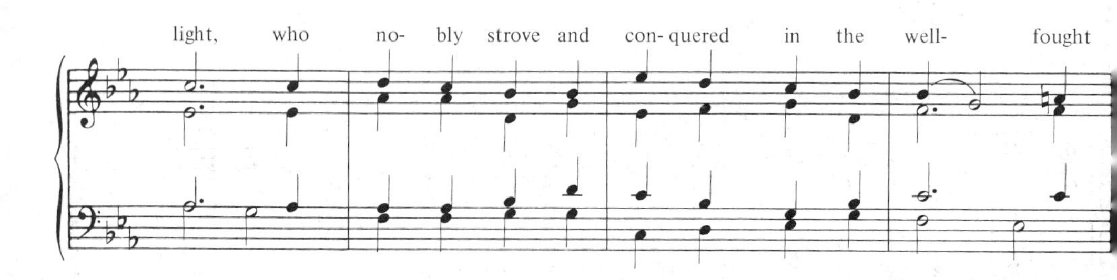

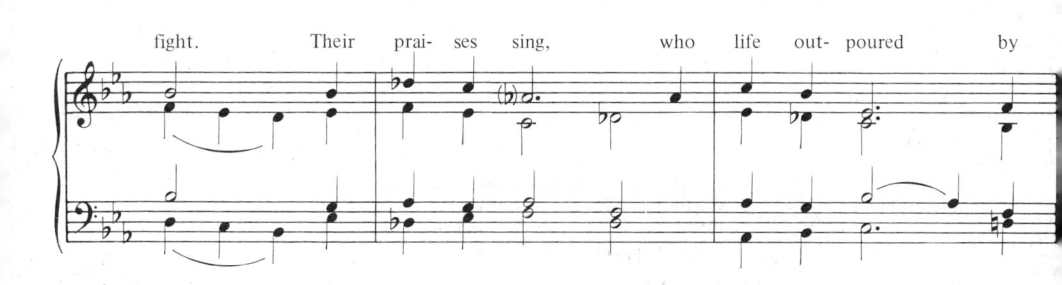

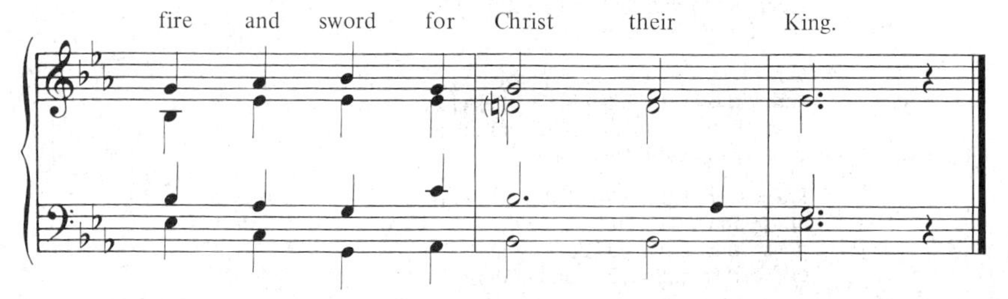

This tune may be found in a lower key at Hymn 337

2. Thanks be to thee, O Lord,
for saints thy Spirit stirred
in humble paths to live thy life and
speak thy word.
Unnumbered they,
whose candles shine
to lead our footsteps after thine.

3. Lord God of truth and love,
'thy kingdom come', we pray;
give us thy grace to know thy truth and
walk thy way:
that here on earth
thy will be done,
till saints in earth and heaven are one.

Words: Howard Charles Adie Gaunt (1902-83)
Music: John Ireland (1879-1962)

GOD BE IN MY HEAD

('God be in my head' Irregular)

Words: 'Book of Hours' (1514)
Music: Walford Davies (1869-1941)

GOD FORGAVE MY SIN **(Freely, freely)**

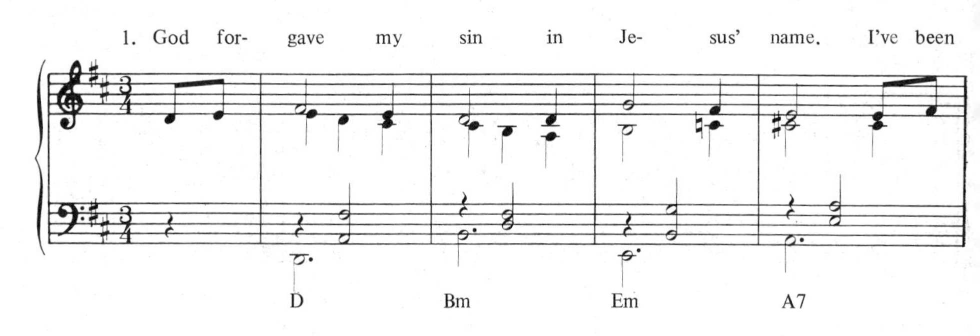

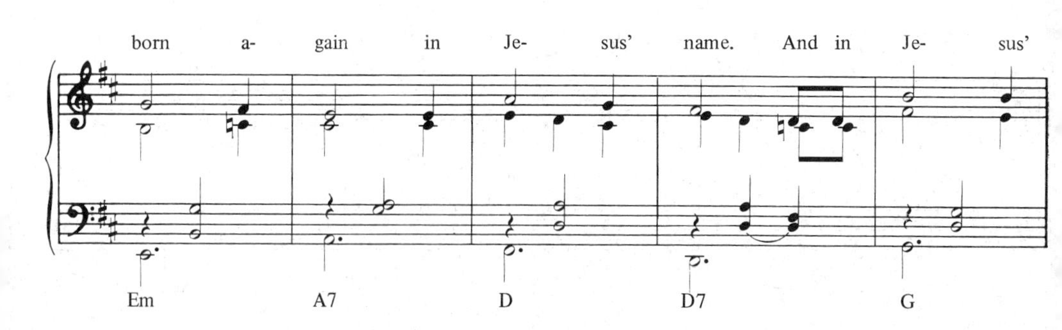

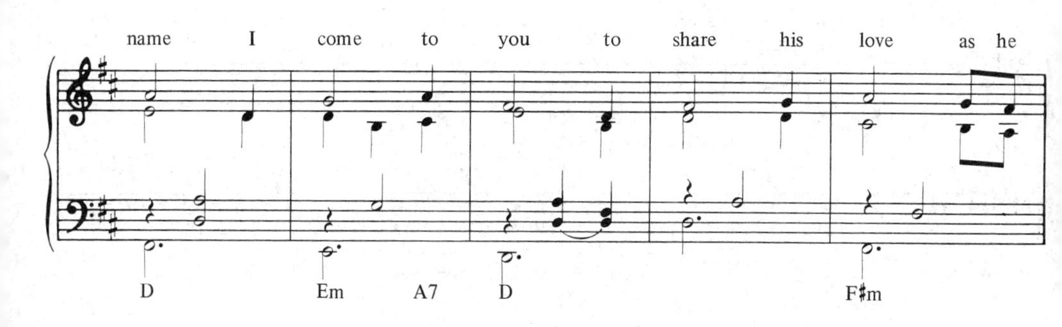

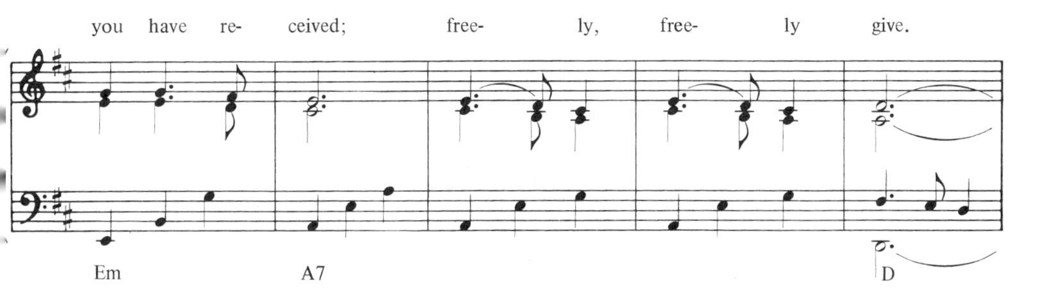

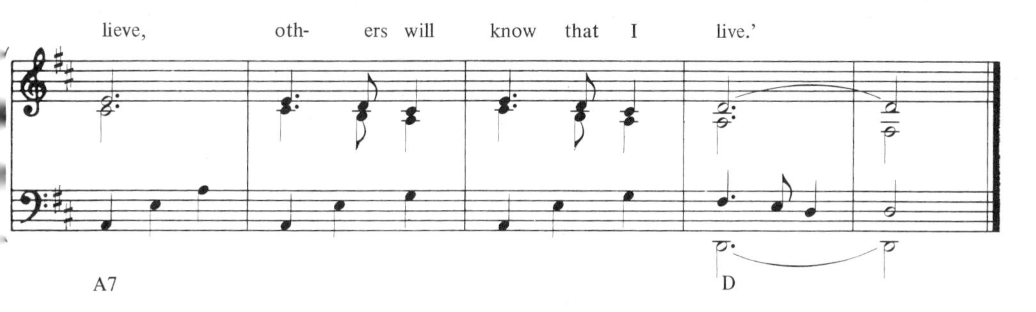

2. All pow'r is giv'n in Jesus' name,
in earth and heav'n in Jesus' name.
And in Jesus' name I come to you
to share his pow'r as he told me to.

3. God gives us life in Jesus' name,
he lives in us in Jesus' name.
And in Jesus' name I come to you
to share his peace as he told me to.

Words and Music: Jimmy and Carol Owens,
(from 'Come together')

GOD GIVES PEACE LIKE A RIVE

2. God gives hope, hope forever,
hope, hope forever.
God gives hope, hope forever
for my soul.

3. God brings life, life forever,
life, life forever.
God brings life, life forever
to us all.

4. Let's bring peace like a river,
peace like a river,
let's bring peace like a river
to the world.

Words: Verse 1 - Unknown
Verses 2-4 - Robert B. Kelly
Music: Unknown, arranged by John Rombaut

GOD IS LOVE: HIS THE CARE

('Theodoric' 666.66.55.3.9.)

152

Verse

Je - sus came to show him, that man- kind might know him! *Chorus* Sing a - loud,

C Am G C G C

2. None can see God above;
all have here man to love;
thus may we Godward move,
finding him in others,
holding all men brothers.

3. Jesus lived here for men:
strove and died, rose again,
rules our hearts now as then;
for he came to save us
by the truth he gave us.

4. To our Lord praise we sing,
light and life, friend and king,
coming down love to bring,
pattern for our duty,
showing God in beauty.

Words: Percy Dearmer (1867-1936)
Music: from 'Piae Cantiones' 1582
arranged by John Rombaut

GOD IS LOVE: LET HEAVEN ADORE HIM

('Alleluia' 87.87.D.)

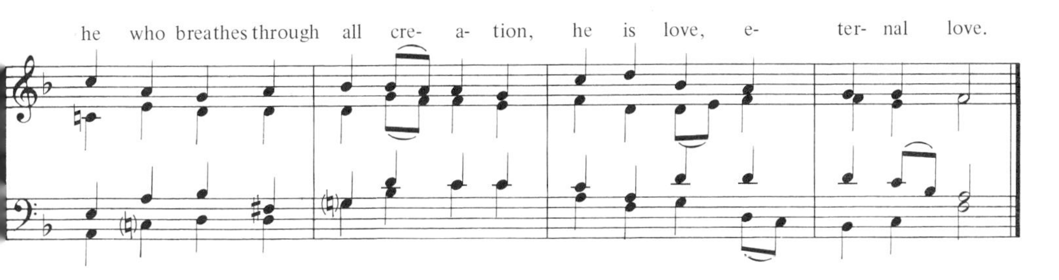

2. God is Love: and he enfoldeth
all the world in one embrace;
with unfailing grasp he holdeth
every child of every race.
And when human hearts are breaking
under sorrow's iron rod,
then they find that selfsame aching
deep within the heart of God.

3. God is Love: and though with blindness
sin afflicts the souls of men,
God's eternal loving-kindness
holds and guides them even then.
Sin and death and hell shall never
o'er us final triumph gain;
God is Love, so Love for ever
o'er the universe must reign.

Words: Timothy Rees (1874-1939)
Music: Samuel Sebastian Wesley (1810-76)

GOD IS WORKING HIS PURPOSE OUT

(First tune: 'Benson' Irregular)

[HARMONY]

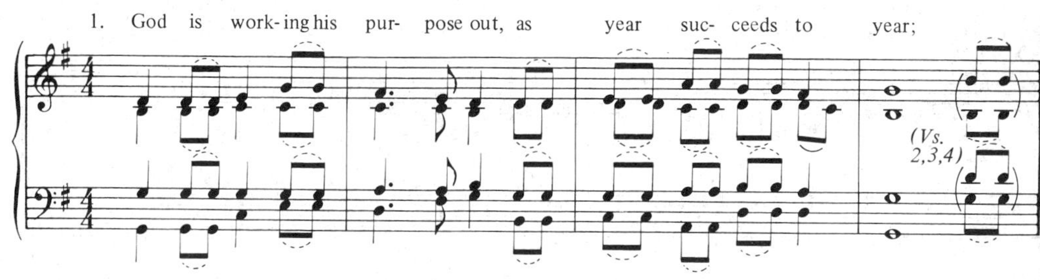

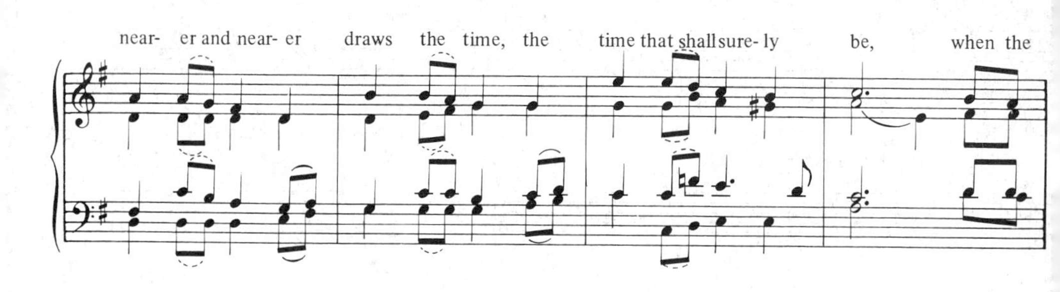

2. From utmost east to utmost west
where'er man's foot hath trod,
by the mouth of many messengers
goes forth the voice of God,
'Give ear to me, ye continents,
ye isles, give ear to me,
that the earth may be filled
with the glory of God
as the waters cover the sea.'

3. What can we do to work God's work,
to prosper and increase
the brotherhood of all mankind,
the reign of the Prince of Peace?
What can we do to hasten the time,
the time that shall surely be,
when the earth shall be filled
with the glory of God
as the waters cover the sea.

4. March we forth in the strength of God
with the banner of Christ unfurled,
that the light of the glorious gospel of truth
may shine throughout the world.
Fight we the fight with sorrow and sin,
to set their captives free,
that the earth may be filled
with the glory of God
as the waters cover the sea.

5. All we can do is nothing worth
unless God blesses the deed;
vainly we hope for the harvest-tide
till God gives life to the seed;
yet nearer and nearer draws the time,
the time that shall surely be,
when the earth shall be filled
with the glory of God
as the waters cover the sea.

Words: Arthur C. Ainger (1841-1919)
Music: First tune - Millicent D. Kingham (1866-1927)
Second tune overleaf

GOD IS WORKING HIS PURPOSE OU

(Second tune: 'Purpose' Irregula

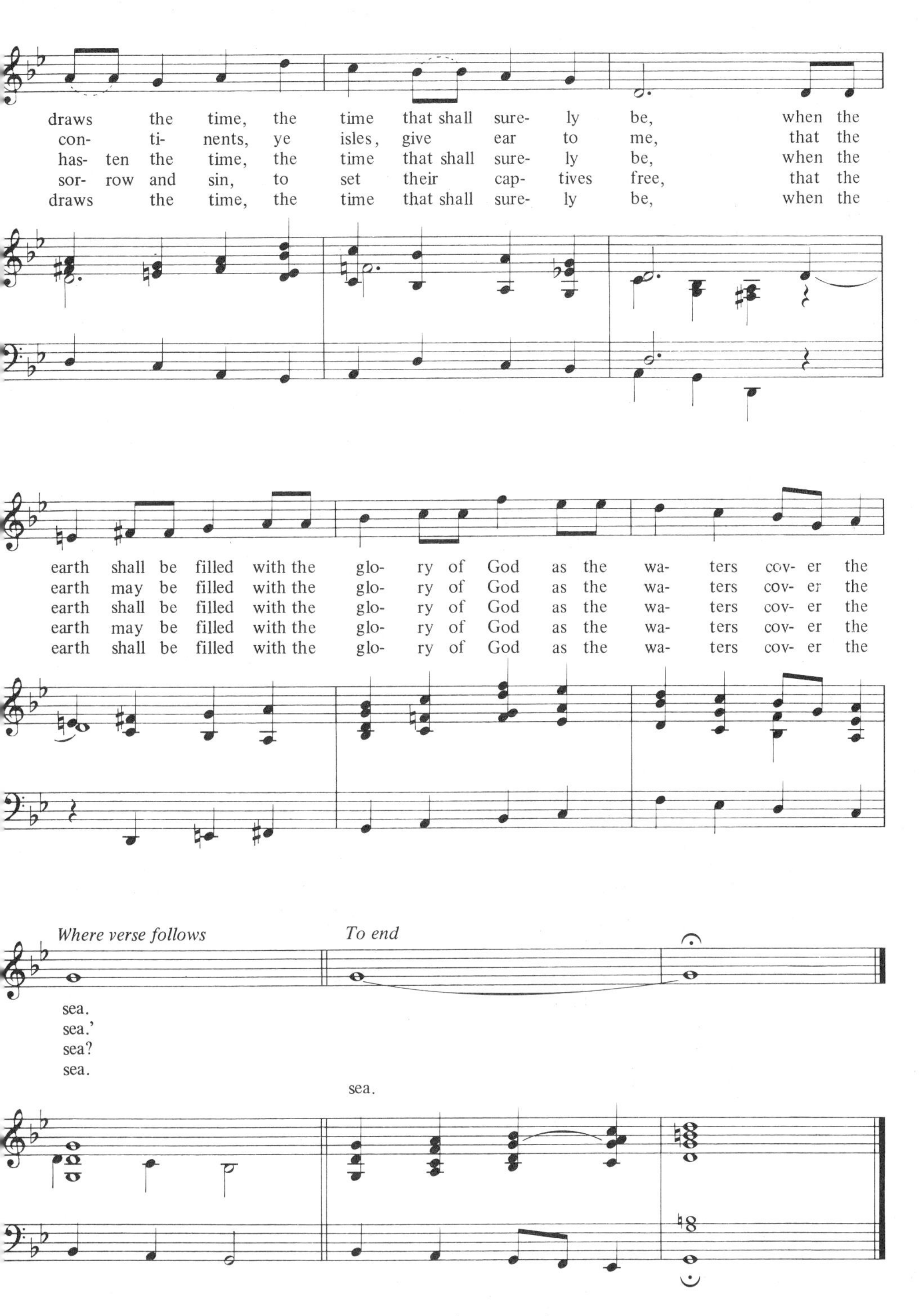

Words: Arthur C. Ainger (1841-1919)
Music: Second tune - Martin Shaw (1875-1958)

155

GOD MOVES IN A MYSTERIOUS WAY
('London New' C.M.)

[HARMONY]

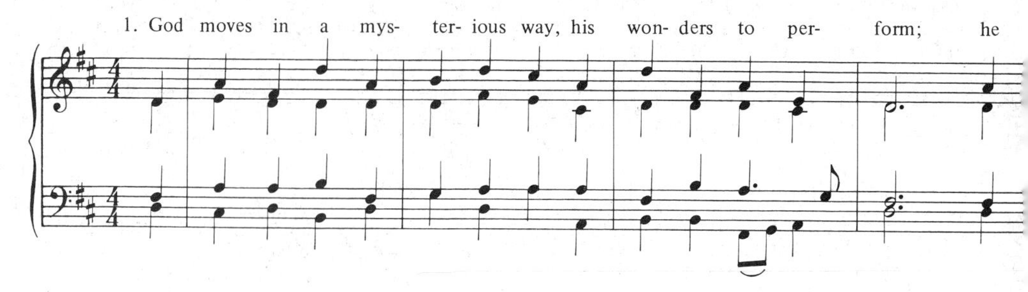

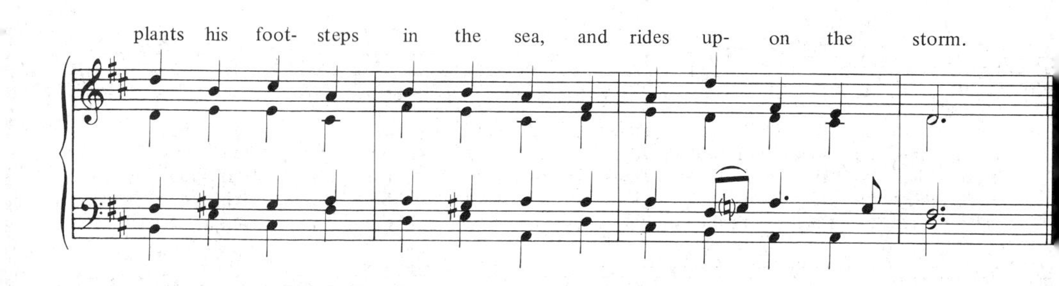

2. Deep in unfathomable mines
 of never-failing skill
 he treasures up his bright designs,
 and works his sovereign will.

3. Ye fearful saints, fresh courage take;
 the clouds ye so much dread
 are big with mercy, and shall break
 in blessings on your head.

4. Judge not the Lord by feeble sense,
 but trust him for his grace;
 behind a frowning providence
 he hides a smiling face.

5. His purposes will ripen fast,
 unfolding every hour;
 the bud may have a bitter taste,
 but sweet will be the flower.

6. Blind unbelief is sure to err,
 and scan his work in vain;
 God is his own interpreter,
 and he will make it plain.

Words: William Cowper (1731-1800)
Music: 'Playford's Psalms' (1671)

GOD OF MERCY, GOD OF GRACE

('Heathlands' 77.77.77.)

[HARMONY]

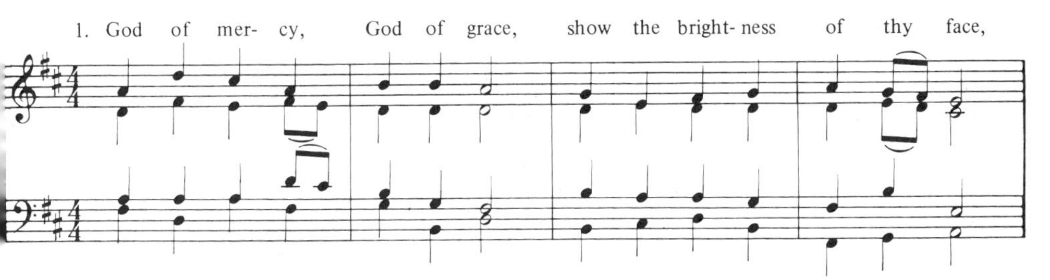

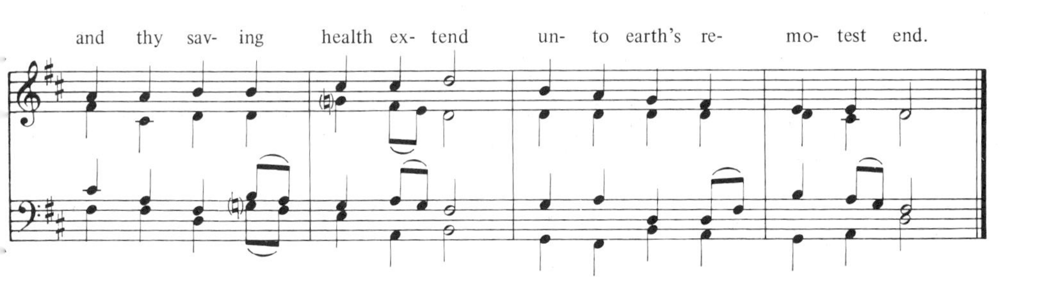

2. Let the people praise thee, Lord;
be by all that live adored;
let the nations shout and sing
glory to their Saviour King;
at thy feet their tribute pay,
and thy holy will obey.

3. Let the people praise thee, Lord;
earth shall then her fruits afford;
God to man his blessing give,
man to God devoted live;
all below, and all above,
one in joy and light and love.

Words: Henry F. Lyte (1793-1847)
Music: Henry Smart (1813-79)

GOD REST YOU MERRY, GENTLEME

('God rest you merry, gentlemen' Irregular

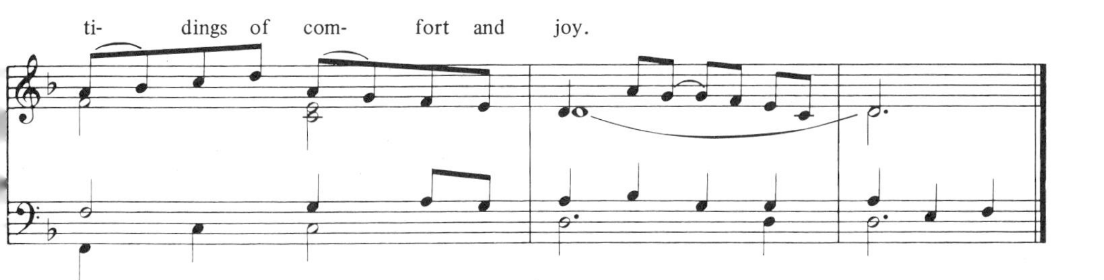

2. In Bethlehem in Jewry
this blessed babe was born,
and laid within a manger,
upon this blessed morn;
the which his mother Mary
did nothing take in scorn.

3. From God our heavenly Father
a blessed angel came,
and unto certain shepherds
brought tidings of the same,
how that in Bethlehem was born
the Son of God by name:

4. 'Fear not,' then said the angel,
'let nothing you affright,
this day is born a Saviour,
of virtue, power and might;
so frequently to vanquish all
the friends of Satan quite:

5. The shepherds at those tidings
rejoicèd much in mind,
and left their flocks a-feeding,
in tempest, storm and wind,
and went to Bethlehem straightway
this blessed babe to find:

6. But when to Bethlehem they came,
whereat this infant lay,
they found him in a manger,
where oxen feed on hay;
his mother Mary kneeling,
unto the Lord did pray:

7. Now to the Lord sing praises,
all you within this place,
and with true love and brotherhood
each other now embrace;
this holy tide of Christmas
all others doth efface:

Words: Unknown (18th century)
Music: Traditional melody,
arranged by Frances M. Kelly

GOD SAVE OUR GRACIOUS QUEEN

('National Anthem' 664.6664.)

158

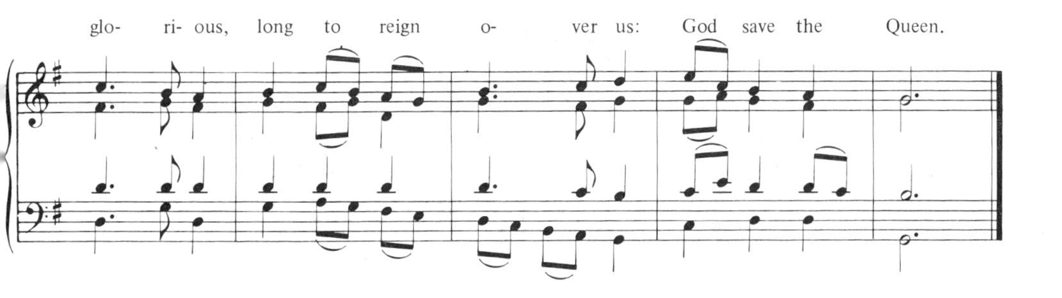

2. Thy choicest gifts in store
on her be pleased to pour,
long may she reign.
May she defend our laws,
and ever give us cause
to sing with heart and voice,
God save the Queen.

3. God bless our native land,
may heaven's protecting hand
still guard our shore;
may peace her power extend,
foe be transformed to friend,
and Britain's rights depend
on war no more.

4. May just and righteous laws
uphold the public cause
and bless our isle.
Home of the brave and free,
the land of liberty,
we pray that still on thee
kind heaven may smile.

5. Nor on this land alone,
but be God's mercies known
from shore to shore.
Lord, make the nations see
that all should brothers be
and form one family
the wide world o'er.

Words: *vv. 1 & 2 unknown (17th or 18th century),*
vv. 3-5 William E. Hickson (1803-70)
Music: *Source unknown*

159

GOD SENT HIS SON **(Because he lives)**

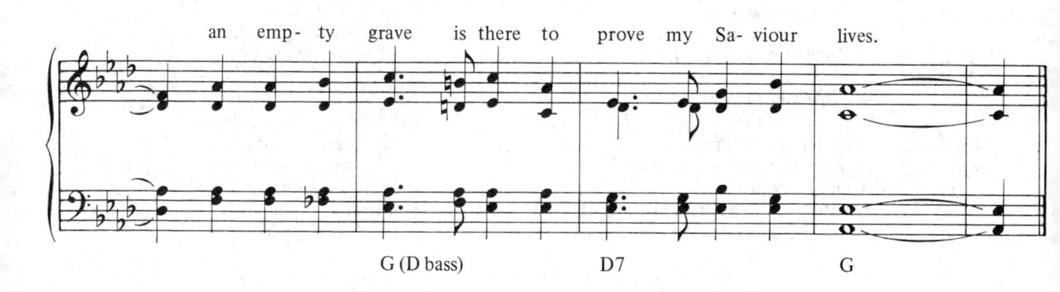

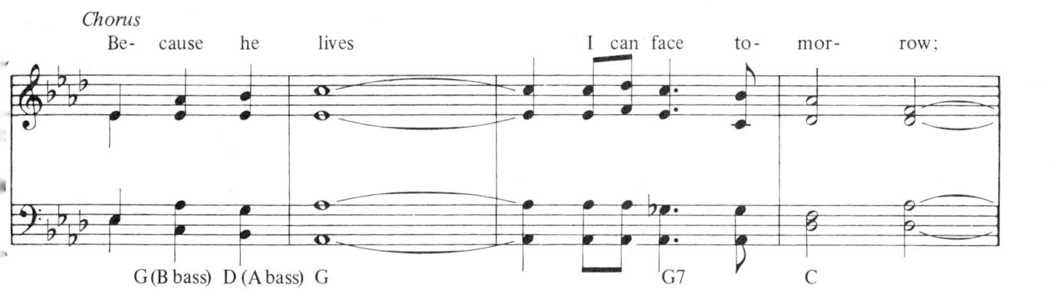

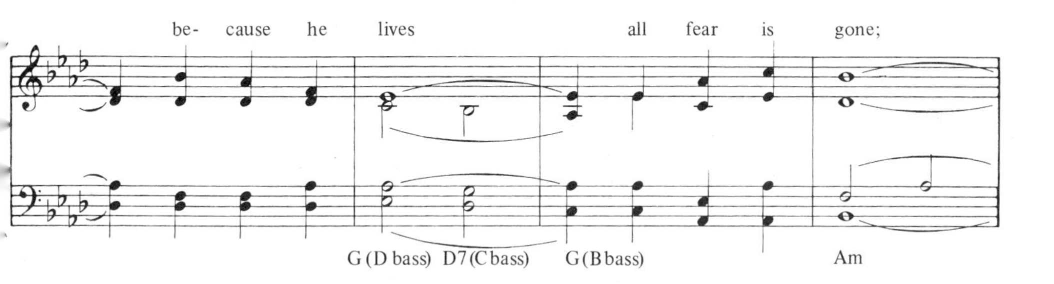

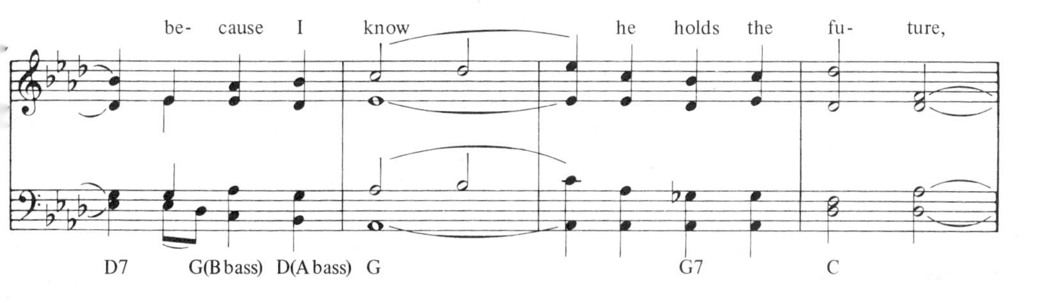

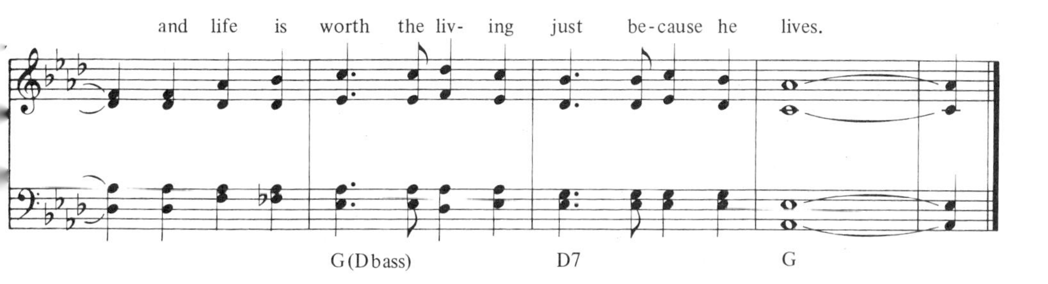

2. How sweet to hold a new-born baby,
   and feel the pride and joy he gives;
   but greater still the calm assurance,
   this child can face uncertain days
   because he lives.

3. And then one day I'll cross the river;
   I'll fight life's final war with pain;
   and then as death gives way to vict'ry,
   I'll see the lights of glory and
   I'll know he lives.

Words: Gloria and William J. Gaither
Music: William J. Gaither

Verse
1. God's Spi - rit is in my heart. He has called me and
Am
Dm
set me a - part. This is what I have to do,
Am
E
Am
what I have to do.
Chorus
He sent me to
mf
E7 Am E7
A
give the Good News to the poor, tell pris - 'ners that they are
E7
A
pris - 'ners no more, tell blind peo - ple that they can see,
E7
A
D

2. Just as the Father sent me
so I'm sending you out to be
my witnesses throughout the world,
the whole of the world.

3. Don't carry a load in your pack,
you don't need two shirts on your back.
A workman can earn his own keep,
can earn his own keep.

4. By dying, I'm going away,
but I'll be with you every day
as the Spirit of love in your heart,
the love in your heart.

5. Myself you will no longer see,
but if you love as God has loved me
then people will see me in you,
will see me in you.

6. Don't worry what you have to say,
don't worry because on that day
God's Spirit will speak in your heart,
will speak in your heart.

Words, from Scripture, and Music:
Hubert J. Richards

161

GOD, THAT MADEST EARTH AND HEAVEN

('Ar hyd y nos' 84.84.88.84.)

[HARMONY]

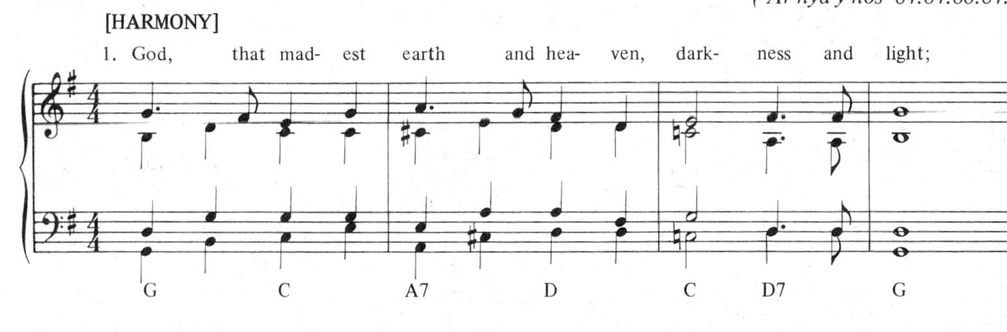

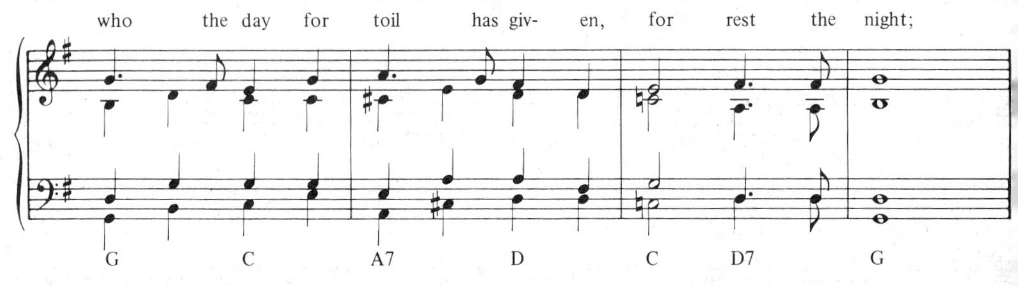

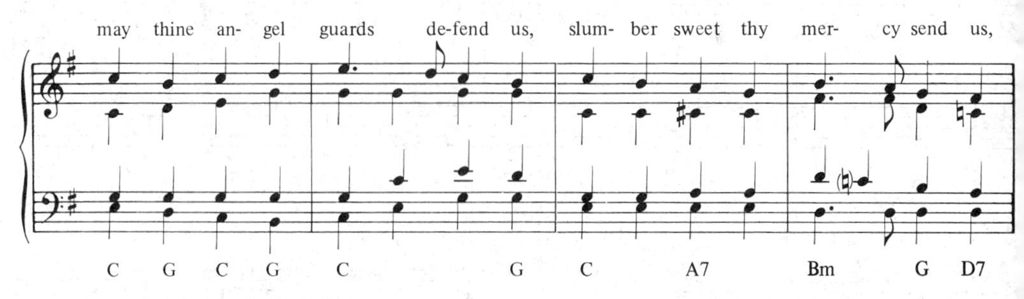

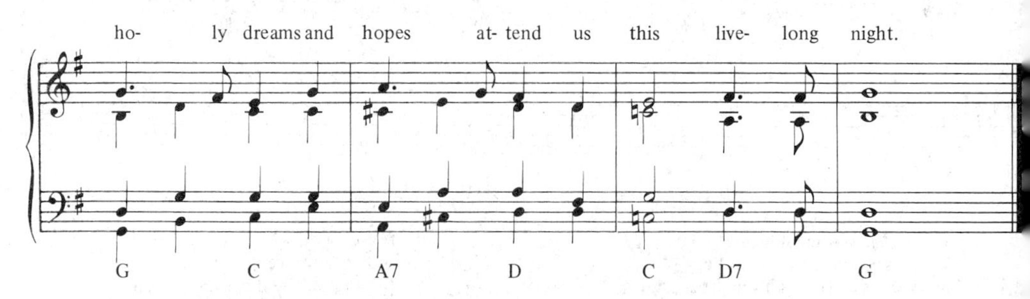

2. Guard us waking, guard us sleeping,
 and, when we die,
 may we in thy mighty keeping
 all peaceful lie:
 when the last dread call shall wake us,
 do not thou our God forsake us,
 but to reign in glory take us
 with thee on high.

Words: verse 1 - Reginald Heber (1783-1826)
verse 2 - Richard Whately (1787-1863)
Music: Welsh traditional melody,
arranged by John Rombaut

GOD WHO MADE THE EARTH
('Sommerlied' 56.64.)

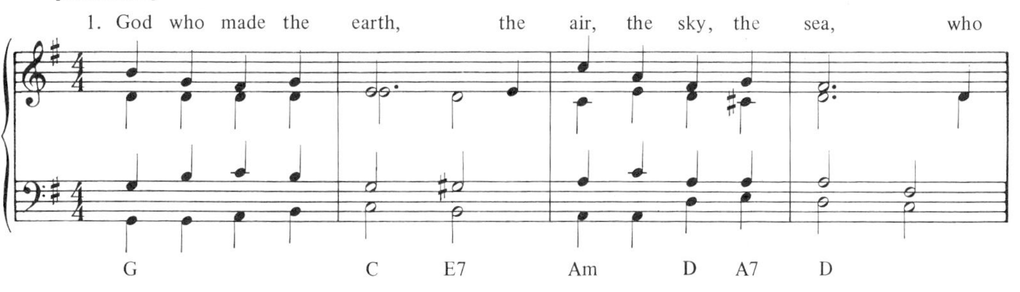

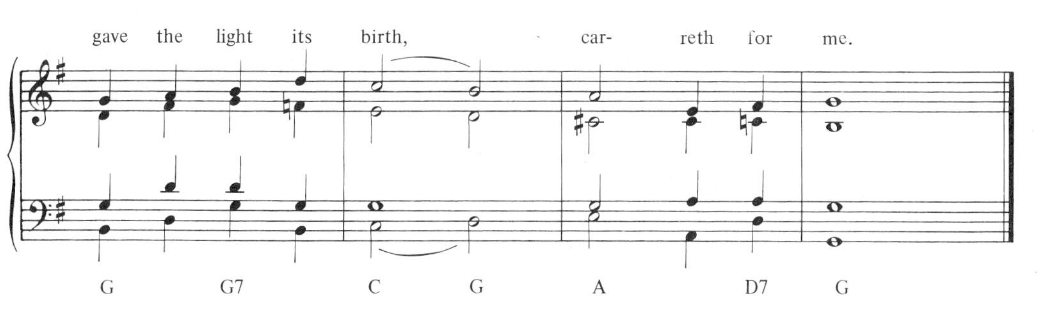

2. God who made the grass,
the flower, the fruit, the tree,
the day and night to pass,
careth for me.

3. God who made the sun,
the moon, the stars, is he
who when life's clouds come on,
careth for me.

4. God who sent his Son
to die on Calvary,
he, if I lean on him,
will care for me.

Words, based on Genesis 1: S. B. Rhodes († 1904)
Music: Hermann von Muller (1859-1938)

163

GOD, WHOSE FARM IS ALL CREATION
('Gott will's machen' 87.87.)

[HARMONY]

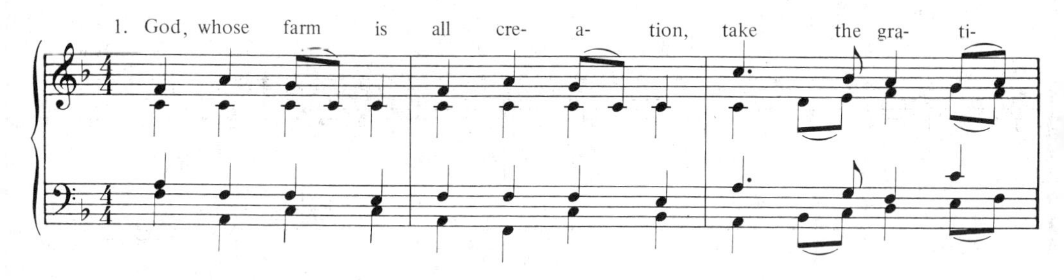

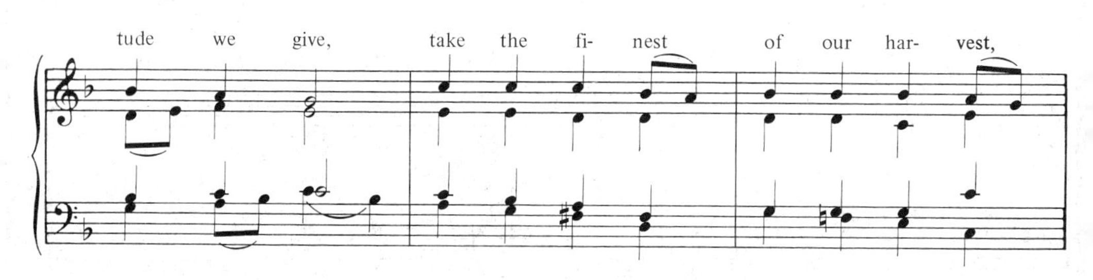

2. Take our ploughing, seeding, reaping,
hopes and fears of sun and rain,
all our thinking, planning, waiting,
ripened in this fruit and grain.

3. All our labour, all our watching,
all our calendar of care,
in these crops of your creation,
take, O God: they are our prayer.

Words: Leslie Thomas John Arlott (b. 1914)
Music: Johann Ludwig Steiner (1688-1761)

GO FORTH AND TELL
('Yanworth' 10 10.10 10.)

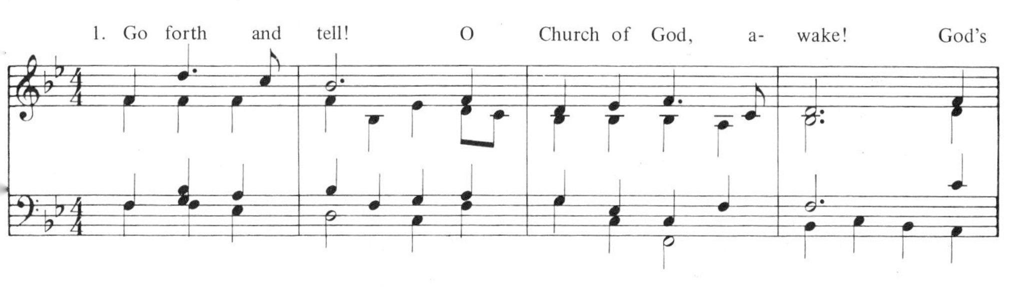

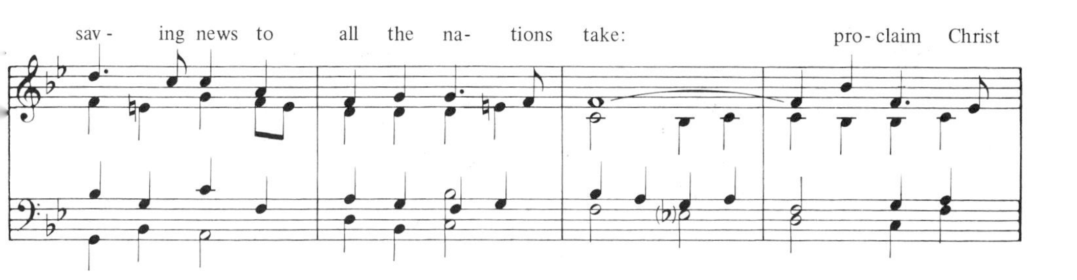

2. Go forth and tell! God's love embraces all;
he will in grace respond to all who call:
how shall they call if they have never heard
the gracious invitation of his Word?

3. Go forth and tell! Men still in darkness lie;
in wealth or want, in sin they live and die:
give us, O Lord, concern of heart and mind,
a love like yours which cares for all mankind.

4. Go forth and tell! The doors are open wide:
share God's good gifts - let no one be denied;
live out your life as Christ your Lord shall choose,
your ransomed powers for his sole glory use.

5. Go forth and tell! O Church of God, arise!
Go in the strength which Christ your Lord supplies;
go till all nations his great name adore
and serve him, Lord and King for evermore.

Words: James E. Seddon (b.1915)
Music: John Barnard (b.1948)

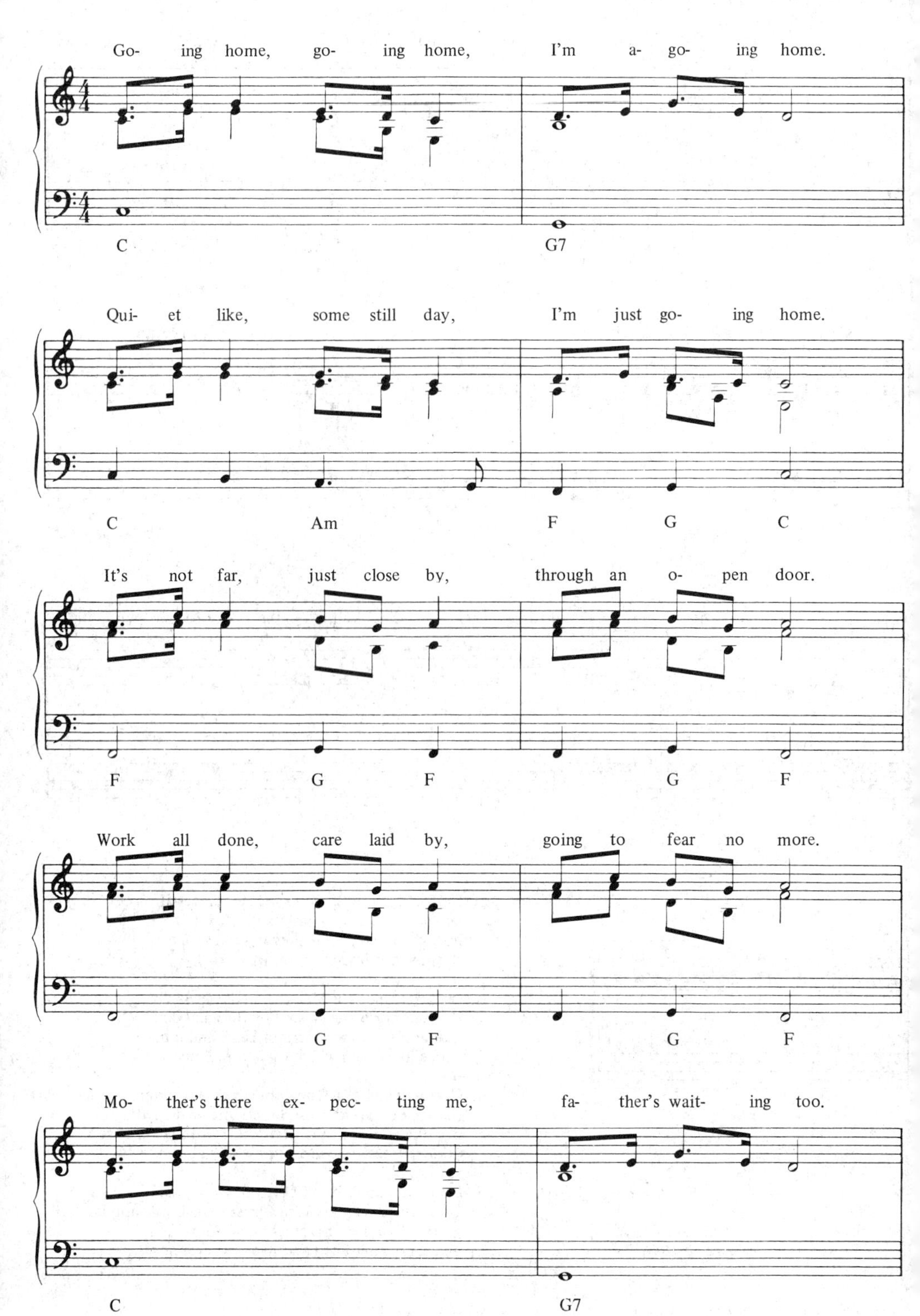
Go- ing home, go- ing home, I'm a- go- ing home.
C G7
Qui- et like, some still day, I'm just go- ing home.
C Am F G C
It's not far, just close by, through an o- pen door.
F G F G F
Work all done, care laid by, going to fear no more.
G F G F
Mo- ther's there ex- pec- ting me, fa- ther's wait- ing too.
C G7

2. Morning star lights the way,
restless dreams all done.
Shadows gone, break of day,
real life just begun.
There's no break, there's no end,
just a living on,
wide awake, with a smile,
going on and on.
Going home, going home,
I'm just going home.
It's not far, just close by,
through an open door.
I'm just going home.

Words: William Arms Fisher
Music: Traditional Spiritual, based on a tune by Antonin Dvorak, arranged by Sarah Fletcher

166 GO IN PEACE TO BE CHRIST'S BOD

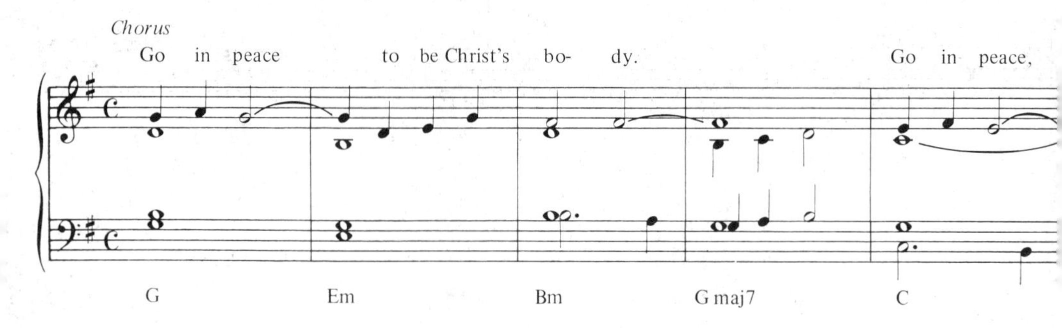

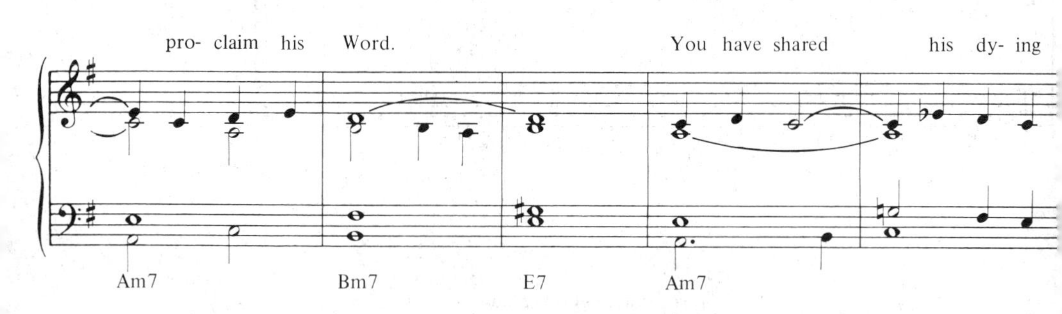

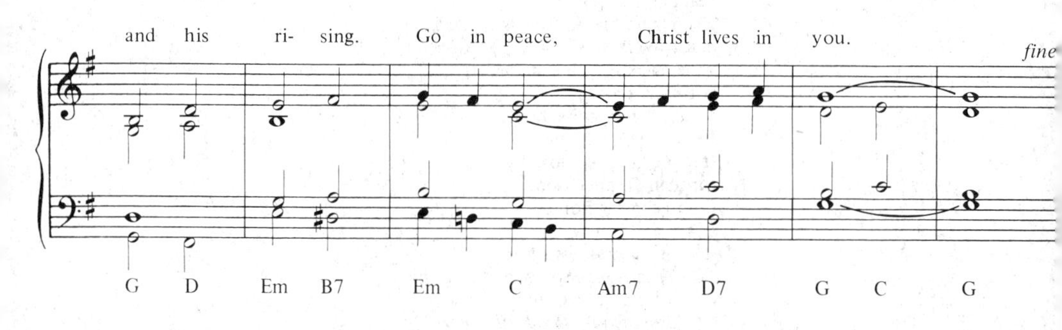

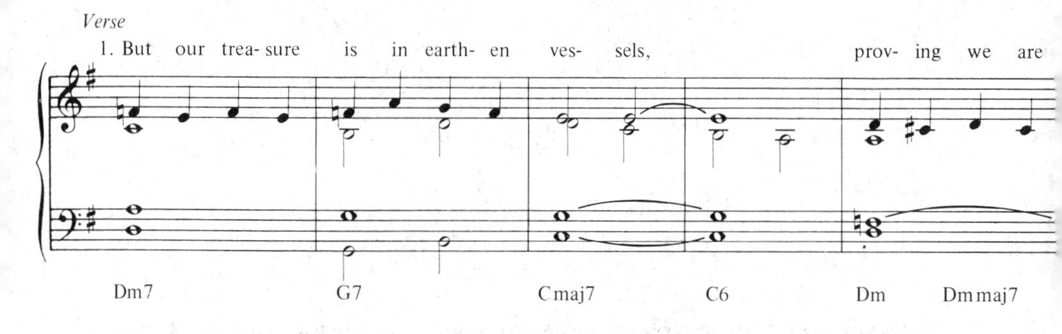

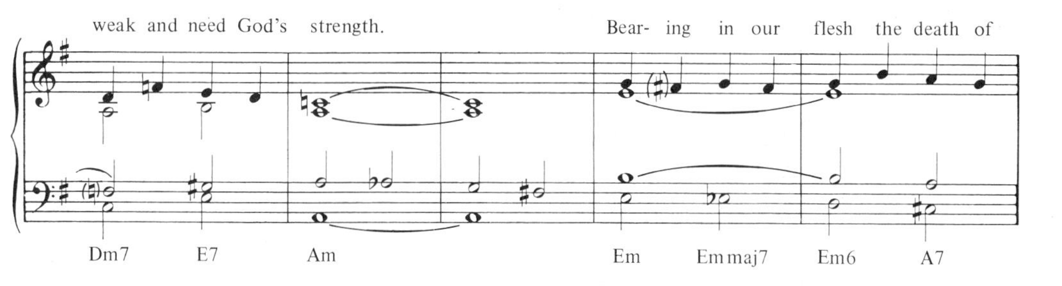

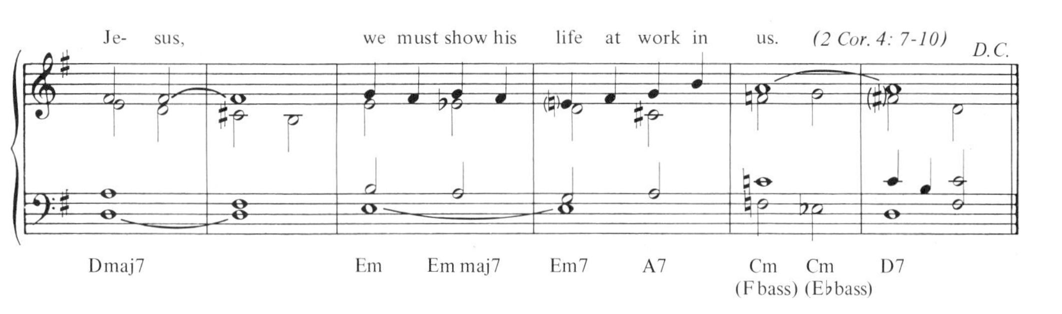

2. Though our outer nature may seem wasted,
daily is the inner self renewed.
For the love of Jesus Christ controls us,
since we know that one man died for all. *(2 Cor. 4: 16 & 5: 14)*

Words, based on Scripture, and Music: Aniceto Nazareth,
arranged by Frances M. Kelly

GONNA LAY DOWN MY SWORD **(Down by the riverside)**

2. Gonna walk with the Prince of peace . . .

3. Gonna shake hands around the world . . .

Words and Music: Traditional Spiritual

GOOD KING WENCESLAUS
('Tempus adest floridum' 76.76.D.)

Introduction (and optional interlude between verses)

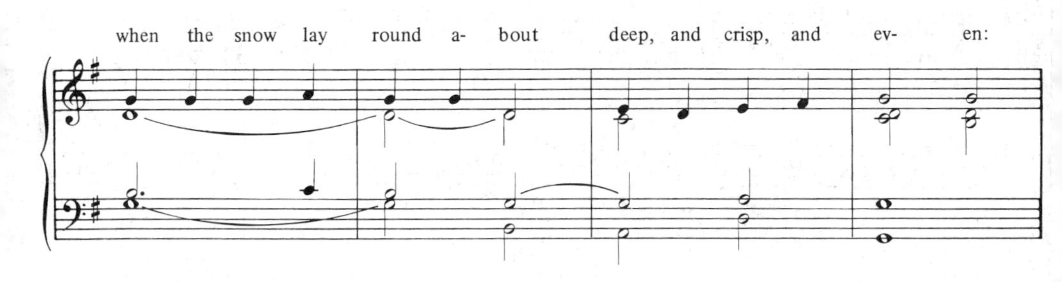

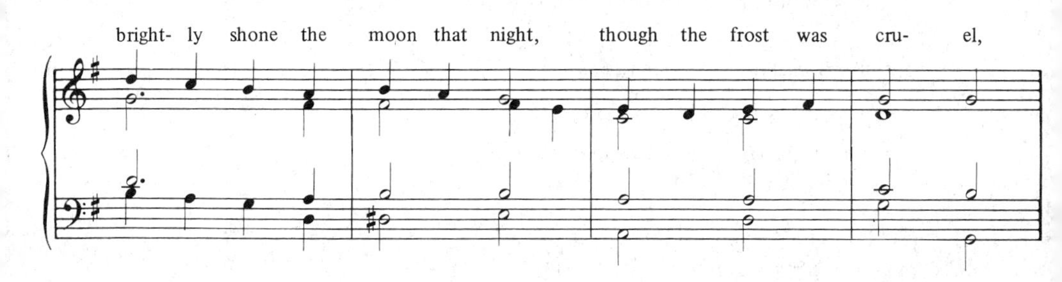

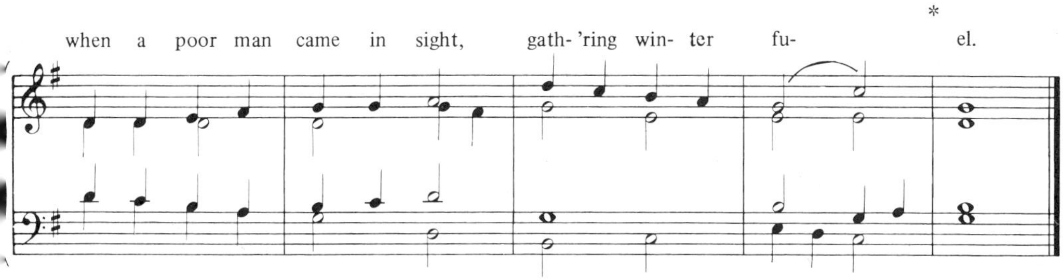

when a poor man came in sight, gath- 'ring win- ter fu- * el.

* *If using the Interlude, da Capo from here;*
if not, play the final bar, and then repeat dal Segno.

2. 'Hither, page, and stand by me,
   if thou know'st it, telling,
   yonder peasant, who is he,
   where and what his dwelling?'
   'Sire, he lives a good league hence,
   underneath the mountain,
   right against the forest fence,
   by Saint Agnes' fountain.'

3. 'Bring me flesh, and bring me wine,
   bring me pine logs hither;
   thou and I will see him dine,
   when we bring them thither.'
   Page and monarch, forth they went,
   forth they went together;
   through the rude wind's wild lament,
   and the bitter weather.

4. 'Sire, the night is darker now,
   and the wind blows stronger;
   fails my heart, I know not how;
   I can go no longer.'
   'Mark my footsteps, good my page;
   tread thou in them boldly:
   thou shalt find the winter's rage
   freeze thy blood less coldly.'

5. In his master's steps he trod,
   where the snow lay dinted;
   heat was in the very sod
   which the Saint had printed.
   Therefore, Christian men, be sure,
   wealth or rank possessing,
   ye who now will bless the poor,
   shall yourselves find blessing.

Words: John M. Neale (1818-66)
Music: melody from 'Piae Cantiones',
arranged by Frances M. Kelly

GOOD SHEPHERD, YOU HAVE SHOWN (Feed my sheep)

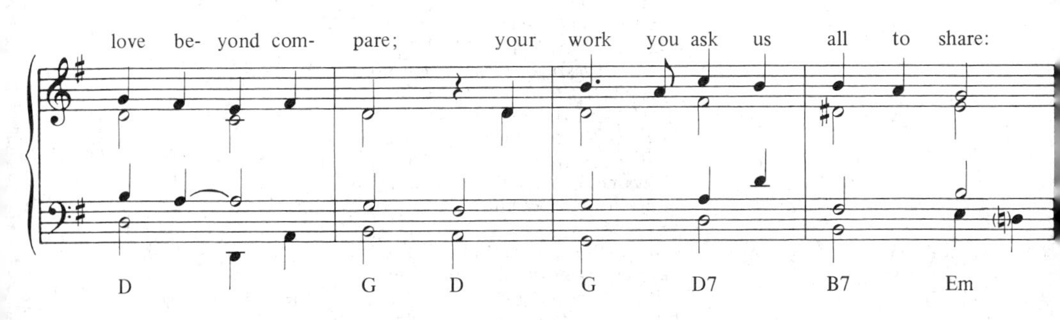

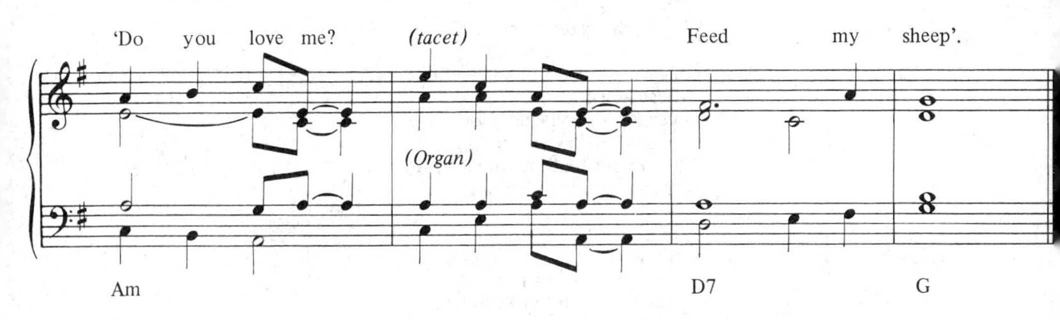

2. O Lord, the pasture you prepare
both young and old must share;
you ask disciples ev'rywhere:
'Do you love me? Feed my lambs'.

3. Good shepherd, lead us as we dare
your ministry to share;
teach us that love demands we care:
'Do you love me? Feed my sheep'.

Words, based on John 21, and Music: Patrick Appleford,
arranged by Frances M. Kelly

GO, TELL IT ON THE MOUNTAIN

2. And lo, when they had seen it,
   they all bowed down and prayed;
   they travelled on together
   to where the babe was laid.

3. When I was a seeker,
   I sought both night and day:
   I asked my Lord to help me
   and he showed me the way.

4. He made me a watchman
   upon the city wall,
   and if I am a Christian,
   I am the least of all.

Words and Music: Traditional, arranged by John Rombaut

GREAT INDEED ARE YOUR WORKS

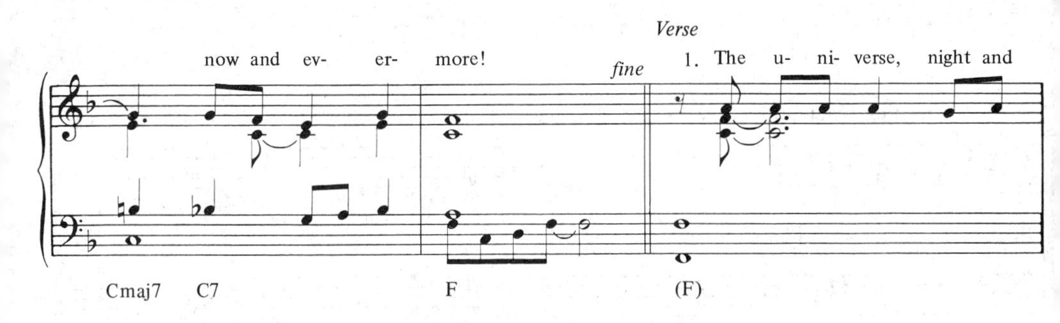

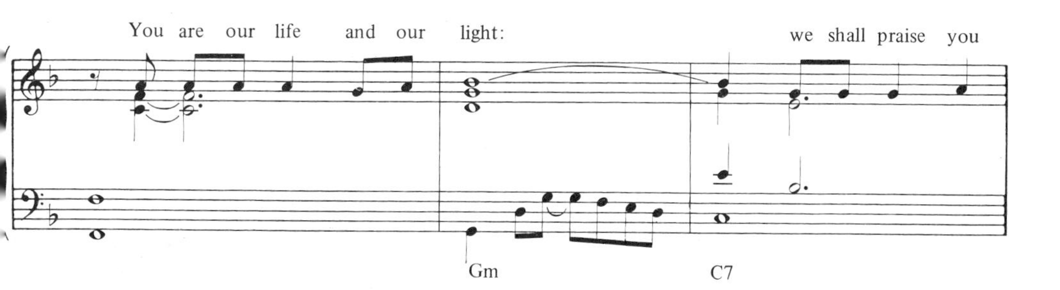

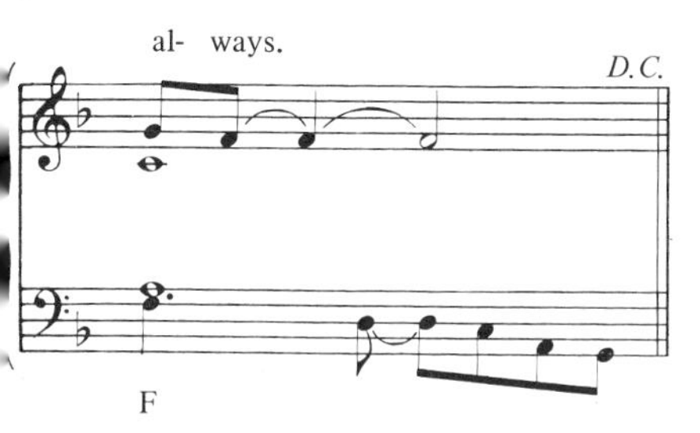

2. You are the path which we tread,
   you will lead us onward.
   From ev'ry corner of earth
   all the nations gather.

3. You lead them all by the hand
   to the heavenly kingdom.
   Then, at the end of all times,
   you will come in glory.

Words, based on Psalm 111, and Music: Aniceto Nazareth,
arranged by Frances M. Kelly

GREAT IS THY FAITHFULNESS
('Great is thy faithfulness' 11 10.11 10. & Chorus)

[HARMONY]

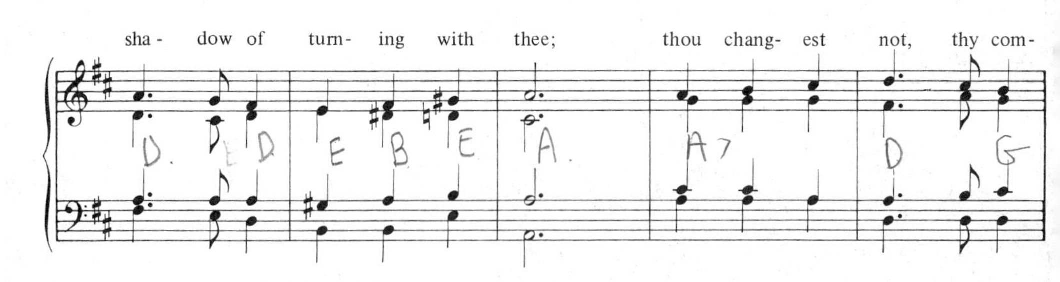

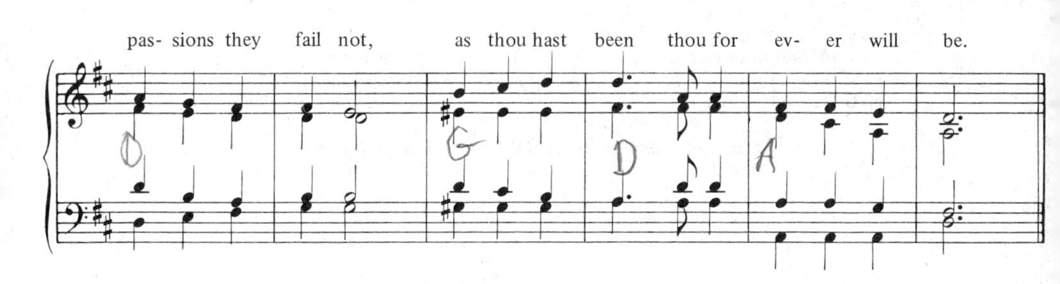

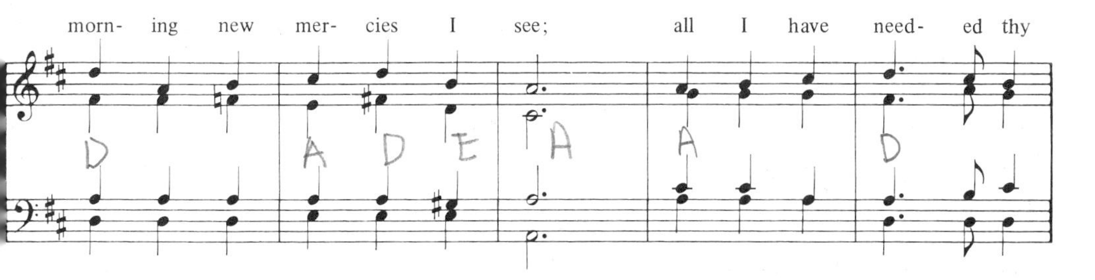

2. Summer and winter, and spring-time and harvest,
   sun, moon and stars in their courses above,
   join with all nature in manifold witness
   to thy great faithfulness, mercy and love.

3. Pardon for sin and a peace that endureth,
   thine own dear presence to cheer and to guide;
   strength for today and bright hope for tomorrow,
   blessings all mine, with ten thousand beside!

Words: Thomas Obadiah Chisholm (1866-1960)
Music: W. M. Runyan (1870-1957)

173

GUIDE ME, O THOU GREAT REDEEMER

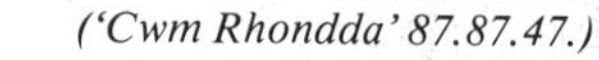

[HARMONY]

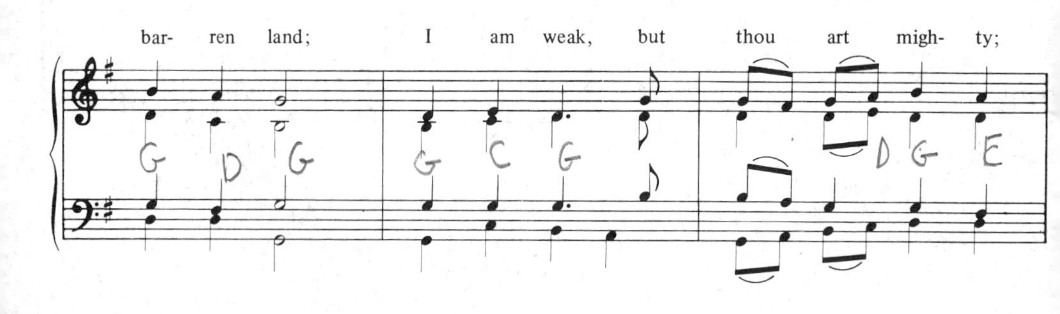

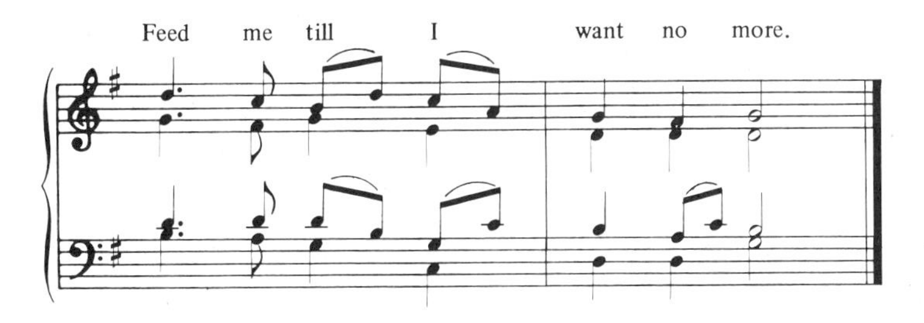

2. Open now the crystal fountain,
whence the healing stream doth flow;
let the fiery cloudy pillar
lead me all my journey through;
strong deliverer, strong deliverer,
be thou still my strength and shield,
be thou still my strength and shield.

3. When I tread the verge of Jordan,
bid my anxious fears subside,
death of death, and hell's destruction,
land me safe on Canaan's side;
songs and praises, songs and praises,
I will ever give to thee,
I will ever give to thee.

Words: Original Welsh - William Williams (1717-91),
tr. Peter Williams (1727-96)
Music: J. Hughes (1873-1932)

HAIL THE DAY THAT SEES HIM RISE

('Llanfair' 74.74.D.) [HARMONY]

1. Hail the day that sees him rise, al- le- lu- ia!
to his throne a- bove the skies; al- le- lu- ia!
Christ, the Lamb for sin- ners given, al- le- lu- ia!
en- ters now the high- est heav'n, al- le- lu- ia!

2. There for him high triumph waits;
lift your heads, eternal gates!
He hath conquered death and sin;
take the King of glory in!

3. Lo, the heaven its Lord receives,
yet he loves the earth he leaves;
though returning to his throne,
still he calls mankind his own.

4. See! he lifts his hands above,
see! he shows the prints of love;
hark! his gracious lips bestow
blessings on his Church below.

5. Still for us he intercedes,
his prevailing death he pleads;
near himself prepares our place,
he the first-fruits of our race.

6. Lord, though parted from our sight,
far above the starry height,
grant our hearts may thither rise,
seeking thee above the skies.

Words: Charles Wesley (1707-88),
Thomas Cotterill (1779-1823),
et al.
Music: R. Williams (1781-1821)

175

HAIL THEE, FESTIVAL DAY! (EASTER DAY)

('Salve Festa Dies' Irregular)

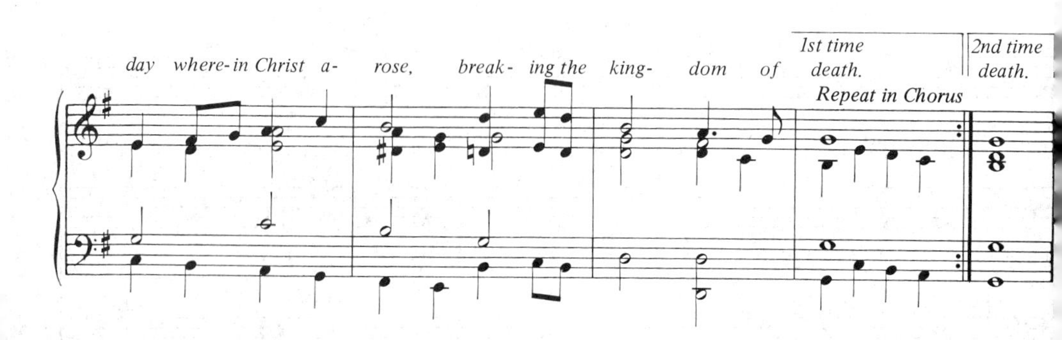

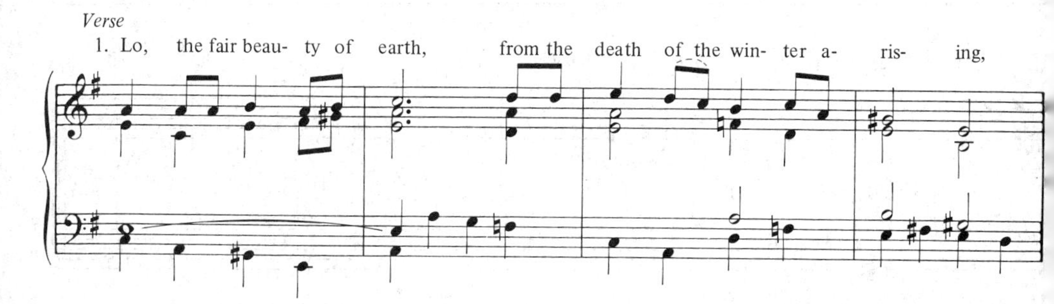

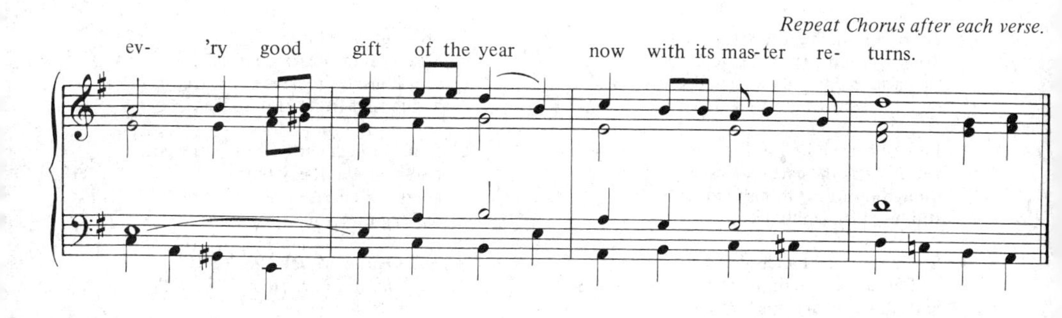

3. God of all pity and power,
let thy Word be assured to the doubting;
light on the third day returns:
rise, Son of God, from the tomb!

5. Ill it beseemeth that thou,
by whose hand all things are encompassed,
captive and bound should remain,
deep in the gloom of the rock.

7. Mourning they laid thee to rest,
who art author of life and creation;
treading the pathway of death,
life thou bestowedst on man.

9. Out of the prison of death
thou art rescuing numberless captives;
freely they tread in the way
whither their maker has gone.

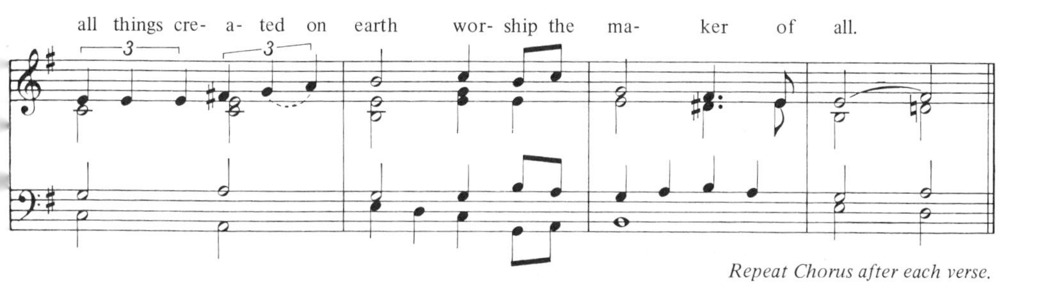

Repeat Chorus after each verse.

4. Ill doth it seem that thy limbs
should linger in lowly dishonour,
ransom and price of the world,
veiled from the vision of men.

6. Rise now, O Lord, from the grave
and cast off the shroud that enwrapped thee;
thou art sufficient for us:
nothing without thee exists.

8. Show us thy face once more,
that the ages may joy in thy brightness;
give us the light of day,
darkened on earth at thy death.

10. Jesus has harrowed hell;
he has led captivity captive:
darkness and chaos and death
flee from the face of the light.

Words: Venantius Fortunatus (530-609),
tr. Maurice F. Bell
Music: Ralph Vaughan Williams (1872-1958)

176 HAIL THEE, FESTIVAL DAY! (ASCENSION DAY

('Salve Festa Dies' Irregular

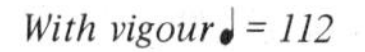

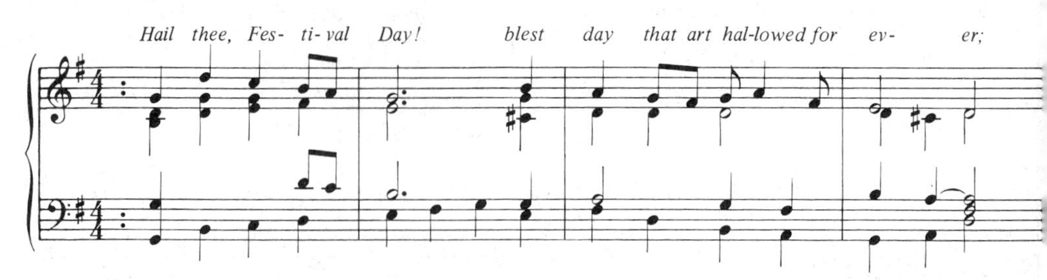

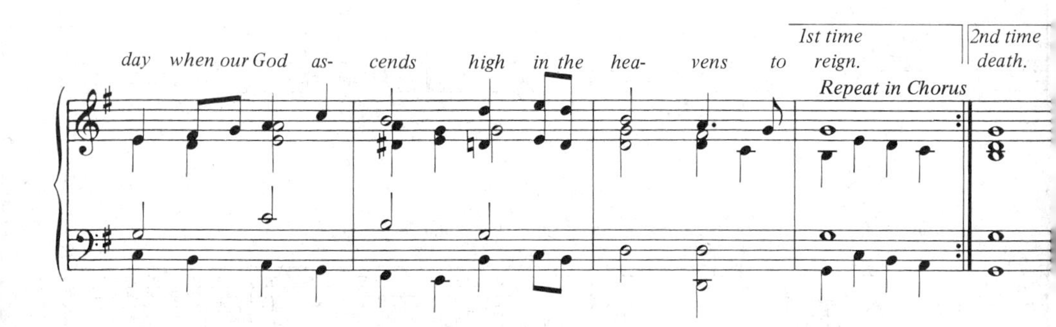

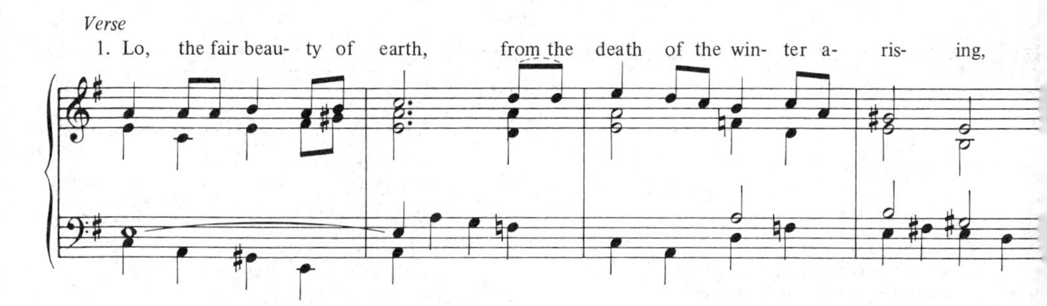

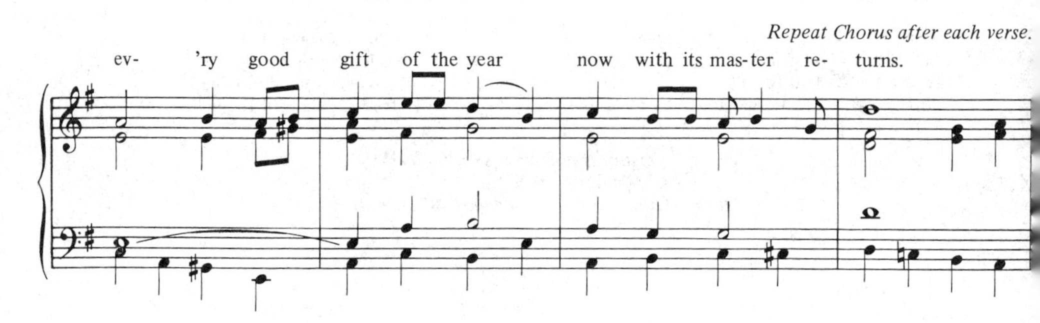

3. Christ in his triumph ascends,
who hath vanquished the devil's dominion;
gay is the woodland with leaves,
bright are the meadows with flowers.

5. Loosen, O Lord, the enchained,
the spirits imprisoned in darkness;
rescue, recall into life
those who are rushing to death.

7. Jesus, the health of the world,
enlighten our minds, thou Redeemer,
Son of the Father supreme,
only-begotten of God!

9. And it was thou, blessed Lord,
who discerning humanity's sorrow,
humblest thyself for our race,
taking our flesh for thine own.

Repeat Chorus after each verse.

4. Christ overwhelms the domain
of hades and rises to heaven;
fitly the light gives him praise -
meadows and ocean and sky.

6. So shall thou bear in thine arms
an immaculate people to heaven,
bearing them pure unto God,
pledge of thy victory here.

8. Equal art thou, co-eternal,
in fellowship ay with the Father;
in the beginning by thee
all was created and made.

Words: Venantius Fortunatus (530-609)
tr. Percy Dearmer
Music: Ralph Vaughan Williams (1872-1958)

177

HAIL THEE, FESTIVAL DAY! (WHIT SUNDAY)

('Salve Festa Dies' Irregular)

With vigour ♩ = 112

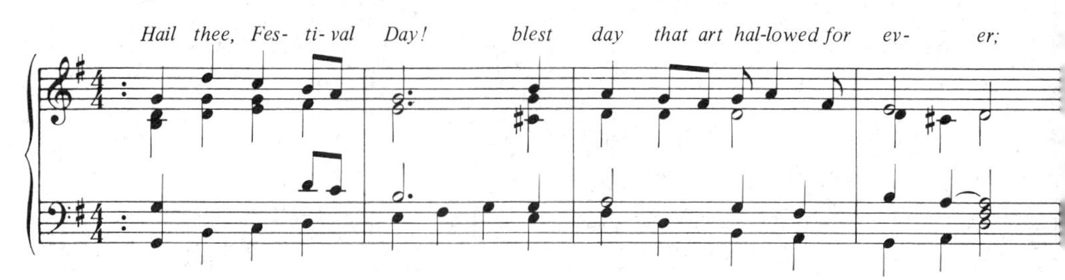

Repeat Chorus after each verse.

he whom the Lord fore- told, sud- den- ly, swift-ly, de- scends.

3. Hark! in a hundred tongues
Christ's own, his chosen apostles,
preach to a hundred tribes
Christ and his wonderful works.

5. God, who art giver of all good gifts
and lover of concord,
pour thy balm on our souls,
order our way in thy peace.

7. Kindle our lips with the live bright coal
from the hands of the seraph;
shine in our minds with thy light;
burn in our hearts with thy love.

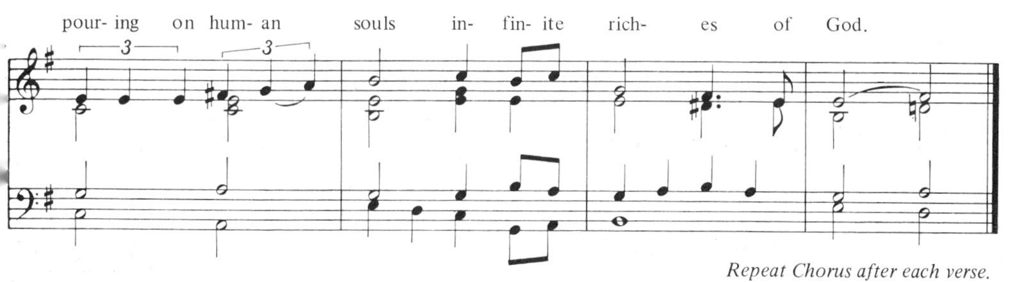

Repeat Chorus after each verse.

4. Praise to the Spirit of life,
all praise to the fount of our being,
light that dost lighten all,
life that in all dost abide.

6. God Almighty, who fillest the heaven,
the earth and the ocean,
guard us from harm without,
cleanse us from evil within.

Words: York Processional (14th century),
tr. G. Gillet
Music: Ralph Vaughan Williams (1872-1958)

178

HAIL THEE, FESTIVAL DAY! (DEDICATION)

('Salve Festa Dies' Irregular)

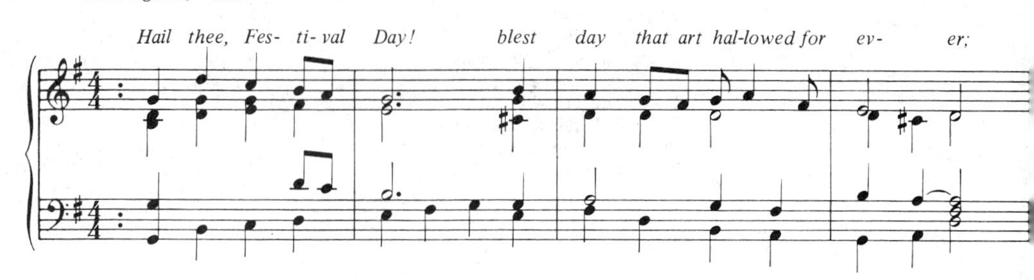

3. Mystical also the new
   and the heavenly city of Zion,
   fitly adorned for her spouse,
   clad with the light from on high.

5. Tower of David is this;
   here are pledges of life and salvation,
   if with unwavering feet
   swift to his stronghold we run.

7. Ladder of Jacob, by none but by thee
   we can mount to the heavens;
   grant that thy people, O Lord,
   thither ascending may reign.

Repeat Chorus after each verse.

4. Here, at his holy font,
   does the heavenly King and the righteous
   grace for their cleansing and growth
   grant to his people on earth.

6. Here is the ark of God,
   a refuge of grace to the faithful;
   safe to the heaven it bears
   mariners tossed by the waves.

Words: York Processional (13th century)
tr. Maurice F. Bell
Music: Ralph Vaughan Williams (1872-1958)

179

HAIL TO THE LORD'S ANOINTED

('Crüger' 76.76.D.)

[HARMONY]

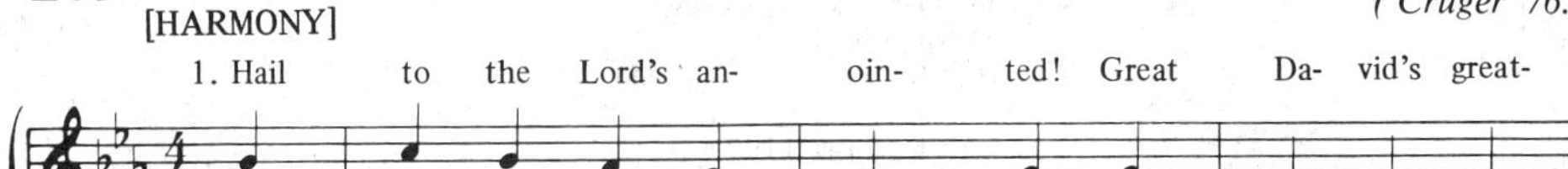

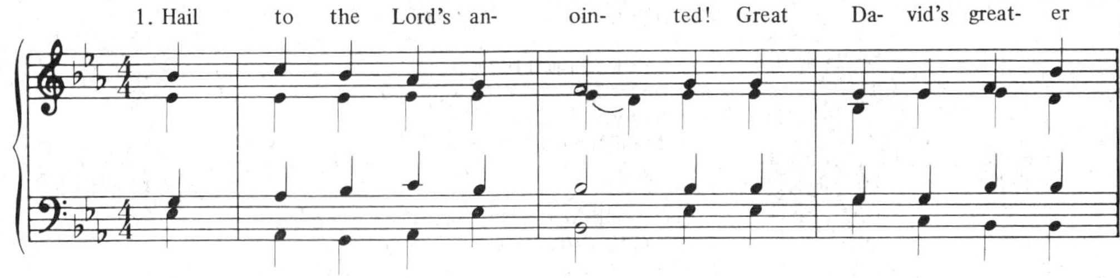

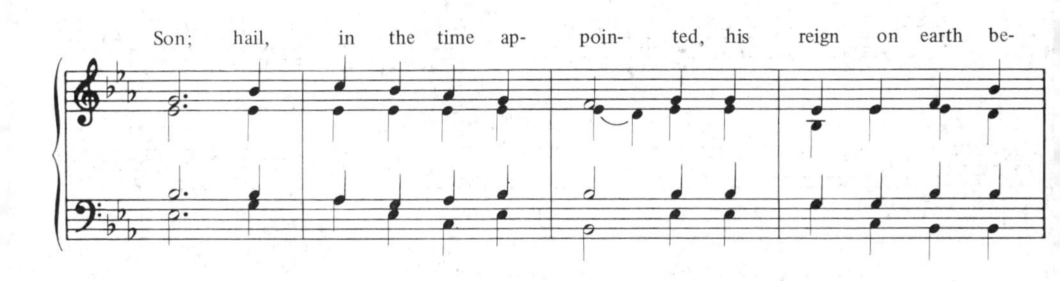

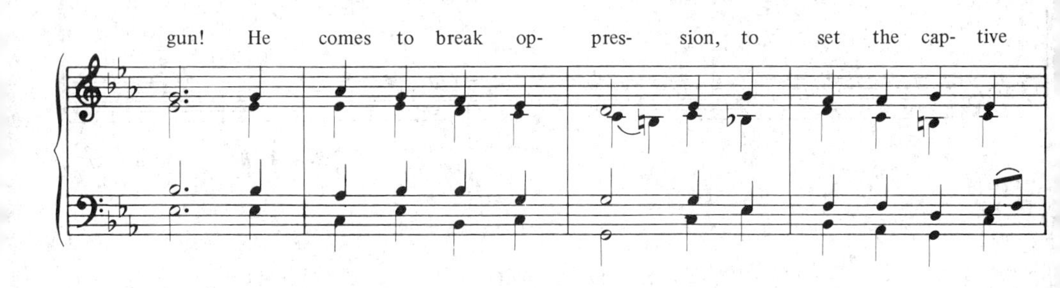

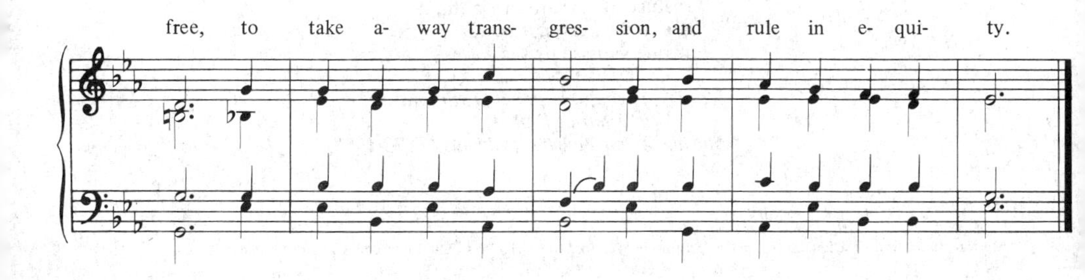

2. He shall come down like showers
upon the fruitful earth,
and love, joy, hope, like flowers,
spring in his path to birth:
before him on the mountains
shall Peace, the herald, go;
and righteousness in fountains
from hill to valley flow.

3. Kings shall fall down before him,
and gold and incense bring;
all nations shall adore him,
his praise all people sing;
to him shall prayer unceasing
and daily vows ascend;
his kingdom still increasing,
a kingdom without end.

4. O'er every foe victorious
he on his throne shall rest,
from age to age more glorious,
all-blessing and all blest;
the tide of time shall never
his covenant remove;
his name shall stand for ever;
that name to us is love.

Words, based on Psalm 72: James Montgomery (1771-1854)
Music: from a melody in Johann Cruger's 'Gesangbuch', adapted by W. H. Monk (1823-89)

With quiet devotion
Hal- le- lu- jah, my Fa- ther, for
giv- ing us your Son; send- ing him into the world to be giv- en up for men,
know- ing we would bruise him and smite him from the
earth. Hal- le- lu- jah, my Fa- ther, in his

Words and Music: Tim Cullen

HAPPY ARE THEY, THEY THAT LOVE GOD

('Binchester' C.M.)

[HARMONY]

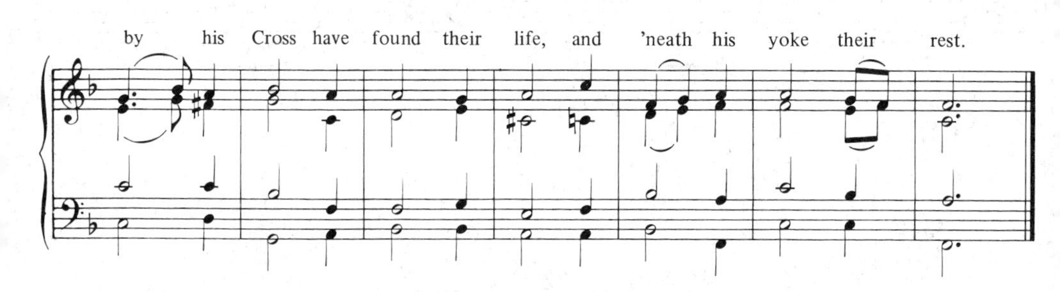

2. Glad is the praise, sweet are the songs,
   when they together sing;
   and strong the prayers that bow the ear
   of heaven's eternal King.

3. Christ to their homes giveth his peace,
   and makes their loves his own:
   but ah, what tares the evil one
   hath in his garden sown!

4. Sad were our lot, evil this earth,
   did not its sorrows prove
   the path whereby the sheep may find
   the fold of Jesus' love.

5. Then shall they know, they that love him,
   how all their pain is good;
   and death itself cannot unbind
   their happy brotherhood.

Words: 'Yattendon Hymnal' (1899),
based on Charles Coffin ***tr. Robert Bridges***
Music: William Croft (1678-1727)

HARK! A HERALD VOICE IS CALLING

('Merton' 87.87.)

This tune may be found in a higher key at Hymn 255

2. Startled at the solemn warning,
let the earth-bound soul arise;
Christ, her sun, all sloth dispelling,
shines upon the morning skies.

3. Lo! the Lamb, so long expected,
comes with pardon down from heav'n;
let us haste, with tears of sorrow,
one and all to be forgiv'n.

4. So when next he comes with glory,
wrapping all the earth in fear,
may he then as our defender
on the clouds of heaven appear.

5. Honour, glory, virtue, merit,
to the Father and the Son,
with the co-eternal Spirit,
while unending ages run.

Words: Fifth or sixth century,
tr. Edward Caswall (1814-78)
Music: William H. Monk (1823-89)

HARK! HARK, MY SOUL!
('Pilgrims' 11 10.11 10.9 11.)

[HARMONY]

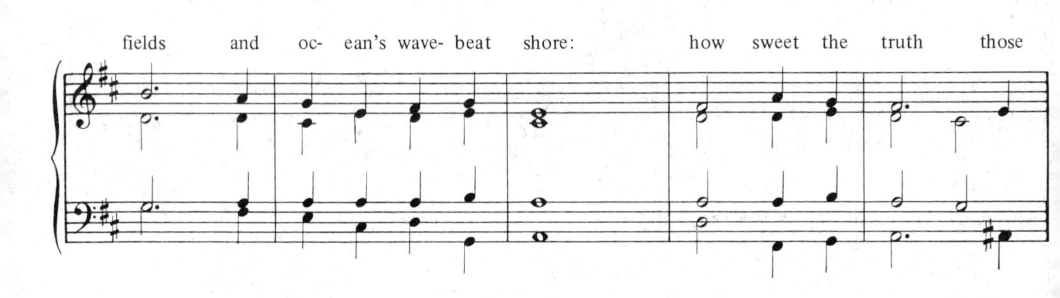

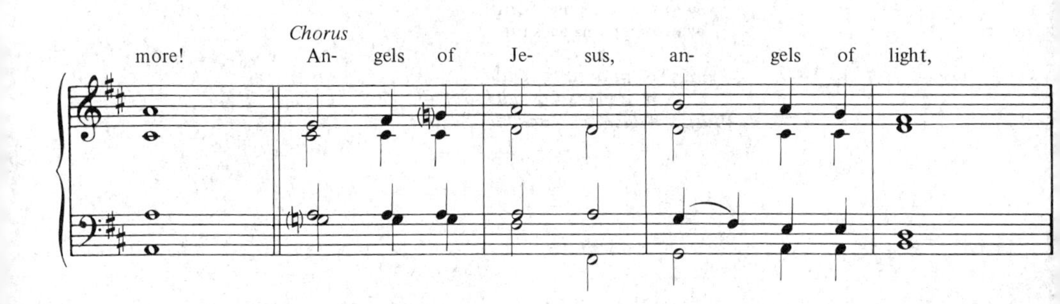

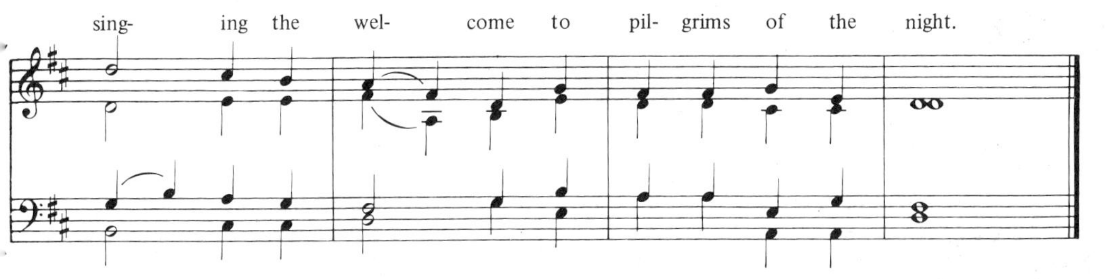

2. Onward we go, for still we hear them singing,
   'Come, weary souls, for Jesus bids you come;'
   and through the dark, its echoes sweetly ringing,
   the music of the Gospel leads us home.

3. Far, far away, like bells at evening pealing,
   the voice of Jesus sounds o'er land and sea,
   and laden souls, by thousands meekly stealing,
   kind Shepherd, turn their weary steps to thee.

4. Rest comes at length: though life be long and dreary,
   the day must dawn, and darksome night be past;
   faith's journey ends in welcome to the weary,
   and heaven, the heart's true home, will come at last.

5. Angels, sing on, your faithful watches keeping,
   sing us sweet fragments of the songs above;
   till morning's joy shall end the night of weeping,
   and life's long shadows break in cloudless love.

Words: Frederick William Faber (1814-1863)
Music: Henry Smart (1813-79)

HARK, MY SOUL! IT IS THE LORD

('St Bees' 77.77.)

[HARMONY]

2. 'I delivered thee when bound,
   and, when wounded, healed thy wound;
   sought thee wandering, set thee right,
   turned thy darkness into light.

3. 'Can a woman's tender care
   cease towards the child she bare?
   yes, she may forgetful be,
   yet will I remember thee.

4. 'Mine is an unchanging love,
   higher than the heights above,
   deeper than the depths beneath,
   free and faithful, strong as death.

5. 'Thou shalt see my glory soon,
   when the work of grace is done,
   partner of my throne shalt be:
   say, poor sinner, lov'st thou me?'

6. Lord, it is my chief complaint
   that my love is weak and faint;
   yet I love thee, and adore;
   O for grace to love thee more!

Words: William Cowper (1731-1800)
Music: John B. Dykes (1823-76)

HARK, THE GLAD SOUND!
('Bristol' C.M.)

[HARMONY]

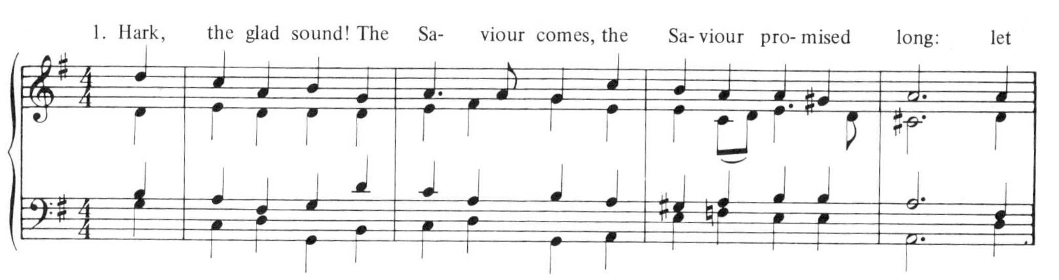

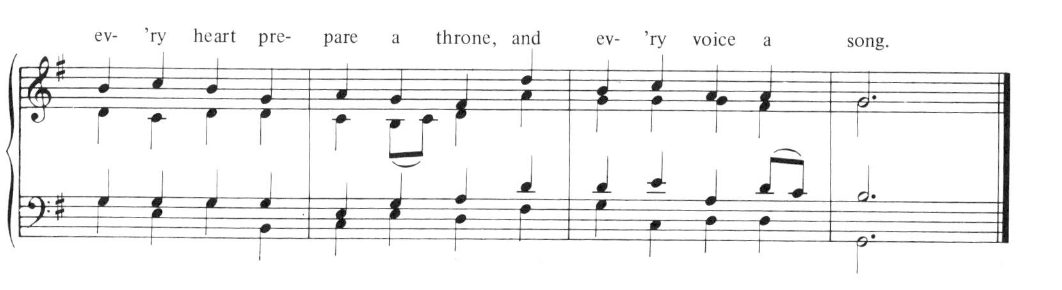

2. He comes, the prisoners to release
in Satan's bondage held;
the gates of brass before him burst,
the iron fetters yield.

3. He comes, the broken heart to bind,
the bleeding soul to cure,
and with the treasures of his grace
to bless the humble poor.

4. Our glad hosannas, Prince of Peace,
thy welcome shall proclaim;
and heaven's eternal arches ring
with thy beloved name.

Words: Philip Doddridge (1702-51)
Music: 'Ravenscroft's Psalter' (1621)

186 [HARMONY]

HARK, THE HERALD ANGELS SING

('Mendelssohn' 77.77.D.)

2. Christ, by highest heaven adored,
   Christ, the everlasting Lord,
   late in time behold him come,
   offspring of a virgin's womb!
   Veiled in flesh the Godhead see,
   hail th'incarnate Deity!
   Pleased as man with man to dwell,
   Jesus, our Emmanuel.

3. Hail the heaven-born Prince of Peace!
   Hail the Sun of Righteousness!
   Light and life to all he brings,
   risen with healing in his wings;
   mild he lays his glory by,
   born that man no more may die,
   born to raise the sons of earth,
   born to give them second birth.

Words: Charles Wesley (1708-88), George Whitefield (1753),
Martin Madan (1760), and others
Music: Felix Mendelssohn (1809-47)

HARK! THE SOUND OF HOLY VOICES
('Deerhurst' 87.87.D.)

[HARMONY]

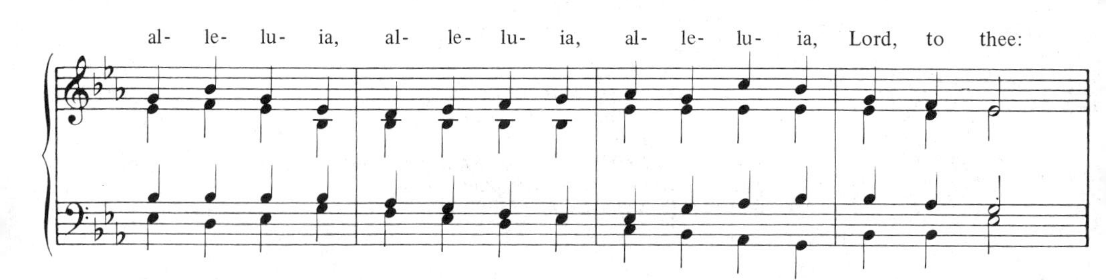

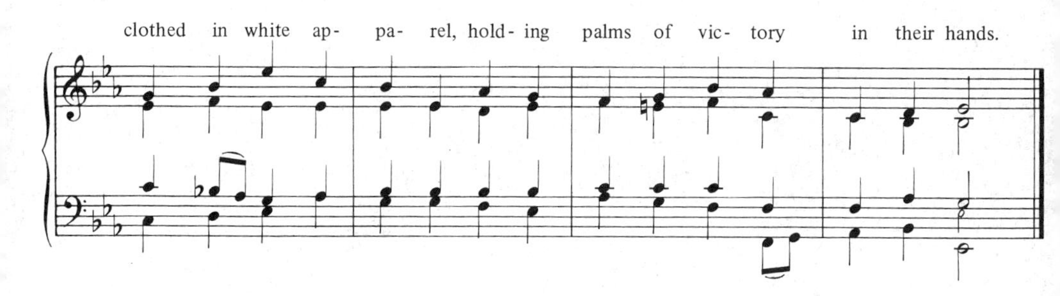

2. Patriarch, and holy prophet,
who prepared the way of Christ,
king, apostle, saint, confessor,
martyr, and evangelist,
saintly maiden, godly matron,
widows who have watched to prayer,
joined in holy concert, singing
to the Lord of all, are there.

3. They have come from tribulation,
and have washed their robes in blood,
washed them in the blood of Jesus;
tried they were, and firm they stood;
mocked, imprisoned, stoned, tormented,
sawn asunder, slain with sword,
they have conquered death and Satan
by the might of Christ the Lord.

4. Marching with thy cross their banner,
they have triumphed following
thee, the captain of salvation,
thee, their Saviour and their King;
gladly, Lord, with thee they suffered;
gladly, Lord, with thee they died,
and by death to life immortal
they were born, and glorified.

5. Now they reign in heavenly glory,
now they walk in golden light,
now they drink, as from a river,
holy bliss and infinite;
love and peace they taste for ever,
and all truth and knowledge see
in the beatific vision
of the Blessèd Trinity.

6. God of God, the one-begotten,
light of light, Emmanuel,
in whose body joined together
all the saints for ever dwell;
pour upon us of thy fullness,
that we may for evermore
God the Father, God the Son, and
God the Holy Ghost adore.

Words: Christopher Wordsworth (1807-85)
Music: J. Langran (1835-1909)

2. Let me stay in your tent;
safe in the shade of your wings.

3. I will echo your praise;
pay my vows day after day.

Words, based on Psalm 61, and Music: Anthony D'Souza,
arranged by Frances M. Kelly

HE BRINGS US INTO HIS BANQUETING TABLE **(His banner over me is love)**

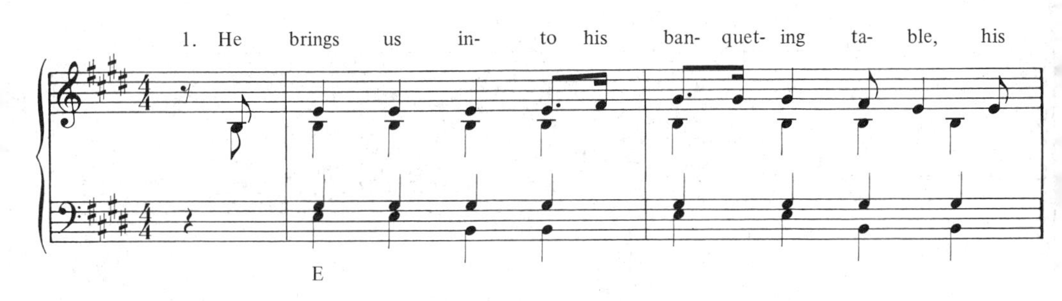

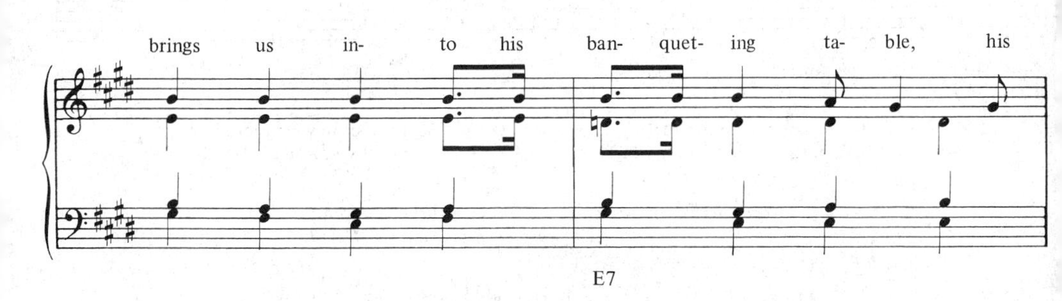

2. The one way to peace is the power of the cross . . .

3. He builds his Church on a firm foundation . . .

4. In him we find a new creation . . .

5. He lifts us up to heavenly places . . .

Words: Verse 1 - Song of Songs 2:4;
Verses 2-5 - unknown
Music: Unknown, arranged by Andy Mills

190 HE IS LORD

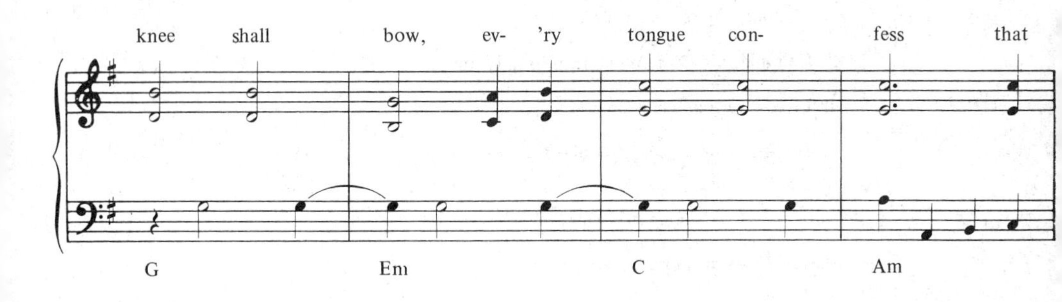

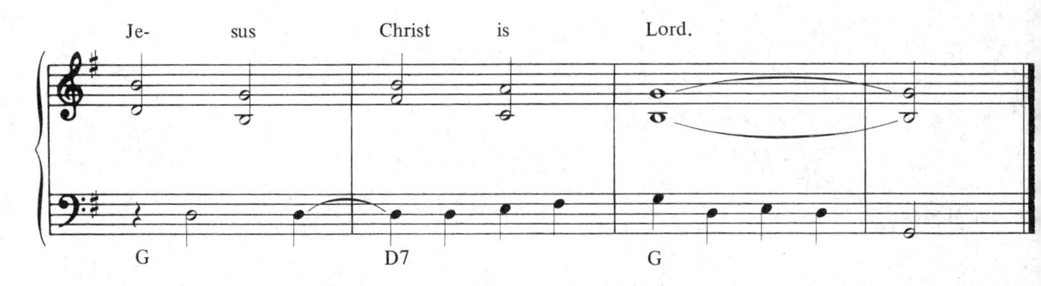

2. He is King . . . 3. He is love . . .

Words: Unknown
Music: Unknown, arranged by John Rombaut

ꟷELP US, O LORD, TO LEARN
"Sandys' S.M.)

[HARMONY]

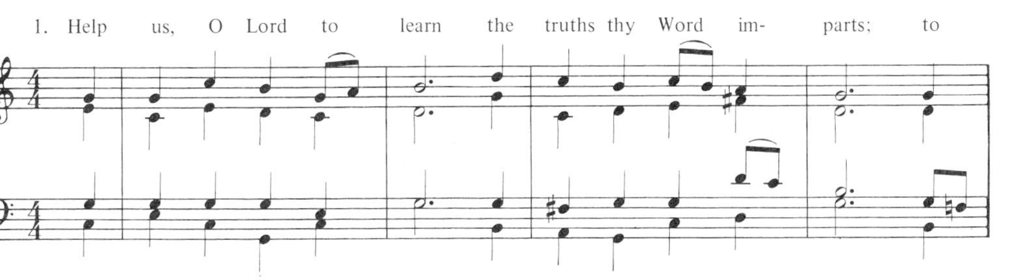

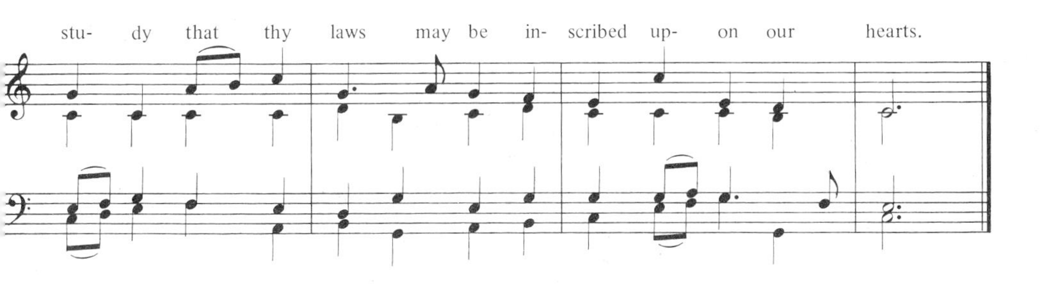

2. Help us, O Lord, to live
the faith which we proclaim,
that all our thoughts and words and deeds
may glorify thy name.

3. Help us, O Lord, to teach
the beauty of thy ways,
that yearning souls may find the Christ,
and sing aloud his praise.

Words: William Watkins Reid (b. 1923)
Music: from William Sandys' 'Christmas Carols' (1833)

HELP US TO HELP EACH OTHER, LORD
('Dunfermline' C.M.)

192

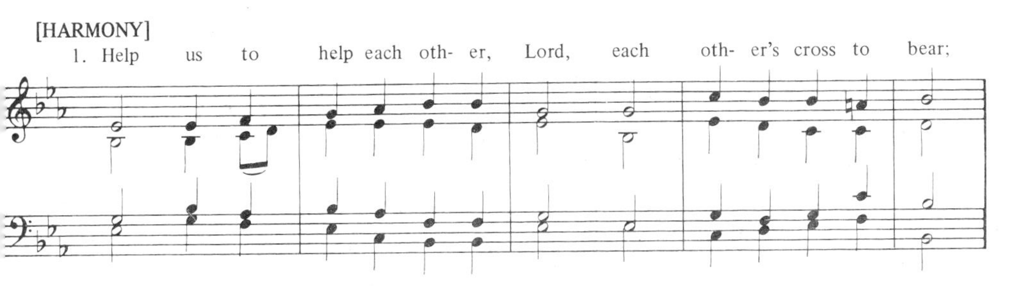

2. Up into thee, our living head,
let us in all things grow,
and by thy sacrifice be led
the fruits of love to show.

3. Drawn by the magnet of thy love
let all our hearts agree;
and ever towards each other move,
and ever move towards thee.

4. This is the bond of perfectness,
thy spotless charity.
O let us still, we pray, possess
the mind that was in thee.

Words: after Charles Wesley (1707-88)
Music: 'Scottish Psalter' (1615)

HERE COMES JESUS

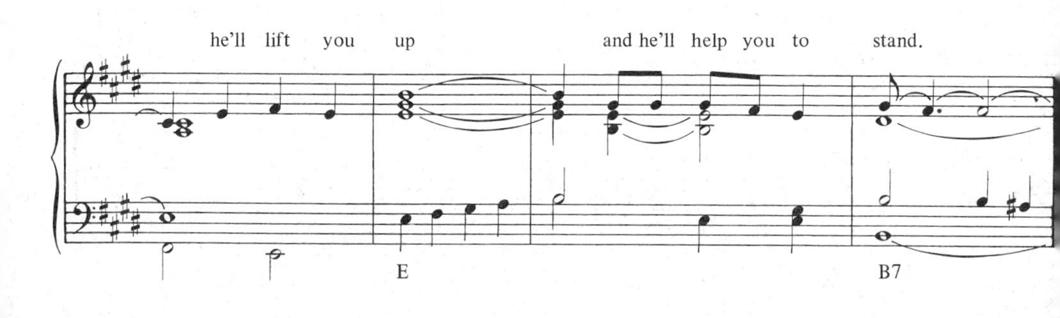

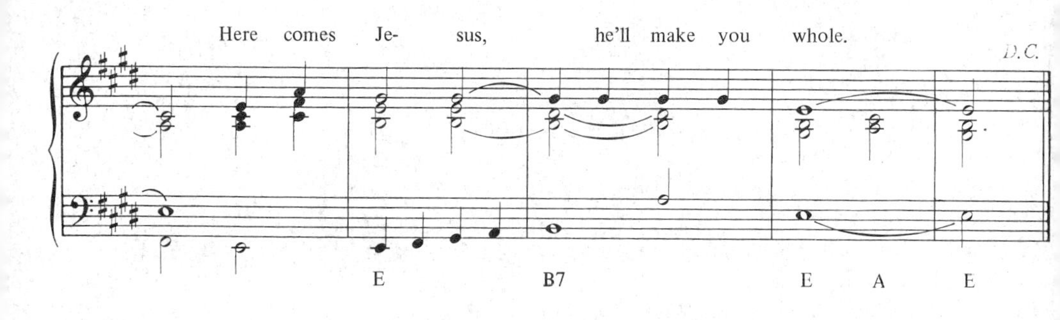

To add interest, try singing
– once through in the key of C;
– repeat, in the key of D;
– repeat again, in the key of E, adding the Coda to finish

Words and Music: Unknown, arranged by Frances M. Kelly

HE'S GOT THE WHOLE WORLD IN HIS HAND

2. He's got you and me, brother . . .

3. He's got you and me, sister . . .

4. He's got the little tiny baby . . .

5. He's got everybody here . . .

Words and Music: Traditional,
arranged by John Rombaut

HE WHO WOULD VALIANT BE
('Monks Gate' 11 11.12 11.)

[HARMONY]

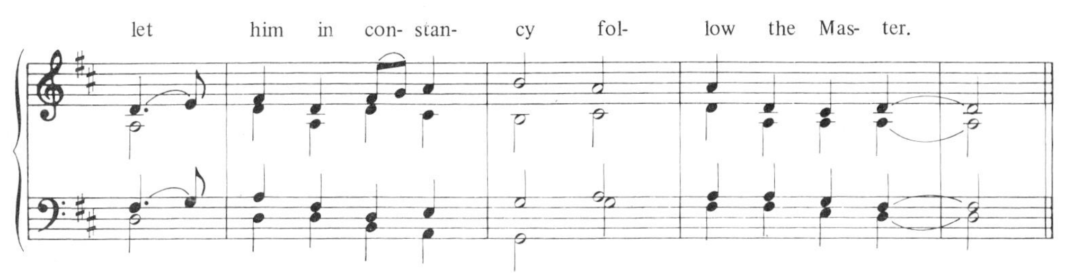

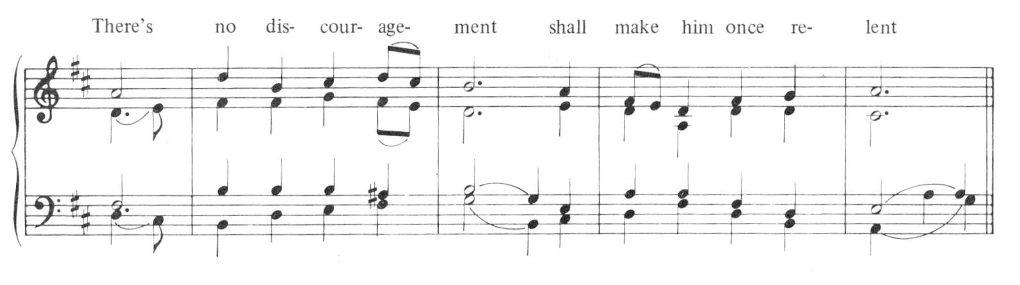

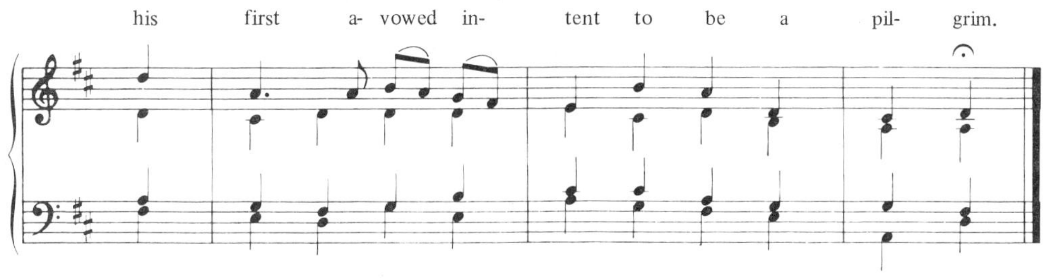

2. Who so beset him round
with dismal stories,
do but themselves confound:
his strength the more is.
No foes shall stay his might
though he with giants fight:
he will make good his right
to be a pilgrim.

3. Since, Lord, thou dost defend
us with thy Spirit,
we know we at the end
shall life inherit.
Then fancies flee away!
I'll fear not what men say,
I'll labour night and day
to be a pilgrim.

Words: Percy Dearmer (1867-1936),
after John Bunyan (1628-88)
Music: adapted from a traditional English
melody by R. Vaughan Williams (1872-1958)

HILLS OF THE NORTH REJOICE
('Little Cornard' 66.66.88.)

2. Isles of the southern seas,
sing to the listening earth,
carry on every breeze
hope of a world's new birth:
in Christ shall all be made anew,
his word is sure, his promise true.

3. Lands of the east, arise,
he is your brightest morn,
greet him with joyous eyes,
praise shall his path adorn:
the God whom you have longed to know
in Christ draws near, and calls you now.

4. Shores of the utmost west,
lands of the setting sun,
welcome the heavenly guest
in whom the dawn has come:
he brings a never-ending light
who triumphed o'er our darkest night.

5. Shout, as you journey on,
songs be in every mouth,
lo, from the north they come,
from east and west and south:
in Jesus all shall find their rest,
in him the sons of earth be blest.

Words: Charles Edward Oakley (1832-65), adapted
Music: Martin Shaw (1875-1958)

HIS NAME IS WONDERFUL

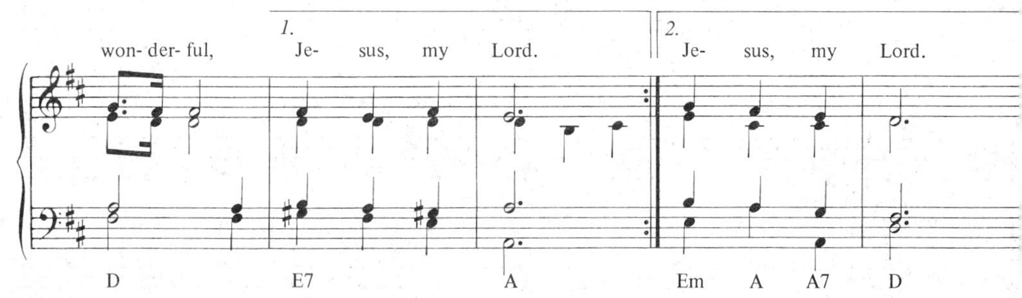

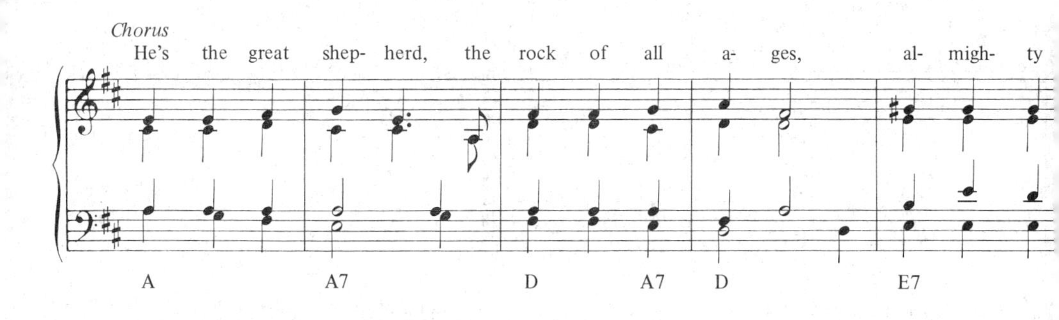

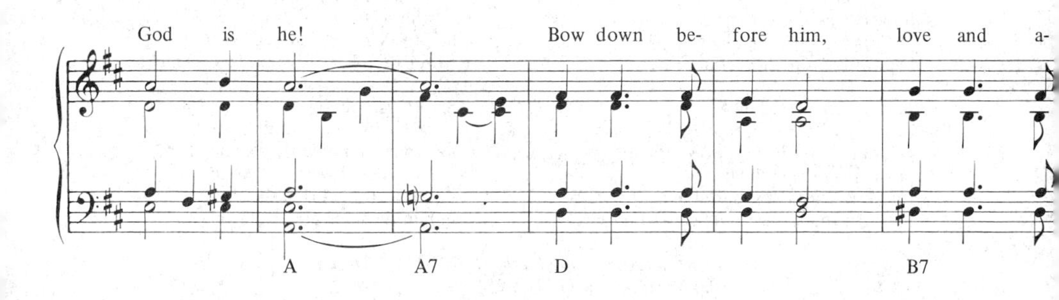

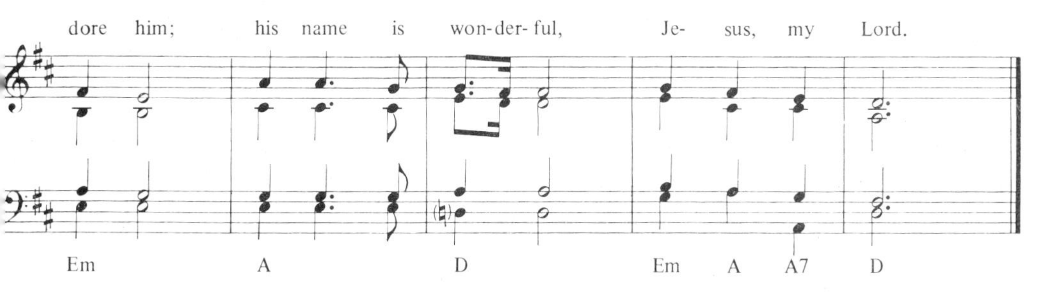

2. He is the mighty King,
master of everything.
His name is wonderful,
Jesus, my Lord.

Words, based on Isaiah 9,
and Music: Audrey Mieier,
arranged by John Rombaut

HOLY, HOLY, HOLY, HOLY

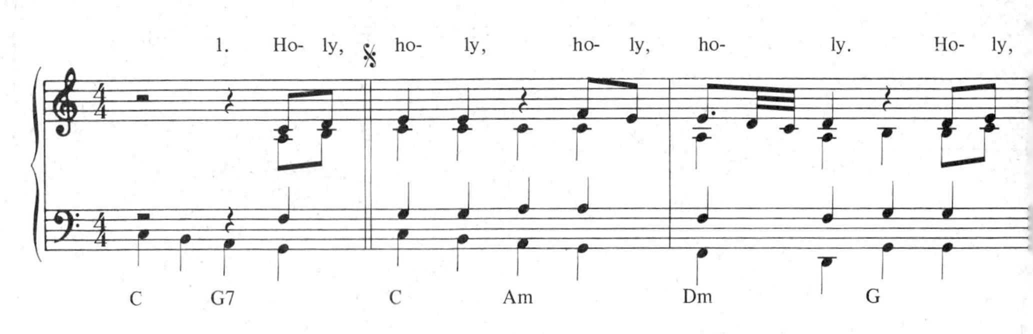

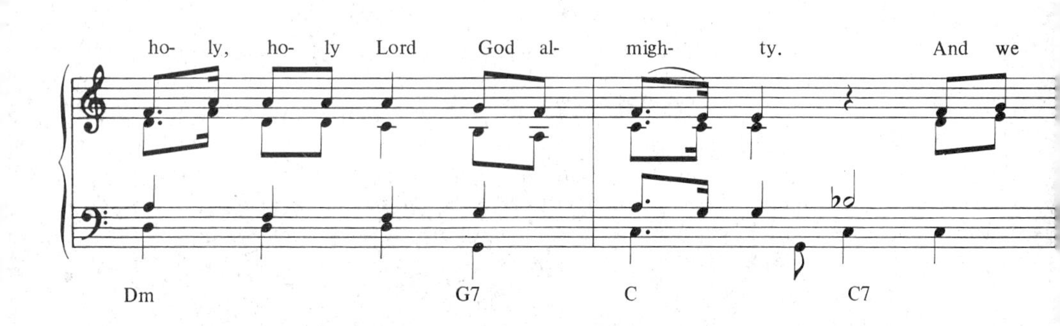

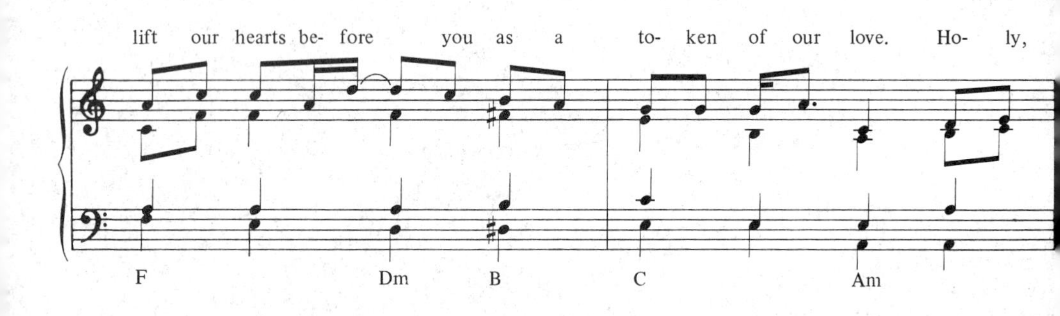

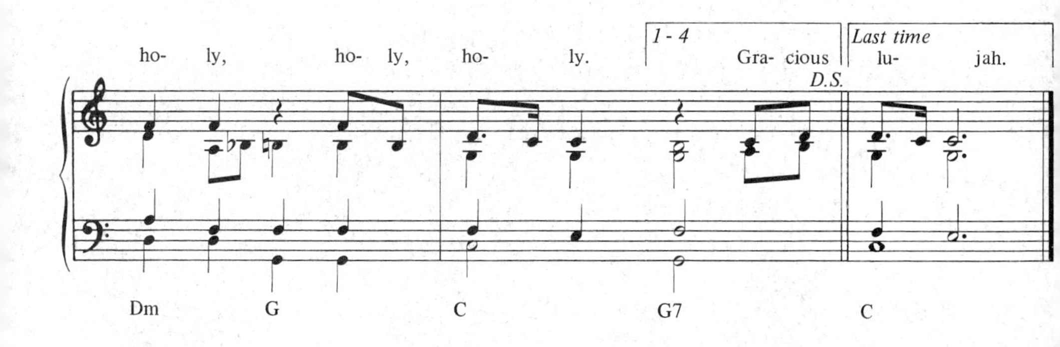

2. Gracious Father, gracious Father,
we are glad to be your children, gracious Father
And we lift our heads before you
as a token of our love,
gracious Father, gracious Father.

3. Risen Jesus, risen Jesus,
we are glad you have redeemed us, risen Jesus.
And we lift our hands before you
as a token of our love,
risen Jesus, risen Jesus.

4. Holy Spirit, Holy Spirit,
come and fill our hearts anew, Holy Spirit.
And we lift our voice before you
as a token of our love,
Holy Spirit, Holy Spirit.

5. Hallelujah, hallelujah,
hallelujah, hallelujah, hallelujah.
And we lift our hearts before you
as a token of our love,
hallelujah, hallelujah.

Words and Music, from 'Come Together': Jimmy and Carol Owens

2. Jesus, Jesus, Jesus is the Lord,
   Jesus is the Lord God almighty: *(2)*
   who was and is, and is to come;
   holy, holy is the Lord.

3. Worthy, worthy, worthy is the Lord,
   worthy is the Lord God almighty: *(2)*
   who was and is, and is to come;
   holy, holy, holy is the Lord.

4. Glory, glory, glory to the Lord,
   glory to the Lord God almighty: *(2)*
   who was and is, and is to come;
   holy, holy, holy is the Lord.

Words and Music: Unknown,
arranged by Frances M. Kelly

HOLY, HOLY, HOLY! LORD GOD ALMIGHTY!
('Nicaea' 11 12.12.10.)

2. Holy, holy, holy!
All the saints adore thee,
casting down their golden crowns
around the glassy sea;
cherubim and seraphim
falling down before thee,
which wert, and art,
and evermore shall be.

3. Holy, holy, holy!
Though the darkness hide thee,
though the eye of sinful man
thy glory may not see,
only thou art holy,
there is none beside thee,
perfect in power,
in love, and purity.

4. Holy, holy, holy!
Lord God almighty!
All thy works shall praise thy name,
in earth, and sky and sea;
holy, holy, holy!
Merciful and mighty!
God in three persons,
blessèd Trinity.

Words: Reginald Heber (1783-1826)
Music: John B. Dykes (1823-76)

HOPE SPRINGS OUT OF EVERY RACE AND NATION

[HARMONY]

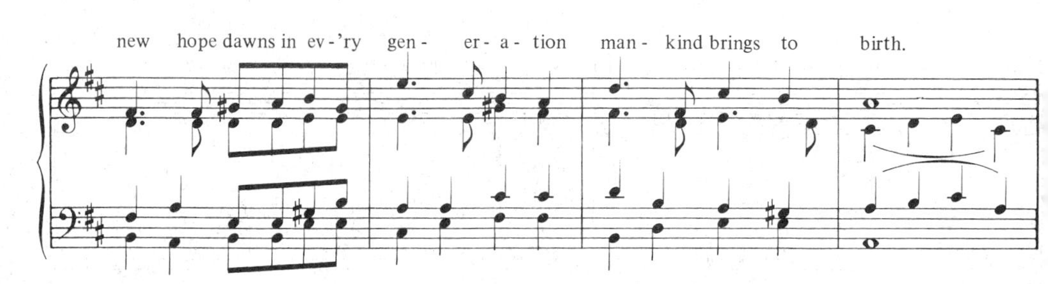

[UNISON]

Words and Music: Patrick Appleford

202

HOW FIRM A FOUNDATION
('Montgomery' 11 11.11 11.)

2. Fear not, he is with thee, O be not dismayed,
for he is thy God and will still give thee aid;
he'll strengthen thee, help thee, and cause thee to stand,
upheld by his righteous, omnipotent hand.

3. In every condition, in sickness, in health,
in poverty's vale, or abounding in wealth;
at home and abroad, on the land, on the sea,
as thy days may demand shall thy strength ever be.

4. When through the deep waters he calls thee to go,
the rivers of grief shall not thee overflow,
for he will be with thee in trouble to bless,
and sanctify to thee thy deepest distress.

5. When through fiery trials thy pathway shall lie,
his grace all-sufficient shall be thy supply;
the flame shall not hurt thee, his only design,
thy dross to consume and thy gold to refine.

6. The soul that on Jesus has leaned for repose,
he will not, he will not, desert to its foes;
that soul, though all hell should endeavour to shake,
he'll never, no never, no never forsake.

Words: Richard Keen (c.1787)
Music: probably S. Jarvis († c.1785)

HOW GOOD IS THE GOD WE ADORE!
('Celeste' L.M.)

[HARMONY]

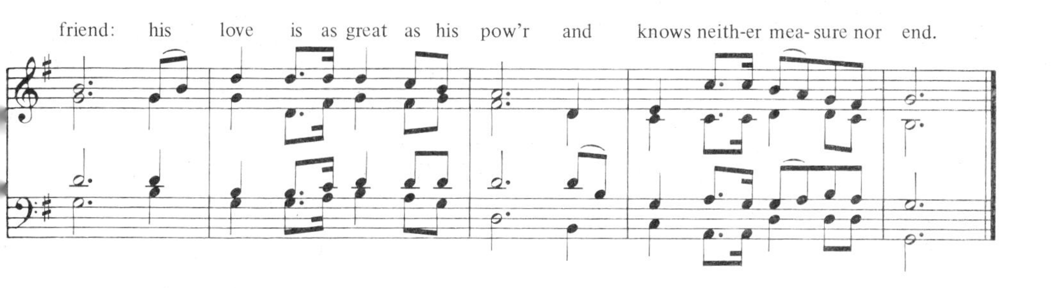

2. For Christ is the first and the last;
his Spirit will guide us safe home;
we'll praise him for all that is past
and trust him for all that's to come.

Words: Joseph Hart (1712-68)
Music: 'Lancashire Sunday School Songs' (1857)

204

HOW GREAT IS OUR GOD

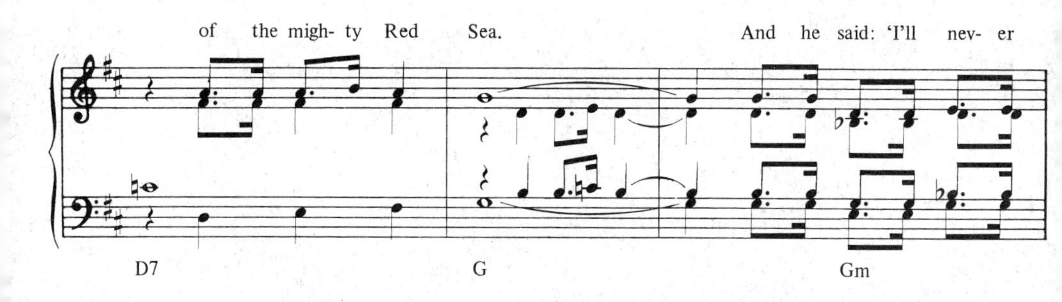

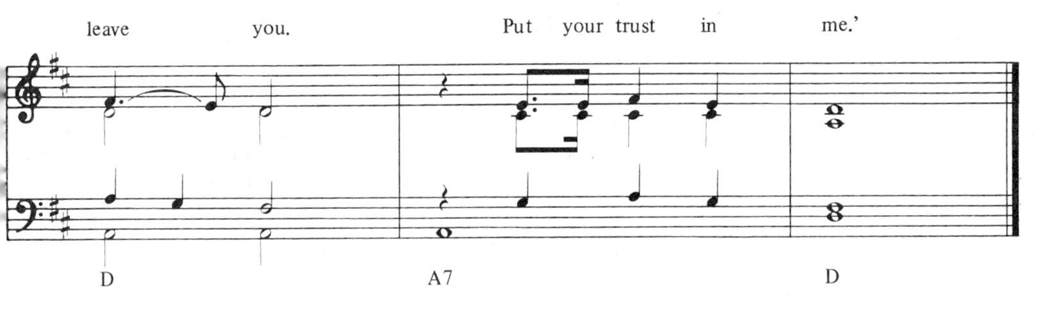

2. How great is our God,
how great is his name!
How great is our God,
for ever the same!
He sent his Son Jesus
to set us all free.
And he said: 'I'll never leave you.
Put your trust in me.'

3. How great is our God,
how great is his name!
How great is our God,
for ever the same!
He gave us his Spirit,
and now we can see.
And he said: 'I'll never leave you.
Put your trust in me.'

Words and Music: Unknown, arranged by Michael Irwin

HOW LOVELY ON THE MOUNTAINS (Our God reigns)

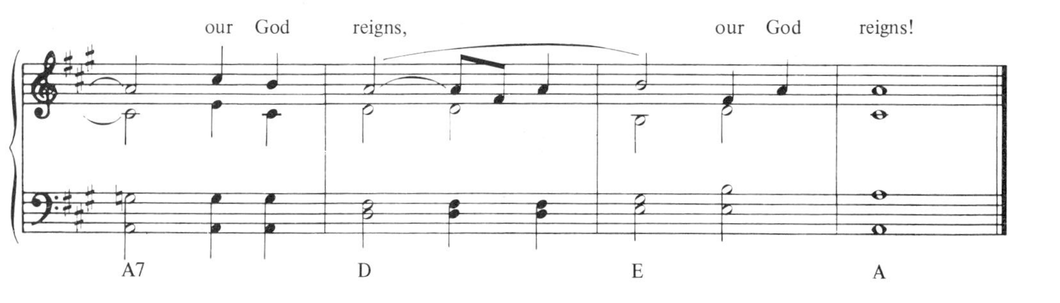

2. You watchmen, lift your voices
   joyfully as one,
   shout for your King, your King!
   See eye to eye,
   the Lord restoring Zion:
   Our God reigns. *(6)*

3. Wasteplaces of Jerusalem,
   break forth with joy!
   We are redeemed, redeemed.
   The Lord has saved
   and comforted his people.
   Our God reigns. *(6)*

4. Ends of the earth, see
   the salvation of our God!
   Jesus is Lord, is Lord!
   Before the nations,
   he has bared his holy arm.
   Our God reigns. *(6)*

Words, based on Isaiah 52 : Verse 1 – Leonard E. Smith Jr.
: Verses 2-4 – Unknown
Music : Leonard J. Smith Jr.

HOW SWEET THE NAME OF JESUS SOUNDS

('St Peter' C.M.)

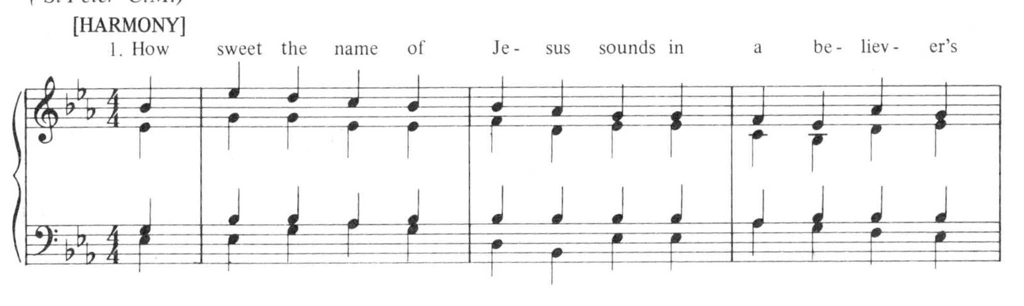

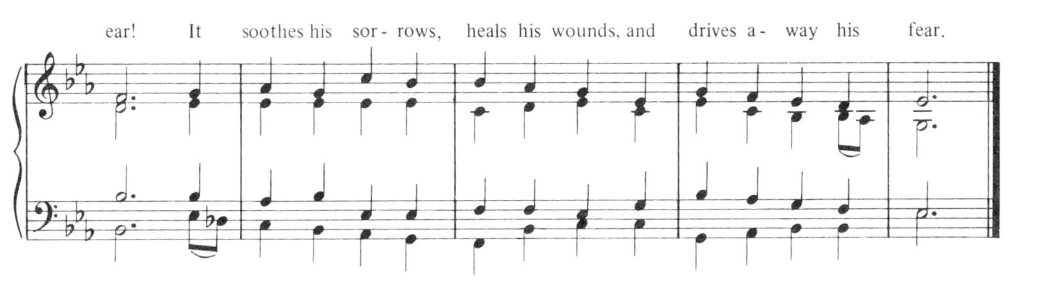

This tune may be found in a lower key at Hymn 330

2. It makes the wounded spirit whole,
and calms the troubled breast;
'tis manna to the hungry soul,
and to the weary rest.

3. Dear name! the rock on which I build,
my shield and hiding-place,
my never-failing treasury filled
with boundless stores of grace.

4. Jesus! my shepherd, brother, friend,
my prophet, priest, and king,
my Lord, my life, my way, my end,
accept the praise I bring.

5. Weak is the effort of my heart,
and cold my warmest thought;
but when I see thee as thou art,
I'll praise thee as I ought.

6. Till then I would thy love proclaim
with every fleeting breath;
and may the music of thy name
refresh my soul in death.

Words: John Newton (1725-1807)
Music: Alexander R. Reinagle (1799-1877)

207
I AM THE BREAD OF LIFE (Toolan)
1. I am the bread of life. He who comes to me shall not
2. The bread that I will give is my flesh for the life of the
3. Un - less you eat of the flesh of the Son of
4. I am the Re - sur - rec - tion, I am the
5. Yes, Lord, I be - lieve that you are the
A C♯m D
(1.) hun - ger. He who be - lieves in me shall not thirst. No one can come to
(2.) world, and he who eats of this bread, he shall live for
(3.) Man and drink of his blood, and drink of his
(4.) life. He who be - lieves in me, ev - en if he
(5.) Christ, the Son of God, who has
E A C♯m D A

Words, based on John 6 & 11, and Music: Suzanne Toolan, S.M.

2. I am the spring of life.
He who hopes in me will never be thirsty.
I will raise him up . . .
I am the spring of life.

3. I am the way of life.
He who follows me will never be lonely.
I will raise him up . . .
I am the way of life.

4. I am the truth of life.
He who looks for me will never seek blindly.
I will raise him up . . .
I am the truth of life.

5. I am the life of life.
He who dies with me will never die vainly.
I will raise him up . . .
I am the life of life.

Words, based on John 6: 31: David Konstant
Music: Kevin Mayhew

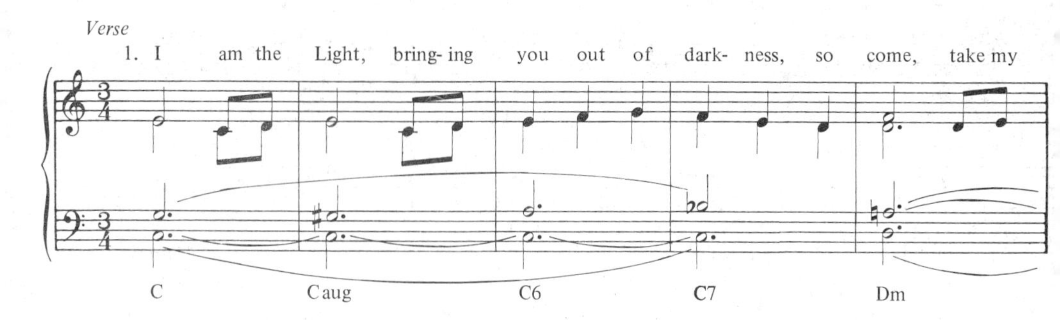
Verse
1. I am the Light, bring- ing you out of dark- ness, so come, take my
C
Caug
C6
C7
Dm

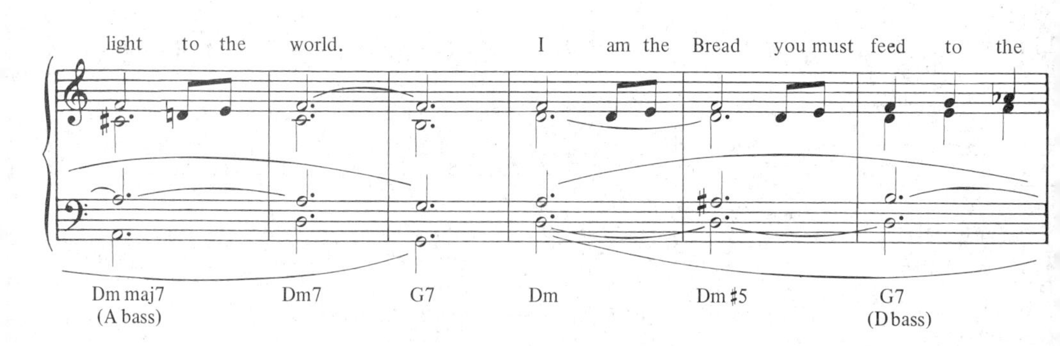
light to the world. I am the Bread you must feed to the
Dm maj7
(A bass)
Dm7
G7
Dm
Dm ♯5
G7
(D bass)

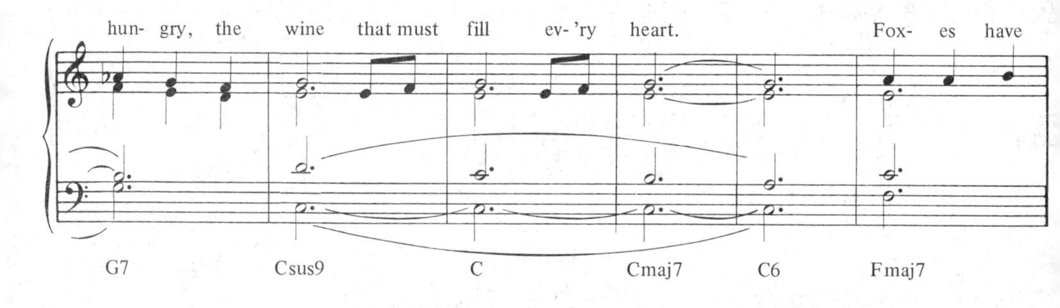
hun- gry, the wine that must fill ev- 'ry heart. Fox- es have
G7
Csus9
C
Cmaj7
C6
Fmaj7

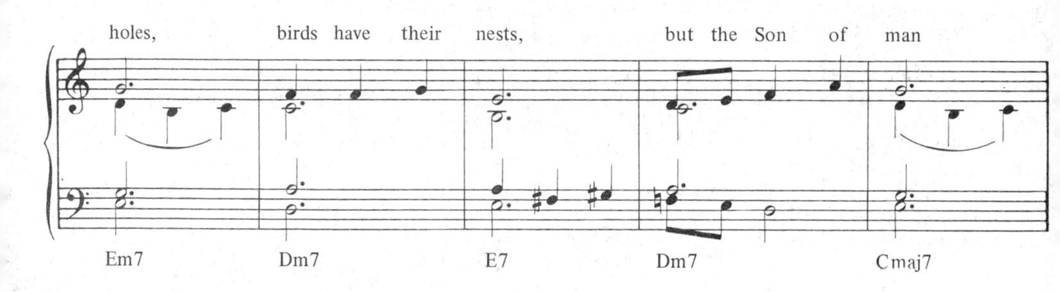
holes, birds have their nests, but the Son of man
Em7
Dm7
E7
Dm7
Cmaj7

2. I am the Life
   that must change ev'ry life
   and the Way that must alter your ways.
   I am the Truth and my word is the cross
   you must take if you want to be free.
   Foxes have holes, birds have their nests,
   but the Son of Man has no place to rest.

3. I am the Sower,
   come, work in my vineyard, my field.
   Tend my vines, sow the grain.
   And should it fall to the ground
   it can only spring up
   with new life, hundredfold.
   Foxes have holes, birds have their nests,
   but the Son of Man has no place to rest.

4. I am the Shepherd,
   come into the sheepfold
   to help feed my lambs, feed my sheep.
   Bring back the straying,
   and bind up their wounds, and rejoice
   when you've found what was lost.
   Foxes have holes, birds have their nests,
   but the Son of Man has no place to rest.

Words, based on the Gospel of John, and Music: Aniceto Nazareth

ASK YOUR BLESSING, LORD
('Blessings')

Very softly and gently

Words: *Graham Jeffery*
Music: *Kevin Mayhew*

I BIND UNTO MYSELF TODAY
('St Patrick's Breastplate' D.L.M.)

Men 2. I bind this day to me for e- ver, by pow- er of
Treble 4. I bind un- to my- self to- day the vir- tues
Full 7. A- gainst all Sa- tan's spells and wiles, a- gainst false
faith, Christ's in- car- na - tion; his bap- tism in the Jor- dan
of the star- lit hea - ven, the glo- rious sun's life - giv- ing
words of he- re- sy, a- gainst the know- ledge that de-
ri- ver; his death on cross for my sal- va- tion,
ray, the white- ness of the moon at ev- en,
files, a- gainst the heart's i- do- la- try,

Full his burst - ing from the spi - cèd tomb; his rid - ing
Full the flash - ing of the light - ning free, the whirl - ing
a - gainst the wiz - ard's ev - il craft, a - gainst the
up the heaven - ly way; his com - ing at the day of
wind's tem - pes - tuous shocks, the sta - ble earth, the deep salt
death - wound and the burn - ing, the chok - ing wave, the poi - soned
doom: I bind un - to my - self to - day.
sea a - round the old e - ter - nal rocks.
shaft, pro - tect me, Christ, till thy re - turn - ing.

Voices in Harmony with Organ
3 I bind un - to my - self the pow - er of the great
5 I bind un - to my - self to - day the pow - er of
6 A - gainst the de - mon snares of sin, the vice that

love of cher - u - bim; the sweet 'Well done!' in judge - ment
God to hold and lead, his eye to watch, his might to
gives temp - ta - tion force, the na - tu - ral lusts that war with -

(Org.)
hour; the ser - vice of the ser - a - phim, con -
stay, his ear to heark - en to my need; the
in, the hos - tile men that mar my course or

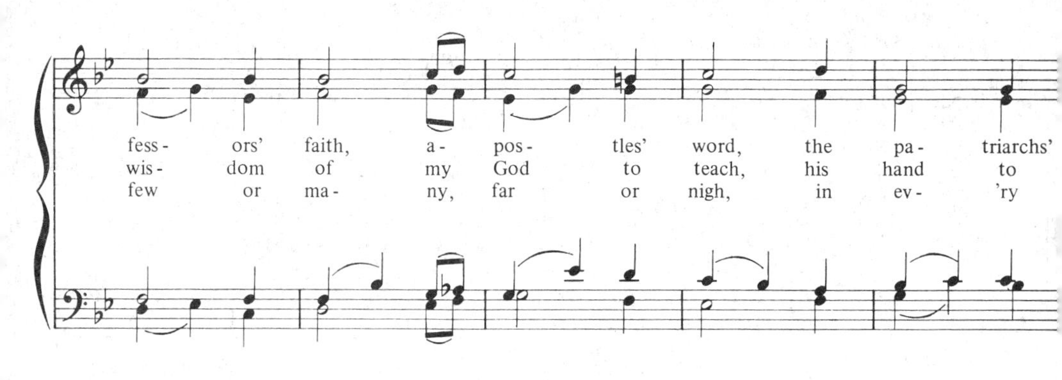
fess- ors' faith, a- pos- tles' word, the pa- triarchs'
wis- dom of my God to teach, his hand to
few or ma- ny, far or nigh, in ev- 'ry

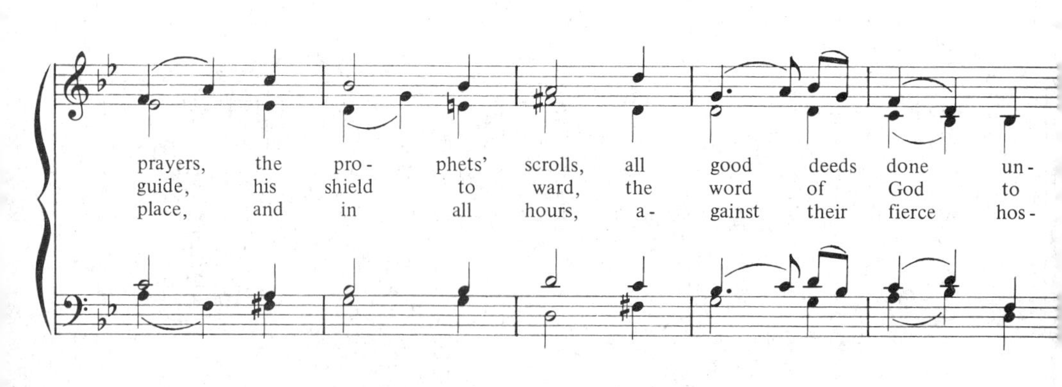
prayers, the pro- phets' scrolls, all good deeds done un-
guide, his shield to ward, the word of God to
place, and in all hours, a- gainst their fierce hos-

to the Lord, and pu- ri- ty of vir- gin souls.
give me speech, his heav'n- ly host to be my guard.
til- i- ty I bind to me these ho- ly powers.

[HARMONY]
8. Christ be with me, Christ with-in me, Christ be- hind me, Christ be-fore me,
Christ be-side me, Christ to win me, Christ to com-fort and re- store me.
Christ be-neath me, Christ a-bove me, Christ in qui- et, Christ in dan- ger,
Christ in hearts of all that love me, Christ in mouth of friend and stran- ger.

9. I bind un- to my- self the name, the strong name of the

Tri- ni- ty, by in- vo- ca- tion of the same, the Three in

One and One in Three of whom all na- ture hath cre-

Words: attributed to Saint Patrick (372-466), tr. C.F. Alexander
Music: Traditional Irish Hymn Melody, arranged by Charles Villiers Stanford (1852-1924)

I CANNOT TELL WHY HE
('Londonderry Air' 11 10.11 10.D.

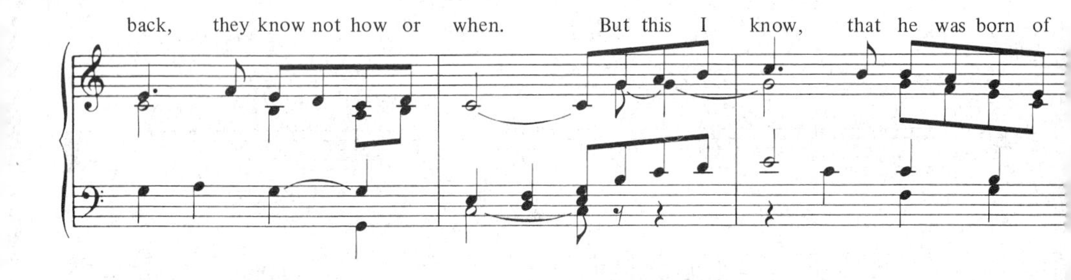

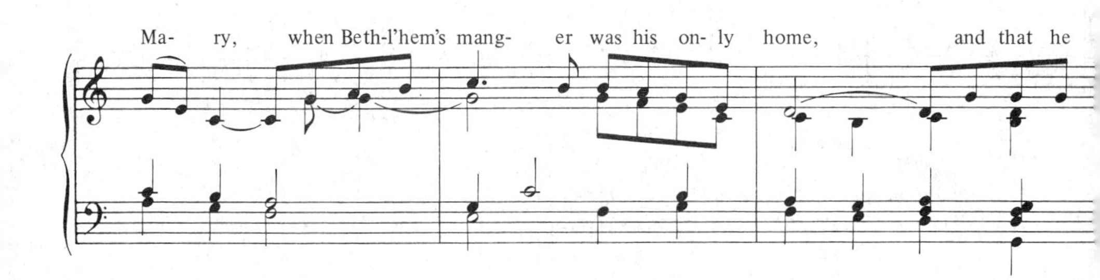

2. I cannot tell how silently he suffered,
as with his peace he graced this place of tears,
or how his heart upon the cross was broken,
the crown of pain to three and thirty years.
But this I know, he heals the broken-hearted,
and stays our sin, and calms our lurking fear,
and lifts the burden from the heavy laden,
for yet the Saviour, Saviour of the world is here.

3. I cannot tell how he will win the nations,
how he will claim his earthly heritage,
how satisfy the needs and aspirations
of east and west, of sinner and of sage.
But this I know, all flesh shall see his glory,
and he shall reap the harvest he has sown,
and some glad day his sun shall shine in splendour
when he the Saviour, Saviour of the world, is known.

4. I cannot tell how all the lands shall worship,
when, at his bidding, every storm is stilled,
or who can say how great the jubilation
when all the hearts of men with love are filled.
But this I know, the skies will thrill with rapture,
and myriad, myriad human voices sing.
And earth to heaven, and heaven to earth, will answer:
at last the Saviour, Saviour of the world, is King!

Words: William Young Fullerton (1857-1932)
Music: Traditional Irish melody,
arranged by Roland Fudge

Verse
1. I danced in the morning when the world was be-gun, and I danced in the moon and the
G
Am

stars and the sun, and I came down from hea-ven and I danced on the earth, at
D
G

Chorus
Beth- le- hem I had my birth. Dance, then, wher- ev-er you may be,
Am
D7
C
G
Em

I am the Lord of the Dance, said he, and I'll lead you all wher-
G
Am
D7
G
C

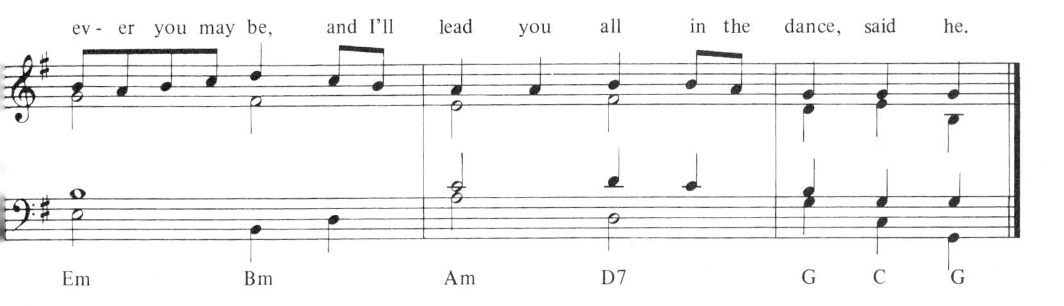

2. I danced for the scribe
and the Pharisee,
but they would not dance
and they wouldn't follow me.
I danced for the fishermen,
for James and John;
they came with me
and the dance went on.

3. I danced on the Sabbath
and I cured the lame.
The holy people they
said it was a shame.
They whipped and they stripped
and they hung me on high,
and they left me there
on the cross to die.

4. I danced on a Friday
when the sky turned black.
It's hard to dance
with the devil on your back.
They buried my body
and they thought I'd gone
but I am the dance
and I still go on.

5. They cut me down
and I leapt up high.
I am the life
that'll never, never die.
I'll live in you
if you'll live in me.
I am the Lord
of the Dance, said he.

Words: Sydney Carter
Music: Traditional Shaker tune,
arranged by Frances M. Kelly

IF I WERE A BUTTERFLY **(The butterfly song)**

2.. If I were an elephant
I'd thank you, Lord, by raising my trunk,
and if I were a kangaroo
you know I'd hop right up to you,
and if I were an octopus
I'd thank you, Lord, for my fine looks,
but I just thank you, Father, for making me me.

3. If I were a wiggly worm
I'd thank you, Lord, that I could squirm,
and if I were a billy goat
I'd thank you, Lord, for my strong throat,
and if I were a fuzzy wuzzy bear
I'd thank you, Lord, for my fuzzy wuzzy hair,
but I just thank you, Father, for making me me.

Words and Music: Brian Howard

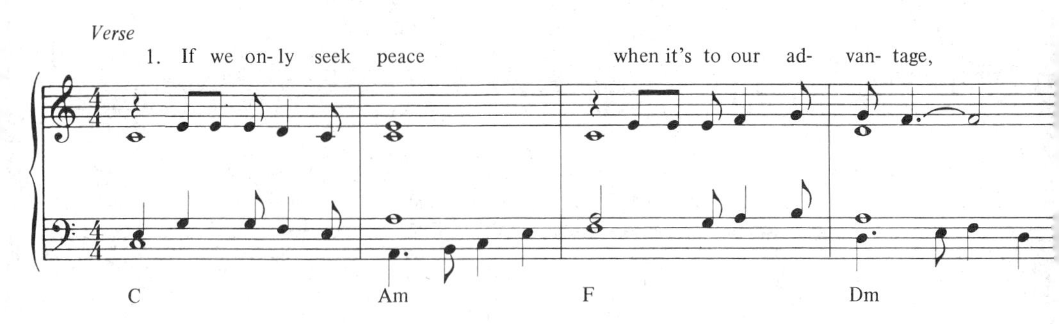
Verse
1. If we on- ly seek peace when it's to our ad- van- tage,
C
Am
F
Dm

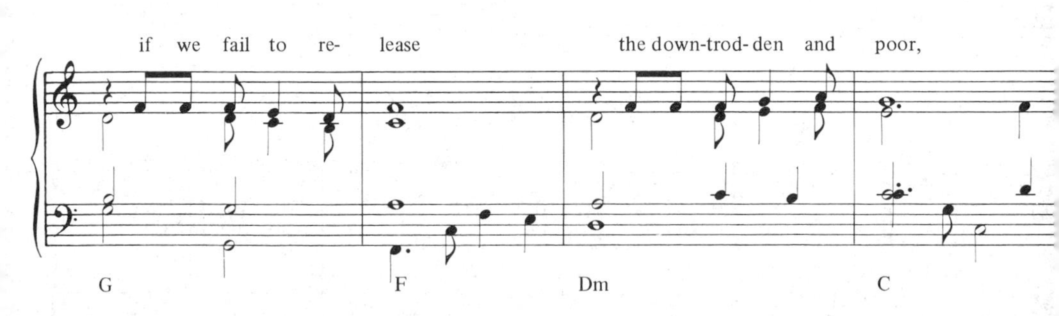
if we fail to re- lease the down-trod- den and poor,
G
F
Dm
C

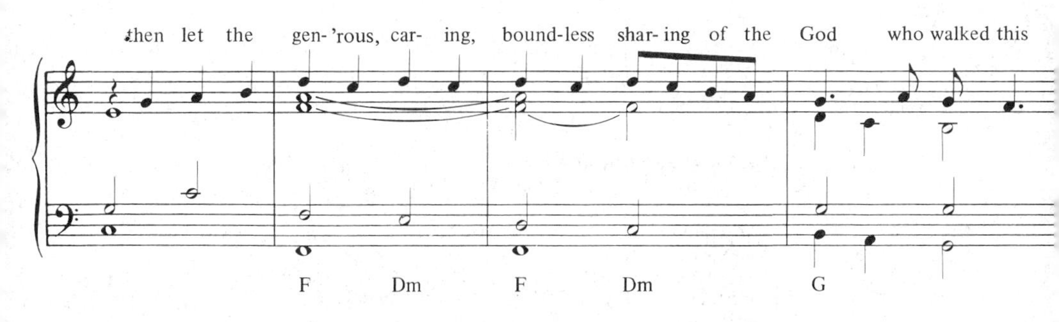
then let the gen- 'rous, car- ing, bound-less shar- ing of the God who walked this
F
Dm
F
Dm
G

earth nou-rish our roots un- til we fruit in the joy of the Lord.
Am
F
Dm
G7
C

2. If we try to avoid
inconvenient giving,
or if love is destroyed
by our failure to serve,
then let the wide, unflinching, selfless giving
of the God who walked this earth
nourish our roots until we fruit
in the joy of the Lord.

3. If we start to object
to the path we are given
and decide to select
other ways of our own,
then let the full acceptance, firm obedience
of the God who walked this earth
nourish our roots until we fruit
in the joy of the Lord.

Words and Music: Susan Sayers,
arranged by Frances M. Kelly

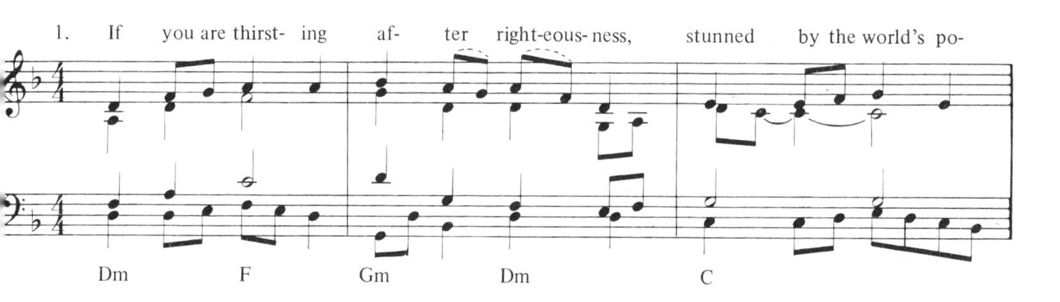

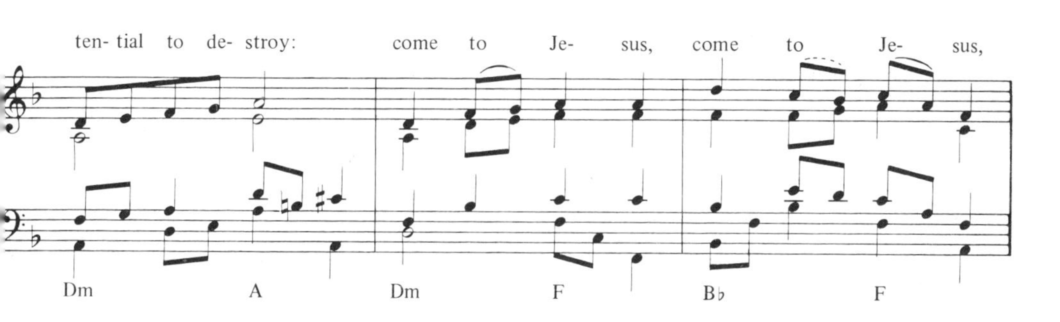

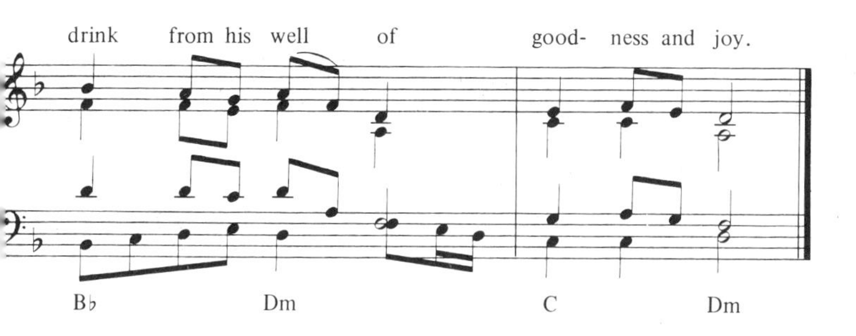

2. If you are weary, heavily laden,
finding a burden difficult to bear:
come to Jesus, he will refresh you,
lighten your load and free you from care.

3. If you are hungry for life's meaning,
faced with disaster, suffering, disease:
come to Jesus, he will feed you,
bread of eternity, truth and peace.

Words, based on John 7: 37,
and Music: Susan Sayers,
arranged by Frances M. Kelly

I GIVE MY HANDS TO DO YOUR WORK

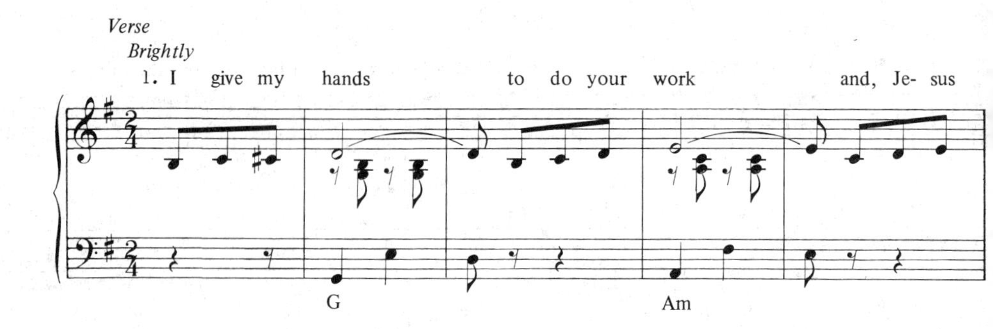

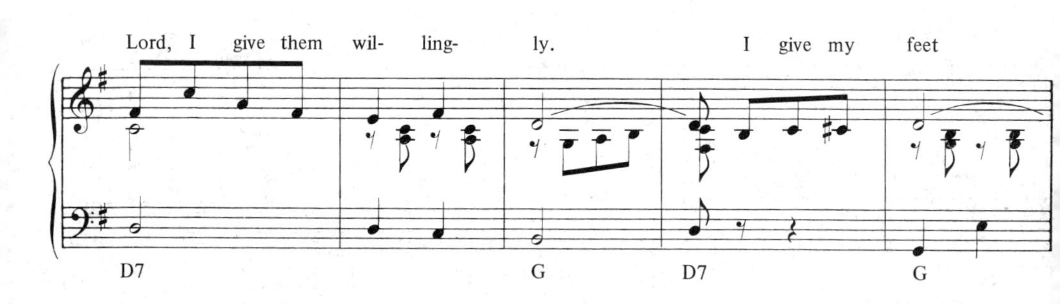

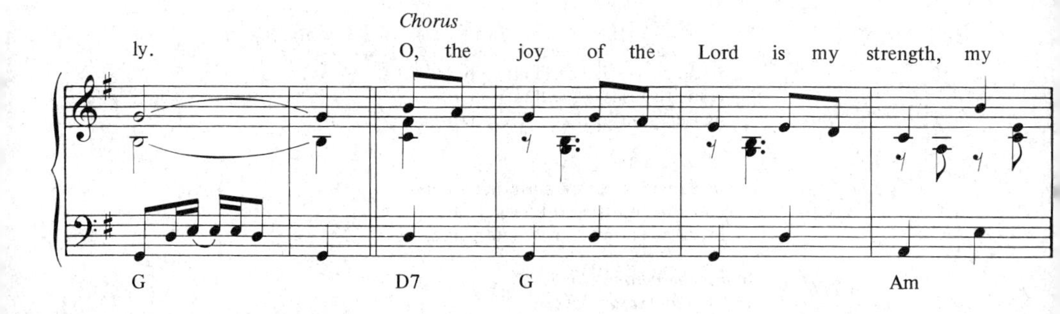

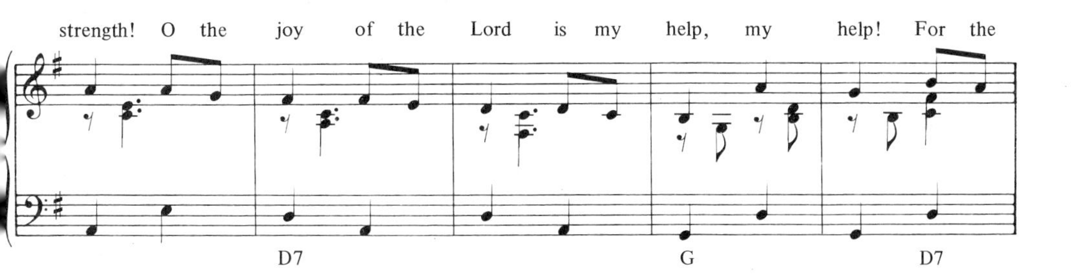

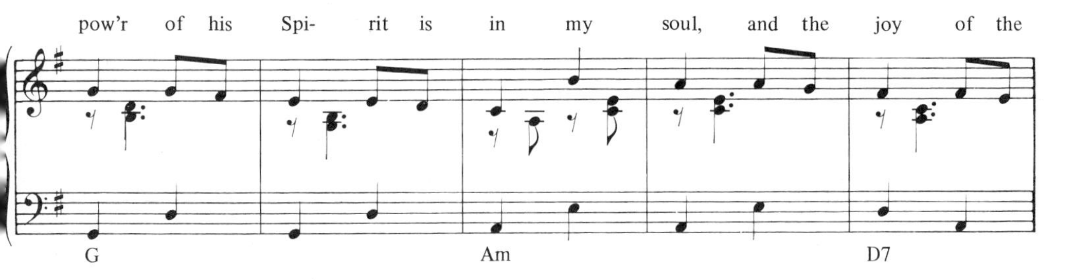

2. I give my eyes to see the world
and everyone, in just the way you do.
I give my tongue to speak your words,
to spread your name and freedom-giving truth.

3. I give my mind in every way
so that each thought I have will come from you.
I give my spirit to you, Lord,
and every day my prayer will spring anew.

4. I give my heart that you may love
in me your Father and the human race.
I give myself that you may grow
in me and make my life a song of praise.

Words and Music: Estelle White

I GIVE YOU PEACE

2. Fear not, my children; peace to you.
My love is with you; all life through.

Words, based on John 14: 1 & 27, and Music: Francesca Leftley, arranged by John Rombaut

219

I HEARD THE LORD CALL MY NAME

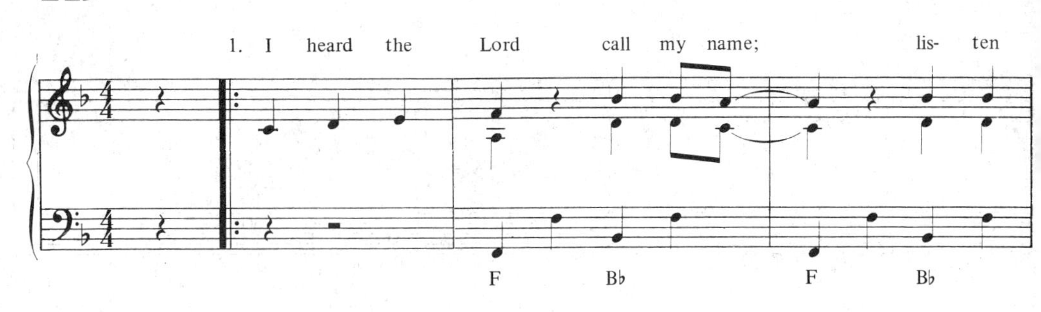

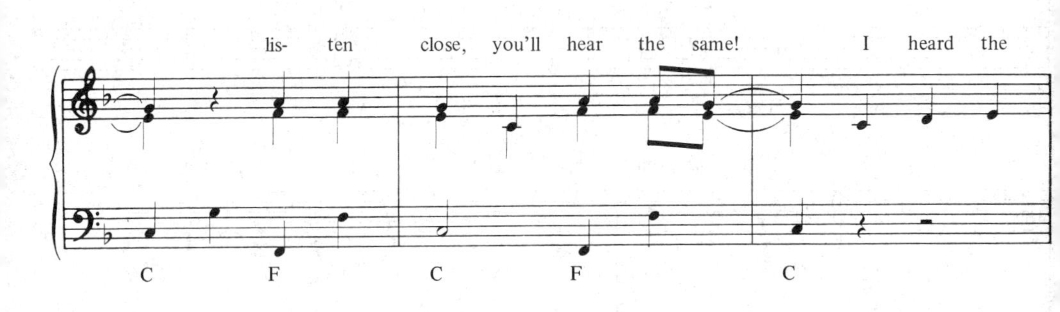

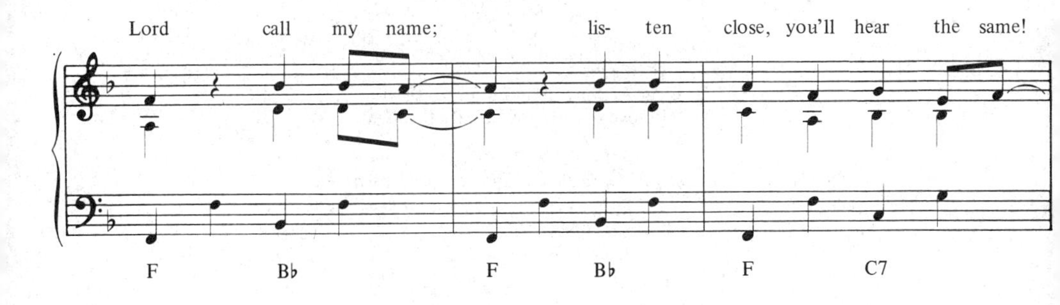

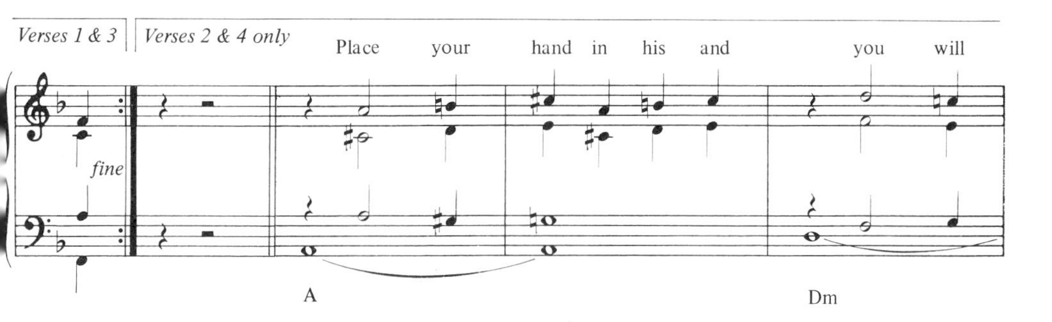

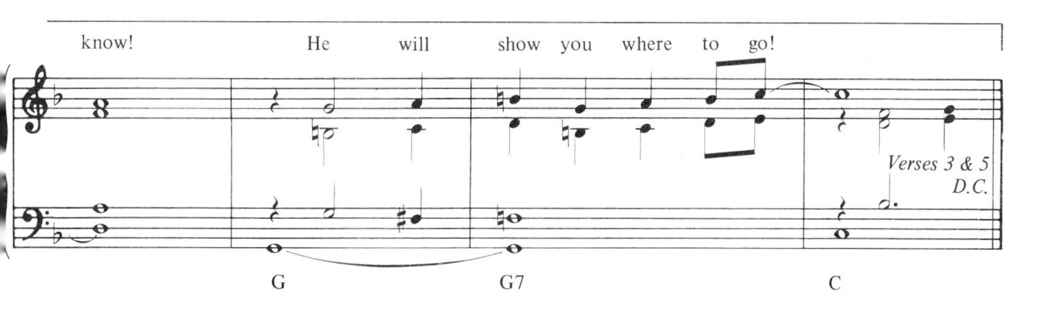

2. His Word is love, love's his word,
that's the message that I heard! *(3)*
Take his hand: we are glory bound!
Place your hand in his and you will know;
he will show you where to go!

3. I felt his love from above
settle on me like a dove. *(3)*
Take his hand; we are glory bound!

4. And to the Father all your days
with the Son and Spirit praise! *(3)*
Take his hand, we are glory bound!
Place your hand in his and you will know;
he will show you where to go!

5. *Repeat Verse 1.*

Words and Music: Jacob Krieger

I HEARD THE VOICE OF JESUS SAY

('Kingsfold' D.C.M.)

2. I heard the voice of Jesus say,
'Behold, I freely give
the living water, thirsty one;
stoop down and drink and live.'
I came to Jesus, and I drank
of that life-giving stream;
my thirst was quenched, my soul revived,
and now I live in him.

3. I heard the voice of Jesus say,
'I am this dark world's light;
look unto me, thy morn shall rise,
and all thy day be bright.'
I looked to Jesus, and I found
in him my star, my sun;
and in that light of life I'll walk
till travelling days are done.

Words: Horatius Bonar (1808-89)
Music: Traditional melody, harmonised by Ralph Vaughan Williams (1872-1958)

221 I HEAR THE SOUND OF RUSTLING

Verse
With pace

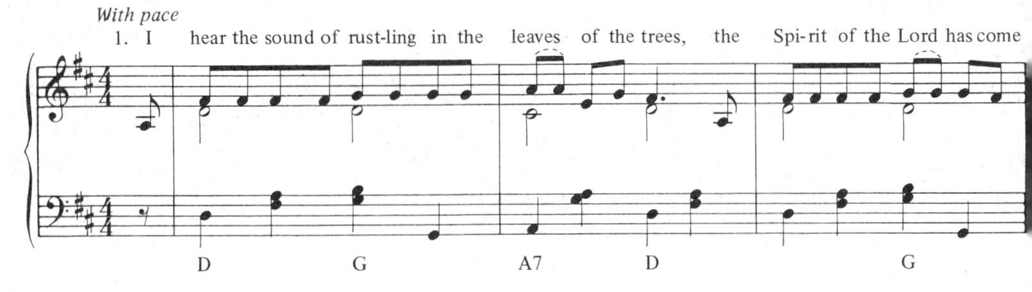

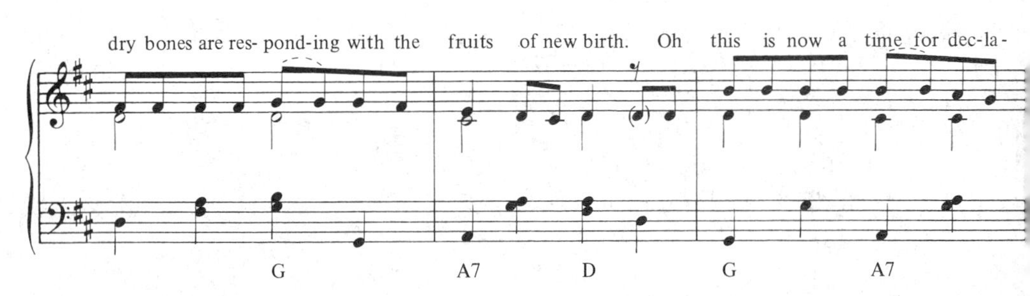

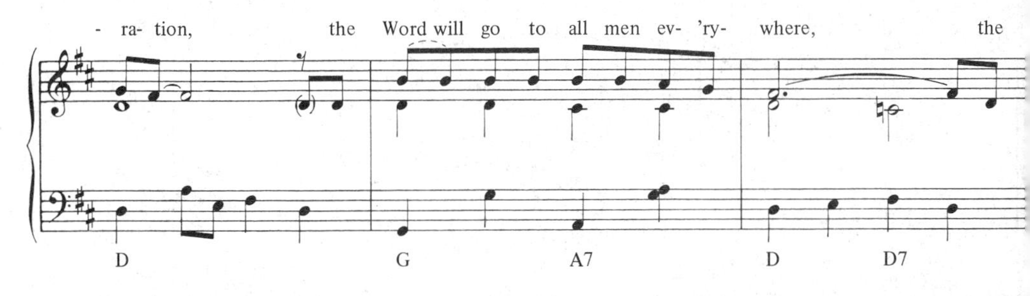

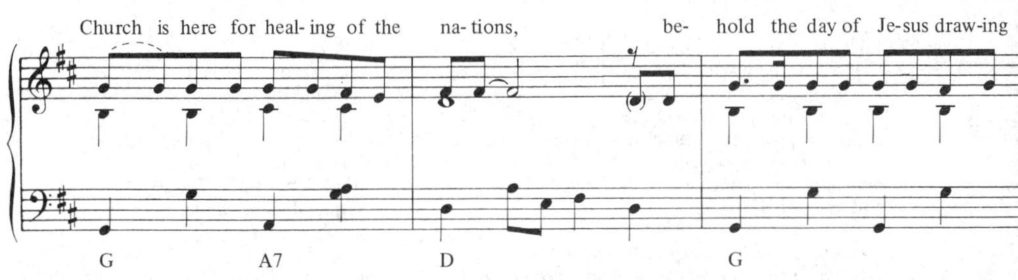

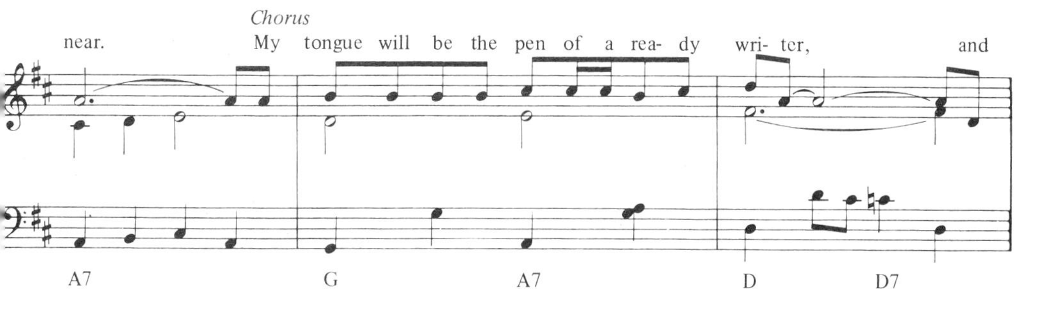

2. And all around the world the body waits expectantly
the promise of the Father is now ready to fall.
The watchmen on the tower all exhort us to prepare,
and the Church responds - a people who will answer the call.
And this is not a phase which is passing,
it's the start of the age that is to come.
And where is the wise man and the scoffer?
Before the face of Jesus they are dumb.

3. A body now prepared by God and ready for war,
the prompting of the Spirit is our word of command.
We rise, a mighty army, at the bidding of the Lord,
the devils see and fear, for their time is at hand.
And children of the Lord hear our commission
that we should love and serve our God as one.
The Spirit won't be hindered by division
in the perfect work that Jesus has begun.

Words, based on Ezekiel 37: R. Wilson
Music: R. Wilson

I KNEEL IN PRAYER TO THE FATHER **(Paul's prayer)**

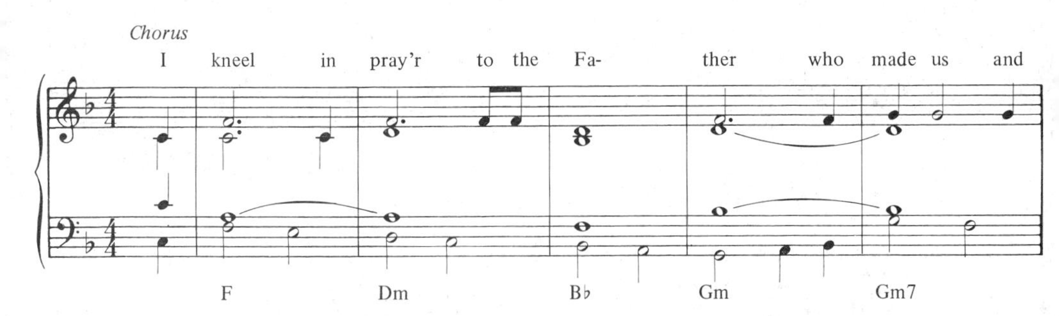

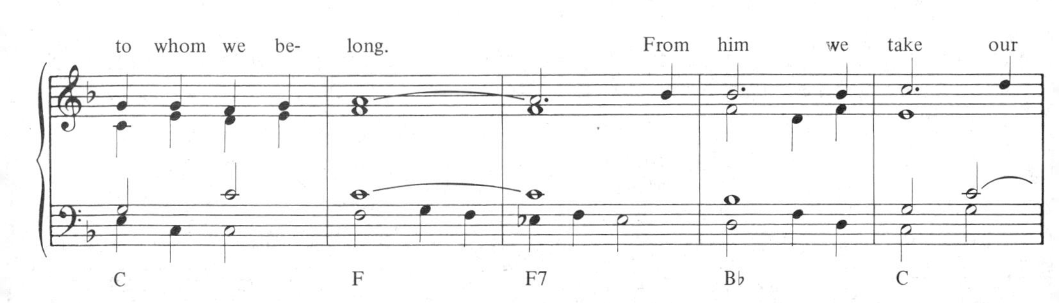

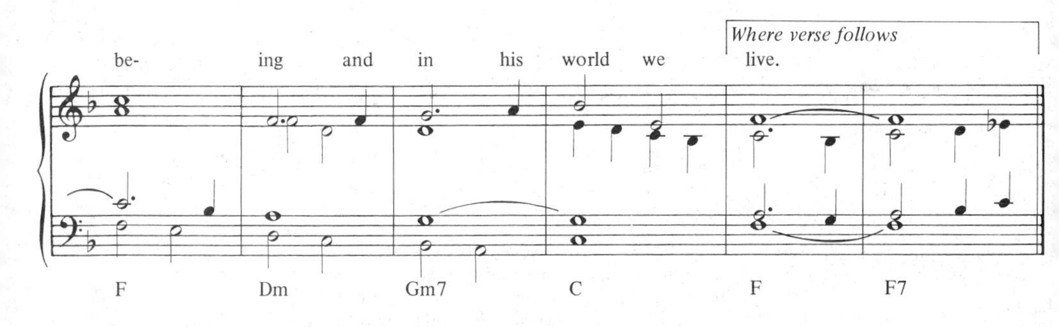

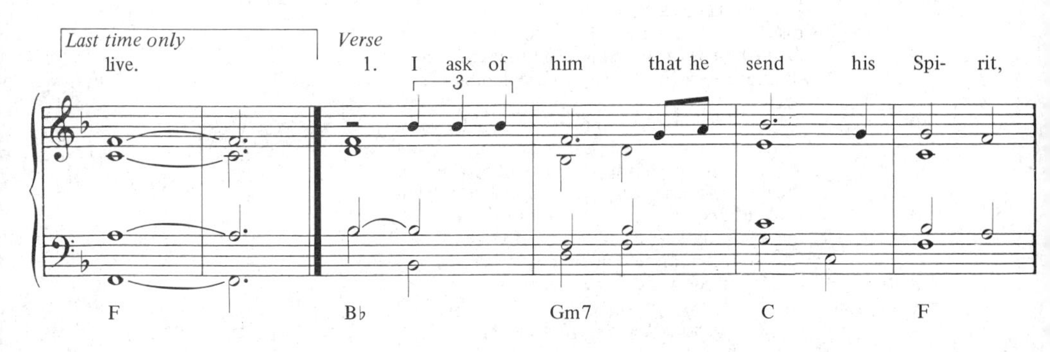

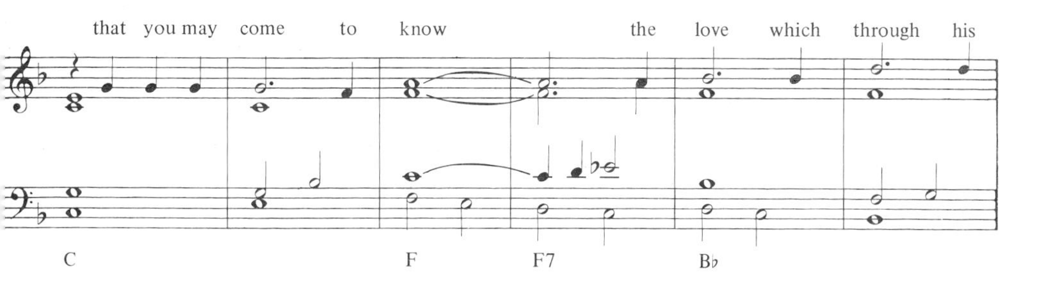

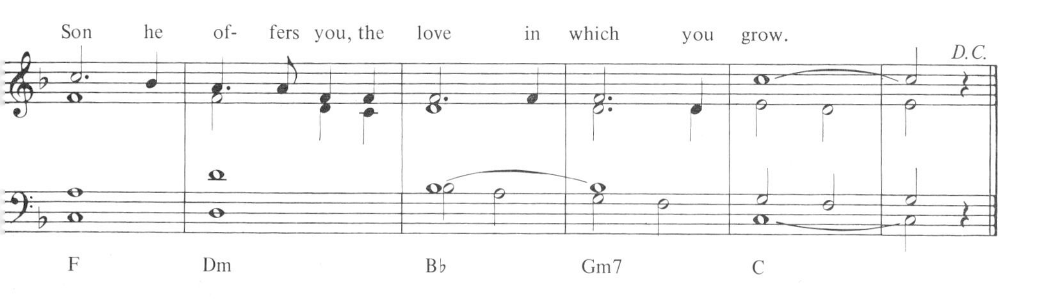

2. I ask of him that his Son, Christ Jesus,
   may live within your hearts,
   that you may come to know and understand
   how deep, how vast his love.

3. I ask of him that the love you're sharing
   may deepen as you grow,
   that you reflect his love, though far beyond
   what you can understand.

4. Glory to God for the love he shows us
   and in whose love we grow;
   glory to Father, Son and Holy Spirit,
   Blessed Trinity.

Words, based on Ephesians 3: 14-21, and Music: Christine McCann,
arranged by Frances M. Kelly

223

I KNOW THAT MY REDEEMER LIVES!
(First tune: 'Church triumphant' L.M.)

[HARMONY]

2. He lives, to bless me with his love;
he lives, to plead for me above;
he lives, my hungry soul to feed;
he lives, to help in time of need.

3. He lives, and grants me daily breath;
he lives, and I shall conquer death;
he lives, my mansion to prepare;
he lives, to lead me safely there.

4. He lives, all glory to his name;
he lives, my Saviour, still the same;
what joy the blest assurance gives!
I know that my Redeemer lives!

Words: Samuel Medley (1738-99)
Music: First tune - J. W. Elliott (1883-1915)

I KNOW THAT MY REDEEMER LIVES!
(Second tune: 'Philippine' L.M.)

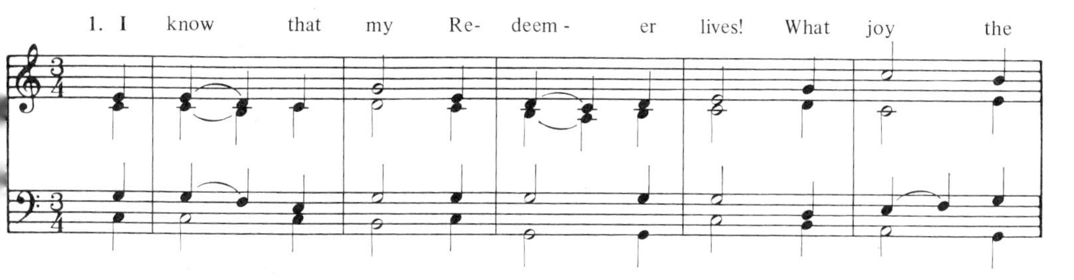

2. He lives, to bless me with his love;
he lives, to plead for me above;
he lives, my hungry soul to feed;
he lives, to help in time of need.

3. He lives, and grants me daily breath;
he lives, and I shall conquer death;
he lives, my mansion to prepare;
he lives, to lead me safely there.

4. He lives, all glory to his name;
he lives, my Saviour, still the same;
what joy the blest assurance gives!
I know that my Redeemer lives!

Words: Samuel Medley (1738-99)
Music: Second tune - R.E.Roberts (1878-1940)

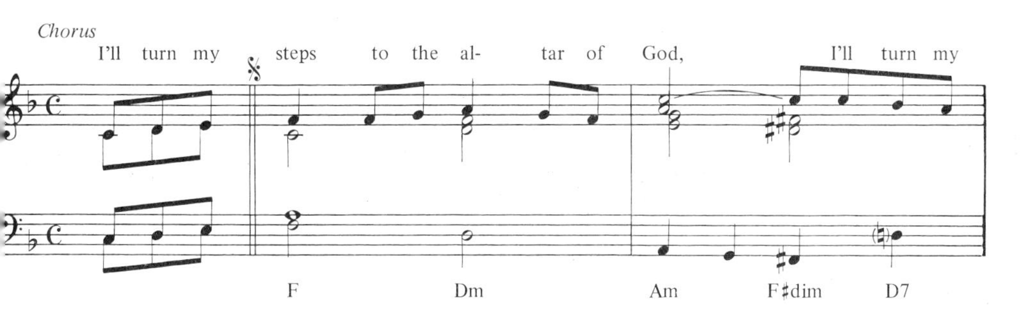

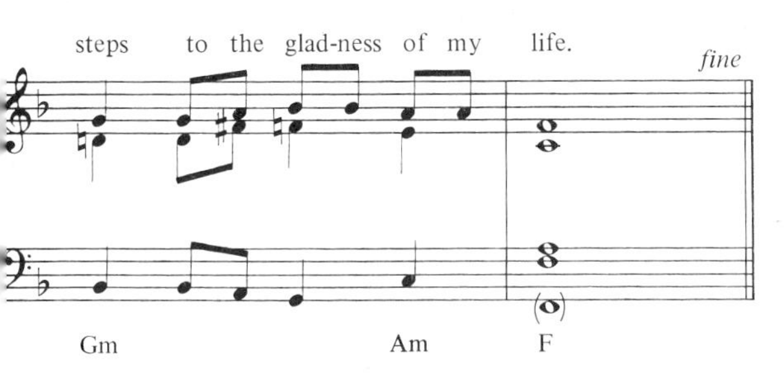

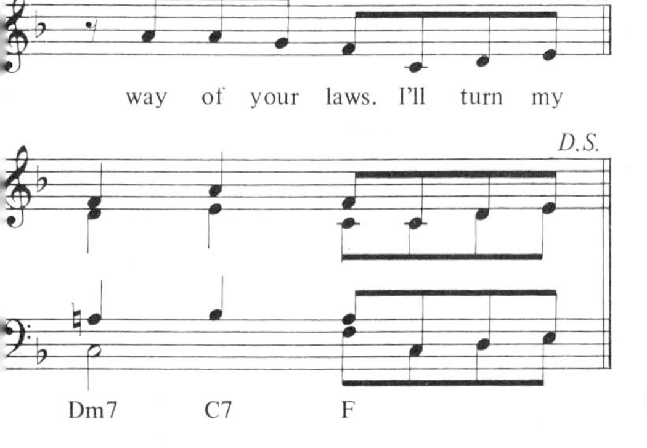

2. Lead me on with your power and strength,
then my courage will never be spent.

3. Fill my heart with your truth and your light
as I enter with joy in your sight.

4. Holy praises of God will I sing;
I will trust and will hope in my King.

5. Glory be to the Father, the Son,
and the Spirit, while ages run.

Words, based on Psalm 43, and Music: Aniceto Nazareth

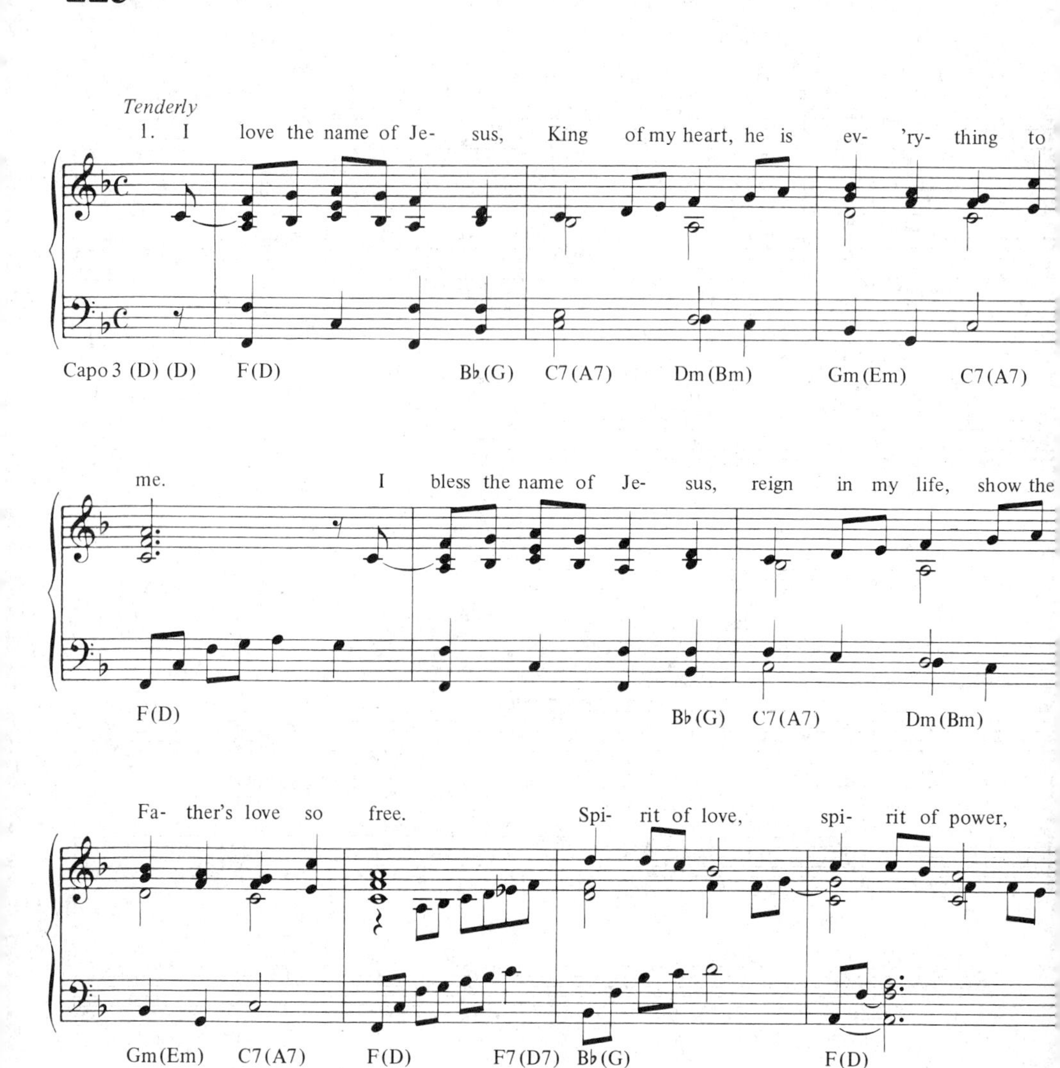
Tenderly
1. I love the name of Je- sus, King of my heart, he is ev- 'ry- thing to
Capo 3 (D) (D) F(D) B♭(G) C7(A7) Dm(Bm) Gm(Em) C7(A7)
me. I bless the name of Je- sus, reign in my life, show the
F(D) B♭(G) C7(A7) Dm(Bm)
Fa- ther's love so free. Spi- rit of love, spi- rit of power,
Gm(Em) C7(A7) F(D) F7(D7) B♭(G) F(D)

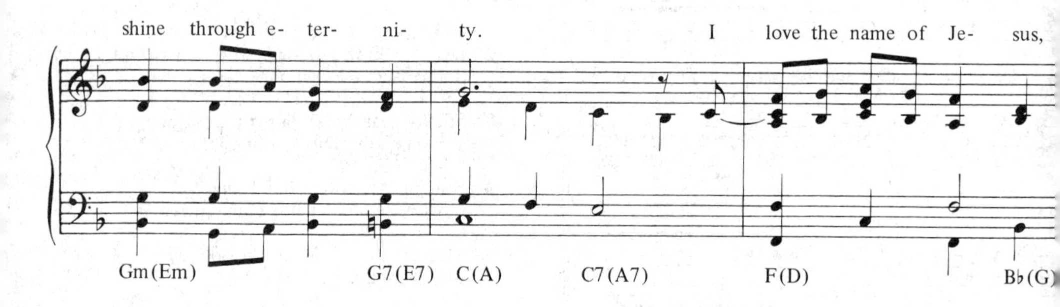
shine through e- ter- ni- ty. I love the name of Je- sus,
Gm(Em) G7(E7) C(A) C7(A7) F(D) B♭(G)

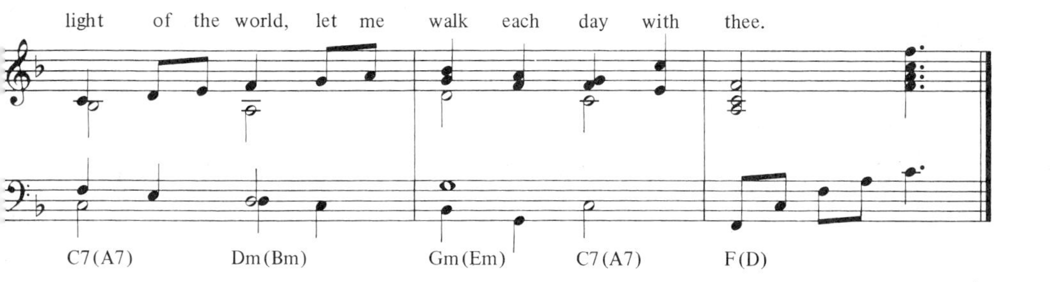

2. I love the name of Jesus, risen above,
   and he loves and prays for me.
   I bless the name of Jesus, ruling on high
   with a glorious majesty.
   Spirit of love, spirit of power,
   shine through eternity.
   I praise the name of Jesus, Lord of my life,
   for he died to set me free.

3. I love the name of Jesus, splendour of God,
   and his face I long to see.
   I bless the name of Jesus, shepherd of men;
   by his side I now can be.
   Spirit of love, spirit of power,
   shine through eternity.
   I praise the name of Jesus, for he is love,
   and that love he gives to me.

Words and Music: Kathleen Thomerson

I LOVE TO HEAR THE STO

(First tune: 'I love to hear the story' 76.76.

2. I'm glad my blessèd Saviour
was once a child like me,
to show how pure and holy
his little ones might be;
and if I try to follow
his footsteps here below,
he never will forget me,
because he loves me so.

3. To tell his love and mercy
my sweetest songs I'll raise;
and though I cannot see him,
I know he hears my praise;
for he himself has promised
that even I may go
to sing among his angels,
because he loves me so.

I LOVE TO HEAR THE STORY
(Second tune: 'Gosterwood' 76.76.D.)

Words: *Emily Miller (1833-1913)*
Music: *First tune - Henry J. Gauntlett (1805-76)*
Second tune - English traditional melody

227 IMMORTAL, INVISIBLE

[HARMONY]

('St Denio' 11 11.11 11.)

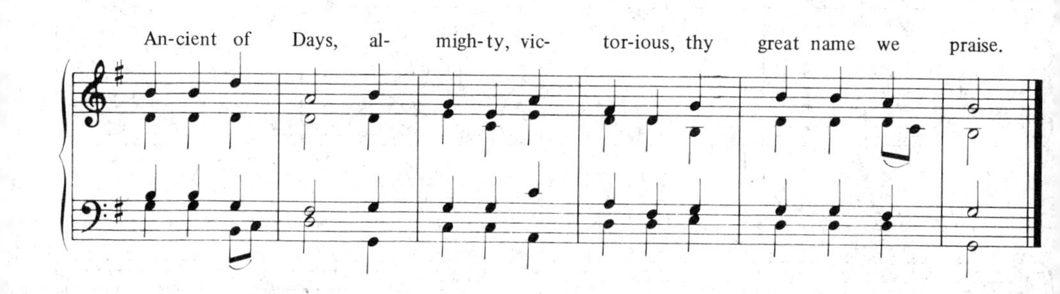

2. Unresting, unhasting,
and silent as light;
nor wanting, nor wasting,
thou rulest in might -
thy justice like mountains
high-soaring above
thy clouds which are fountains
of goodness and love.

3. To all life thou givest,
to both great and small;
in all life thou livest,
the true life of all;
we blossom and flourish
as leaves on the tree,
and wither and perish;
but naught changeth thee.

4. Great Father of glory,
pure Father of light,
thine angels adore thee,
all veiling their sight;
all laud we would render:
O help us to see
'tis only the splendour
of light hideth thee.

Words: W. Chalmers Smith (1824-1908), based on 1 Tim 1: 17
Music: Welsh Hymn Melody (1839)

IMMORTAL LOVE FOR EVER FULL **228**

('Bishopthorpe' C.M.)

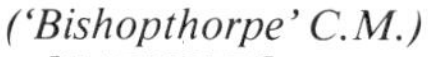

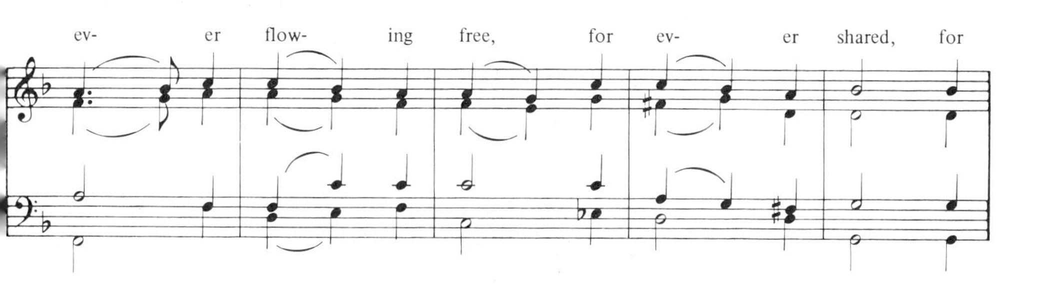

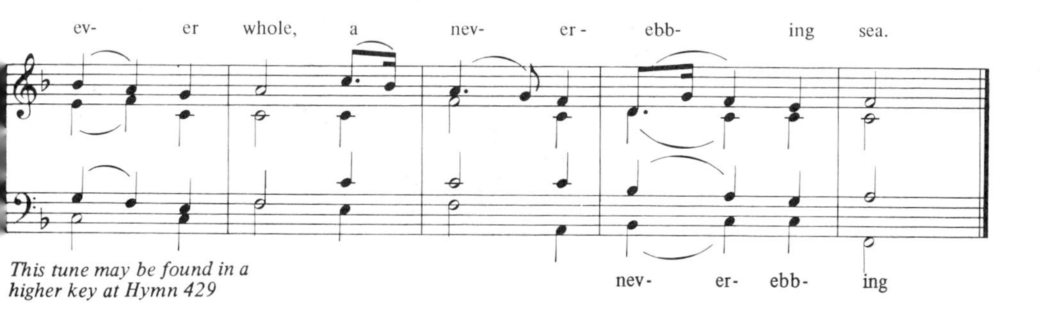

This tune may be found in a higher key at Hymn 429

2. Our outward lips confess the name
all other names above;
love only knoweth whence it came
and comprehendeth love.

3. We may not climb the heavenly steeps
to bring the Lord Christ down;
in vain we search the lowest deeps,
for him no depths can drown:

4. But warm, sweet, tender, even yet
a present help is he;
and faith has still its Olivet,
and love its Galilee.

5. The healing of his seamless dress
is by our beds of pain;
we touch him in life's throng and press,
and we are whole again.

6. Through him the first fond prayers are said
our lips of childhood frame;
the last low whispers of our dead
are burdened with his name.

7. Alone, O Love ineffable,
thy saving name is given;
to turn aside from thee is hell,
to walk with thee is heaven.

Words: John G. Whittier (1807-92)
Music: Jeremiah Clark (1670-1707)

I'M NOT ASHAMED TO OWN MY LORD
('Jackson' C.M.)

[HARMONY]

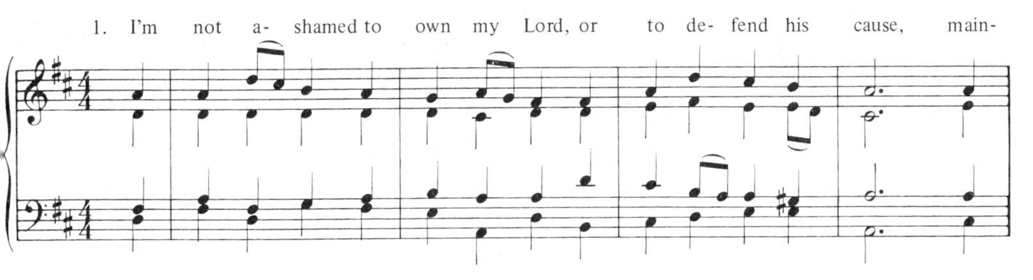

2. Jesus, my God! I know his name,
   his name is all my trust;
   nor will he put my soul to shame,
   nor let my hope be lost.

3. Firm as his throne his promise stands,
   and he can well secure
   what I've committed to his hands,
   till the decisive hour.

4. Then will he own my worthless name
   before his Father's face;
   and, in the New Jerusalem,
   appoint my soul a place.

Words: Isaac Watts (1674-1748)
Music: Thomas Jackson (1715-81)

IN BREAD WE BRING YOU, LORD

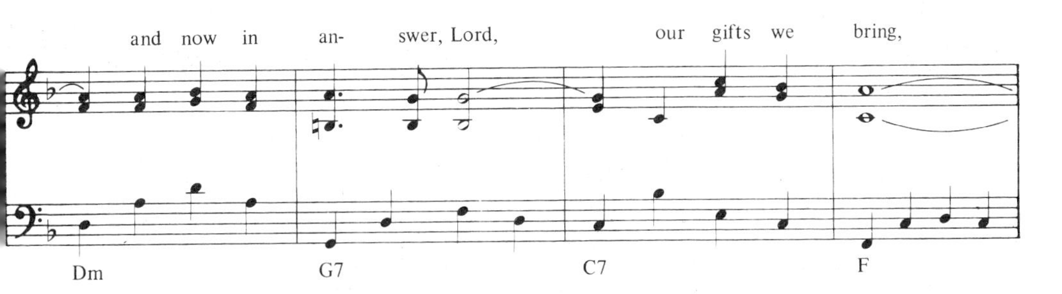

2. The bread we offer you
 is blessed and broken,
 and it becomes for us
 our spirits' food.
 Over the cup we bring
 your Word is spoken;
 make it your gift to us,
 your healing blood.
 Take all that daily toil
 plants in our hearts poor soil,
 take all we start and spoil,
 each hopeful dream,
 the chances we have missed,
 the graces we resist,
 Lord, in thy eucharist,
 take and redeem.

Words and Music: Kevin Nichols

IN CHRIST THERE IS NO EAST OR WEST

(First tune: 'Kilmarnock' C.M.)

[HARMONY]

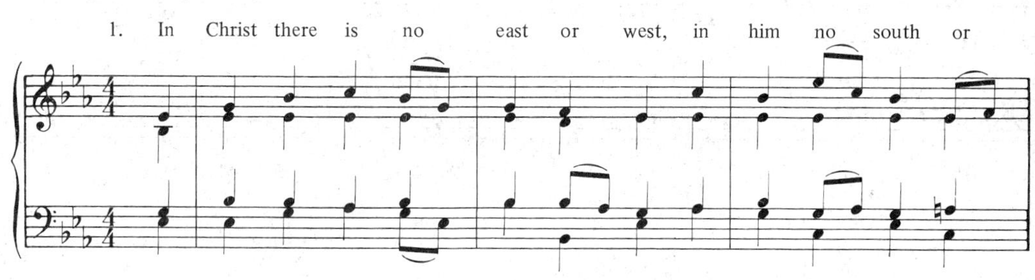

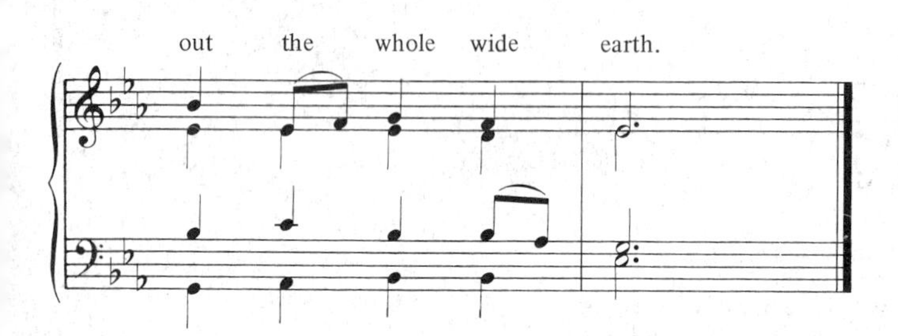

2. In him shall true hearts everywhere
their high communion find;
his service is the golden cord,
close binding all mankind.

3. Join hands, then, brothers of the faith,
whate'er your race may be;
who serves my Father as a son
is surely kin to me.

4. In Christ now meet both east and west,
in him meet south and north;
all Christlike souls are one in him,
throughout the whole wide earth.

Words: John Oxenham (1852-1941)
Music: First tune - Neil Dougall (1776-1862)

N CHRIST THERE IS NO EAST OR WEST
econd tune: 'McKee' C.M.)

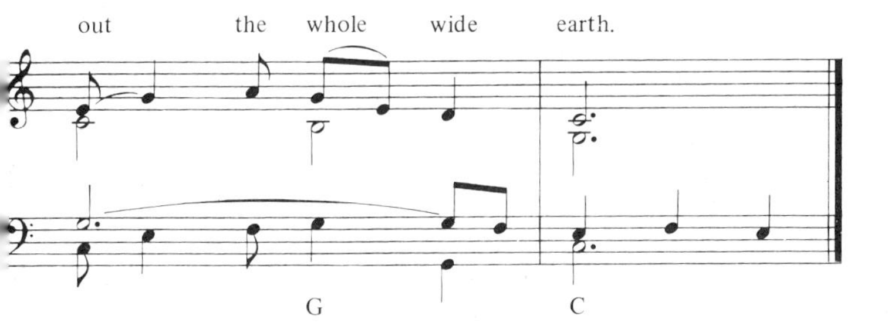

2. In him shall true hearts ev'rywhere
their high communion find.
His service is the golden cord
close-binding all mankind.

3. Join hands, then, brothers of the faith
whate'er your race may be.
Who serves my Father as a son
is surely kin to me.

4. In Christ now meet both east and west,
in him meet south and north.
All Christlike souls are one in him
throughout the whole wide earth.

Words: John Oxenham (1852-1941)
Music: Second tune - Traditional spiritual, arranged by Frances M. Kelly

INFANT HOLY, INFANT LOWLY

('Wzlobie lezy' 87.87.88.77.)

2. Flocks were sleeping, shepherds keeping
vigil till the morning new;
saw the glory, heard the story,
tidings of a gospel true.
Thus rejoicing, free from sorrow,
praises voicing, greet the morrow,
Christ the babe was born for you!
Christ the babe was born for you!

Words: Polish carol, tr. Edith M.G. Reed (1885-1933)
Music: Traditional Polish melody, arranged by Frances M. Kelly

IN FULL AND GLAD SURRENDER

('St Alphege' 76.76.)

[HARMONY]

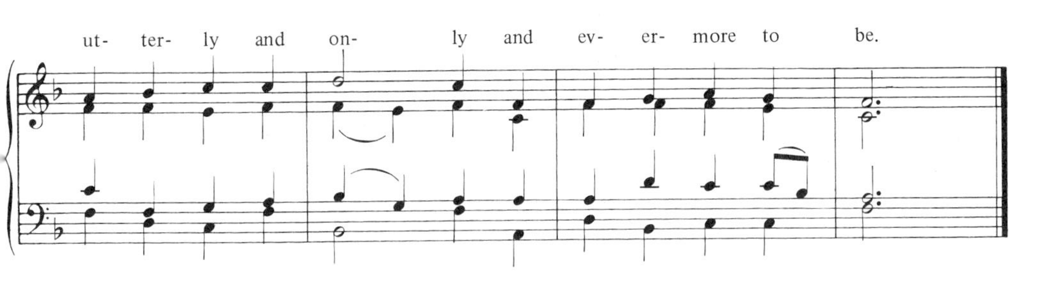

2. O Son of God, who lov'st me,
   I will be thine alone;
   and all I have and am, Lord,
   shall henceforth be thine own!

3. Reign over me, Lord Jesus;
   O make my heart thy throne;
   it shall be thine, dear Saviour,
   it shall be thine alone.

4. O come and reign, Lord Jesus;
   rule over everything!
   And keep me always loyal,
   and true to thee, my King.

Words: Frances Ridley Havergal (1836-79)
Music: Henry John Gauntlett (1805-76)

234

IN HEAVENLY LOVE ABIDING
('Penlan' 76.76.D.)

[HARMONY]

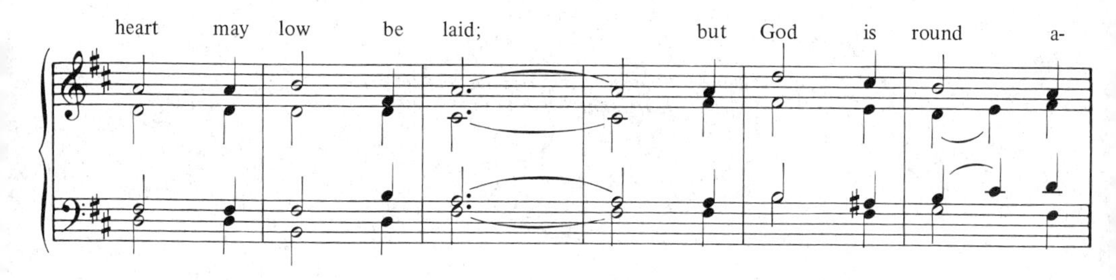

2. Wherever he may guide me,
 no want shall turn me back;
 my Shepherd is beside me,
 and nothing can I lack:
 his wisdom ever waketh,
 his sight is never dim;
 he knows the way he taketh,
 and I will walk with him.

3. Green pastures are before me,
 which yet I have not seen;
 bright skies will soon be o'er me,
 where the dark clouds have been:
 my hope I cannot measure,
 my path to life is free;
 my Saviour has my treasure,
 and he will walk with me.

Words, based on Psalm 23: Anna Laetitia Waring (1820-1910)
Music: D. Jenkins (1849-1915)

235 [HARMONY]

IN OUR DAY OF THANKSGIVING
('Was lebet' Irregular)

2. In the morning of life, and at noon, and at even,
he called them away from our worship below;
but not till his love, at the font and the altar,
had girt them with grace for the way they should go.

3. These stones that have echoed their praises are holy,
and dear is the ground where their feet have once trod;
yet here they confessed they were strangers and pilgrims,
and still they were seeking the city of God.

4. Sing praise, then, for all who here sought and here found him,
whose journey is ended, whose perils are past:
they believed in the light; and its glory is round them,
where the clouds of earth's sorrow are lifted at last.

Words: William Henry Draper (1855-1933)
Music: from Rheinhardt Ms (Üttingen, 1754)

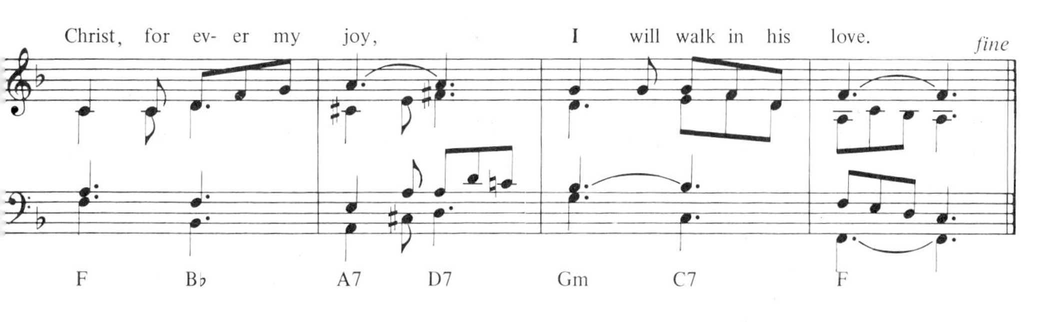

2. Christ on my right, my left, around.
Christ to the world with joy I must bring.

3. Christ is my way, my peace, my light,
Christ to the world with joy I must bring.

4. Christ is my rock, my shield, my strength,
Christ to the world with joy I must bring.

5. Christ is my Lord, my God, my all,
Christ to the world with joy I must bring.

Words and Music: Aniceto Nazareth

237 IN THE BLEAK MID-WINTE

('Cranham' Irregula

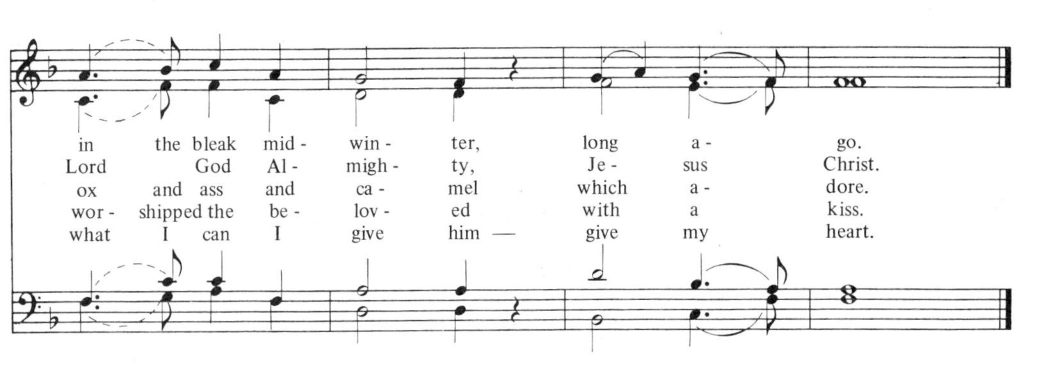

Words: Christina G. Rossetti (1830-94)
Music: Gustav Holst (1874-1934)

238

IN THE CROSS OF CHRIST I GLORY
('Wychbold' 87.87.)

[HARMONY]

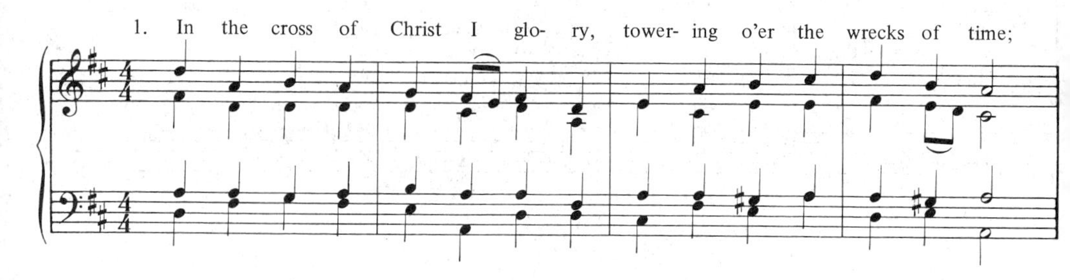

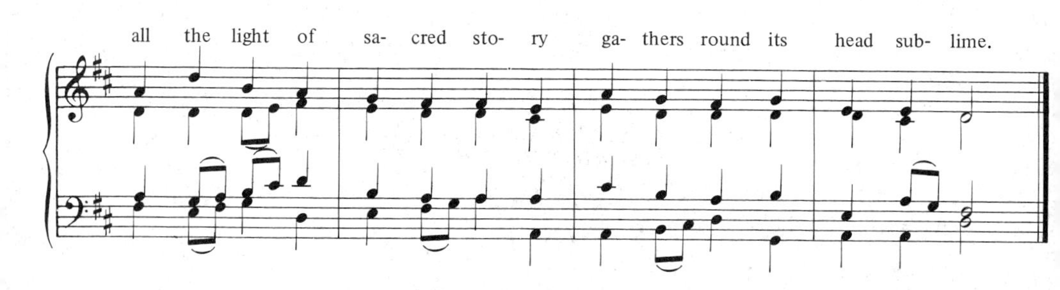

2. When the woes of life o'ertake me,
hopes deceive and fears annoy,
never shall the cross forsake me,
lo! it glows with peace and joy.

3. When the sun of bliss is beaming
light and love upon my way,
from the cross the radiance streaming,
adds more lustre to the day.

4. Bane and blessing, pain and pleasure,
by the cross are sanctified;
peace is there that knows no measure,
joys that through all time abide.

Words, based on Galatians 6: 14:
John Bowring (1792-1872)
Music: W.G. Whinfield (†1919)

IN TOKEN THAT THOU SHALT NOT FEAR
('St Stephen (Abridge)' C.M.)

[HARMONY]

2. In token that thou shalt not blush
to glory in his name,
we blazon here upon thy front
his glory and his shame.

3. In token that thou shalt not flinch
Christ's quarrel to maintain,
but 'neath his banner manfully
firm at thy post remain;

4. In token that thou too shalt tread
the path he travelled by,
endure the cross, despise the shame,
and sit thee down on high;

5. Thus outwardly and visibly
we seal thee for his own;
and may the brow that wears his cross
hereafter share his crown.

Words: Henry Alford (1810-71)
Music: William Jones (1726-1800)

Chorus
I re- joiced when I heard them say,
A
D
'Let us go to God's house to- day!' I re- joiced when I
E
A
Last time to Coda
heard them say, 'Let us go to God's house.'
D
E
A
Verse
1. And now our
2. Je- ru- sa- lem is
3. For the peace of Je-
4. For love of my
D
A

Words, based on Psalm 122, and Music: Betty Pulkingham

241

I SEE YOUR HANDS AND SIDE LORD
('True marks')

Fairly slowly and gently

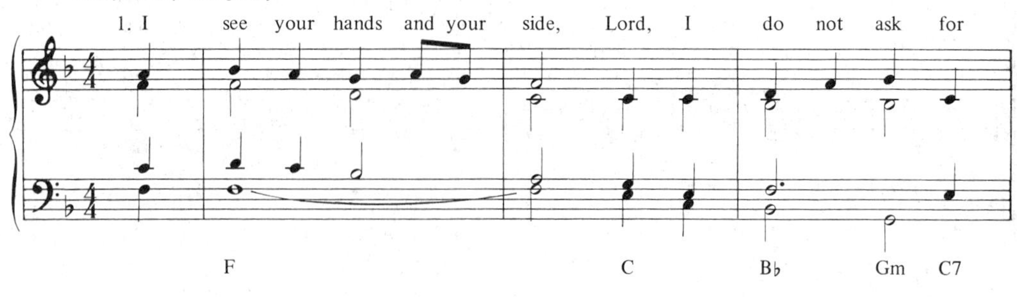

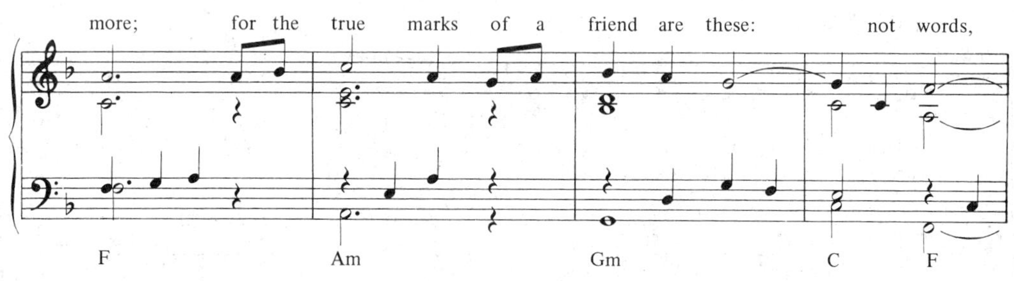

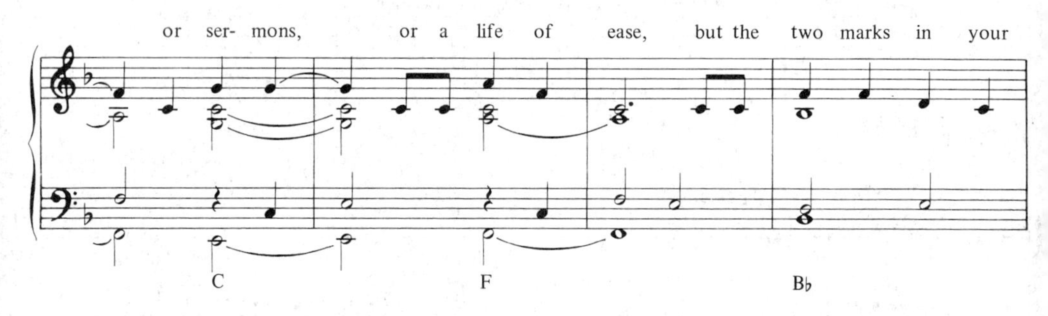

2. I see your hands and your side, Lord,
I do not ask for more;
for the true marks of your Church are these:
not words, or sermons, or a life of ease,
but the two marks in your hands, Lord,
and the sword-mark in your side.

3. I see your hands and your side, Lord,
I do not ask for more;
for the true marks of my life shall be
not words, or sermons, or a life of ease,
but the two marks in my hands, Lord,
and your sword-mark in my side.

Words: Graham Jeffery
Music: Kevin Mayhew

IT CAME UPON THE MIDNIGHT CLEAR

('Noel' D.C.M.)

2. Yet with the woes of sin and strife
the world has suffered long;
beneath the angel-strain have rolled
two thousand years of wrong;
and man, at war with man, hears not
the love-song which they bring:
O hush the noise, ye men of strife,
and hear the angels sing!

3. For lo, the days are hastening on,
by prophets seen of old,
when with the ever-circling years
shall come the time foretold,
when the new heaven and earth shall own
the Prince of Peace, their King,
and all the world send back the song
which now the angels sing.

Words: Edmund H. Sears (1810-76), altered
Music: Traditional English melody, arranged by Arthur Sullivan (1842-1900)

243

IT IS A THING MOST WONDERFUL
(First tune: 'Herongate' L.M.)

[HARMONY]

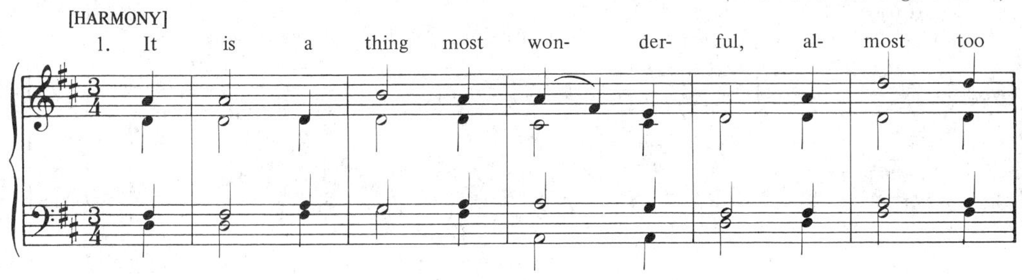

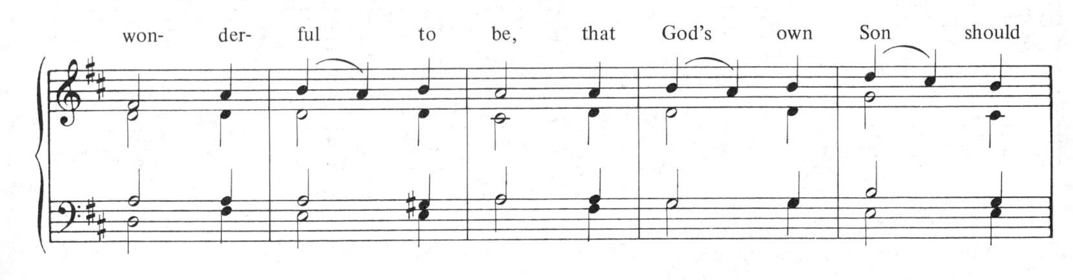

2. And yet I know that it is true:
he chose a poor and humble lot,
and wept and toiled and mourned and died
for love of those who loved him not.

3. I cannot tell how he could love
a child so weak and full of sin;
his love must be most wonderful,
if he could die my love to win.

4. I sometimes think about the cross,
and shut my eyes, and try to see
the cruel nails and crown of thorns,
and Jesus crucified for me.

5. But even could I see him die,
I could but see a little part
of that great love which, like a fire,
is always burning in his heart.

6. It is most wonderful to know
his love for me so free and sure;
but 'tis more wonderful to see
my love for him so faint and poor.

7. And yet I want to love thee, Lord;
O light the flame within my heart,
and I will love thee more and more,
until I see thee as thou art.

Words: William Walsham How (1823-97)
Music: First tune - English Traditional Melody

IT IS A THING MOST WONDERFUL

(Second tune: 'Brookfield' L.M.)

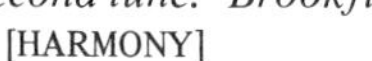

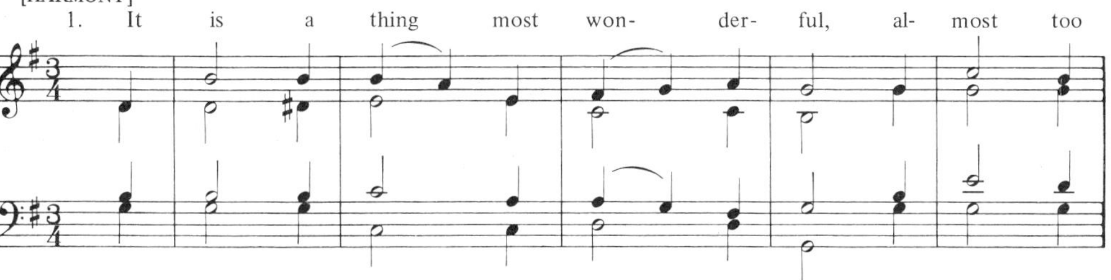

2. And yet I know that it is true,
   he chose a poor and humble lot,
   and wept and toiled and mourned and died
   for love of those who loved him not.

3. I cannot tell how he could love
   a child so weak and full of sin;
   his love must be most wonderful,
   if he could die, my love to win.

4. I sometimes think about the cross,
   and shut my eyes, and try to see
   the cruel nails and crown of thorns,
   and Jesus crucified for me.

5. But even could I see him die,
   I could but see a little part
   of that great love which, like a fire,
   is always burning in his heart.

6. It is most wonderful to know
   his love for me so free and sure;
   but 'tis more wonderful to see
   my love for him so faint and poor.

7. And yet I want to love thee, Lord,
   O light the flame within my heart,
   and I will love thee more and more,
   until I see thee as thou art.

Words: William Walsham How (1823-97)
Music: Second tune - T. B. Southgate (1814-68)

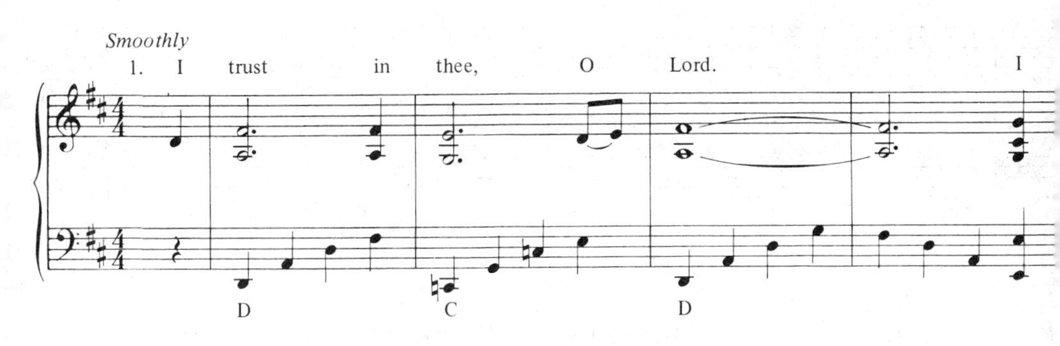
Smoothly
1. I trust in thee, O Lord. I
D
C
D

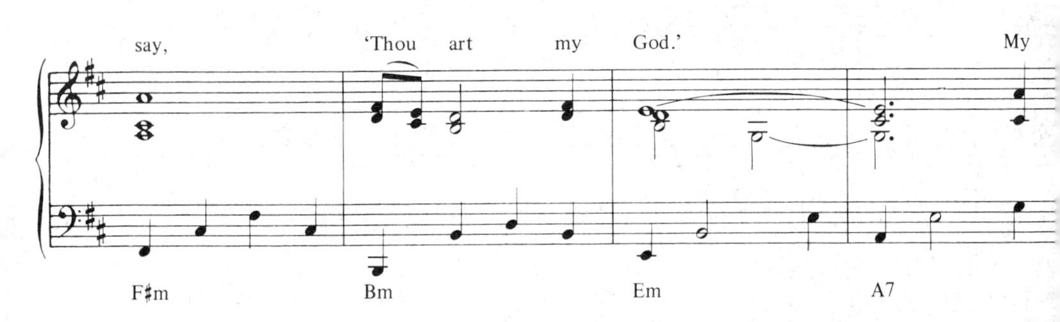
say, 'Thou art my God.' My
F♯m
Bm
Em
A7

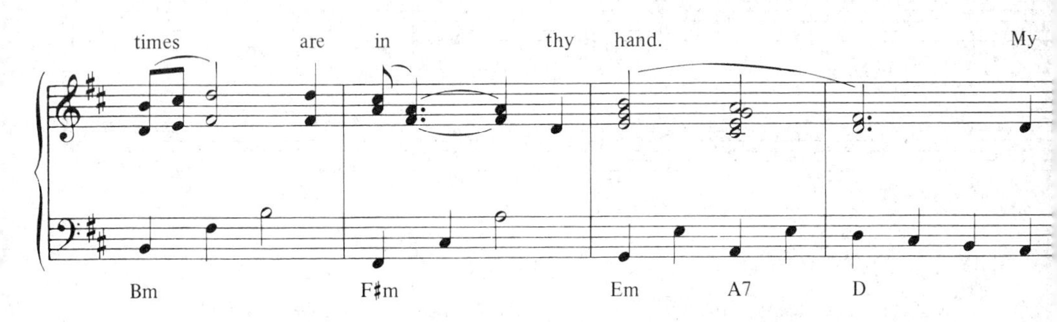
times are in thy hand. My
Bm
F♯m
Em
A7
D

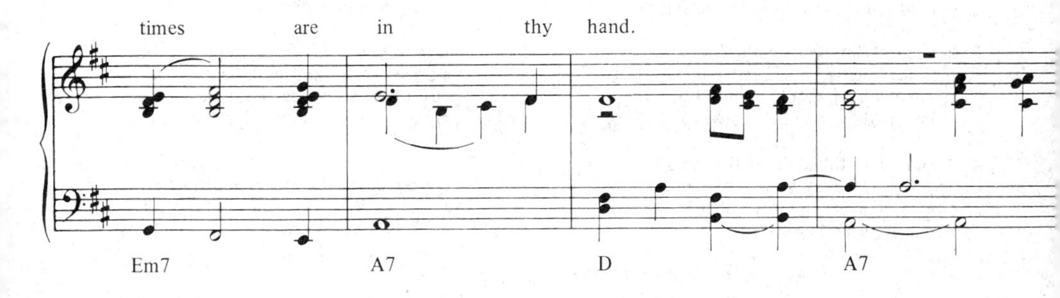
times are in thy hand.
Em7
A7
D
A7

Words, based on Psalm 31: Marion Warrington
Music: Marion Warrington, arranged by Jeanne Harper

Chorus
It's me, it's me, it's me, O Lord, stan- din' in the need of
G C D

pray'r. It's me, it's me, it's me, O Lord, stan- din' in the need of
G C D

Verse
pray'r. 1. Not my bro- ther or my sis- ter, but it's
fine
G

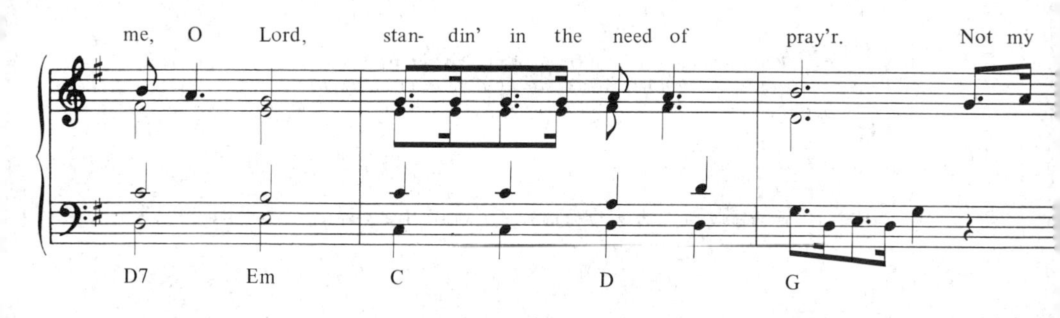
me, O Lord, stan- din' in the need of pray'r. Not my
D7 Em C D G

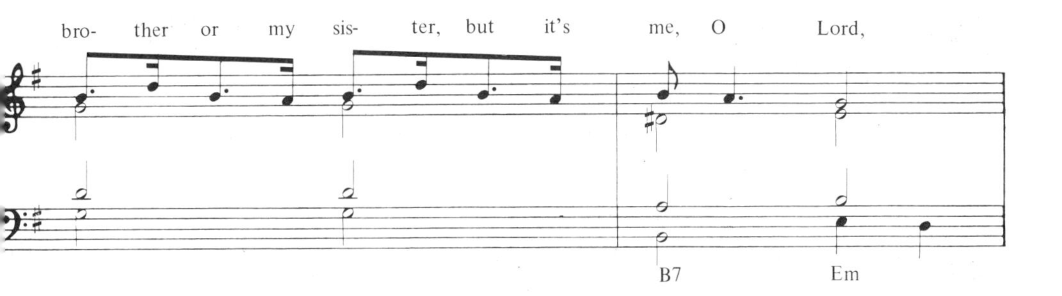

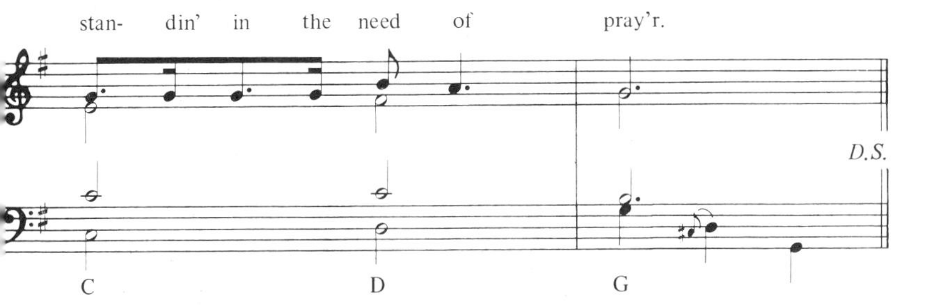

2. Not my mother or my father,
   but it's me, O Lord,
   standin' in the need of prayer.
   Not my mother or my father,
   but it's me, O Lord,
   standin' in the need of prayer.

3. Not the stranger or my neighbour,
   but it's me, O Lord,
   standin' in the need of prayer.
   Not the stranger or my neighbour,
   but it's me, O Lord,
   standin' in the need of prayer.

Words and Music: Traditional Spiritual,
arranged by John Rombaut

I VOW TO THEE, MY COUNTRY
('Thaxted' 13 13.13 13.13 13.

2. And there's another country, I've heard of long ago,
most dear to them that love her, most great to them that know;
we may not count her armies, we may not see her King;
her fortress is a faithful heart, her pride is suffering;
and soul by soul and silently her shining bounds increase,
and her ways are ways of gentleness and all her paths are peace.

Words: Cecil Spring Rice (1859-1918)
Music: Gustav Holst (1874-1934)

Chorus
I will be with you wher- ev- er you go.
Go now through- out the world!
I will be with you in all that you say.
Go now and spread my word!
Capo 5:
D
D(F♯ bass)
G
D(F♯ bass)
G
G6
A7
D
D9
D
D9
D
D(F♯ bass
G
D (F♯ bass)
G
G6
A7
D
D9
D4
D
fine

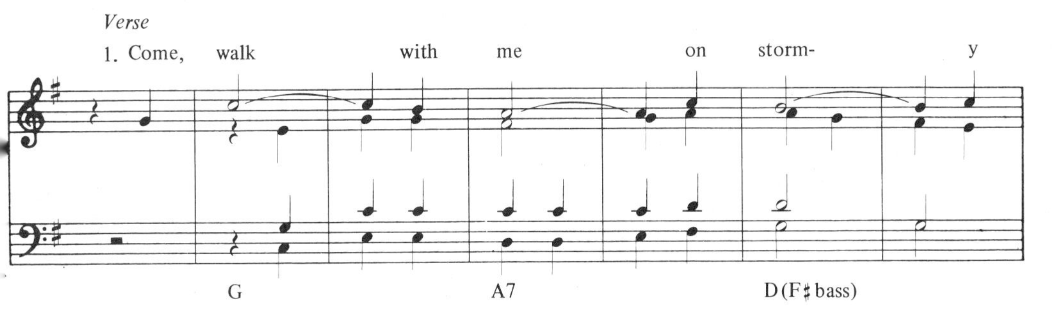

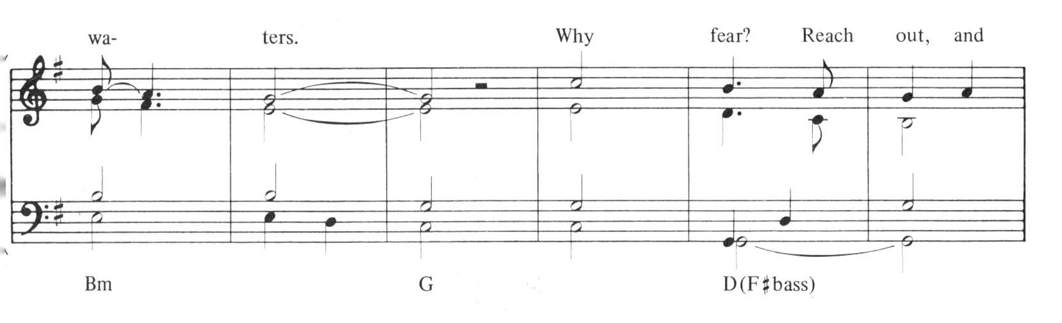

2. And you, my friend, will you now leave me,
   or do you know me as your Lord?

3. Your life will be transformed with power
   by living truly in my name.

4. And if you say: 'Yes, Lord, I love you!',
   then feed my lambs and feed my sheep.

Words, based on the Gospels, and Music: Gerard Markland

WILL ENTER HIS GATES

248

With pace and swing

Words, based on Scripture: Leona Vonbrethorst
Music: Unknown, arranged by Margaret Evans

This needs a good steady beat with the two main beats of the bars accented particularly in the verses. The chorus, which is meant to be a rousing one, has two parts, the second hopefully keeping the first one steady.

2. Yes, my soul rejoices in Yahweh;
   he's my help, my strength and shield.
   My hope in him has rested
   and I trust his holy name.

3. I will always pray to Yahweh,
   and he'll answer with great love.
   Yes, he'll come to my side and redeem me,
   and lift up my soul from death.

4. I'll proclaim the greatness of Yahweh;
   he gives all the things I need.
   My soul is full of his glory.
   Let everyone hear and rejoice!

Words and Music: Clare Lee

I WILL SING, I WILL SING

250

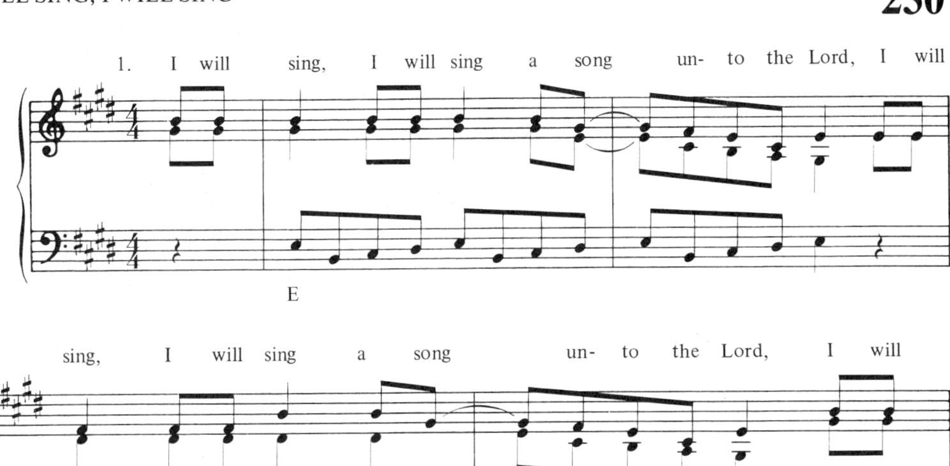

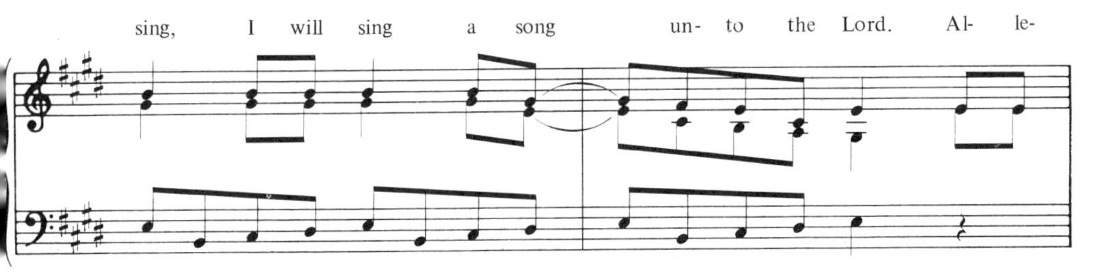

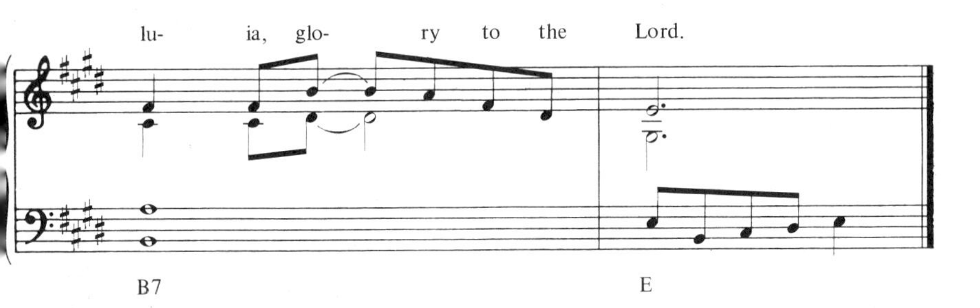

Chorus (to the same melody)
Allelu, alleluia, glory to the Lord. (3)
Alleluia, glory to the Lord.

2. We will come, we will come as one before the Lord. *(3)*
   Alleluia, glory to the Lord.

3. If the Son, if the Son shall make you free, *(3)*
   you shall be free indeed.

4. They that sow in tears shall reap in joy. *(3)*
   Alleluia, glory to the Lord.

5. Ev'ry knee shall bow and ev'ry tongue confess *(3)*
   that Jesus Christ is Lord.

6. In his name, in his name we have the victory. *(3)*
   Alleluia, glory to the Lord.

Words and Music: Max Dyer

This song is most effective when sung without accompaniment, but with light clapping.

I WILL SING THE WONDROUS STORY

('Hyfrydol' 87.87.D.)

[HARMONY]

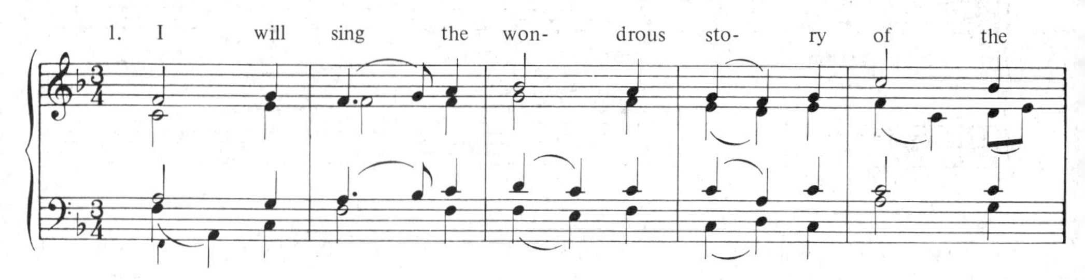

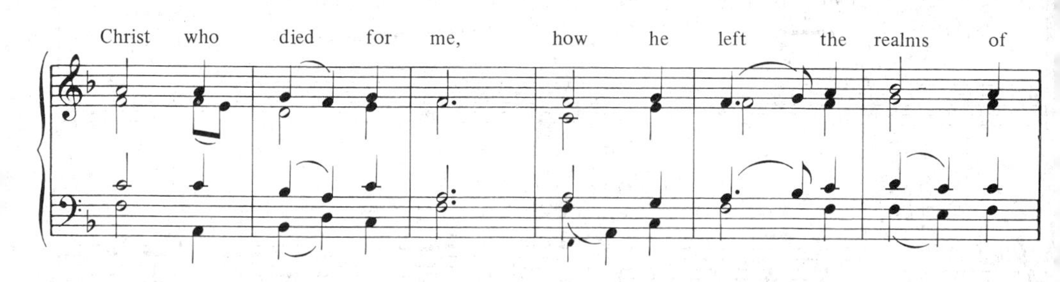

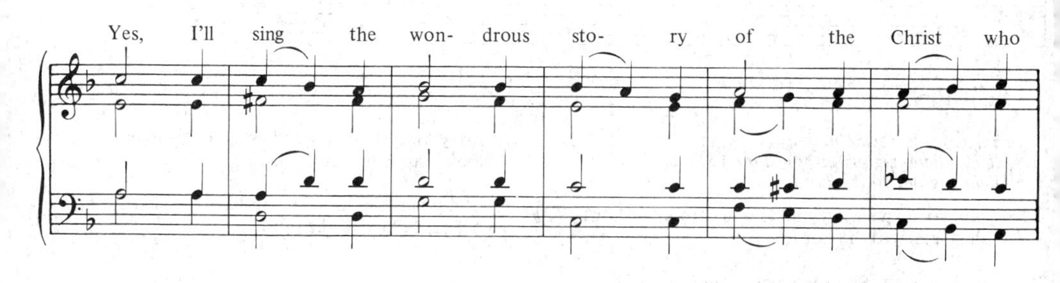

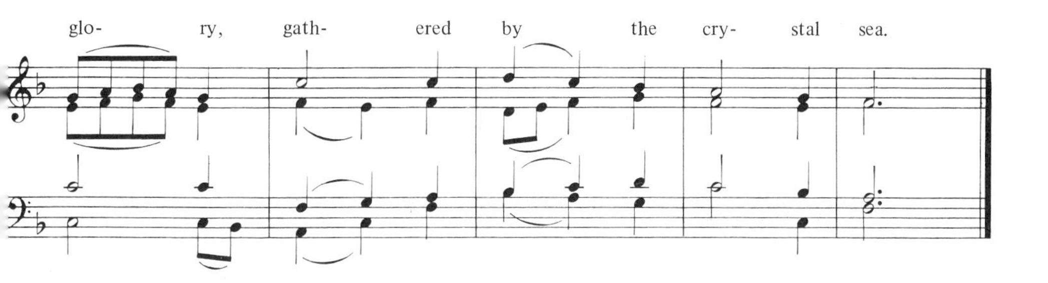

A different harmonisation of this tune may be found at Hymn 592

2. I was lost: but Jesus found me,
found the sheep that went astray,
raised me up and gently led me
back into the narrow way.
Days of darkness still may meet me,
sorrow's path I oft may tread;
but his presence still is with me,
by his guiding hand I'm led.

3. He will keep me till the river
rolls its waters at my feet:
then he'll bear me safely over,
made by grace for glory meet.
Yes, I'll sing the wondrous story
of the Christ who died for me, -
sing it with his saints in glory,
gathered by the crystal sea.

Words: F.H. Rawley (1854-1952)
Music: Melody by R.H. Prichard (1811-87)

252 I WILL SING UNTO THE LORD (The canticle of Moses)

Words: Exodus 15:1-2 *Music: Unknown, arranged by Frances M. Kelly*

I WONDER AS I WANDER

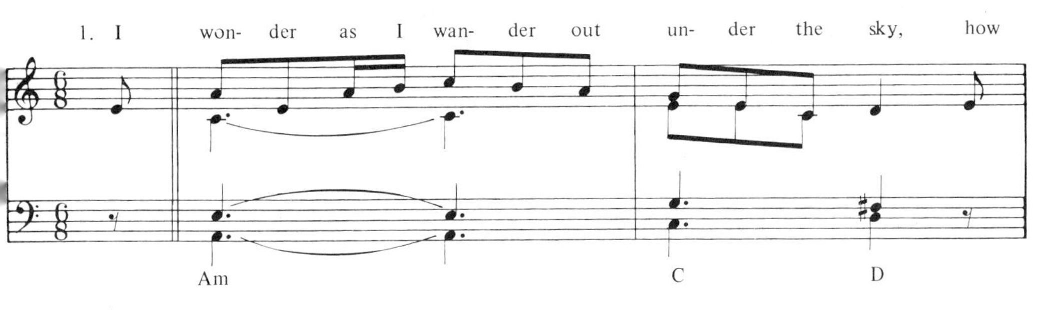

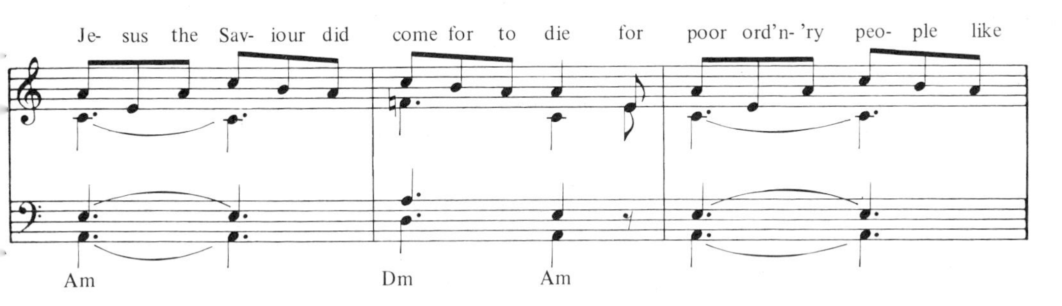

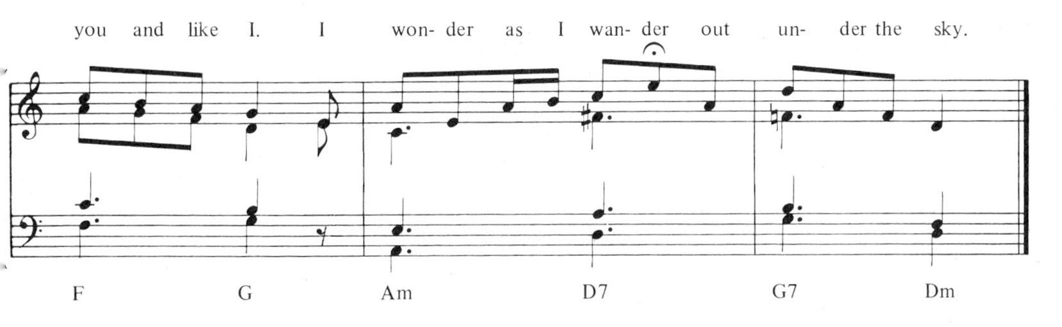

2. When Mary birthed Jesus, 'twas in a cow's stall
with wise men and farmers and shepherds and all.
But high from God's heaven a star's light did fall,
and the promise of ages it did then recall.

3. If Jesus had wanted for any wee thing,
a star in the sky, or a bird on the wing,
or all of God's angels in heav'n for to sing,
he surely could have it, 'cause he was the King.

Words and Music: Traditional North American

254

JERUSALEM THE GOLDEN
('Ewing' 76.76.D.)

2. They stand, those halls of Zion,
all jubilant with song,
and bright with many an angel,
and all the martyr throng;
the prince is ever in them,
the daylight is serene;
the pastures of the blessed
are decked in glorious sheen.

3. There is the throne of David;
and there, from care released,
the shout of them that triumph,
the song of them that feast;
and they, who with their leader
have conquered in the fight,
for ever and for ever
are clad in robes of white.

4. O sweet and blessed country,
the home of God's elect!
O sweet and blessed country,
that eager hearts expect!
Jesus, in mercy bring us
to that dear land of rest;
who art, with God the Father
and Spirit, ever blest.

Words: from 'De Contemptu Mundi' by St Bernard of Cluny (c. 1140),
translated by J. M. Neale (1818-66)
Music: Alexander Ewing (1830-95)

JESUS CALLS US O'ER THE TUMULT

(First tune: 'St Andrew' 87.87.)

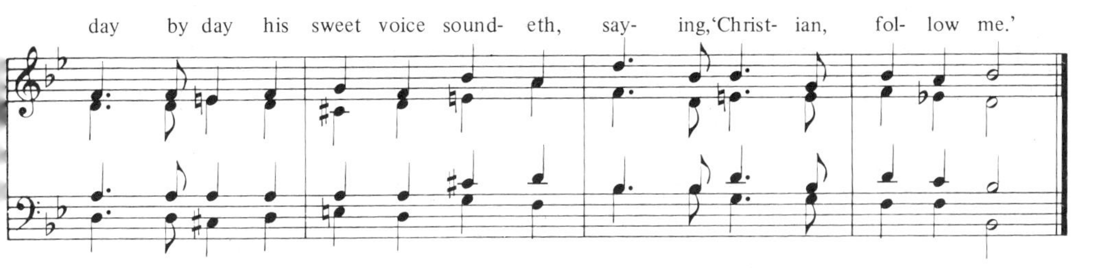

JESUS CALLS US O'ER THE TUMULT

(Second tune: 'Merton' 87.87.)

[HARMONY]

This tune may be found in a lower key at Hymn 182

2. As of old Saint Andrew heard it
   by the Galilean lake,
   turned from home and toil and kindred,
   leaving all for his dear sake.

3. Jesus calls us from the worship
   of the vain world's golden store,
   from each idol that would keep us,
   saying, 'Christian, love me more.'

4. In our joys and in our sorrows,
   days of toil and hours of ease,
   still he calls, in cares and pleasures,
   that we love him more than these.

5. Jesus calls us: by thy mercies,
   Saviour, make us hear thy call,
   give our hearts to thine obedience,
   serve and love thee best of all.

Words: Cecil Frances Alexander (1818-95)
Music: First tune - Edward H. Thorne (1834-1916)
Second tune - William H. Monk (1823-89)

JESUS CHRIST IS RISEN TODAY
('Easter Hymn' 77. 77. & Alleluias)

[HARMONY]

2. Hymns of praise then let us sing,
unto Christ, our heavenly King,
who endured the cross and grave,
sinners to redeem and save.

3. But the pains that he endured,
our salvation have procured;
now above the sky he's King,
where the angels ever sing.

Words: from 'Lyra Davidica' (1708) and the Supplement (1816)
Music: from 'Lyra Davidica' (1708)

JESU, GENTLEST SAVIOUR

(First tune: 'Eudoxia' 65.65.)

[HARMONY]

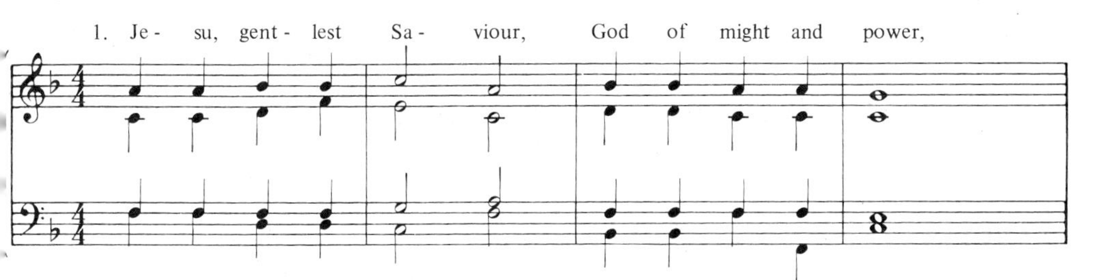

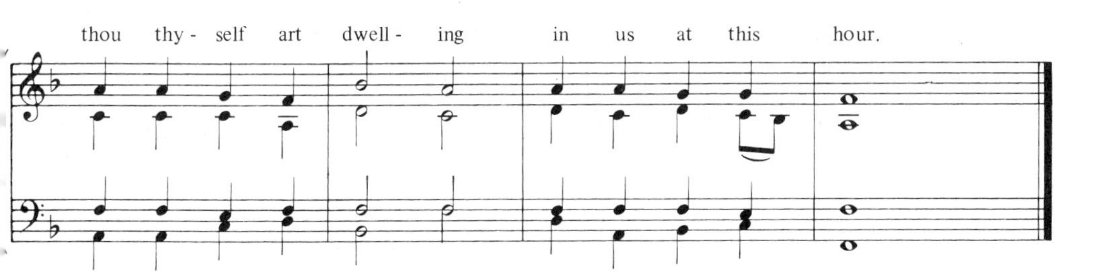

2. Nature cannot hold thee
heaven is all too strait
for thine endless glory
and thy royal state.

3. Out beyond the shining
of the furthest star
thou art ever stretching
infinitely far.

4. Yet the hearts of children
hold what words cannot,
and the God of wonders
loves the lowly spot.

5. Jesu, gentlest Saviour,
thou art in us now;
fill us full of goodness
till our hearts o'erflow.

6. Multiply our graces,
chiefly love and fear,
and, dear Lord, the chiefest,
grace to persevere.

Words: Frederick William Faber (1814-63)
Music: Sabine Baring-Gould (1834-1924)

Second tune overleaf

[HARMONY]

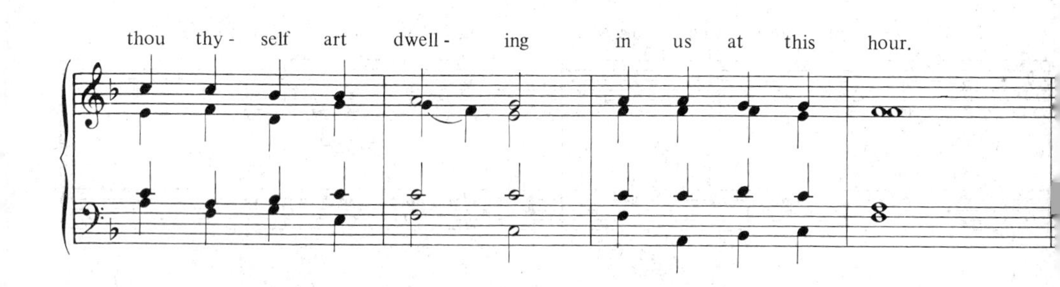

2. Nature cannot hold thee,
heaven is all too strait
for thine endless glory
and thy royal state.

3. Out beyond the shining
of the furthest star
thou art ever stretching
infinitely far.

4. Yet the hearts of children
hold what words cannot,
and the God of wonders
loves the lowly spot.

5. Jesu, gentlest Saviour,
thou art in us now;
fill us full of goodness
till our hearts o'erflow.

6. Multiply our graces,
chiefly love and fear,
and, dear Lord, the chiefest,
grace to persevere.

Words: Frederick William Faber (1814-63)
Music: F. Filitz (1804-76)

First tune overleaf

JESUS GOOD ABOVE ALL OTHER
('Quem pastores laudavere' 88.87.)

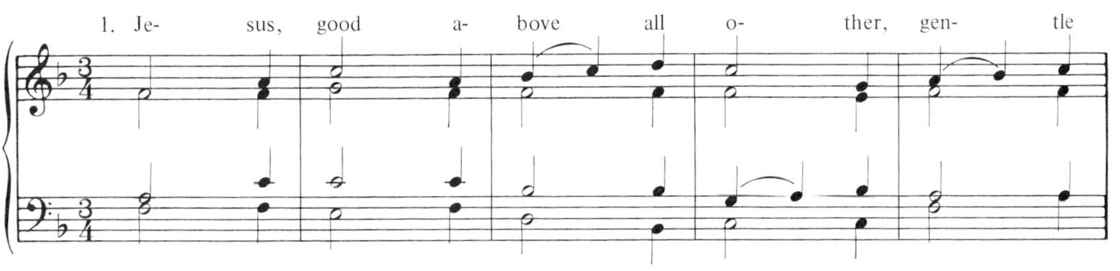

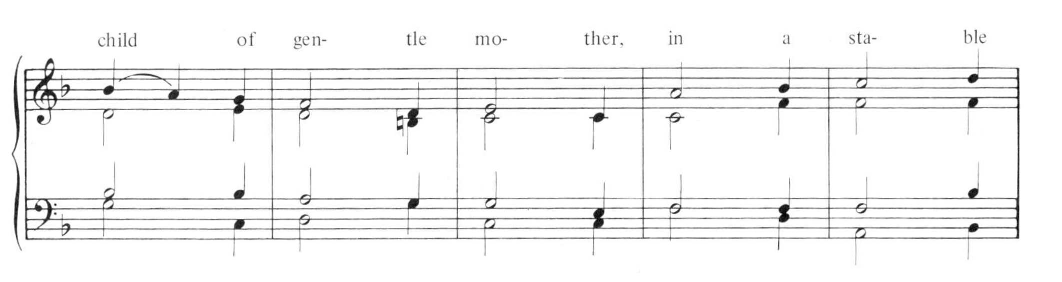

2. Jesus, cradled in a manger,
for us facing every danger,
living as a homeless stranger,
make we thee our King most dear.

3. Jesus, for thy people dying,
risen Master, death defying,
Lord in heaven, thy grace supplying,
keep us to thy presence near.

4. Jesus, who our sorrows bearest,
all our thoughts and hopes thou sharest,
thou to man the truth declarest;
help us all thy truth to hear.

5. Lord, in all our doings guide us;
pride and hate shall ne'er divide us;
we'll go on with thee beside us,
and with joy we'll persevere.

*Words: Percy Dearmer (1867-1936),
after John M. Neale (1818-66)
Music: German Carol Melody (14th century),
harmonised by Ralph Vaughan Williams (1872-1958)*

JESUS HUMBLE WAS YOUR BIRTH

(First tune: 'Buckland' 77.77.)

[HARMONY]

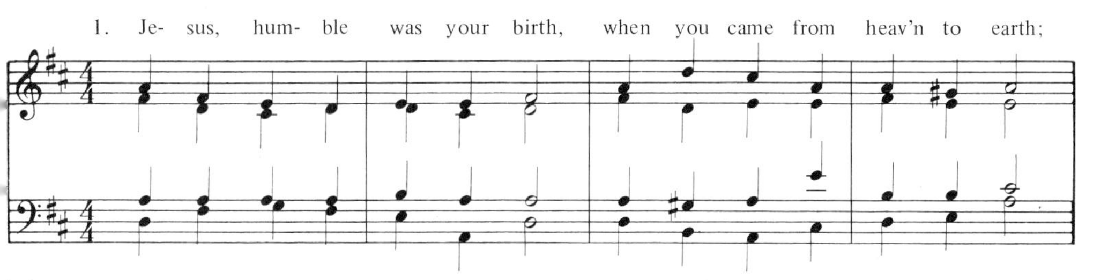

2. Jesus, strong to help and heal,
showing that your love is real;
every day in all we do,
make us strong and kind like you.

3. Jesus, when you were betrayed,
still you trusted God and prayed;
every day in all we do,
help us trust and pray like you.

4. Jesus, risen from the dead,
with us always, as you said;
every day in all we do,
help us live and love like you.

Words: Patrick Appleford
Music: First tune - Leighton George Hayne (1836-83)

Second tune overleaf

JESUS HUMBLE WAS YOUR BIRTH
(Second tune: 'Catherine' 77.77.)

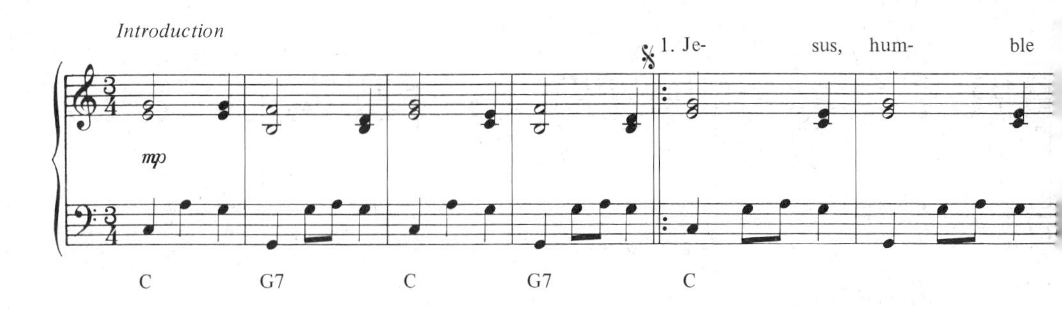

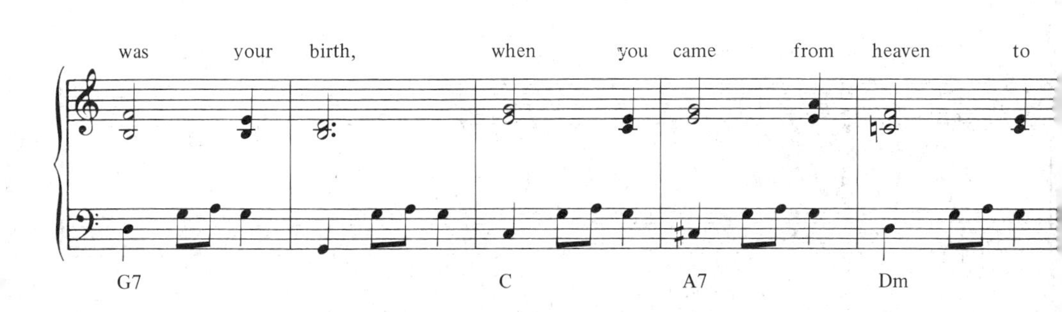

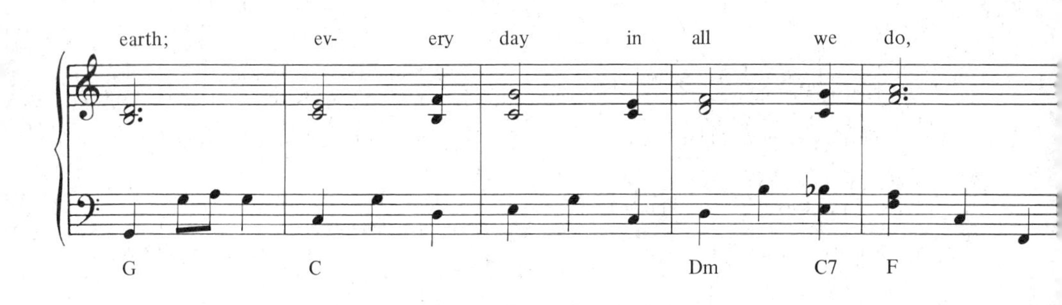

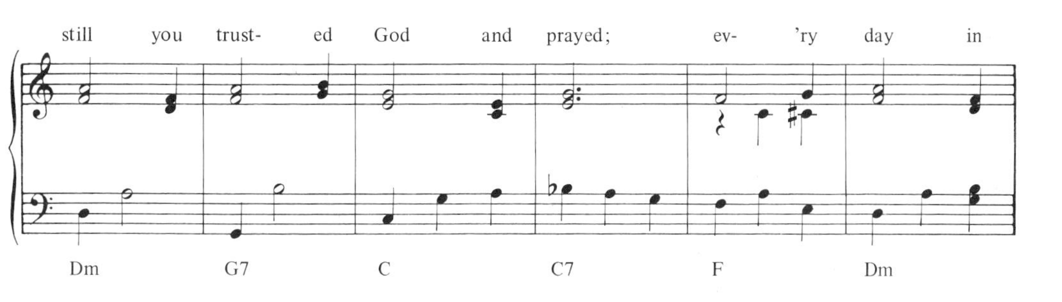

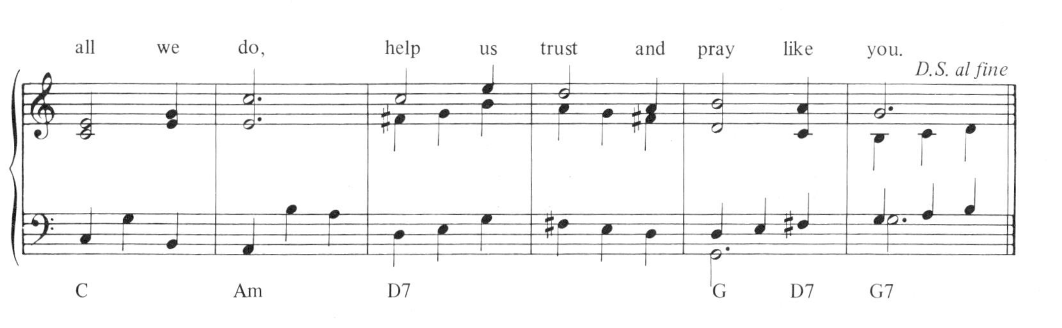

2. Jesus, strong to help and heal,
showing that your love is real;
every day in all we do,
make us strong and kind like you.

4. Jesus, risen from the dead,
with us always, as you said;
every day in all we do,
help us live and love like you.

Words: Patrick Appleford
Music: Second tune - Geoffrey Beaumont
First tune overleaf

JESUS IS LORD!

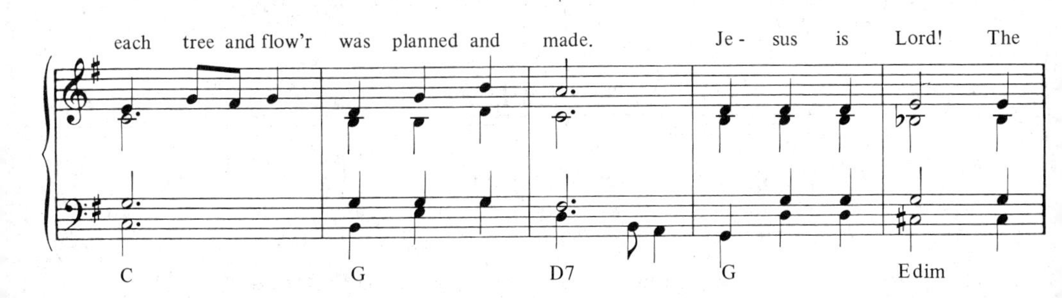

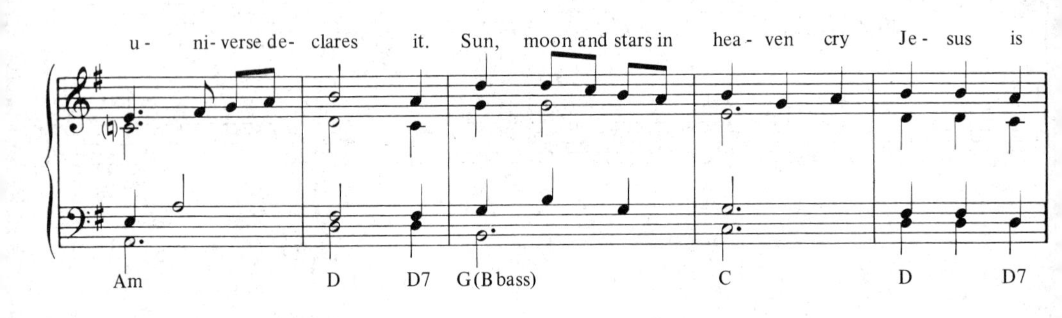

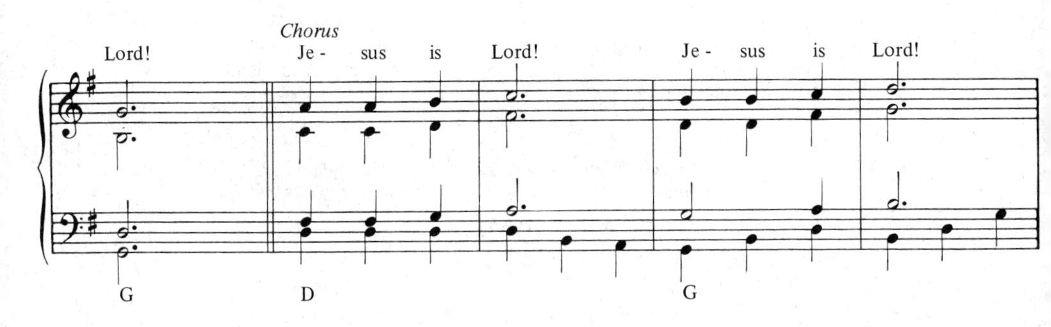

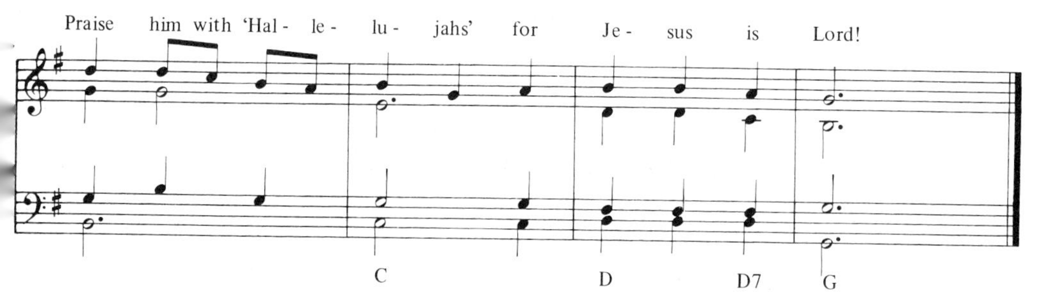

2. Jesus is Lord! Yet from his throne eternal
   in flesh he came to die in pain on Calv'ry's tree.
   Jesus is Lord! From him all life proceeding,
   yet gave his life a ransom thus setting us free.

3. Jesus is Lord! O'er sin the mighty conqu'ror,
   from death he rose and all his foes shall own his name.
   Jesus is Lord! God sends his Holy Spirit
   to show by works of power that Jesus is Lord.

Words and Music: David J. Mansell

261 JESUS, JESUS, JESUS, NEVER HAVE I HEARD

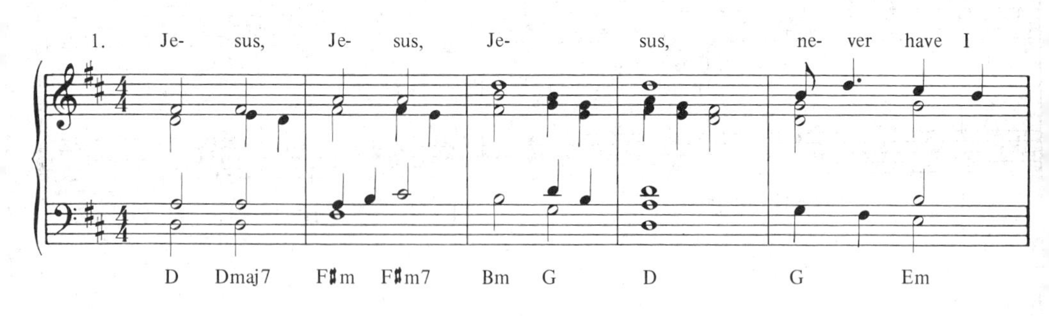

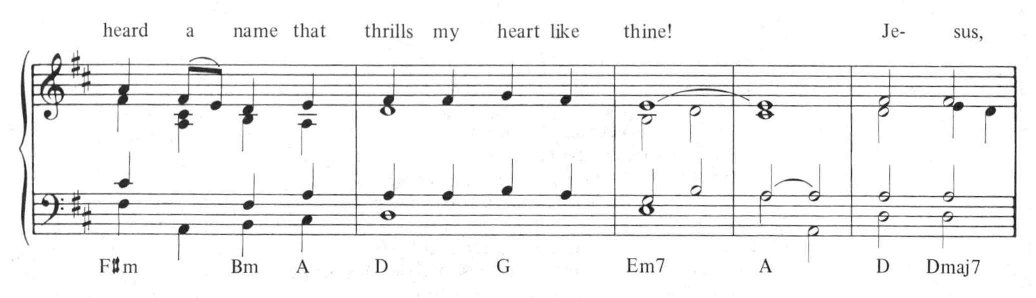

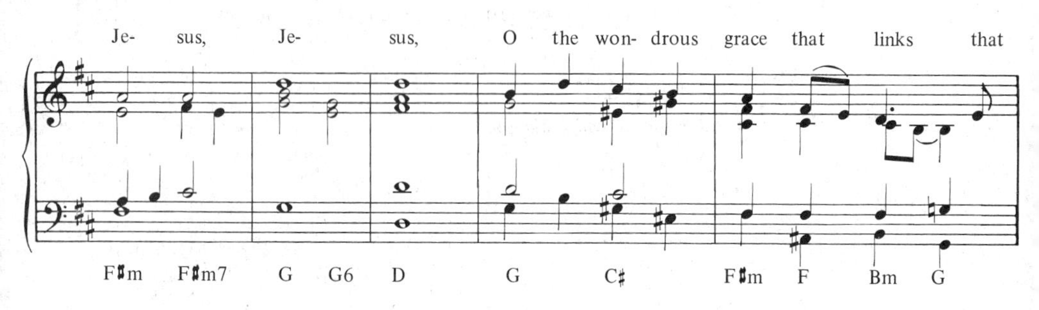

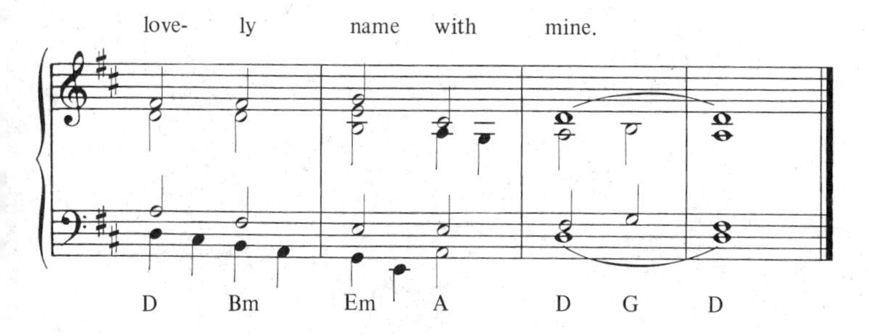

2. Father, Father, Father,
never have I known a love
that fills my life like thine!
Father, Father, Father,
O the wondrous grace that links
thy holy life with mine!

3. Spirit, Spirit, Spirit,
never have I known a pow'r
that fills my life like thine!
Spirit, Spirit, Spirit,
O the wondrous grace that fills
my life with pow'r divine.

Words: Verse 1 – Traditional,
Verses 2 & 3 – Robert B. Kelly
Music: Unknown, arranged by Frances M. Kelly

JESUS LIVES! THY TERRORS NOW

('St Albinus & Alleluia' 78.78.4.)

[HARMONY]

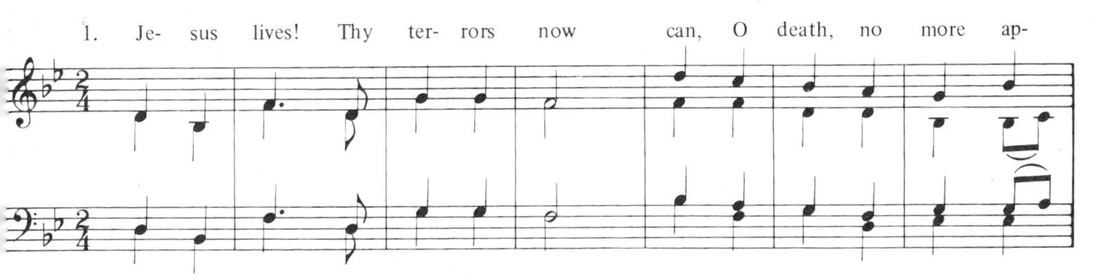

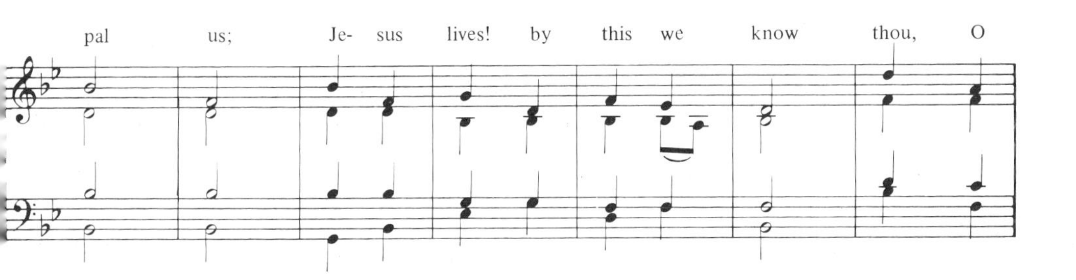

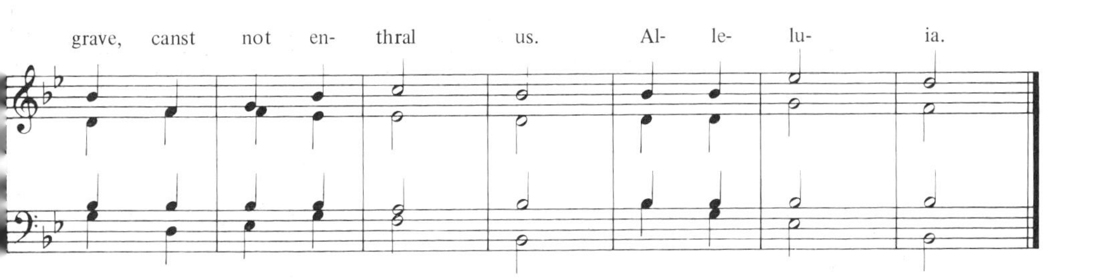

2. Jesus lives! henceforth is death
but the gate of life immortal:
this shall calm our trembling breath,
when we pass its gloomy portal.
Alleluia.

3. Jesus lives! for us he died;
then, alone to Jesus living,
pure in heart may we abide,
glory to our Saviour giving.
Alleluia.

4. Jesus lives! our hearts know well
nought from us his love shall sever;
life, nor death, nor powers of hell
tear us from his keeping ever.
Alleluia.

5. Jesus lives! to him the throne
over all the world is given:
may we go where he is gone,
rest and reign with him in heaven.
Alleluia.

Words: Christian F. Gellert (1715-69),
tr. Frances E. Cox
Music: Henry J. Gauntlett (1805-76)

263

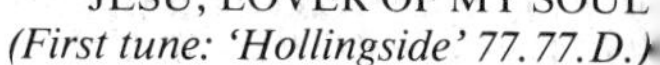

JESU, LOVER OF MY SOUL
(First tune: 'Hollingside' 77.77.D.)

[HARMONY]

2. Other refuge have I none;
hangs my helpless soul on thee;
leave, ah! leave me not alone,
still support and comfort me.
All my trust on thee is stayed,
all my help from thee I bring;
cover my defenceless head
with the shadow of thy wing.

3. Thou, O Christ, art all I want;
more than all in thee I find:
raise the fallen, cheer the faint,
heal the sick, and lead the blind.
Just and holy is thy name;
I am all unrighteousness;
false and full of sin I am,
thou art full of truth and grace.

4. Plenteous grace with thee is found,
grace to cover all my sin;
let the healing streams abound;
make and keep me pure within.
Thou of life the fountain art;
freely let me take of thee;
spring thou up within my heart,
rise to all eternity.

Words: Charles Wesley (1707-88)
Music: First tune John B. Dykes (1823-76)

JESU, LOVER OF MY SOUL

(Second tune: 'Aberystwyth' 77.77.D.)

2. Other refuge have I none;
hangs my helpless soul on thee;
leave, ah! leave me not alone,
still support and comfort me.
All my trust on thee is stayed,
all my help from thee I bring;
cover my defenceless head
with the shadow of thy wing.

3. Thou, O Christ, art all I want;
more than all in thee I find:
raise the fallen, cheer the faint,
heal the sick, and lead the blind.
Just and holy is thy name;
I am all unrighteousness;
false and full of sin I am,
thou art full of truth and grace.

4. Plenteous grace with thee is found,
grace to cover all my sin;
let the healing streams abound;
make and keep me pure within.
Thou of life the fountain art;
freely let me take of thee;
spring thou up within my heart,
rise to all eternity.

Words: Charles Wesley (1707-88)
Music: Second tune – Joseph Parry (1841-1903)

264 JESU, MY LORD, MY GOD, MY ALL

[HARMONY]

('St Chrysostom' 88.88.88.)

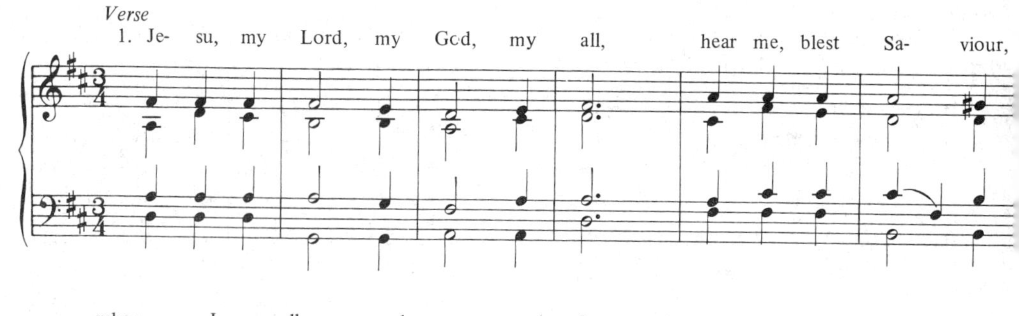

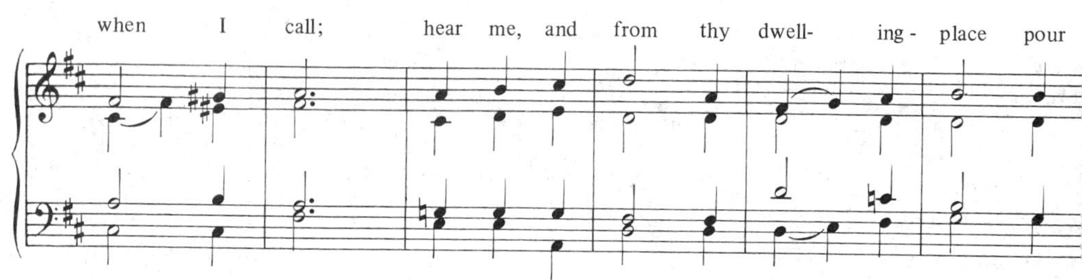

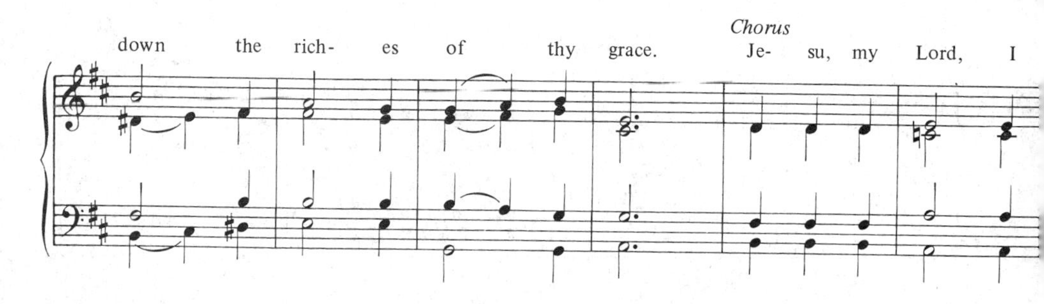

2. Jesu, too late I thee have sought,
how can I love thee as I ought?
And how extol thy matchless fame,
the glorious beauty of thy name?

3. Jesu, what didst thou find in me,
that thou hast dealt so lovingly?
How great the joy that thou hast brought,
so far exceeding hope or thought!

4. Jesu, of thee shall be my song,
to thee my heart and soul belong;
all that I have or am is thine,
and thou, sweet Saviour, thou art mine.

Words: H. Collins (1827-1919)
Music: J. Barnby (1833-96)

Words: N. Hearn
Music: N. Hearn, arranged by Roland Fudge

JESUS SHALL REIGN WHERE'ER THE SUN

('Truro' L.M.)

266

[HARMONY]

2. People and realms of every tongue
   dwell on his love with sweetest song,
   and infant voices shall proclaim
   their early blessings on his name.

3. Blessings abound where'er he reigns:
   the prisoner leaps to lose his chains;
   the weary find eternal rest,
   and all the sons of want are blest.

4. Let every creature rise and bring
   peculiar honours to our King;
   angels descend with songs again,
   and earth repeat the loud Amen.

Words: Isaac Watts (1674-1748)
Music: from 'Psalmodia Evangelica' (1789)

JESUS, STAND AMONG US AT THE MEETING OF OUR LIVE

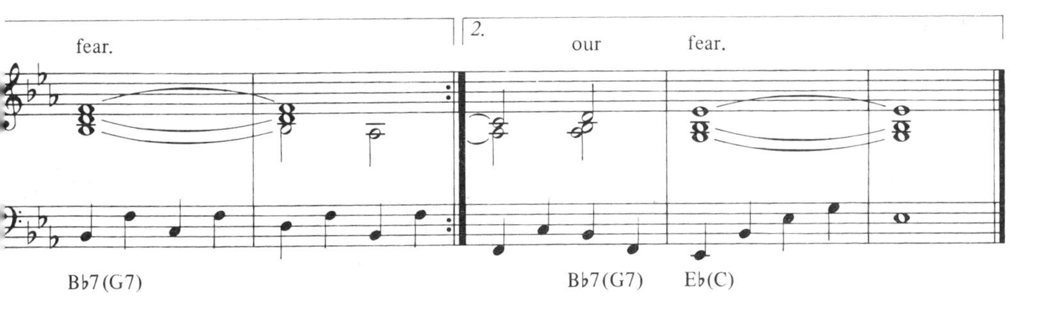

2. So to you we're gathering out of each and every land,
Christ the love between us at the joining of our hands;
O Jesus, we love you, so we gather here,
join our hearts in unity and take away our fear.

Words and Music: Graham Kendrick

268

JESUS, STAND AMONG US IN THY RISEN POWER
('Caswall' 65.65.)

[HARMONY]

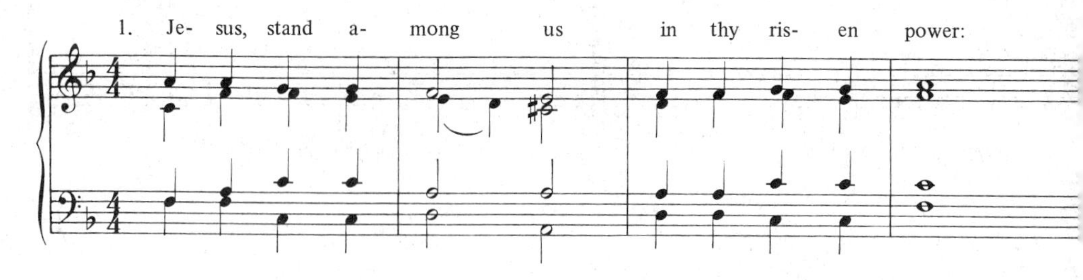

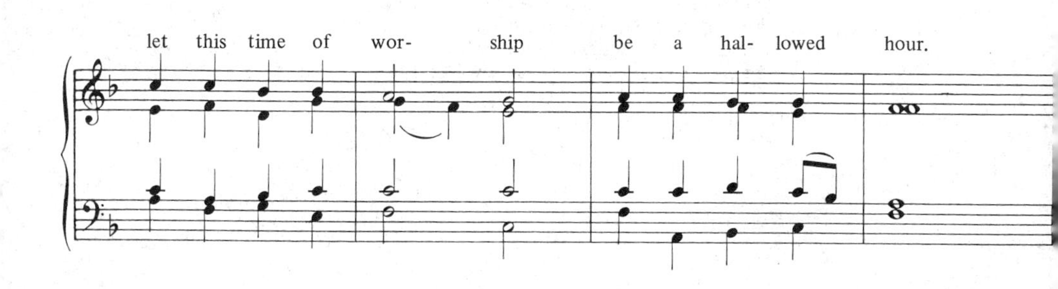

2. Breathe the Holy Spirit
   into every heart:
   bid the fears and sorrows
   from each soul depart.

3. Thus with quickened footsteps
   we'll pursue our way,
   watching for the dawning
   of eternal day.

Words: William Pennefather (1816-73)
Music: F. Filitz (1804-76)

JESUS, THE JOY OF LOVING HEARTS

('Maryton' L.M.)

[HARMONY]

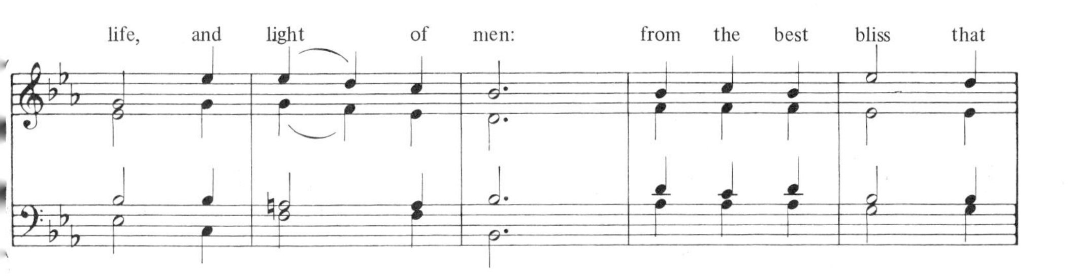

2. Your truth unchanged has ever stood,
you rescue those who on you call;
to those yet seeking, you are good –
to those who find you, all-in-all.

3. We taste of you, the living bread,
and long to feast upon you still;
we drink from you, the fountain-head,
our thirsty souls from you we fill.

4. Our restless spirits long for you,
whichever way our lot is cast,
glad when your gracious smile we view,
blessed when our faith can hold you fast.

5. Jesus, for ever with us stay,
make all our moments calm and bright;
chase the dark night of sin away,
spread through the world your holy light.

Words: from the Latin (12th century),
tr. R. Palmer
Music: H.P. Smith (1825-98)

JESUS, THESE EYES HAVE NEVER SEEN

('Nun danket all' (Grafenberg) C.M.)

[HARMONY]

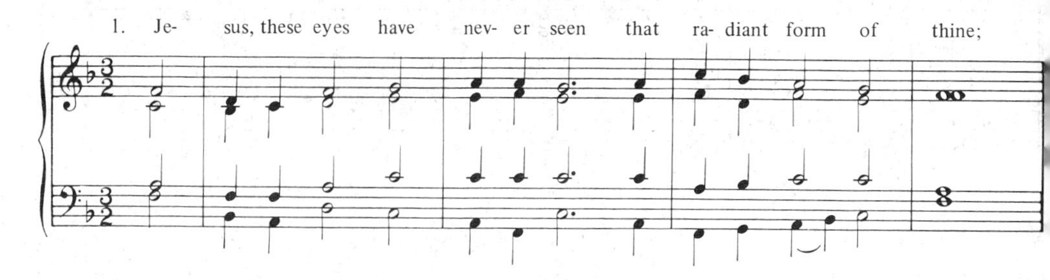

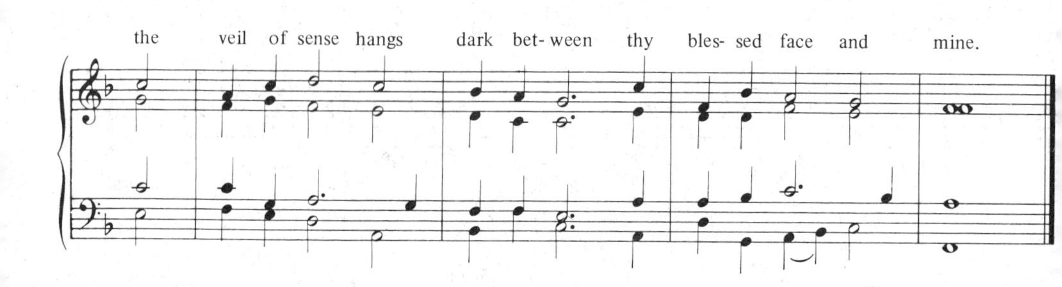

2. I see thee not, I hear thee not,
   yet art thou oft with me;
   and earth has ne'er so dear a spot
   as where I meet with thee.

3. Yet, though I have not seen, and still
   must rest in faith alone,
   I love thee, dearest Lord, and will,
   unseen, but not unknown.

4. When death these mortal eyes shall seal,
   and still this throbbing heart,
   the rending veil shall thee reveal
   all glorious as thou art.

Words: Ray Palmer (1808-87)
Music: from 'Praxis Pietatis' (1647)

JESU, THE VERY THOUGHT OF THEE
('St Botolph' C.M.)

[HARMONY]

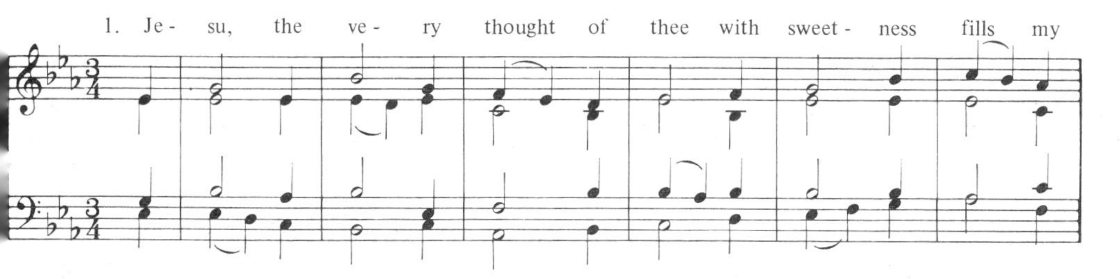

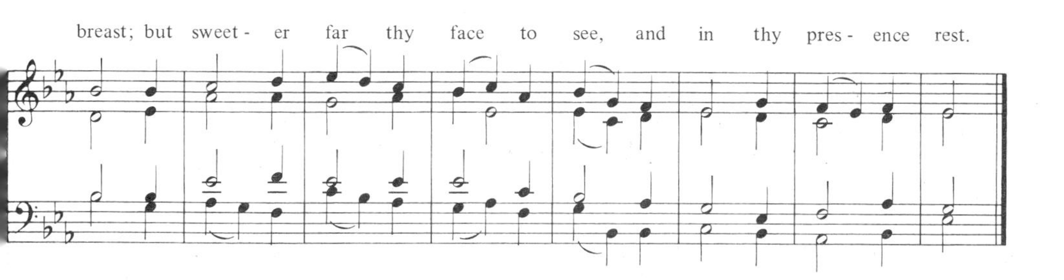

2. Nor voice can sing, nor heart can frame
nor can the memory find
a sweeter sound than thy blest name,
O Saviour of mankind.

3. O hope of every contrite heart,
O joy of all the meek;
to those who fall, how kind thou art,
how good to those who seek!

4. But what to those who find? Ah, this
nor tongue nor pen can show;
the love of Jesus, what it is
none but his lovers know.

5. Jesus, our only joy be thou,
as thou our prize wilt be;
Jesu, be thou our glory now,
and through eternity.

Words: attributed to St Bernard of Clairvaux (1091-1153),
tr. Edward Caswall
Music: Gordon Slater

JESUS, WHERE'ER THY PEOPLE MEET

('St Sepulchre' L.M.)

[HARMONY]

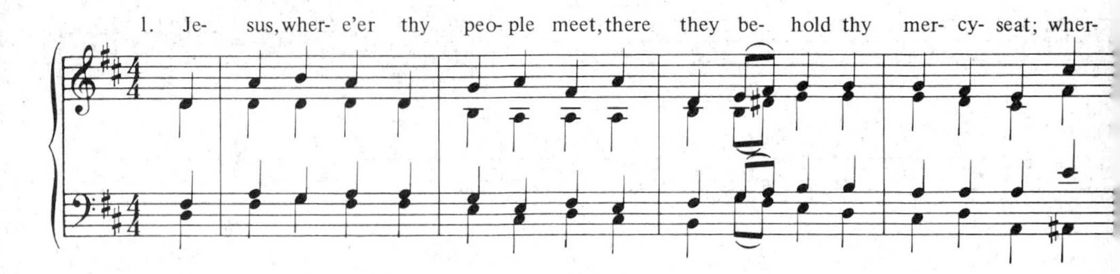

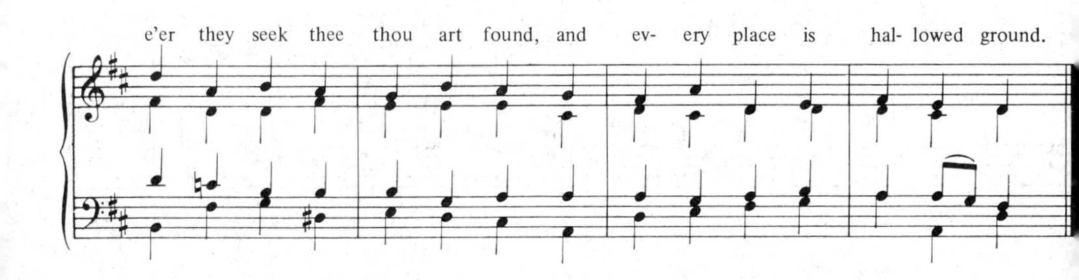

2. For thou, within no walls confined,
   inhabitest the humble mind;
   such ever bring thee when they come,
   and, going, take thee to their home.

3. Dear Shepherd of thy chosen few,
   thy former mercies here renew;
   here to our waiting hearts proclaim
   the sweetness of thy saving name.

4. Here may we prove the power of prayer
   to strengthen faith and sweeten care,
   to teach our faint desires to rise,
   and bring all heaven before our eyes.

5. Lord, we are few, but thou art near;
   nor short thine arm, nor deaf thine ear:
   O rend the heavens, come quickly down,
   and make a thousand hearts thine own!

Words: William Cowper (1731-1800)
Music: G. Cooper (1820-76)

JOY TO THE WORLD

('Antioch' C.M.)

2. Joy to the earth! the Saviour reigns:
let men their songs employ;
while fields and floods, rocks hills and plains
repeat the sounding joy,
repeat the sounding joy,
repeat, repeat the sounding joy.

3. No more let sins and sorrows grow,
nor thorns infest the ground;
he comes to make his blessings flow
far as the curse is found,
far as the curse is found,
far as, far as the curse is found.

4. He rules the world with truth and grace,
and makes the nations prove
the glories of his righteousness,
and wonders of his love,
and wonders of his love,
and wonders, and wonders of his love.

Words: Isaac Watts (1674-1748)
Music: George F. Handel (1695-1759)

JUBILATE, EV'RYBODY (Jubilate Deo)

Words and Music: F. Dunn

JUDGE ETERNAL, THRONED IN SPLENDOUR

('Rhuddlan' 87.87.87.)

[HARMONY]

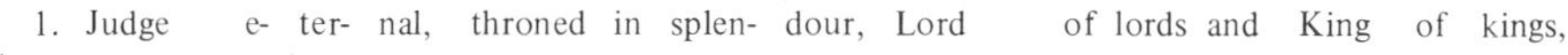

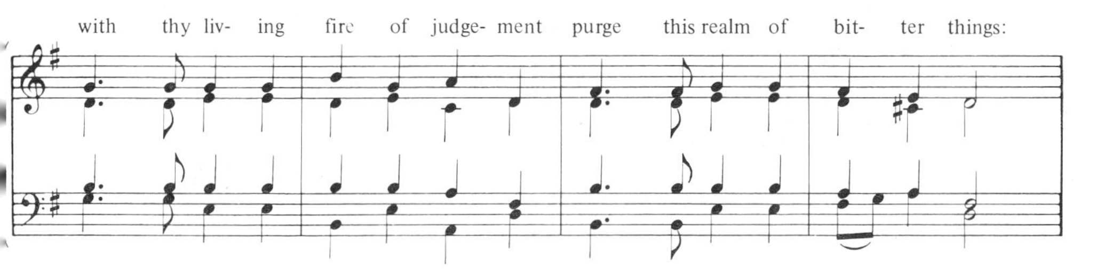

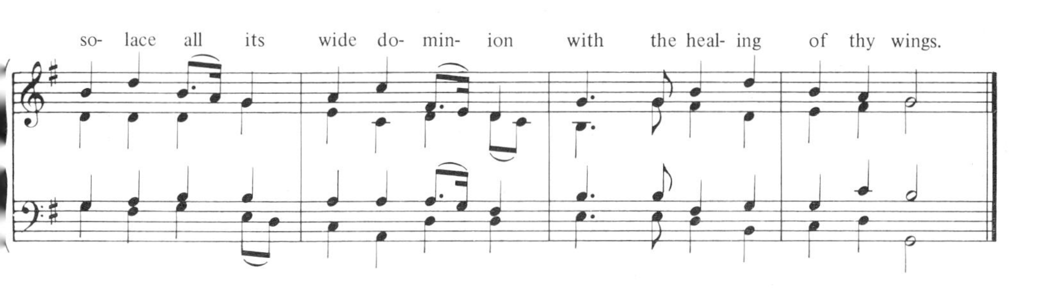

2. Still the weary folk are pining
for the hour that brings release:
and the city's crowded clangour
cries aloud for sin to cease;
and the homesteads and the woodlands
plead in silence for their peace.

3. Crown, O God, thine own endeavour:
cleave our darkness with thy sword:
feed the faint and hungry heathen
with the richness of thy Word:
cleanse the body of this empire
through the glory of the Lord.

Words: Henry Scott Holland (1847-1918)
Music: Welsh traditional melody from 'Musical Relicks of the Welsh Bards' (1800)

JUST A CLOSER WALK WITH THEE

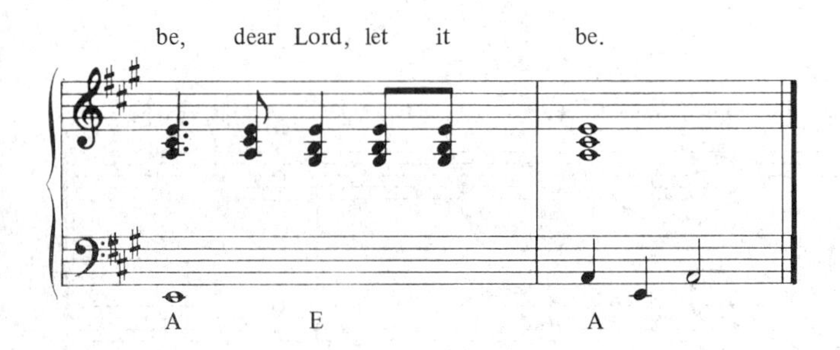

2. Through the day of toil that's near,
if I fall, dear Lord, who cares?
Who with me my burden shares?
None but thee, dear Lord, none but thee.

3. When my feeble life is o'er,
time for me will be no more.
Guide me gently, safely on
to the shore, dear Lord, to the shore.

Words and Music: Traditional, arranged by Michael Irwin

JUST AS I AM, WITHOUT ONE PLEA

('Saffron Walden' 88.86.)

[HARMONY]

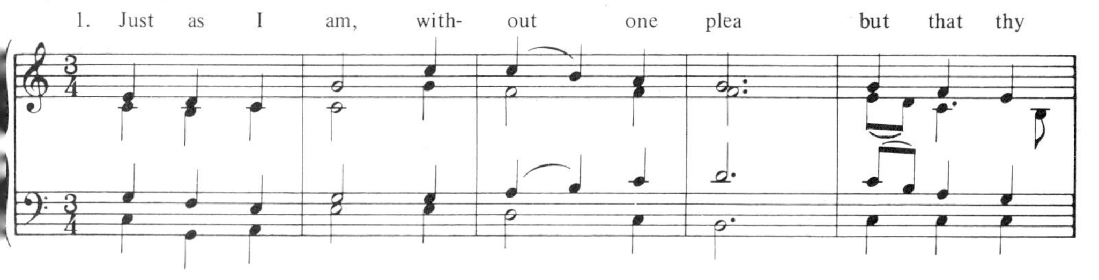

2. Just as I am, though tossed about
   with many a conflict, many a doubt,
   fightings and fears within, without,
   O Lamb of God, I come.

3. Just as I am, poor, wretched, blind;
   sight, riches, healing of the mind,
   yea, all I need, in thee to find,
   O Lamb of God, I come.

4. Just as I am, thou wilt receive,
   wilt welcome, pardon, cleanse, relieve:
   because thy promise I believe,
   O Lamb of God, I come.

5. Just as I am (thy love unknown
   has broken every barrier down),
   now to be thine, yea, thine alone,
   O Lamb of God, I come.

6. Just as I am, of that free love
   the breadth, length, depth, and height to prove,
   here for a season, then above,
   O Lamb of God, I come.

Words: Charlotte Elliott (1789-1871)
Music: Arthur H. Brown (1830-1926)

278

KING OF GLORY, KING OF PEACE
('Gwalchmai' 74.74.D.)

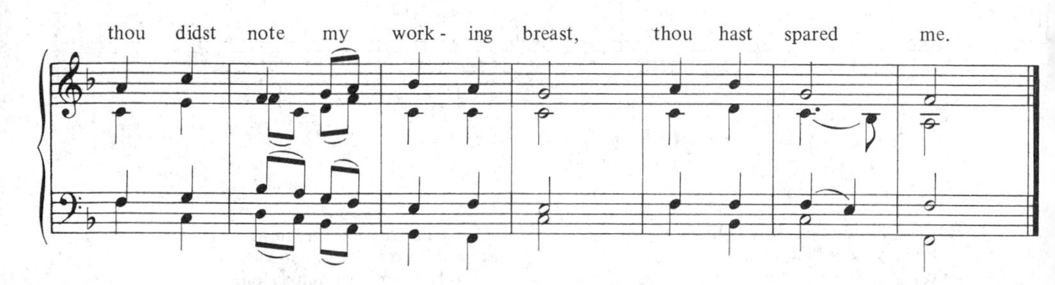

2. Wherefore with thy utmost art
I will sing thee,
and the cream of all my heart
I will bring thee.
Though my sins against me cried,
thou didst clear me,
and alone, when they replied,
thou didst hear me.

3. Sev'n whole days, not one in sev'n,
I will praise thee;
in my heart, though not in heav'n.
I can raise thee.
Small it is, in this poor sort
to enrol thee:
e'en eternity's too short
to extol thee.

Words: George Herbert (1593-1633)
Music: J. D. Jones (1827-70)

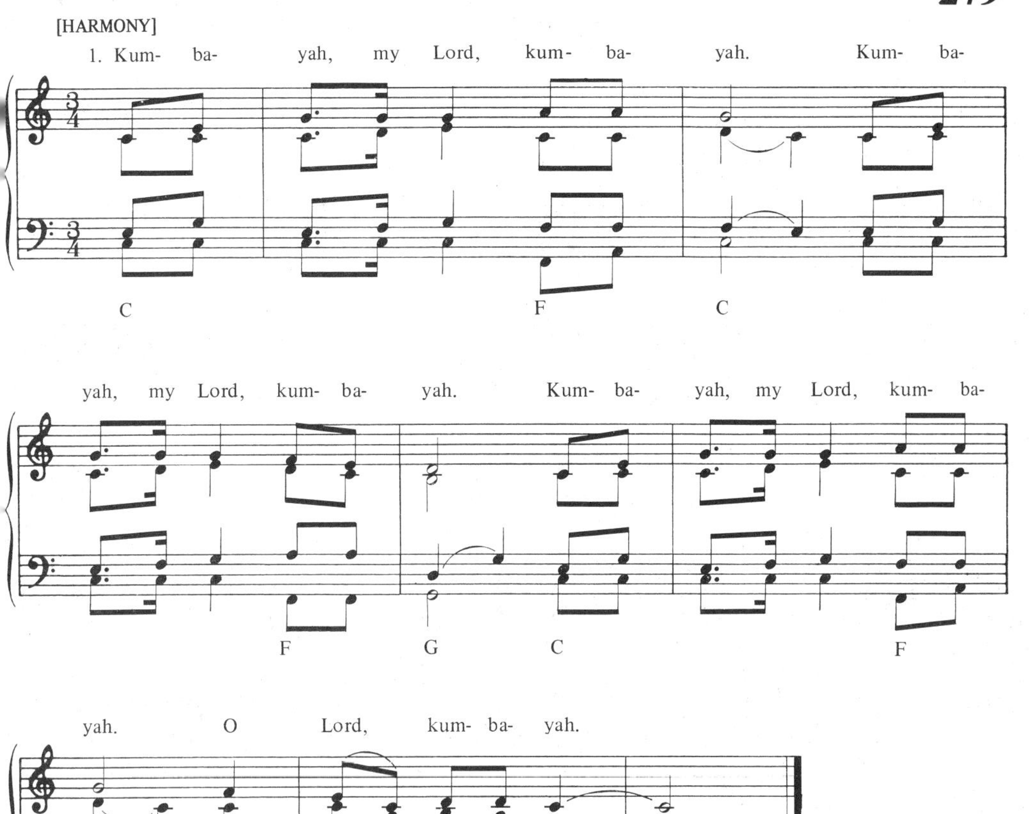

2. Someone's crying, Lord . . .

3. Someone's singing, Lord . . .

4. Someone's praying, Lord . . .

Words and Music: Traditional Angolan, arranged by John Rombaut

LEAD, KINDLY LIGHT
('Lux benigna' 10 4.10 4.10 10.)

[HARMONY]

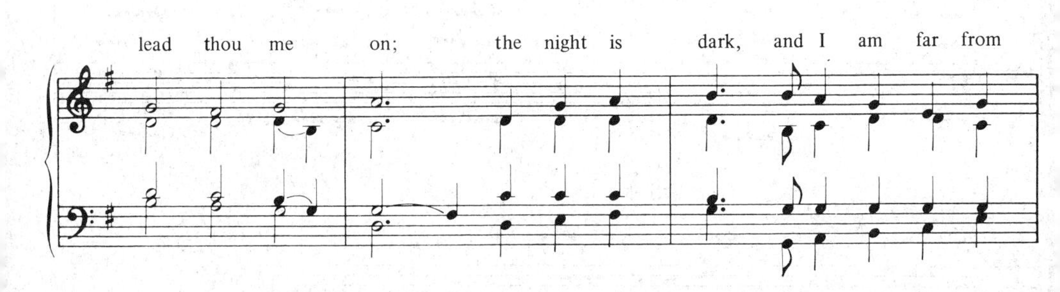

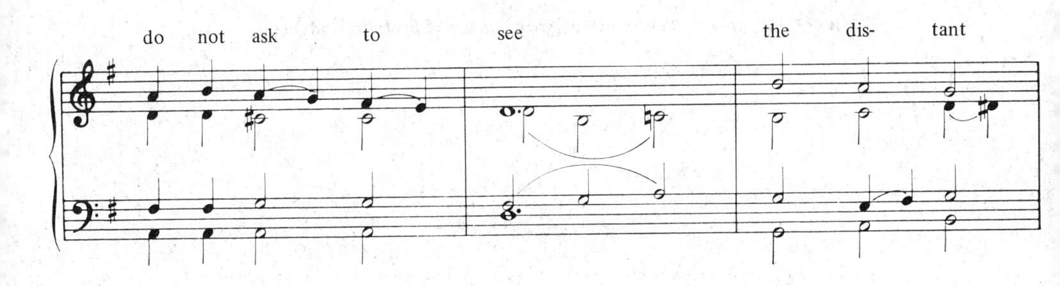

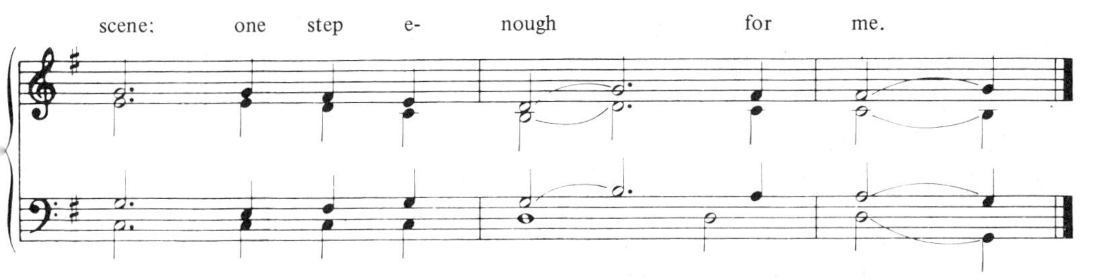

2. I was not ever thus, nor prayed that thou
   shouldst lead me on;
   I loved to choose and see my path, but now
   lead thou me on;
   I loved the garish day, and, spite of fears,
   pride ruled my will: remember not past years.

3. So long thy power hast blest me, sure it still
   will lead me on,
   o'er moor and fen, o'er crag and torrent, till
   the night is gone,
   and with the morn those angel faces smile,
   which I have loved long since, and lost awhile.

Words: John Henry Newman (1801-90)
Music: John Bacchus Dykes (1823-76)

281

LEAD US HEAVENLY FATHER, LEAD US

('Mannheim' 87.87.87.)

2. Saviour, breathe forgiveness o'er us,
all our weakness thou dost know,
thou didst tread this earth before us,
thou didst feel its keenest woe;
lone and dreary, faint and weary,
through the desert thou didst go.

3. Spirit of our God, descending,
fill our hearts with heavenly joy,
love with every passion blending,
pleasure that can never cloy;
thus provided, pardoned, guided,
nothing can our peace destroy.

Words: James Edmeston (1791-1867)
Music: Friedrich Filitz (1804-76)

LET ALL MORTAL FLESH KEEP SILENCE
('Picardy' 87.87.87.)

2. King of kings, yet born of Mary,
as of old on earth he stood –
Lord of lords, in human vesture –
in the body and the blood.
He will give to all the faithful
his own self for heavenly food.

3. Rank on rank the host of heaven
spreads its vanguard on the way,
as the Light of light descendeth
from the realms of endless day,
that the powers of hell may vanish
as the darkness clears away.

4. At his feet the six-winged seraph;
cherubim with sleepless eye,
veil their faces to the presence,
as with ceaseless voice they cry,
alleluia, alleluia,
alleluia, Lord most high.

Words: Liturgy of St. James,
tr. G. Moultrie (1829-85)
Music: Traditional French Carol

283

[HARMONY]

LET ALL THE WORLD IN EVERY CORNER SING

('Luckington' 10 4.66.66.10 4.)

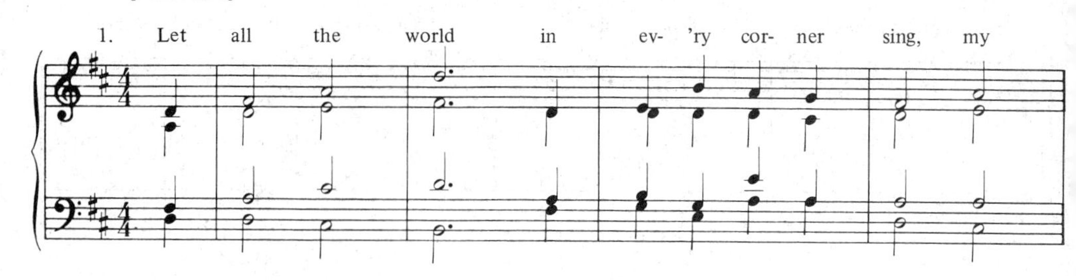

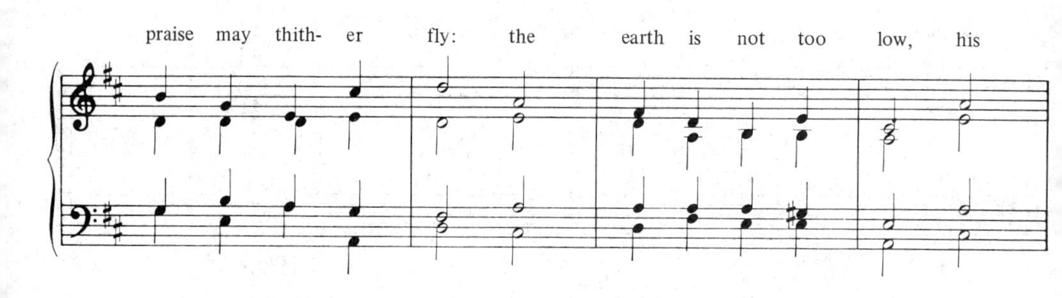

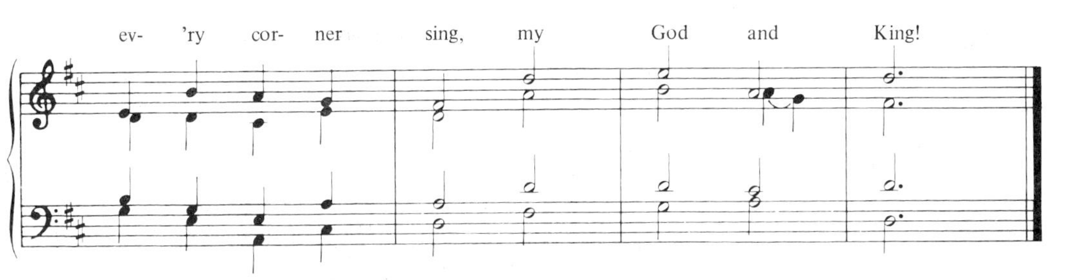

2. Let all the world in every corner sing,
   my God and King!
   The Church with psalms must shout,
   no door can keep them out;
   but, above all, the heart
   must bear the longest part.
   Let all the world in every corner sing,
   my God and King!

Words: George Herbert (1593-1633)
Music: Basil Harwood (1859-1949)

[HARMONY]

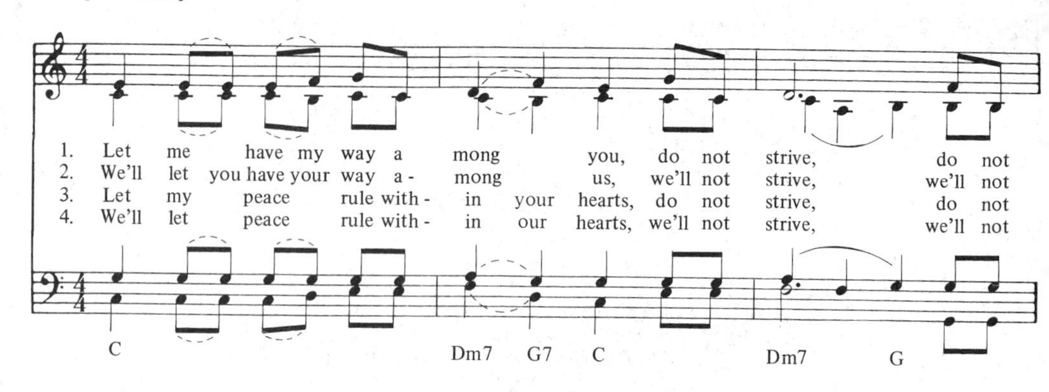
1. Let me have my way a mong you, do not strive, do not
2. We'll let you have your way a- mong us, we'll not strive, we'll not
3. Let my peace rule with- in your hearts, do not strive, do not
4. We'll let peace rule with- in our hearts, we'll not strive, we'll not
C Dm7 G7 C Dm7 G

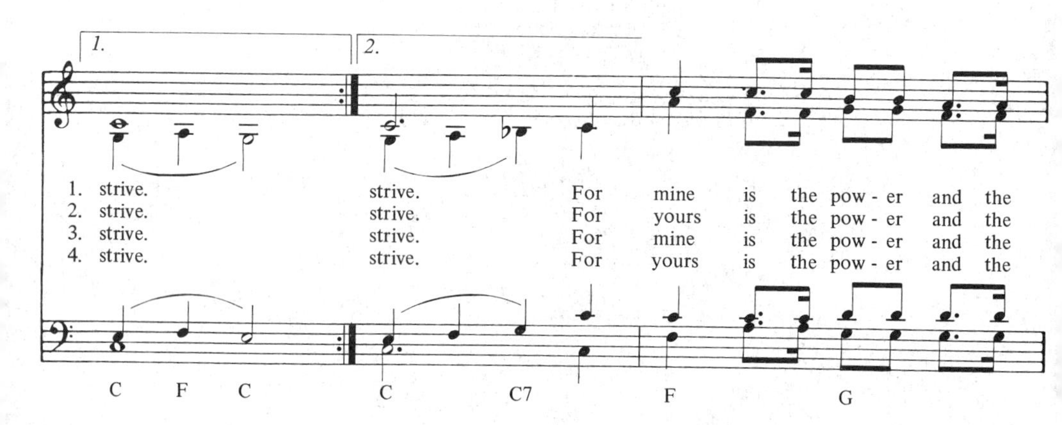
1. 2.
1. strive. strive. For mine is the pow-er and the
2. strive. strive. For yours is the pow-er and the
3. strive. strive. For mine is the pow-er and the
4. strive. strive. For yours is the pow-er and the
C F C C C7 F G

1. glo-ry for ev-er and ev-er the same.
2. glo-ry for ev-er and ev-er the same.
3. glo-ry for ev-er and ev-er the same.
4. glo-ry for ev-er and ev-er the same.
C Am Dm7 D7 G G7

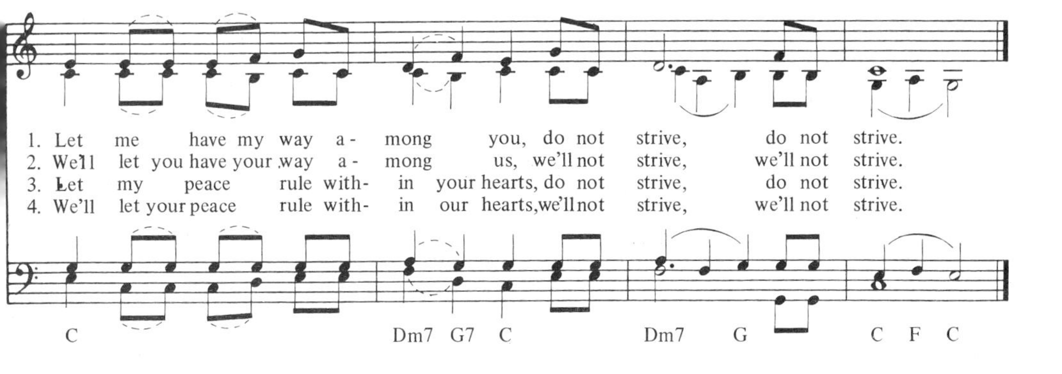

Words and Music: Graham Kendrick

[HARMONY]
Slowly
1. Let there be peace on earth and let it be - gin with me; let there be peace on earth, the peace that was meant to be, with God as our Fa - ther, bro - thers all are
2. Let there peace be - gin with me, let this be the mo- ment now. With ev'- ry step I take, let this be my sol- emn vow: to
2nd time
C Am Dm7 G6 C F
C Dm7 G7 C B7
Em G7
Am Em F G7

Words and Music: Sy Miller and Jill Jackson

LET US BREAK BREAD TOGETHER

2. Let us drink wine together . . .

3. Let us praise God together . . .

Words and Music: Unknown, arranged by John Rombaut

Alternative version

1. Let us break bread together all as one.
   When I fall on my knees with my face to the rising sun,
   Oh Lord, have mercy on me.
2. Let us drink wine together all as one . . .
3. Let us praise God together all as one . . .

2. Let us seek God together,
let us pray,
let us seek his forgiveness
as we pray.
He will cleanse us from all sin,
he will help us the fight to win,
his name be exalted on high.

3. Let us serve God together,
him obey;
let our lives show his goodness
through each day.
Christ the Lord is the world's true light,
let us serve him with all our might,
his name be exalted on high.

Words: J. E. Seddon
Music: Unknown, arranged by John Rombaut

LET US WITH A GLADSOME MIND

('Monkland' 77.77.)

2. Let us blaze his name abroad,
   for of gods he is the God;

3. He, with all-commanding might,
   filled the new-made world with light;

4. He the golden tressèd sun
   caused all day his course to run:

5. And the moon to shine at night,
   'mid her starry sisters bright:

6. All things living he doth feed,
   his full hand supplies their need:

7. Let us, with a gladsome mind,
   praise the Lord, for he is kind.

Words: John Milton (1608-74), based on Psalm 136
Music: Unknown original, arranged by John B. Wilkes (1785-1869)

LIFT HIGH THE CROSS
('Crucifer' 10 10. & Chorus)

2. Each new-born soldier of the crucified
bears on his brow the seal of him who died:

3. This is the sign that Satan's armies fear
and angels veil their faces to revere:

4. Saved by the cross on which their Lord was slain,
see Adam's children their lost home regain:

5. From north and south, from east and west they raise
in growing unison their songs of praise:

6. Let every race and every language tell
of him who saves our souls from death and hell!

7. O Lord, once lifted on the tree of pain,
draw all the world to seek you once again:

8. Set up your throne, that earth's despair may cease
beneath the shadow of its healing peace:

Words: George William Kitchin (1827-1912), and Michael Robert Newbolt (1874-1956)
Music: S.H. Nicholson (1875-1947)

LIFT UP YOUR HEARTS!

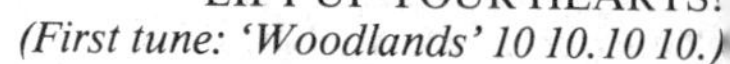

2. Lift every gift that thou thyself hast given:
low lies the best till lifted up to heaven;
low lie the bounding heart, the teeming brain,
till, sent from God, they mount to God again.

3. Then, as the trumpet-call in after years,
'Lift up your hearts!' rings pealing in our ears,
still shall those hearts respond with full accord,
'We lift them up, we lift them to the Lord.'

Words: Henry M. Butler (1833-1918)
Music: Walter Greatorex (1877-1949)

.IFT UP YOUR HEARTS!
(Second tune: 'Cliff Town' 10 10.10 10.)

2. Lift every gift that thou thyself hast given:
low lies the best till lifted up to heaven;
low lie the bounding heart, the teeming brain,
till, sent from God, they mount to God again.

3. Then, as the trumpet-call in after years,
'Lift up your hearts!' rings pealing in our ears,
still shall those hearts respond with full accord,
'We lift them up, we lift them to the Lord!'

Words: Henry M. Butler (1833-1918)
Music: Erik Routley

291

LIGHT'S ABODE, CELESTIAL SALEM
('Regent Square' 87.87.87.)

[HARMONY]

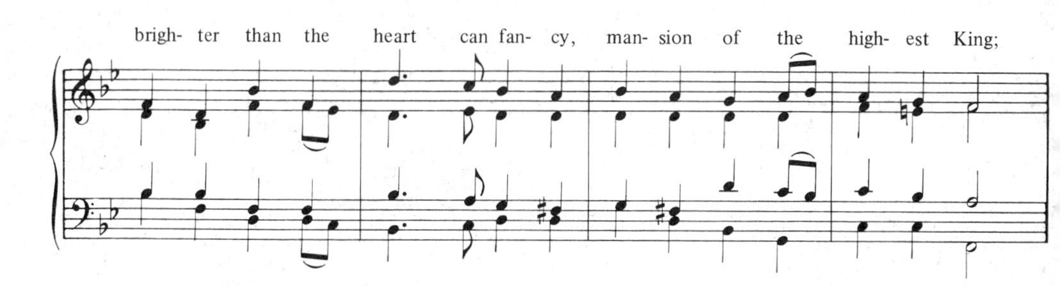

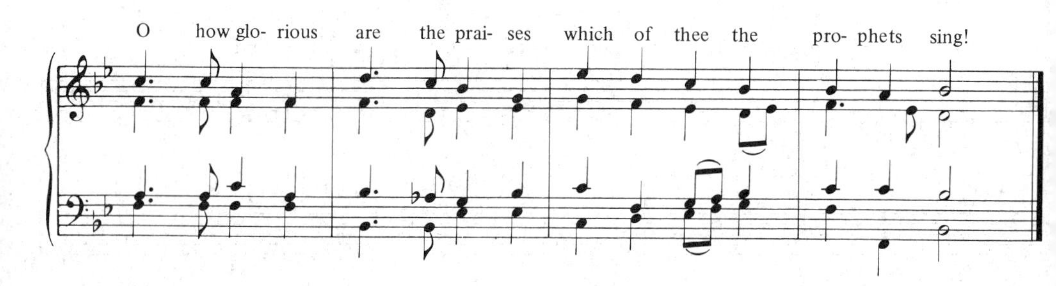

2. There for ever and for ever
 Alleluia is outpoured;
 for unending, for unbroken
 is the feast-day of the Lord;
 all is pure and all is holy
 that within thy walls is stored.

3. There no cloud or passing vapour
 dims the brightness of the air;
 endless noon-day, glorious noon-day,
 from the Sun of suns is there;
 there no night brings rest from labour,
 for unknown are toil and care.

4. O how glorious and resplendent,
 fragile body, shalt thou be,
 when endued with so much beauty,
 full of health and strong and free,
 full of vigour, full of pleasure
 that shall last eternally!

5. Now with gladness, now with courage,
 bear the burden on thee laid,
 that hereafter these thy labours
 may with endless gifts be paid;
 and in everlasting glory
 thou with brightness be arrayed.

6. Laud and honour to the Father,
 laud and honour to the Son,
 laud and honour to the Spirit,
 ever Three and ever One,
 consubstantial, co-eternal,
 while unending ages run.

Words: ascribed to Thomas à Kempis (c.1379-1471),
tr. J. M. Neale
Music: Henry Smart (1813-79)

LIKE A MIGHTY RIVER FLOWING 292

('Old Yeavering' 88.87.)

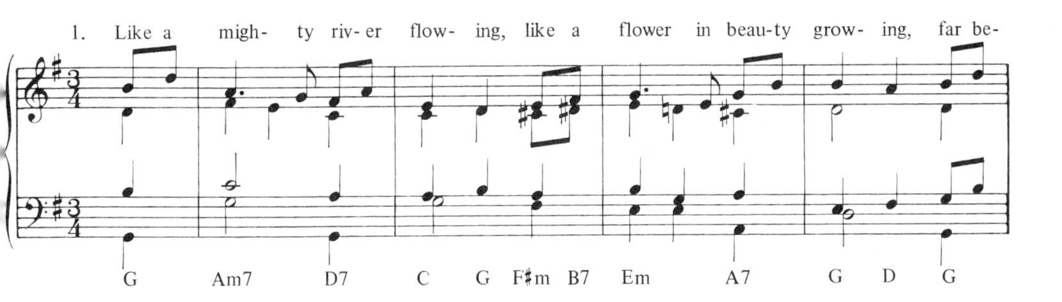

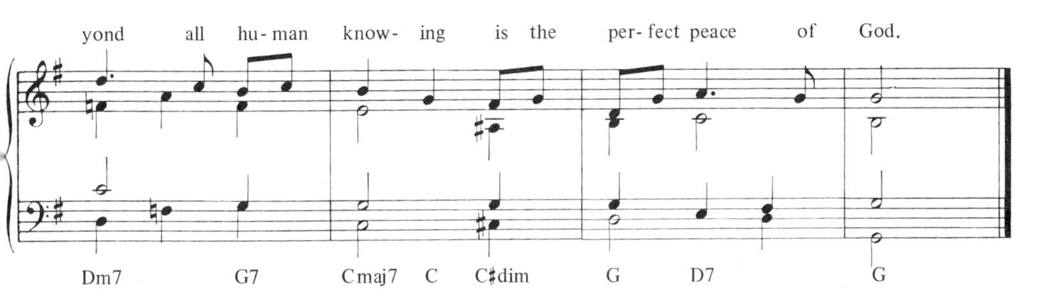

2. Like the hills serene and even,
like the coursing clouds of heaven,
like the heart that's been forgiven
is the perfect peace of God.

3. Like the summer breezes playing,
like the tall trees softly swaying,
like the lips of silent praying
is the perfect peace of God.

4. Like the morning sun ascended,
like the scents of evening blended,
like a friendship never ended,
is the perfect peace of God.

5. Like the azure ocean swelling,
like the jewel all-excelling,
far beyond our human telling
is the perfect peace of God.

Words: Michael Perry (b. 1942)
Music: Noël Tredinnick (b.1949)

LIKE A RIVER GLORIOUS
('Wye Valley' 65.65. Triple)

[HARMONY]

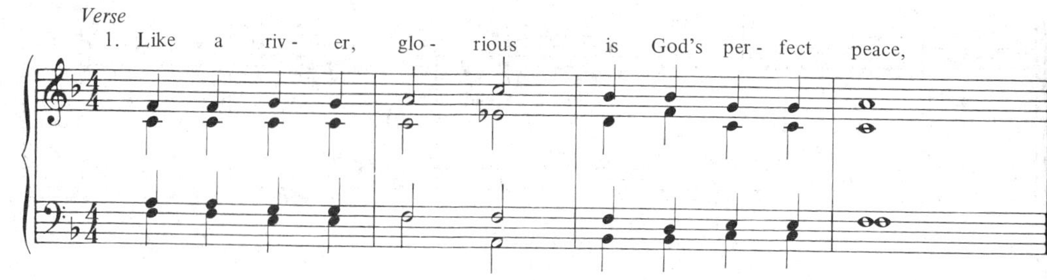

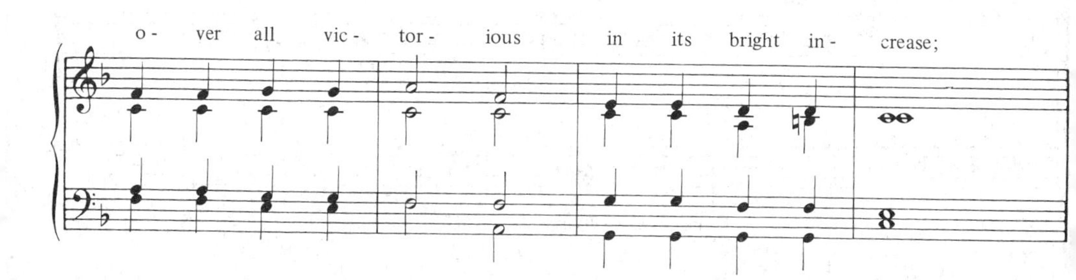

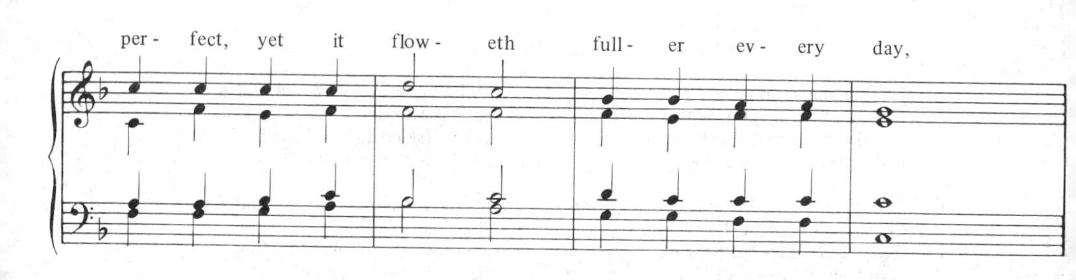

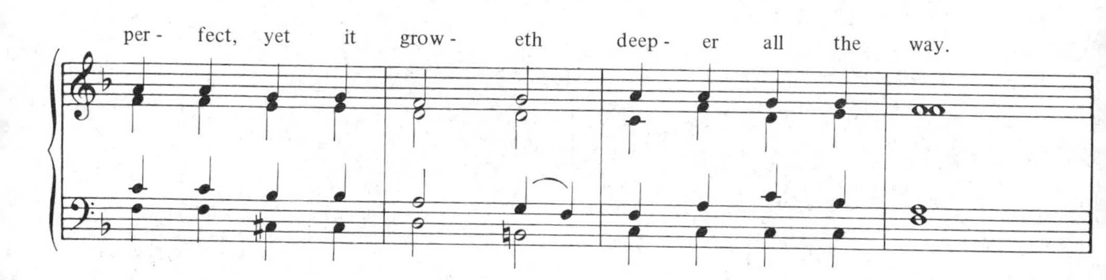

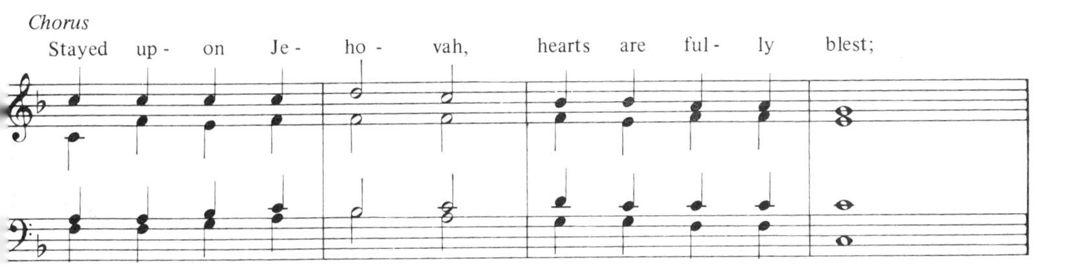

2. Hidden in the hollow
of his blessed hand,
never foe can follow,
never traitor stand;
not a surge of worry,
not a shade of care,
not a blast of hurry
touch the Spirit there.

3. Every joy or trial
falleth from above,
traced upon our dial
by the sun of love.
We may trust him fully
all for us to do:
they who trust him wholly
find him wholly true.

Words: Frances R. Havergal (1836-79)
Music: J. Mountain

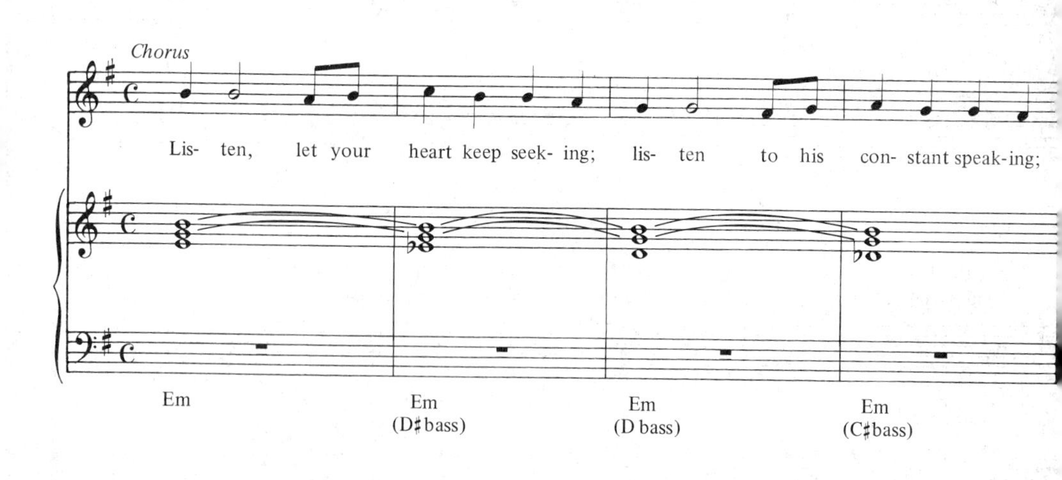
Chorus
Lis- ten, let your heart keep seek- ing; lis- ten to his con- stant speak-ing;
Em
Em
(D♯bass)
Em
(D bass)
Em
(C♯bass)

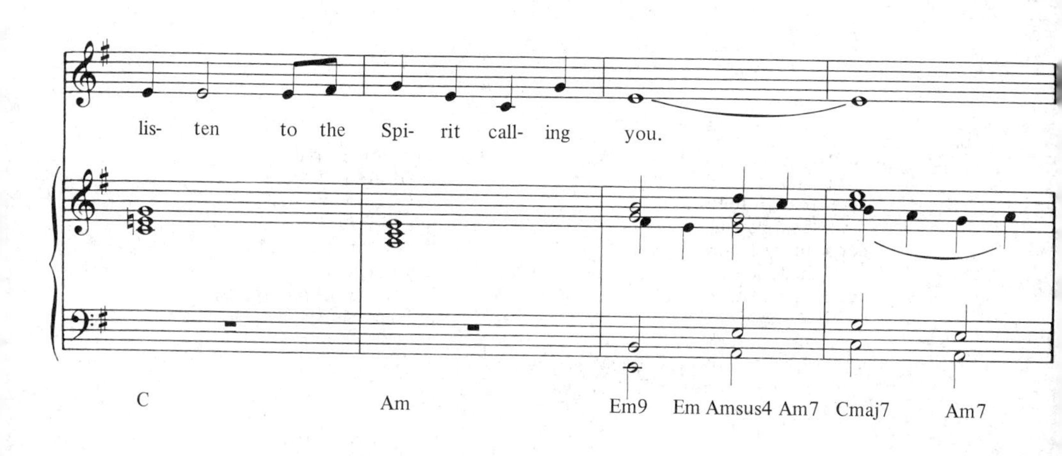
lis- ten to the Spi- rit call- ing you.
C
Am
Em9 Em Amsus4 Am7 Cmaj7 Am7

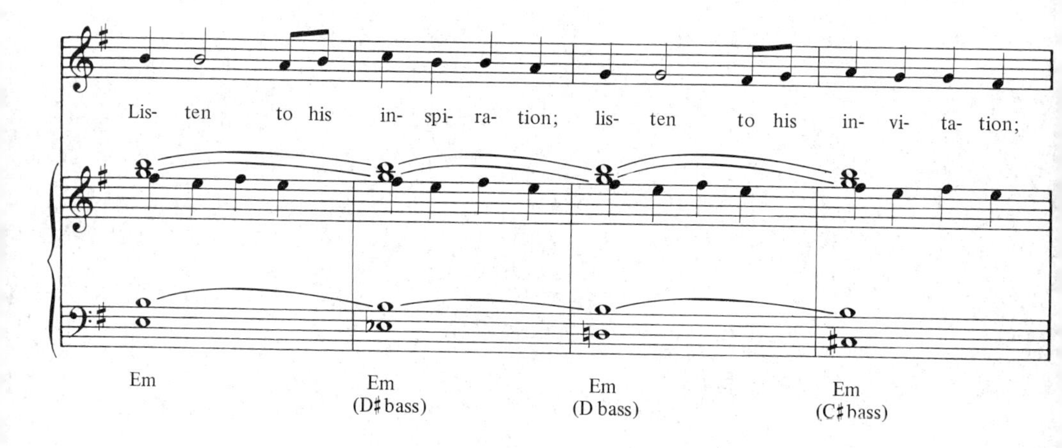
Lis- ten to his in- spi- ra- tion; lis- ten to his in- vi- ta- tion;
Em
Em
(D♯bass)
Em
(D bass)
Em
(C♯bass)

2. He's in the laughter of children,
in the patter of the rain.
Hear him in cries of the suff'ring
in their moaning and their pain.

3. He's in the noise of the city,
in the singing of the birds.
And in the night-time the stillness
helps you listen to his word.

Words and Music: Aniceto Nazareth

LITTLE JESUS, SWEETLY SLEEP
('Rocking' 10 7.88.77.)

2. Mary's little baby sleep,
sweetly sleep,
sleep in comfort, slumber deep;
we will rock you,
rock you, rock you, *(2)*
we will serve you all we can,
darling, darling little man.

Words: Traditional Czech carol, translated by Percy Dearmer (1867-1936)
Music: Traditional Czech carol, arranged by John Rombaut

LO, HE COMES WITH CLOUDS DESCENDING
('Helmsley' 87.87.47.)

[HARMONY]

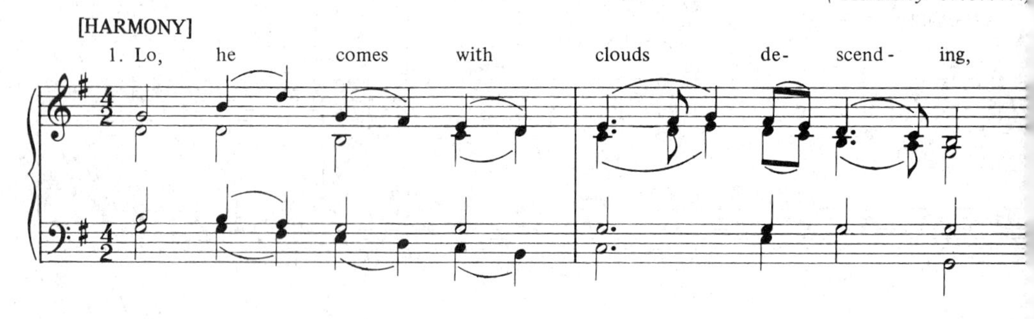

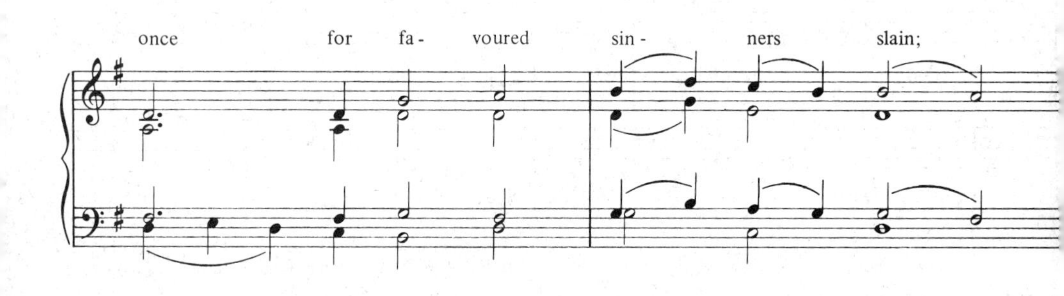

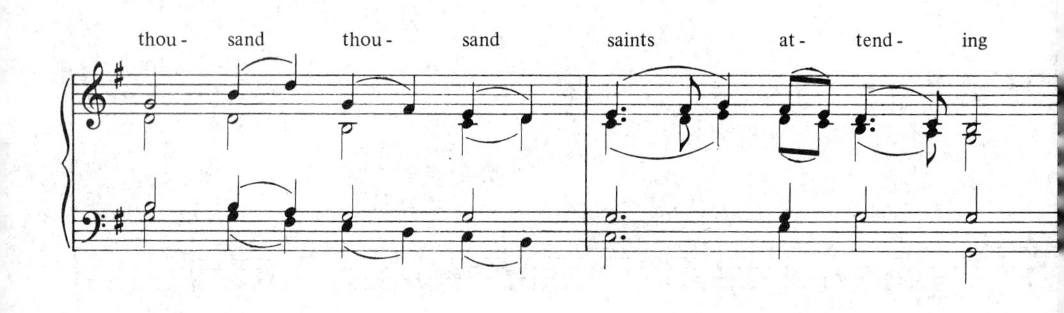

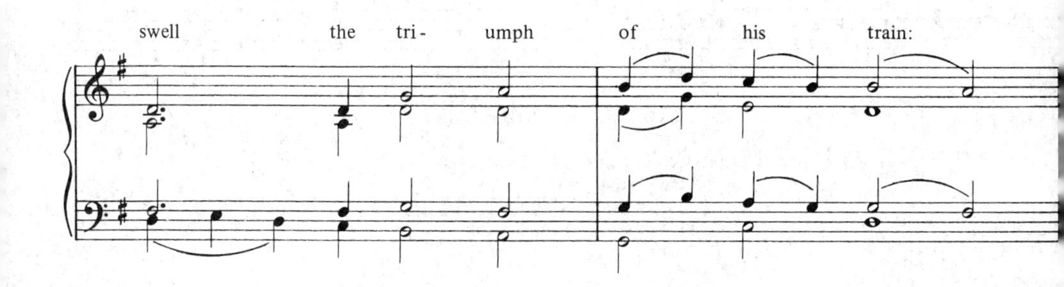

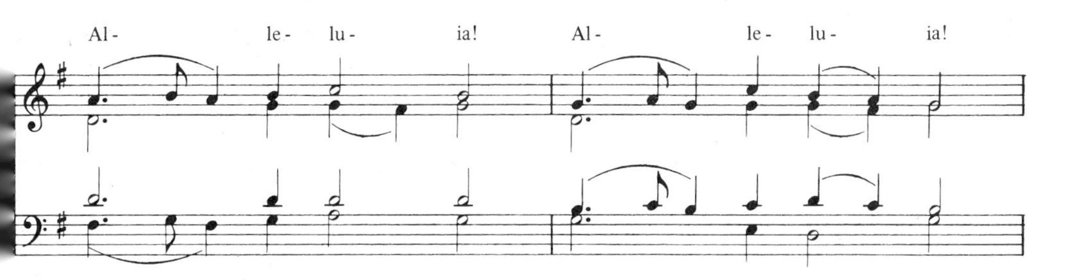

2. Every eye shall now behold him
   robed in dreadful majesty;
   those who set at naught and sold him,
   pierced and nailed him to the Tree,
   deeply wailing, *(3)*
   shall the true Messiah see.

3. Those dear tokens of his passion
   still his dazzling body bears,
   cause of endless exultation
   to his ransomed worshippers:
   with what rapture *(3)*
   gaze we on those glorious scars!

4. Yea, Amen, let all adore thee,
   high on thine eternal throne;
   Saviour, take the power and glory,
   claim the kingdom for thine own:
   Alleluia! *(3)*
   thou shalt reign, and thou alone.

Words: Charles Wesley (1707-88), John Cennick (1718-55),
and Martin Madan (1726-90)
Music: Thomas Olivers (1725-99)

297

LORD CHRIST, WHO ON THY HEART DIDST BEA

('Gonfalon Royal' L.M

2. Thy patience cannot know defeat,
thy pity will not be denied,
thy loving-kindness still is great,
thy tender mercies still abide.

3. O brother Man, for this we pray,
thou brother Man and sovereign Lord,
that we thy brethren, day by day,
may follow thee and keep thy word;

4. that we may care, as thou hast cared,
for sick and lame, for deaf and blind,
and freely share, as thou hast shared,
in all the sorrows of mankind;

5. that ours may be the holy task
to help and bless, to heal and save;
this is the happiness we ask,
and this the service that we crave.

Words: Arnold Thomas (1848-1924)
Music: Percy Carter Buck (1871-1947)

LORD, DISMISS US WITH THY BLESSING
('St Raphael' 87.87.47.)

[HARMONY]

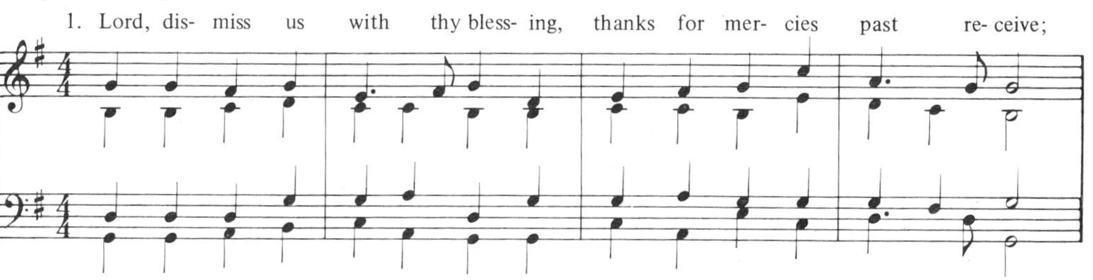

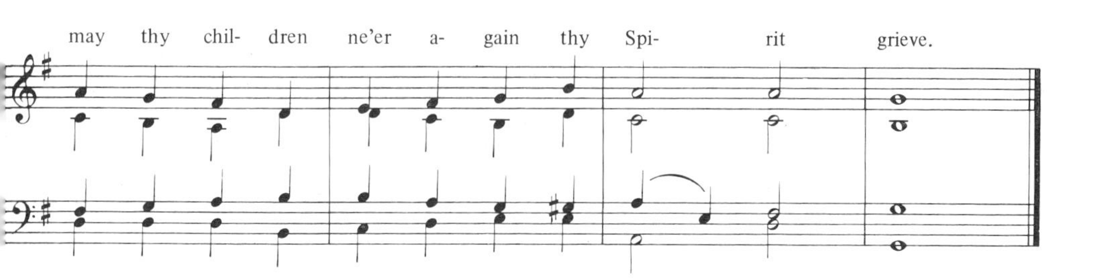

2. Bless thou all our days of leisure,
help us selfish lures to flee;
sanctify our every pleasure;
pure and blameless may it be;
may our gladness
draw us evermore to thee.

3. By thy kindly influence cherish
all the good we here have gained;
may all taint of evil perish
by thy mightier power restrained;
seek we ever
knowledge pure and love unfeigned.

4. Let thy Father-hand be shielding
all who here shall meet no more;
may their seed-time past be yielding
year by year a richer store;
those returning
make more faithful than before.

Words: Henry J. Buckoll (1803-71)
Music: Edward J. Hopkins (1818-1901)

299 LORD, ENTHRONED IN HEAVENLY SPLENDOUR

('St Helen' 87.87.87.)

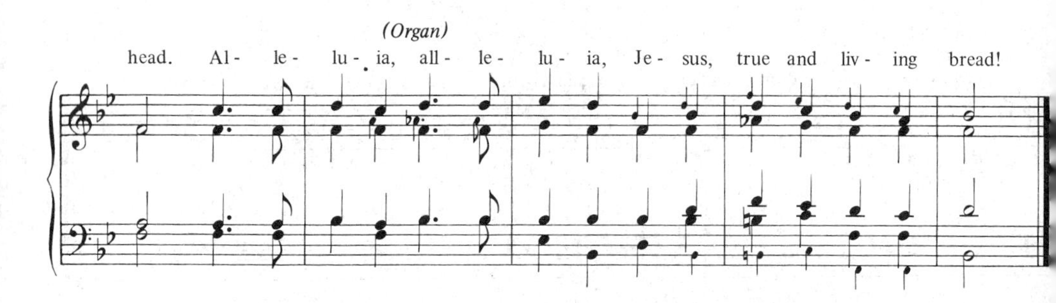

2. Prince of life, for us thou livest,
by thy body souls are healed;
Prince of peace, thy peace thou givest,
by thy blood is pardon sealed;
alleluia, alleluia,
Word of God, in flesh revealed.

3. Paschal Lamb! Thine offering finished,
once for all, when thou wast slain,
in its fullness undiminished
shall for evermore remain,
alleluia, alleluia,
cleansing souls from every stain.

4. Great high priest of our profession,
through the veil thou enteredst in;
by thy mighty intercession
grace and mercy thou canst win;
alleluia, alleluia,
only sacrifice for sin.

5. Life-imparting heavenly manna,
stricken rock, with streaming side,
heaven and earth, with loud hosanna,
worship thee, the Lamb who died;
alleluia, alleluia,
risen, ascended, glorified.

Words, based on Revelation 20: George Hugh Bourne (1840-1925)
Music: G. C. Martin (1844-1916)

300

LORD, FOR THE YEARS

('Lord of the years' 11 10.11 10.)

2. Lord, for that Word, the Word of life which fires us,
speaks to our hearts and sets our souls ablaze,
teaches and trains, rebukes us and inspires us:
Lord of the Word, receive your people's praise.

3. Lord, for our land, in this our generation,
spirits oppressed by pleasure, wealth and care;
for young and old, for commonwealth and nation,
Lord of our land, be pleased to hear our prayer.

4. Lord, for our world, where men disown and doubt you,
loveless in strength, and comfortless in pain,
hungry and helpless, lost indeed without you:
Lord of the world, we pray that Christ may reign.

5. Lord, for ourselves; in living power remake us -
self on the cross and Christ upon the throne,
past put behind us, for the future take us:
Lord of our lives, to live for Christ alone.

Words: Timothy Dudley-Smith
Music: Michael Baughen (b.1930),
arranged by David Iliff (b.1939)

301

LORD, HAVE MERCY
('Ezechiel' 88.88.98.11 7.)

Chorus

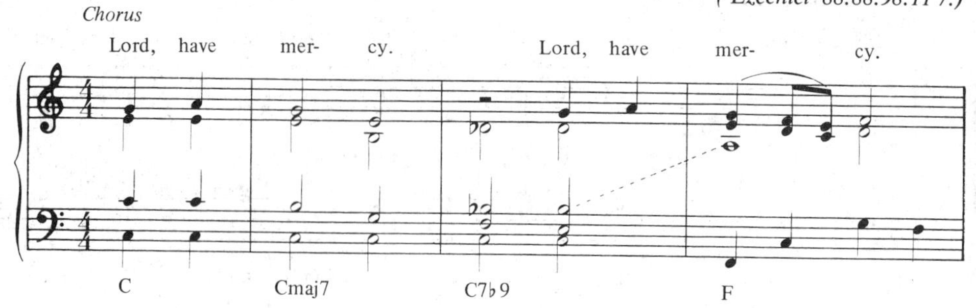

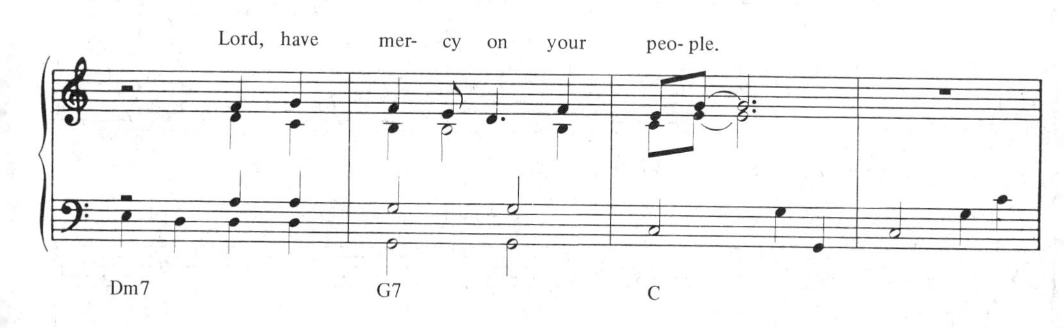

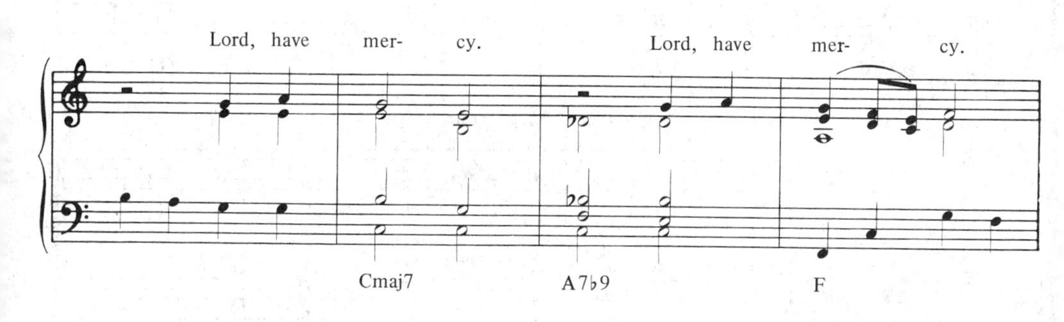

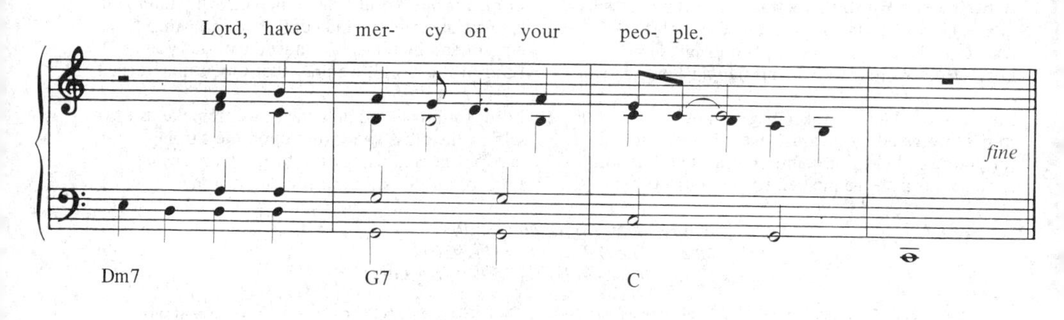

2. You'll find me near the broken-hearted:
those crushed in spirit I will save.
So turn to me, for my pardon is great;
My Word will heal all your wounds.

Words (based on Ezekiel) and Music: Gerard Markland

302 LORD, JESUS CHRIST (**Living Lord**)

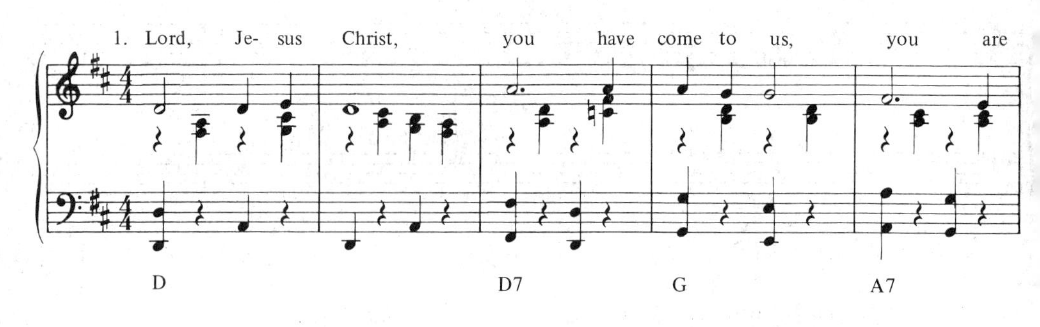

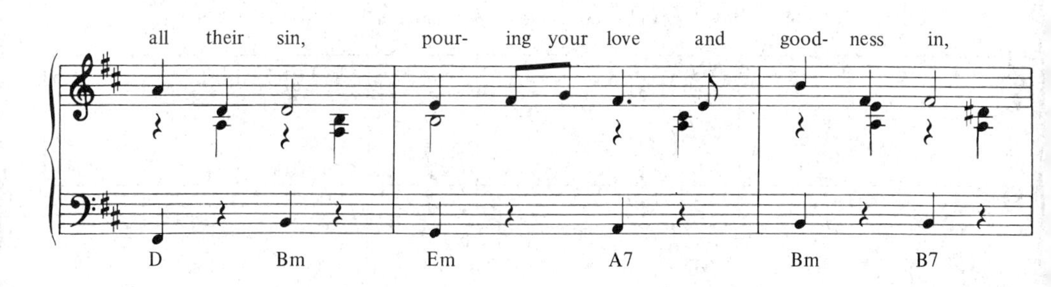

2. Lord Jesus Christ,
now and every day
teach us how to pray, Son of God.
You have commanded us to do
this in remembrance, Lord, of you.
Into our lives your power breaks through,
living Lord.

3. Lord Jesus Christ,
you have come to us,
born as one of us, Mary's son.
Led out to die on Calvary,
risen from death to set us free,
living Lord Jesus, help us see
you are Lord.

4. Lord Jesus Christ,
I would come to you,
live my life for you, Son of God.
All your commands I know are true,
your many gifts will make me new,
into my life your power breaks through,
living Lord.

Words and Music: Patrick Appleford

LORD JESUS, THINK ON ME
('Southwell (Damon)' S.M.)

2. Lord Jesus, think on me,
with care and woe oppressed;
let me thy loving servant be,
and taste thy promised rest.

3. Lord Jesus, think on me
amid the battle's strife;
in all my pain and misery
be thou my health and life.

4. Lord Jesus, think on me,
nor let me go astray;
through darkness and perplexity
point thou the heavenly way.

5. Lord Jesus, think on me,
when flows the tempest high:
when on doth rush the enemy,
O Saviour, be thou nigh.

6. Lord Jesus, think on me,
that, when the flood is past,
I may the eternal brightness see,
and share thy joy at last.

Words: Bishop Synesius (375-430)
tr. A. W. Chatfield (1808-96)
Music: 'Damon's Psalter' (1579)

Slowly, prayerfully and calmly

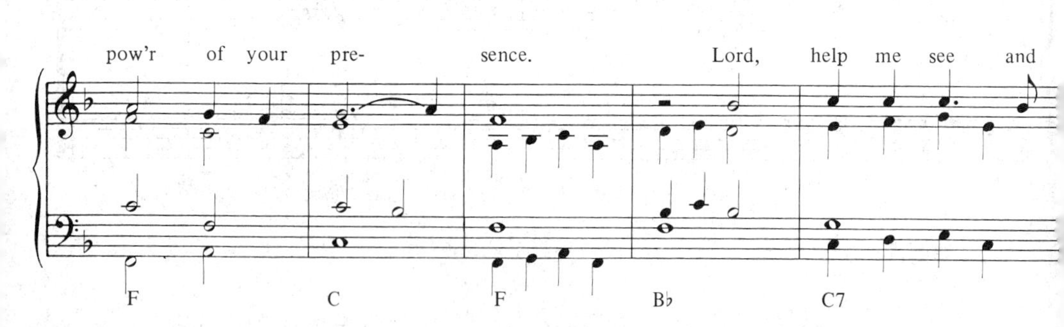

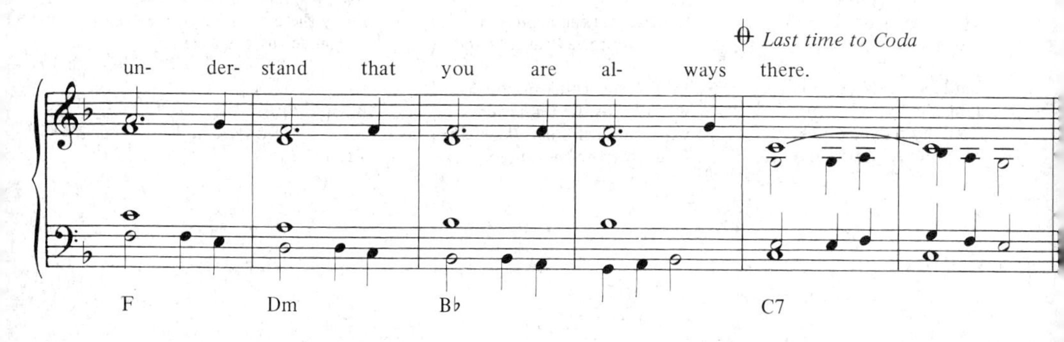

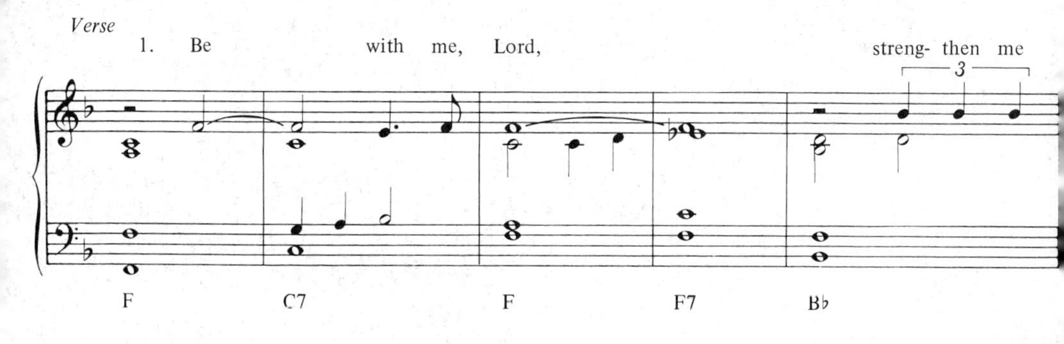

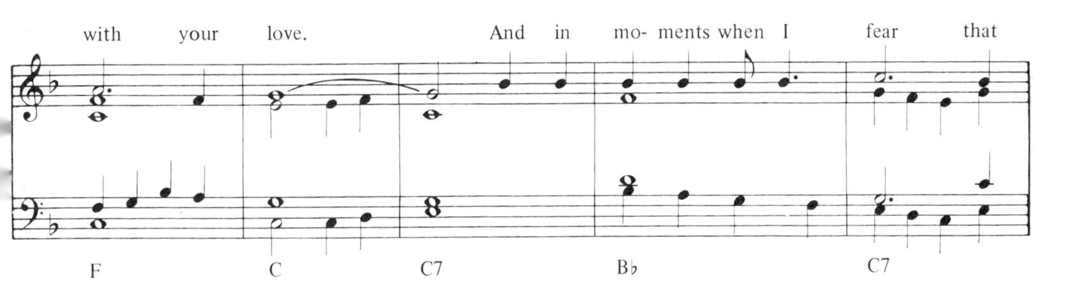

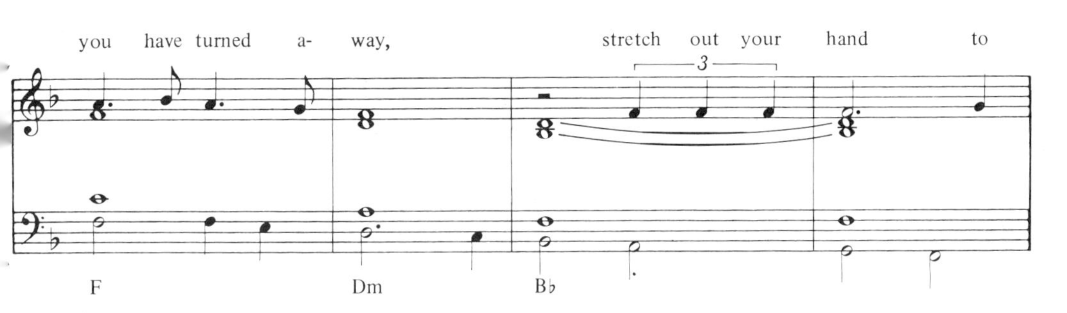

2. Calm all my fears.
   Give me your comfort, Lord.
   Fill me with the presence
   of your Spirit deep within;
   stretch out your hand to me.

3. Stay with me, Lord,
   I put my trust in you.
   Help me, Lord, give back to you
   the love you give to me.
   Stretch out your hand to me.

Words and Music: Christine McCann,
arranged by Frances M. Kelly

305

LORD OF ALL HOPEFULNESS
('Slane' 10 11.11 12.)

[HARMONY]

2. Lord of all eagerness,
Lord of all faith,
whose strong hands were skilled
at the plane and the lathe,
be there at our labours,
and give us, we pray,
your strength in our hearts, Lord,
at the noon of the day.

3. Lord of all kindliness,
Lord, of all grace,
your hands swift to welcome,
your arms to embrace,
be there at our homing,
and give us, we pray,
your love in our hearts, Lord,
at the eve of the day.

4. Lord of all gentleness,
Lord of all calm,
whose voice is contentment,
whose presence is balm,
be there at our sleeping,
and give us, we pray,
your peace in our hearts, Lord,
at the end of the day.

Words: Jan Struther (1901-53)
Music: Traditional Irish melody,
harmonised by Martin Shaw (1875-1958)

A different harmonisation of this tune may be found at Hymn 306

LORD OF ALL POWER
('Slane' 10 11.11 11.)

A different harmonisation of this tune may be found at Hymn 305

2. Lord of all wisdom, I give you my mind,
rich truth that surpasses man's knowledge to find.
What eye has not seen and what ear has not heard
is taught by your Spirit and shines from your Word.

3. Lord of all bounty, I give you my heart;
I praise and adore you for all you impart:
your love to inspire me, your counsel to guide,
your presence to cheer me, whatever betide.

4. Lord of all being, I give you my all;
if e'er I disown you I stumble and fall;
but, sworn in glad service your word to obey,
I walk in your freedom to the end of the way.

Words: Jack C. Winslow (1882-1974)
Music: Irish Traditional Melody,
harmonised by Erik Routley (1917-82)

307

LORD OF LIF

2. 'Come to me,
and I will give you rest.'
Help us see
your Way is richly blest;
guide our questing,
working, resting,
till we hear you calling
'follow me'.

3. Lord, we come,
encouraged by your grace,
Lord, we come,
and things fall into place;
pilgrims ever,
we endeavour,
Lord, to follow as you
bring us home.

4. Lord, may we
bring all our strength and skill;
help us be
prepared to do your will.
Turn our living
into giving
love and service as you
set us free.

5. Glory be
to God for all his love;
here may we
with saints below, above,
go rejoicing,
ever voicing
praise for such a welcome
'Come to me'.

Words and Music: *Patrick Appleford,*
arranged by Frances M. Kelly

308

LORD OF MY LIFE **(Lost in the wonder of all you encompass)**

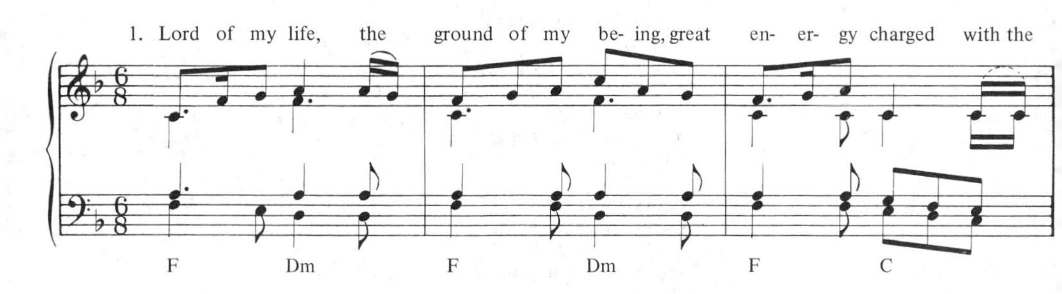

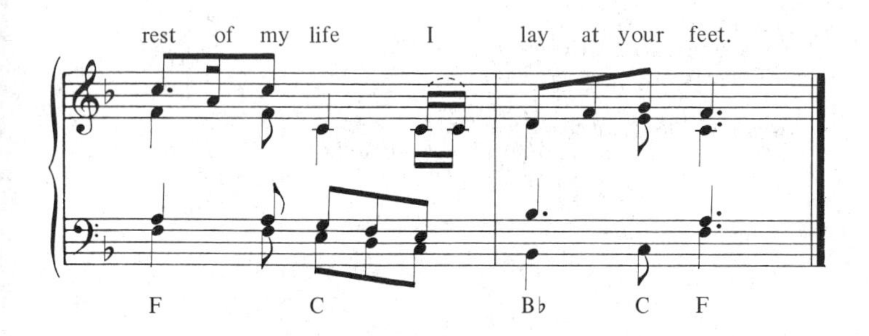

2. Lord of my joy,
   clear stream of refreshment,
   profusion of love
   like blossom in spring.
   Lost in the wonder
   of all you encompass
   my fears and my cares
   to your goodness I bring.

3. Lord of my strength,
   the source of all healing,
   your purity deep
   as the green ocean's floor.
   Lost in the wonder
   of all you encompass
   I ask only this –
   to be yours evermore.

Words and Music: *Susan Sayers,*
arranged by John Rombaut

LORD OF THE CROSS OF SHAME

('Cross of shame' 66.11.D.)

2. Lord of the empty tomb,
born of a Virgin's womb,
triumphant over death, its power defeated;
how gladly now I sing
your praise, my risen King,
and worship you, in heaven's splendour seated.

3. Lord of my life today,
teach me to live and pray
as one who knows the joy of sins forgiven;
so may I ever be,
now and eternally,
one with my fellow-citizens in heaven.

Words: Michael Saward (b.1932)
Music: Michael Baughen (b.1930)

310

LORD, TEACH US HOW TO PRAY ARIGHT
('St Hugh' C.M.)

2. We perish if we cease from prayer;
O grant us power to pray;
and when to meet thee we prepare,
Lord, meet us by the way.

3. God of all grace, we come to thee
with broken contrite hearts;
give, what thine eyes delight to see,
truth in the inward parts;

4. Faith in the only sacrifice
that can for sin atone;
to cast our hopes, to fix our eyes,
on Christ, on Christ alone;

5. Patience to watch, and wait, and weep,
though mercy long delay;
courage our fainting hearts to keep,
and trust thee though thou slay.

6. Give these, and then thy will be done;
thus, strengthened with all might,
we, through thy Spirit and thy Son,
shall pray, and pray aright.

Words, based on Luke 11:1,
James Montgomery (1771-1854)
Music: E. J. Hopkins (1818-1901)

LORD, THY WORD ABIDETH

('Ravenshaw' 66.66.)

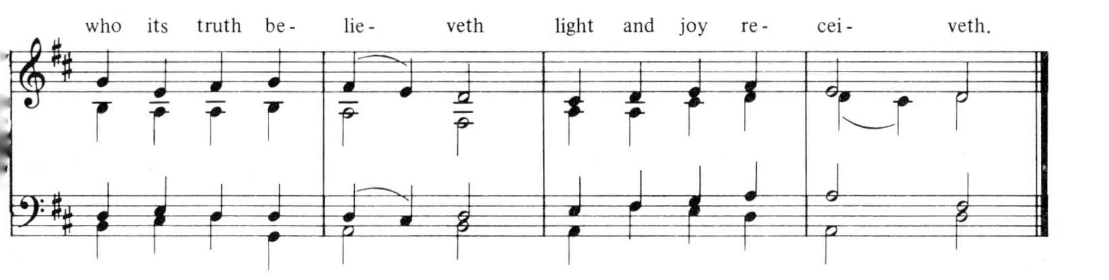

2. When our foes are near us,
then thy word doth cheer us,
word of consolation,
message of salvation.

3. When the storms are o'er us,
and dark clouds before us,
then its light directeth,
and our way protecteth.

4. Who can tell the pleasure,
who recount the treasure,
by thy word imparted
to the simple-hearted?

5. Word of mercy, giving
succour to the living;
word of life, supplying
comfort to the dying!

6. O that we discerning
its most holy learning,
Lord, may love and fear thee,
evermore be near thee.

Words: Henry Williams Baker (1821-77)
Music: 'Weisse's Gesangbuch' (1531), adapted by W.H. Monk

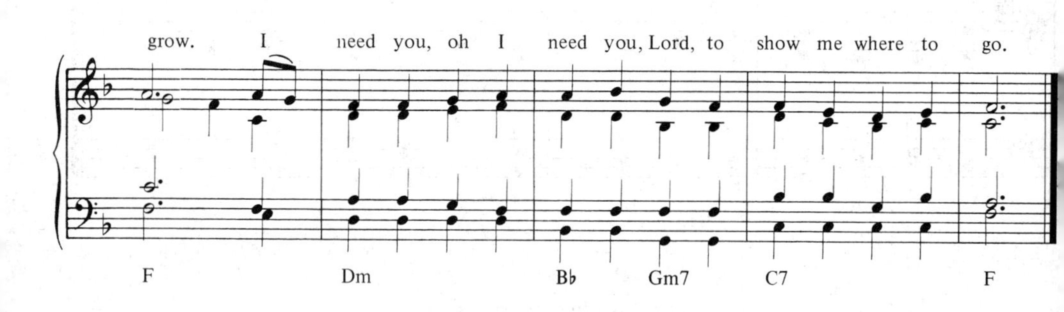

2. With you beside me, Lord, I find
the evils that I face
become instead a joyfulness,
a fountain of your grace.

3. So shape me to your purpose, Lord,
and tell me what to do;
and if I start to turn away,
then turn me back to you.

4. And when the world is over, Lord,
or over just for me,
there is nowhere but with you, Lord,
that I would rather be.

Words and Music: Susan Sayers,
arranged by John Rombaut

LOVE DIVINE, ALL LOVES EXCELLING
('Love divine' 87.87.D.)

[HARMONY]

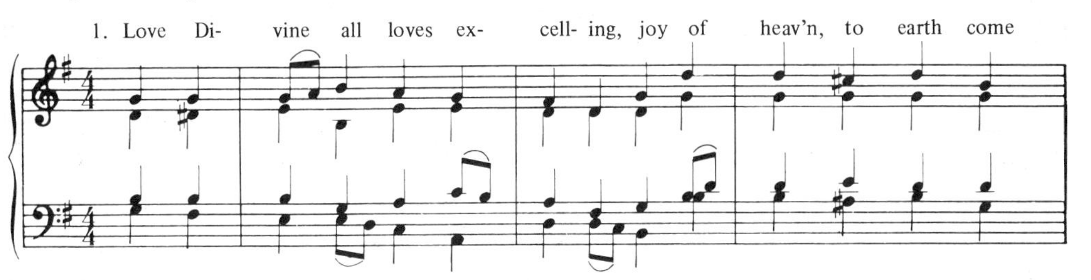

2. Jesus, thou art all compassion,
pure unbounded love thou art;
visit us with thy salvation,
enter every trembling heart.

3. Come, almighty to deliver,
let us all thy life receive;
suddenly return, and never,
never more thy temples leave.

4. Thee we would be always blessing,
serve thee as thy hosts above;
pray, and praise thee without ceasing,
glory in thy perfect love.

5. Finish then thy new creation,
pure and sinless let us be;
let us see thy great salvation
perfectly restored in thee.

6. Changed from glory into glory,
till in heaven we take our place,
till we cast our crowns before thee,
lost in wonder, love, and praise.

Words: Charles Wesley (1707-88)
Music: John Stainer (1840-1901)

314

LOVE IS HIS WORD
('Cresswell' 88.97.10 7.)

2. Love is his way, love is his mark,
sharing his last Passover feast,
Christ at his table, host to the Twelve,
love, only love, is his mark.

3. Love is his mark, love is his sign,
bread for our strength, wine for our joy,
'This is my body, this is my blood,'
love, only, love, is his sign.

4. Love is his sign, love is his news,
'Do this,' he said, 'lest you forget
all my deep sorrow, all my dear blood,'
love, only love, is his news.

5. Love is his news, love is his name,
we are his own, chosen and called,
family, brethren, cousins and kin.
Love, only love, is his name.

6. Love is his name, love is his law.
Hear his command, all who are his,
'Love one another, I have loved you.'
Love, only love, is his law.

7. Love is his law, love is his word:
love of the Lord, Father and Word,
love of the Spirit, God ever one,
love, only love, is his word.

Words: Luke Connaughton
Music: Anthony Milner

LOVE'S REDEEMING WORK IS DONE
('Savannah' 77.77.)

[HARMONY]

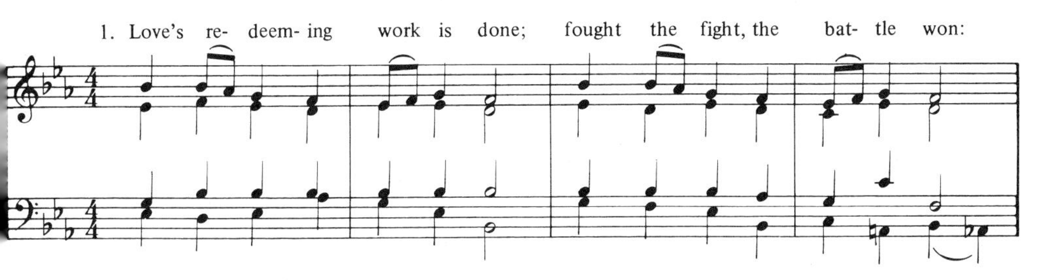

This tune may be found in a lower key at Hymn 425

2. Vain the stone, the watch, the seal;
   Christ has burst the gates of hell;
   death in vain forbids his rise;
   Christ has opened Paradise.

3. Lives again our glorious King;
   where, O death, is now thy sting?
   Dying once, he all doth save;
   where thy victory, O grave?

4. Soar we now where Christ has led,
   following our exalted Head;
   made like him, like him we rise;
   ours the cross, the grave, the skies.

5. Hail the Lord of earth and heaven!
   praise to thee by both be given:
   thee we greet triumphant now;
   hail, the Resurrection thou!

Words: Charles Wesley (1707-88)
Music: John Wesley's 'Foundery Collection' (1742)

LOVING SHEPHERD OF THY SHEEP

316

('Buckland' 77.77.)

[HARMONY]

2. Loving Saviour, thou didst give
thine own life that we might live;
and the hands outstretched to bless
bear the cruel nails' impress.

3. I would bless thee every day,
gladly all thy will obey,
like thy blessed ones above,
happy in thy precious love.

4. Loving Shepherd, ever near,
teach thy lamb thy voice to hear;
suffer not my steps to stray
from the straight and narrow way.

5. Where thou leadest I would go,
walking in thy steps below,
till before my Father's throne
I shall know as I am known.

Words: Jane E. Leeson (1807-82)
Music: L. G. Hayne (1836-83)

LOW IN THE GRAVE HE LAY

('Christ arose' 65.64. & Chorus)

[HARMONY]

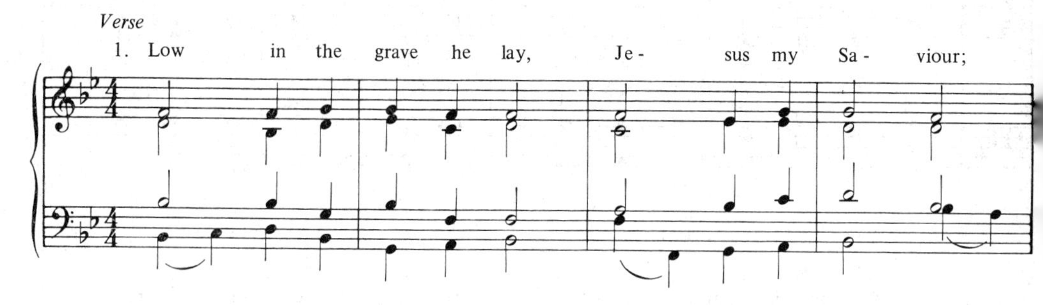

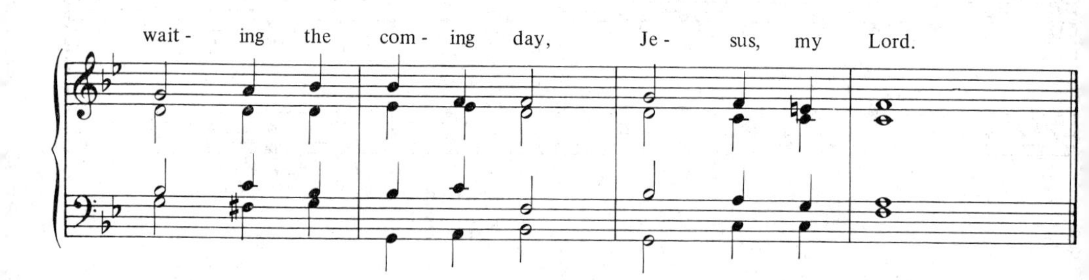

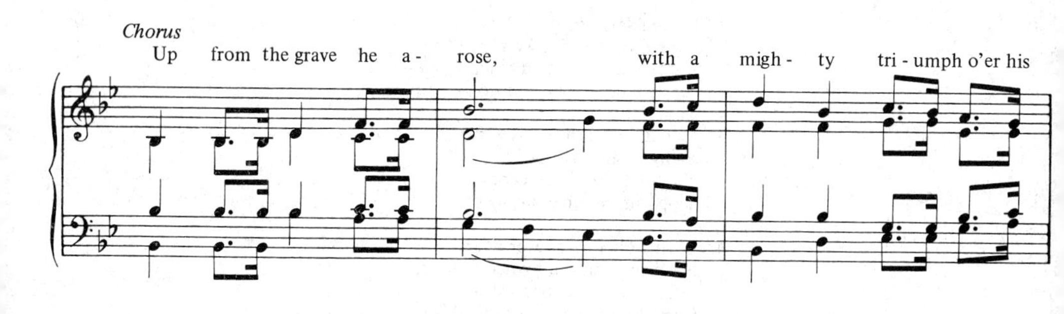

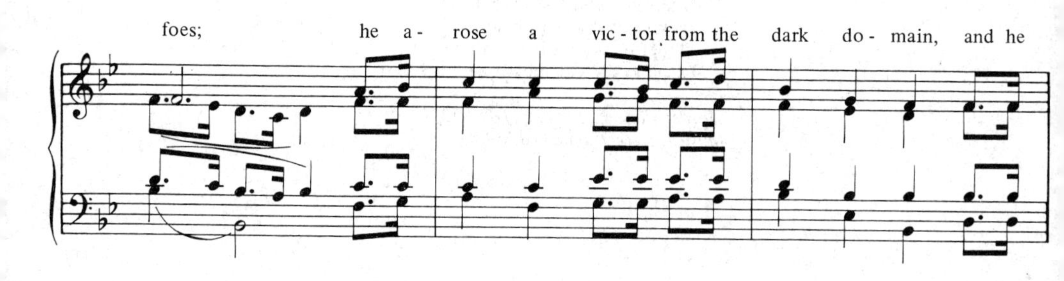

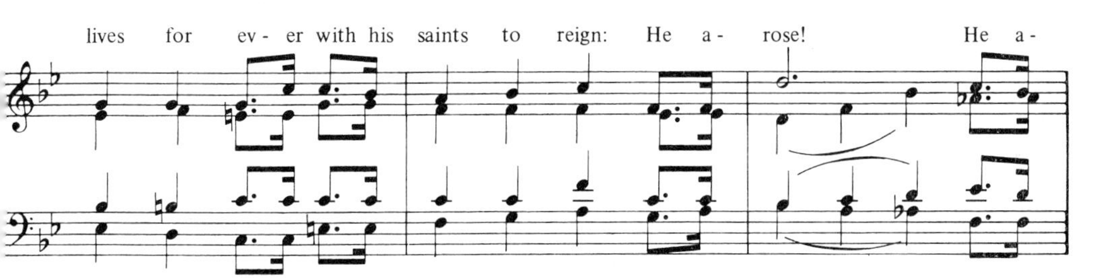

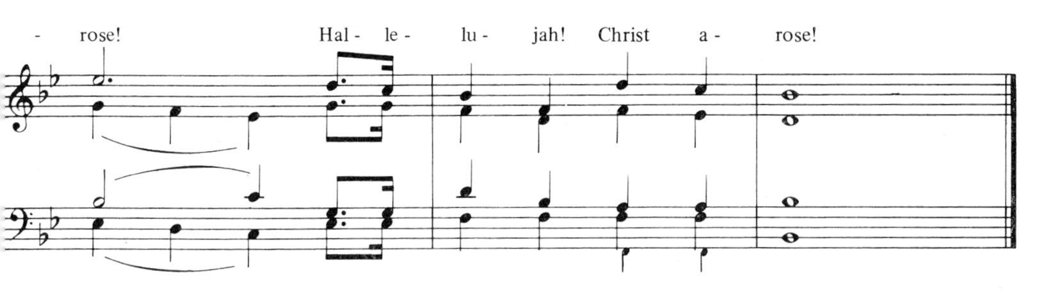

2. Vainly they watch his bed,
   Jesus, my Saviour;
   vainly they seal the dead,
   Jesus, my Lord.

3. Death cannot keep his prey,
   Jesus, my Saviour;
   he tore the bars away,
   Jesus, my Lord.

Words and Music: Robert Lowry (1826-99)

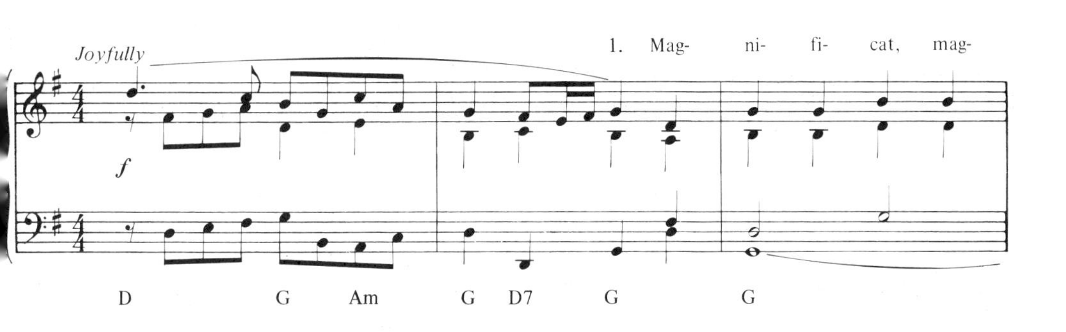
Joyfully
1. Mag- ni- fi- cat, mag-
f
D G Am G D7 G G

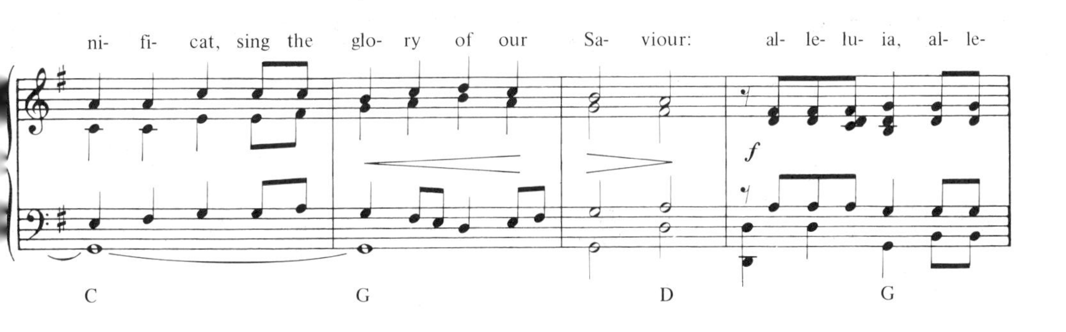
ni- fi- cat, sing the glo- ry of our Sa- viour: al- le- lu- ia, al- le-
f
C G D G

lu- ia, al- le- lu- ia.
ff
D A D G C G D G

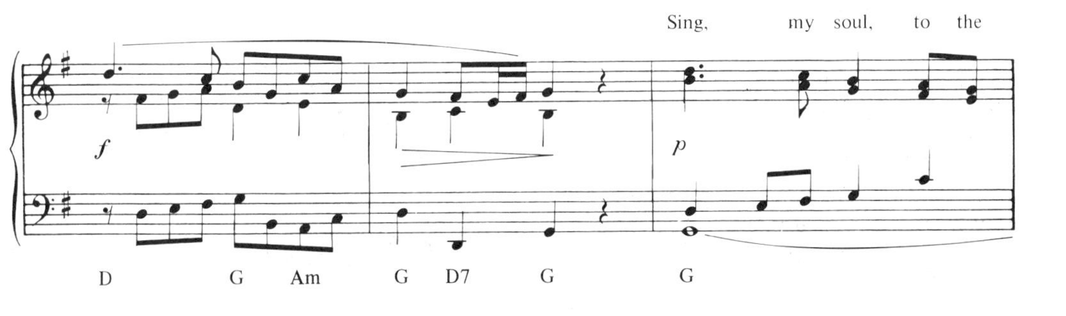
Sing, my soul, to the
f
p
D G Am G D7 G G

glo- ry of my Sa- viour; let all with- in me sing his prai- ses.
D C G D C D G
al- le- lu- ia, al- le- lu- ia, al- le- lu- ia.
f
ff
D G D A D G C G D G
All cre- a- tion, gaze in won- der,
f
D G Am G D7 G C G7 C
see be- fore you God al- migh- ty. Al- le- lu- ia, al- le- lu- ia,
Am D G D A D
al- le- lu- ia.
G C G D G D G Am G D7 G

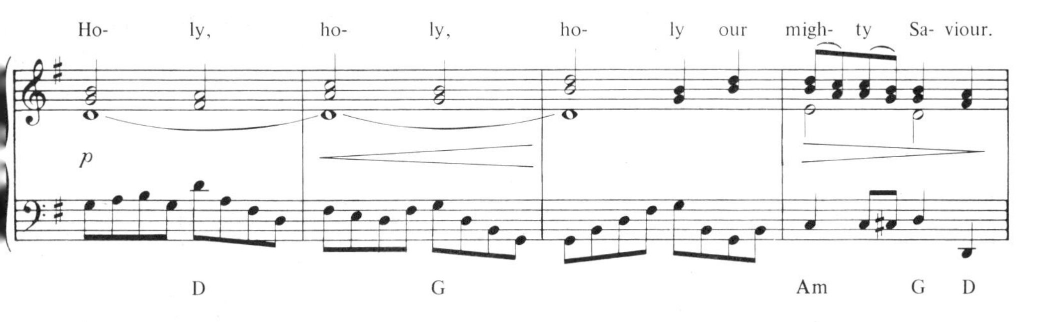

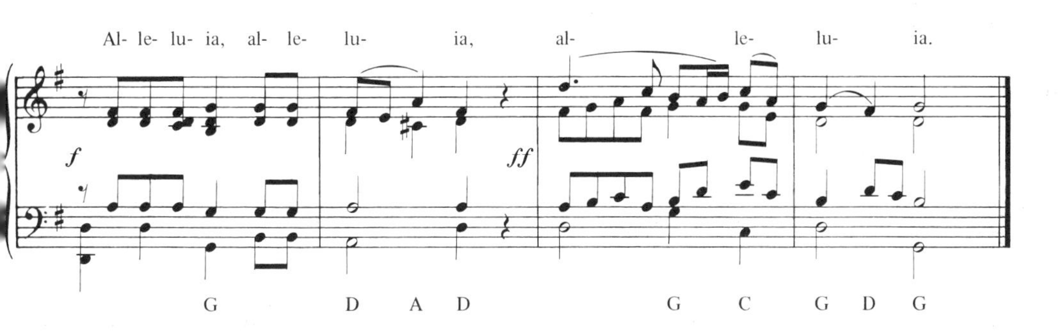

2. Magnificat, magnificat,
sing the glory of our Saviour!
Alleluia, alleluia, alleluia.
Still, my soul, for he raises up the lowly;
the rich and proud he will not welcome.
Alleluia, alleluia, alleluia!
He will feast the poor and hungry
at his banquet of salvation.
Alleluia, alleluia, alleluia!
Holy, holy, holy our mighty Saviour.
Alleluia, alleluia, alleluia!

Words, based on Luke 1: 46-55: Kevin Mayhew
Music: Samuel Webbe (1740-1816), arranged by Kevin Mayhew

MAJESTY, WORSHIP HIS MAJESTY

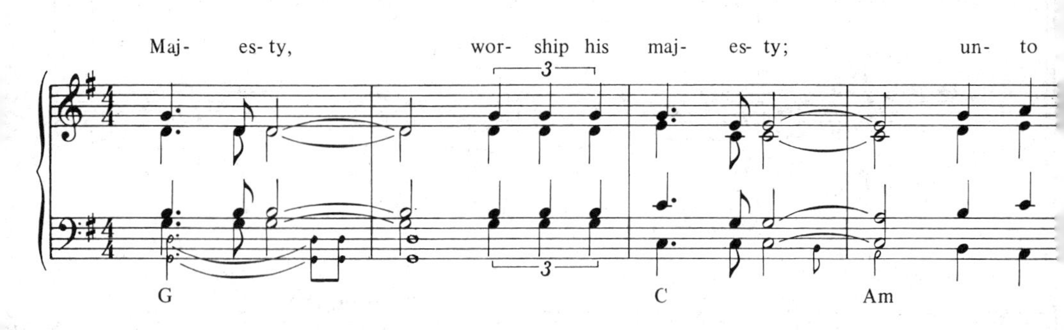

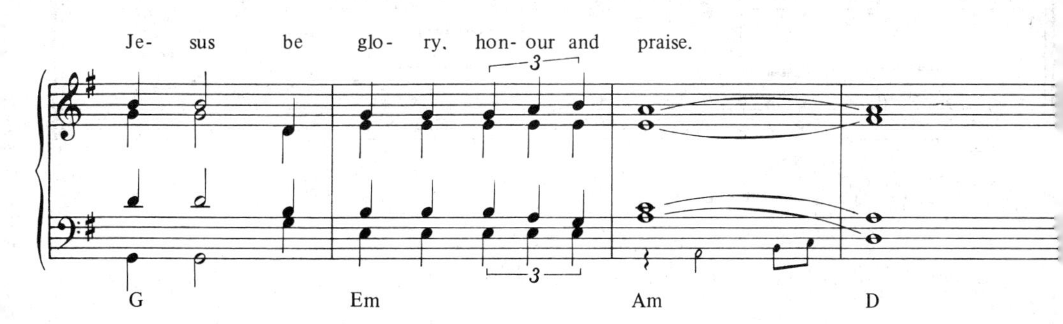

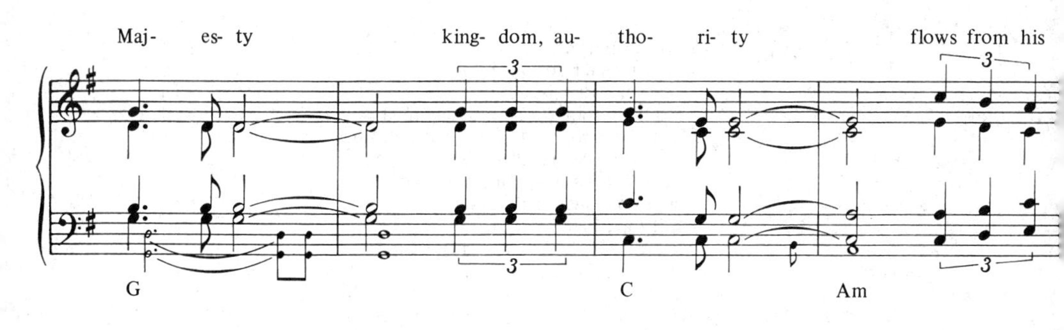

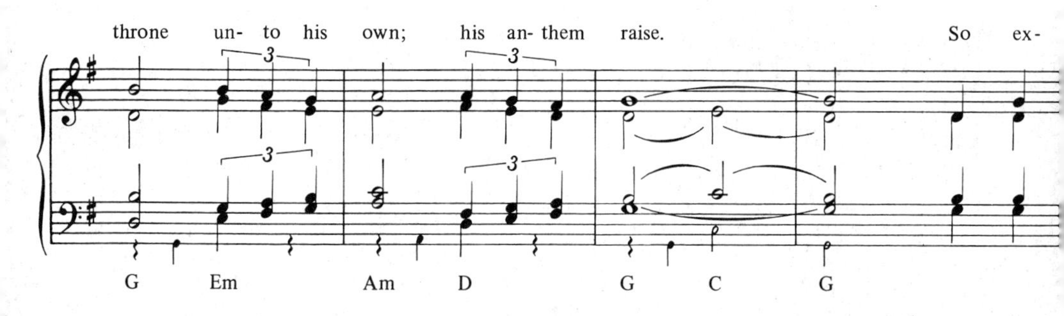

Words and Music: Jack W. Hayford

320

MAKE ME A CHANNEL OF YOUR PEACE

('St Francis')

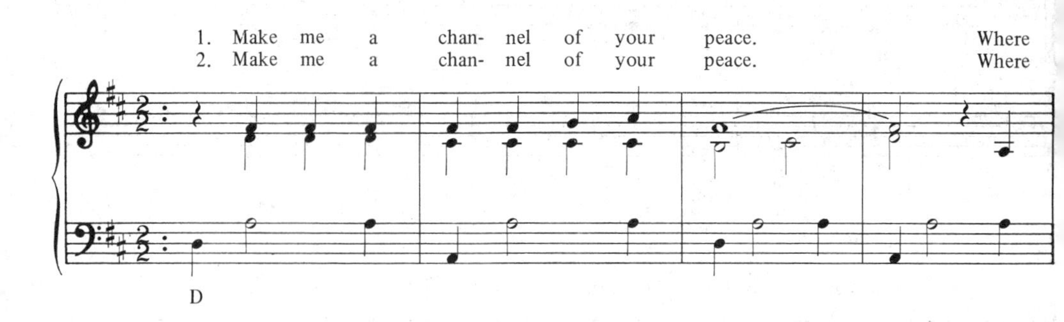

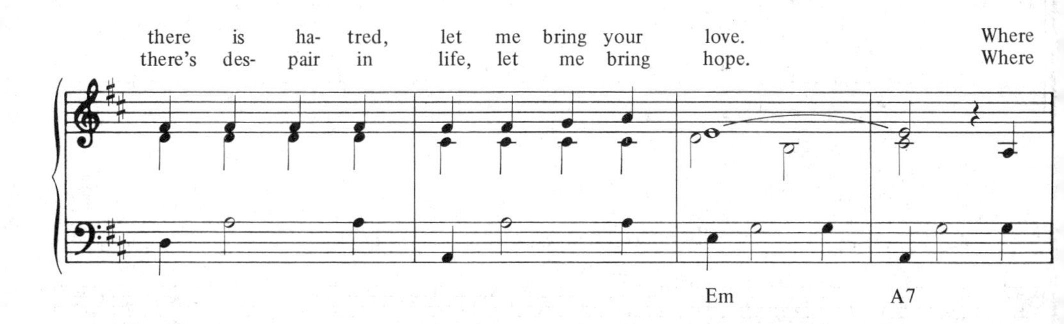

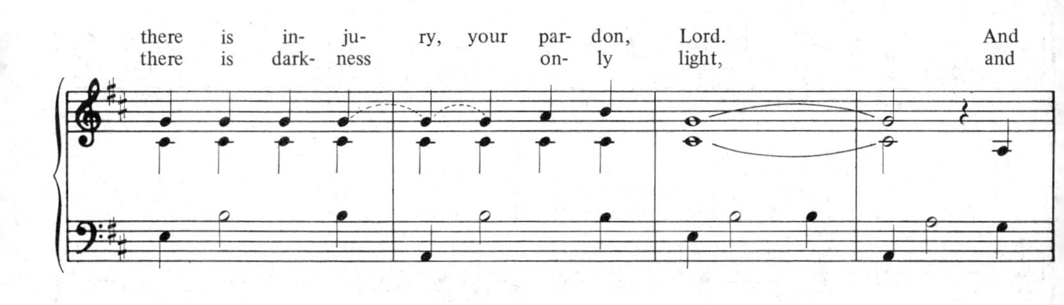

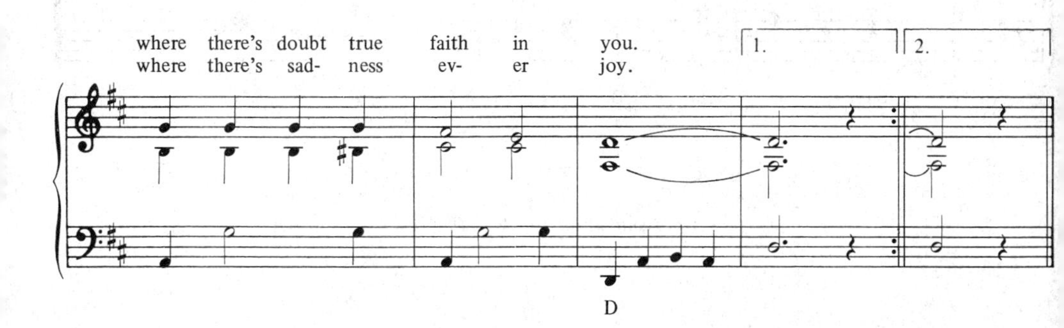

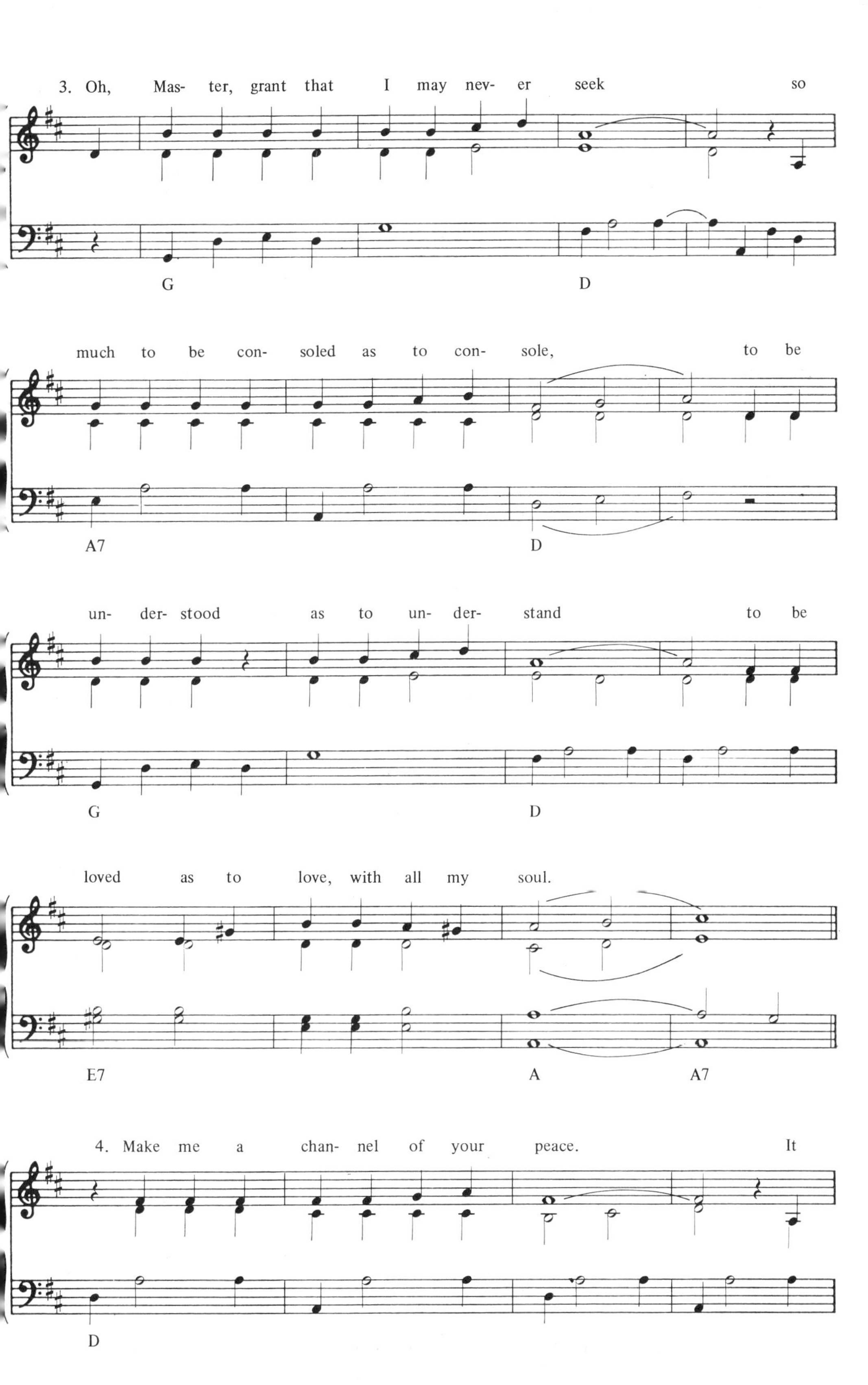
3. Oh, Mas- ter, grant that I may nev- er seek so
G D
much to be con- soled as to con- sole, to be
A7 D
un- der- stood as to un- der- stand to be
G D
loved as to love, with all my soul.
E7 A A7
4. Make me a chan- nel of your peace. It
D

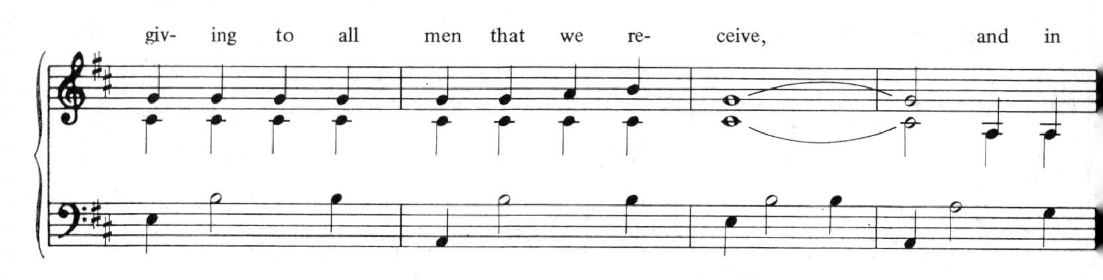

Words, based on Francis of Assisi, and
Music: Sebastian Temple

MARY HAD A BABY

2. What did she name him?
   Yes, Lord.
   What did she name him?
   Yes, my Lord.
   What did she name him?

3. She named him Jesus.
   Yes, Lord.
   She named him Jesus.
   Yes, my Lord.
   She named him Jesus.

4. Where was he born?
   Yes, Lord.
   Where was he born?
   Yes, my Lord.
   Where was he born?

5. Born in a stable.
   Yes, Lord.
   Born in a stable.
   Yes, my Lord.
   Born in a stable.

6. Where did she lay him?
   Yes, Lord.
   Where did she lay him?
   Yes, my Lord.
   Where did she lay him?

7. Laid him in a manger.
   Yes, Lord.
   Laid him in a manger.
   Yes, my Lord.
   Laid him in a manger.

Words and Music: Spiritual, arranged by Frances M. Kelly

Chorus
May all be one in har- mo- ny and love, in spi- rit and in
A D Asus4 A

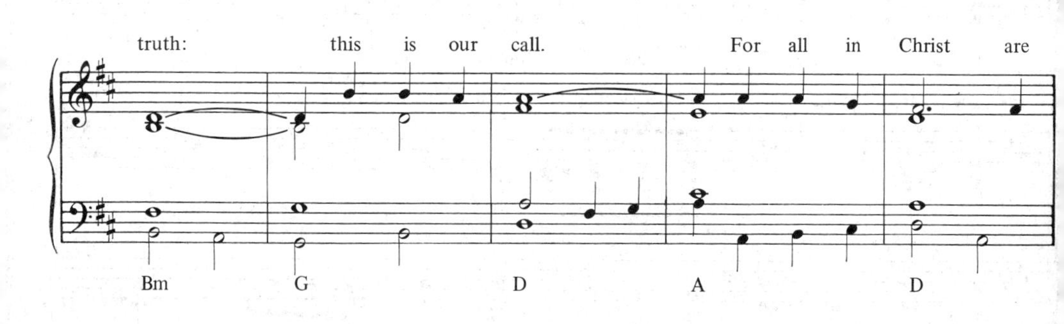
truth: this is our call. For all in Christ are
Bm G D A D

chil- dren of one God, and since he loves us all, we shall be
Asus4 A Bm G A

Where verse follows
one.
Last time
one.
Verse
1. My Fa- ther's
D D G A

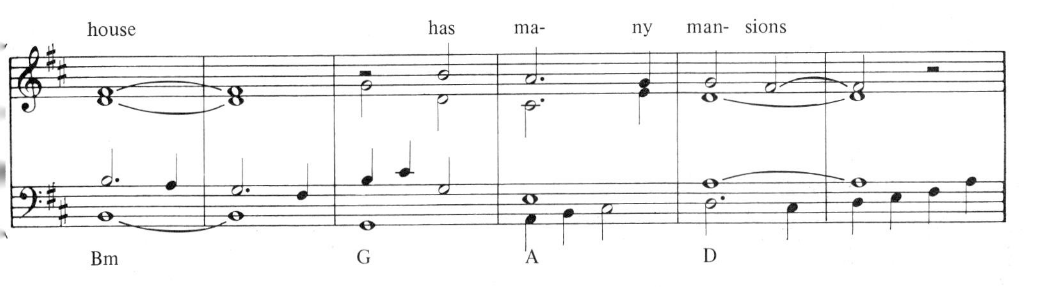

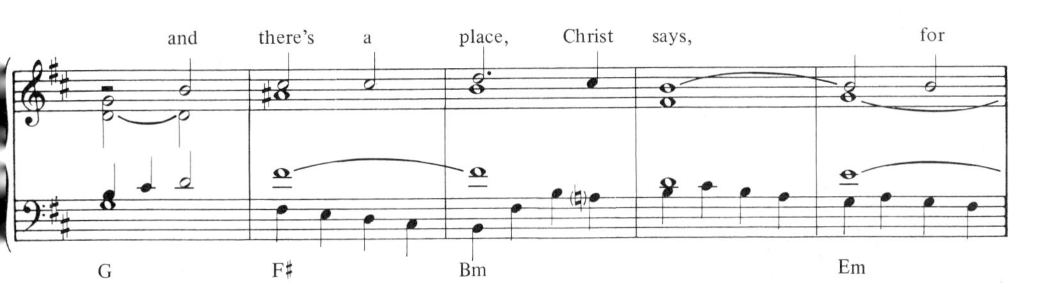

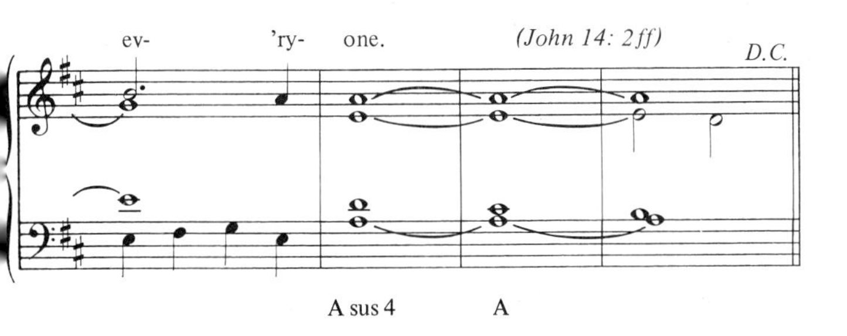

2. There is one Lord, there is one Spirit,
   one birth in me, Christ says, one Father God. *(Ephesians 4: 6)*

3. There is one God; one mediator,
   himself a man, Lord Christ, who ransoms all. *(1 Tim. 2: 5)*

Words, based on Scripture: Andrew Monaghan
Music: Kathleen Donnelly,
arranged by Frances M. Kelly

MAY THE GRACE OF CHRIST OUR SAVIOUR

('Waltham' 87.87.)

[HARMONY]

2. Thus may we abide in union
with each other and the Lord,
and possess, in sweet communion,
joys which earth cannot afford.

Words: John Newton (1725-1807)
Music: Melody by Heinrich Albert (1604-51), harmonised by J. S. Bach (1685-1750)

MAY THE MIND OF CHRIST MY SAVIOUR

('St Leonards' 87.85.)

[HARMONY]

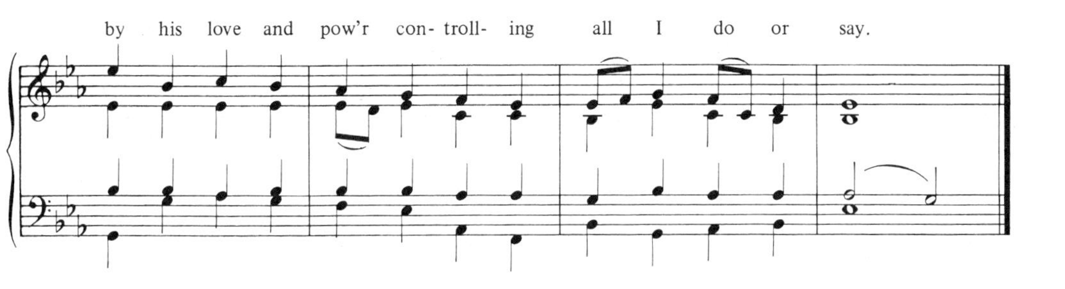

2. May the word of God dwell richly
in my heart from hour to hour,
so that all may see I triumph
only through his power.

3. May the peace of God my Father
rule my life in everything,
that I may be calm to comfort
sick and sorrowing.

4. May the love of Jesus fill me
as the waters fill the sea;
him exalting, self abasing,
this is victory.

5. May I run the race before me,
strong and brave to face the foe,
looking only unto Jesus
as I onward go.

Words: Kate B. Wilkinson (1859-1928)
Music: A.C. Barham Gould (1891-1953)

MINE EYES HAVE SEEN THE GLORY

('Battle hymn' 77.87.87 & Chorus)

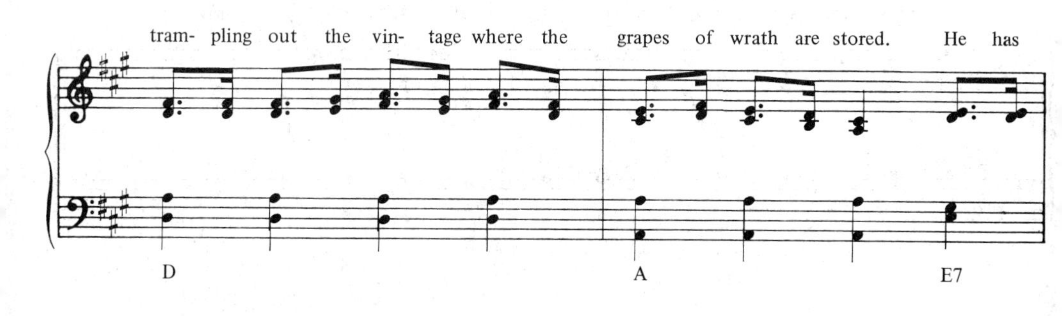

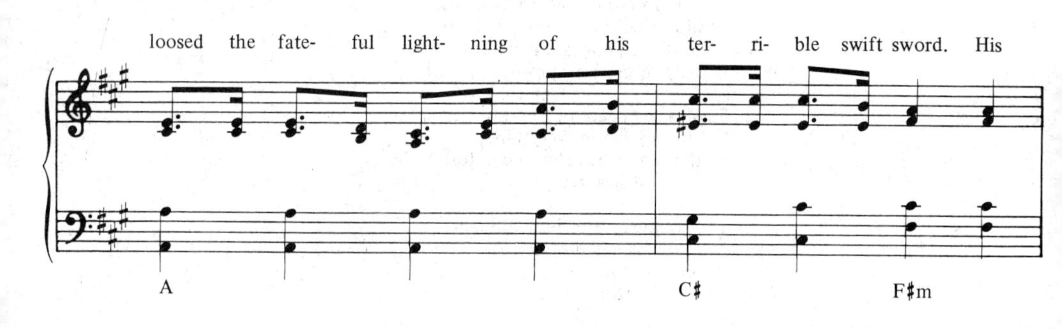

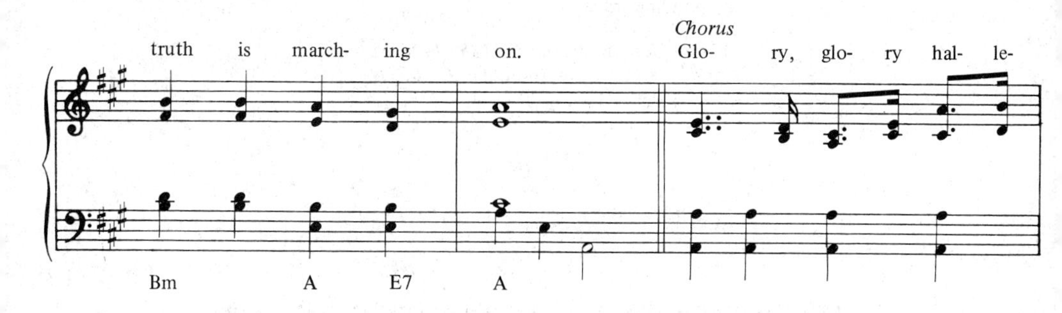

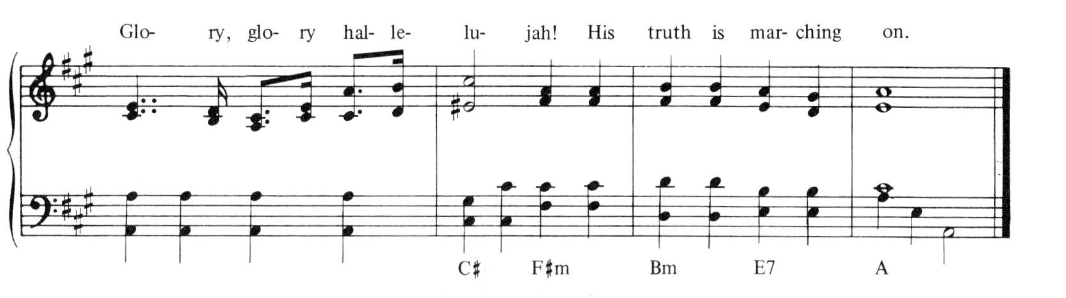

2. I have seen him in the watchfires of a hundred circling camps.
   They have gilded him an altar in the evening dews and damps.
   I can read his righteous sentence by the dim and flaring lamps.
   His day is marching on.

   Glory, glory, hallelujah! Glory, glory, hallelujah!
   Glory, glory, hallelujah! His truth is marching on.

3. He has sounded forth the trumpet that shall never sound retreat.
   He is sifting out the hearts of men before his judgment seat,
   O, be swift my soul to answer him, be jubilant, my feet!
   Our God is marching on.

4. In the beauty of the lilies Christ was born across the sea
   with a glory in his bosom that transfigures you and me.
   As he died to make men holy, let us live to make men free,
   whilst God is marching on.

Words: Julia W. Howe (1819-1910)
Music: (?) William Steffe (c. 1850),
arranged by John Rombaut

MORNING HAS BROKEN
('Bunessan' 55.54.D.)

A different arrangement of this tune is at Hymn 62

2. Sweet the rain's new fall sunlit from heaven,
like the first dew-fall on the first grass.
Praise for the sweetness of the wet garden,
sprung in completeness where his feet pass.

3. Mine is the sunlight! Mine is the morning
born of the one light Eden saw play!
Praise with elation, praise ev'ry morning,
God's re-creation of the new day!

Words: Eleanor Farjeon (1881-1965)
Music: Traditional Gaelic Melody, arranged by John Rombaut

327 MOSES, I KNOW YOU'RE THE MAN (The people of God)

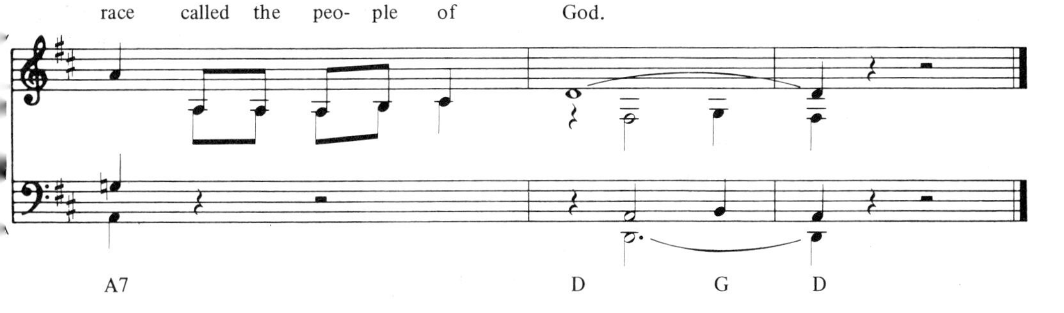

2. 'Don't get too set in your ways,' the Lord said.
'Each step is only a phase,' the Lord said.
'I'll go before you and I shall be a sign
to guide my travelling, wandering race.
You're the people of God.'

3. 'No matter what you may do,' the Lord said,
'I shall be faithful and true,' the Lord said.
'My love will strengthen you as you go along,
for you're my travelling, wandering race.
You're the people of God.'

4. 'Look at the birds in the air,' the Lord said,
'they fly unhampered by care,' the Lord said.
'You will move easier if you're travelling light,
for you're a wandering, vagabond race.
You're the people of God.'

5. 'Foxes have places to go,' the Lord said,
'but I've no home here below,' the Lord said.
'So if you want to be with me all your days,
keep up the moving and travelling on.
You're the people of God.'

Words and Music: Estelle White

MY FAITH IT IS AN OAKEN STAFF

('The staff of faith' 86.86.88.86.)

2. My faith, it is an oaken staff,
O let me on it lean;
my faith, it is a trusty sword,
may falsehood find it keen.
Thy spirit, Lord, to me impart,
O make me what thou ever art,
of patient and courageous heart,
as all true saints have been.

Words: Thomas Lynch
Music: Unknown

MY FAITH LOOKS UP TO THEE

('Olivet' 664.666.4.)

329

2. May thy rich grace impart
strength to my fainting heart,
my zeal inspire;
as thou hast died for me,
O may my love to thee
pure, warm, and changeless be,
a living fire.

3. While life's dark maze I tread,
and griefs around me spread,
be thou my guide;
bid darkness turn to day,
wipe sorrow's tears away,
nor let me ever stray
from thee aside.

4. When ends life's transient dream,
when death's cold sullen stream
shall o'er me roll,
blest Saviour, then in love
fear and distrust remove;
O bear me safe above,
a ransomed soul.

Words: Ray Palmer (1808-87)
Music: Lowell Mason (1792-1872)

MY GOD, ACCEPT MY HEART THIS DAY

(First tune: 'Belmont' C.M.)

[HARMONY]

2. Before the cross of him who died,
behold, I prostrate fall;
let every sin be crucified,
and Christ be all in all.

3. Anoint me with thy heavenly grace,
and seal me for thine own,
that I may see thy glorious face,
and worship at thy throne.

4. Let every thought, and work and word
to thee be ever given,
then life shall be thy service, Lord,
and death the gate of heaven.

5. All glory to the Father be,
all glory to the Son,
all glory, Holy Ghost, to thee
while endless ages run.

Words: Matthew Bridges (1800-94)
Music: First tune - from 'Islington Psalmody' (1854)

MY GOD, ACCEPT MY HEART THIS DAY
(Second tune: 'St Peter' C.M.)

2. Before the cross of him who died,
behold, I prostrate fall;
let every sin be crucified,
and Christ be all in all.

3. Anoint me with thy heavenly grace,
and seal me for thine own.
that I may see thy glorious face,
and worship at thy throne.

4. Let every thought and work and word
to thee be ever given:
then life shall be thy service, Lord,
and death the gate of heaven.

5. All glory to the Father be,
all glory to the Son,
all glory, Holy Ghost, to thee,
while endless ages run.

Words: Matthew Bridges (1800-94)
Music: Second tune - Alexander Robert Reinagle (1799-1877)

This tune may be found in a higher key at Hymn 206

331

MY GOD, AND IS THY TABLE SPREAD

('Rockingham' L.M.)

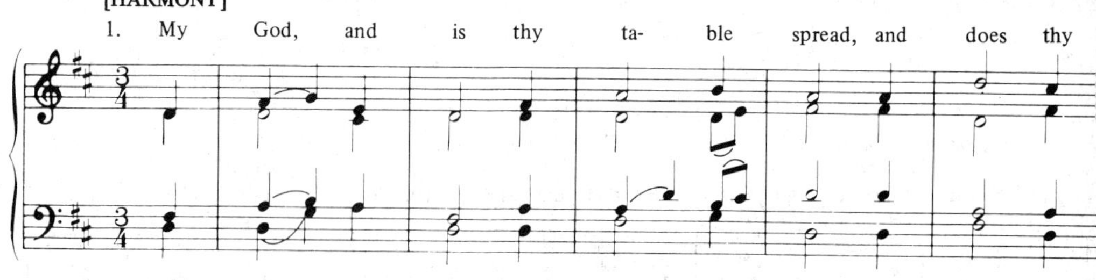

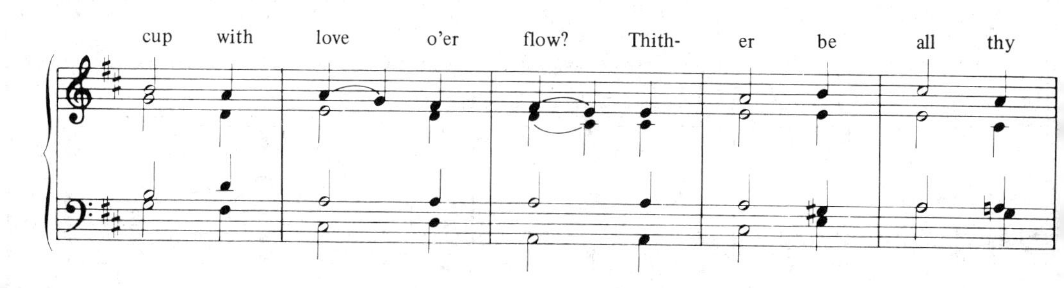

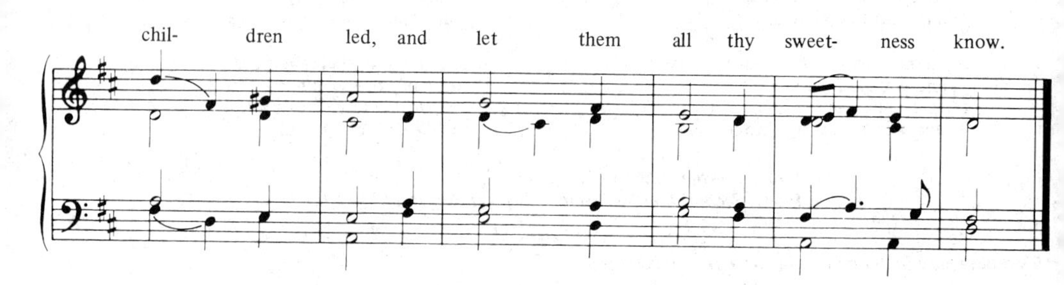

2. Hail, sacred feast, which Jesus makes!
Rich banquet of his flesh and blood!
Thrice happy he, who here partakes
that sacred stream, that heavenly food.

3. O let thy table honoured be,
and furnished well with joyful guests;
and may each soul salvation see,
that here its sacred pledges tastes.

Words: Philip Doddridge (1702-51)
Music: adapted by E. Miller (1735-1807)

MY GOD, HOW WONDERFUL THOU ART
('Westminster' C.M.)

[HARMONY]

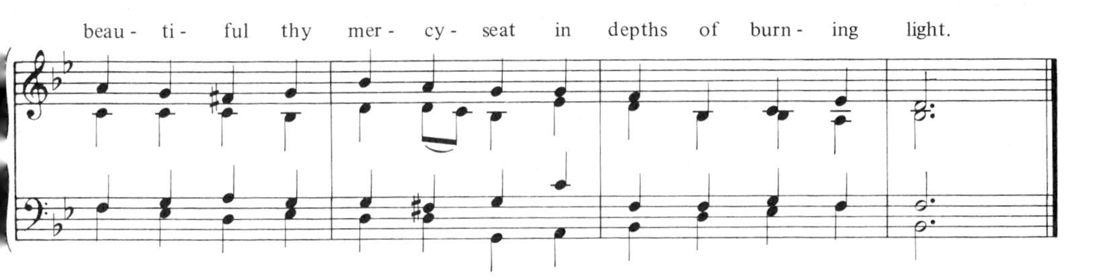

2. How dread are thine eternal years,
   O everlasting Lord!
   By prostrate spirits day and night
   incessantly adored.

3. How wonderful, how beautiful
   the sight of thee must be,
   thine endless wisdom, boundless power
   and awesome purity!

4. Oh, how I fear thee, living God!
   with deepest tenderest fears,
   and worship thee with trembling hope
   and penitential tears.

5. Yet I may love thee too, O Lord,
   almighty as thou art,
   for thou hast stooped to ask of me
   the love of my poor heart.

6. No earthly father loves like thee,
   no mother, e'er so mild,
   bears and forbears as thou hast done
   with me thy sinful child.

7. Father of Jesus, love's reward,
   what rapture will it be,
   prostrate before thy throne to lie,
   and gaze and gaze on thee!

Words: Frederick William Faber (1814-63)
Music: James Turle (1802-82)

MY GOD I LOVE THEE
('St Francis Xavier' C.M.)

[HARMONY]

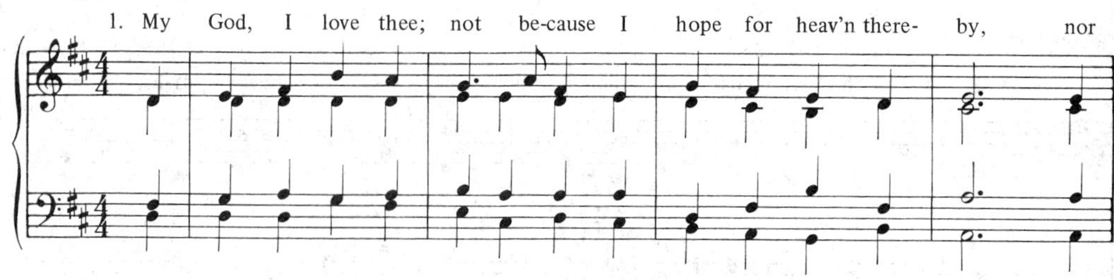

2. Thou, O my Jesus, thou didst me
upon the cross embrace;
for me didst bear the nails and spear,
and manifold disgrace.

3. And griefs and torments numberless,
and sweat of agony;
yea, death itself – and all for me
who was thine enemy.

4. Then why, O blessed Jesu Christ,
should I not love thee well?
not for the sake of winning heaven,
nor of escaping hell;

5. Not from the hope of gaining aught,
not seeking a reward;
but as thyself hast lovèd me,
O ever-loving Lord.

6. E'en so I love thee, and will love,
and in thy praise will sing;
solely because thou art my God,
and my eternal King.

Words: from the Latin (17th century),
tr. E. Caswall
Music: John Stainer (1840-1901)

MY GOD LOVES ME

('Plaisir d'amour')

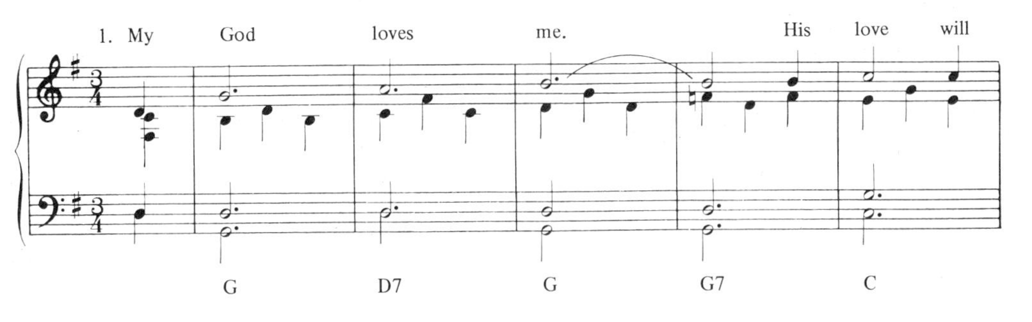

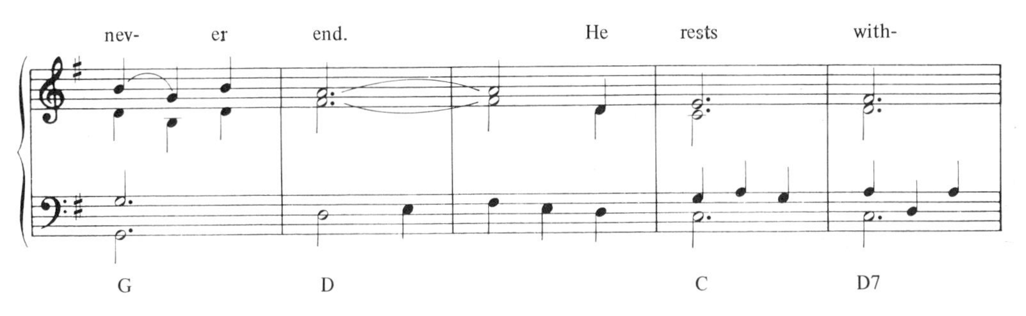

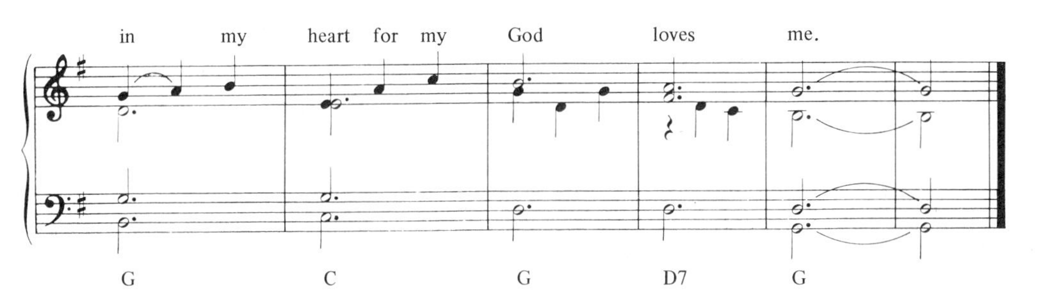

2. His gentle hand he stretches over me.
   Though storm-clouds threaten the day
   he will set me free.

3. He comes to me in sharing bread and wine.
   He brings me life that will reach
   past the end of time.

4. My God loves me, his faithful love endures.
   And I will live like a child
   held in love secure.

5. The joys of love as offerings now we bring.
   The pains of love will be lost
   in the praise we sing.

Words: Verse 1 Unknown,
Verses 2-5 Sandra Joan Billington
Music: Traditional, arranged by Michael Irwin

335

MY HOPE IS BUILT ON NOTHING LESS

(First tune: St Catherine' 88.88.88.)

[HARMONY]

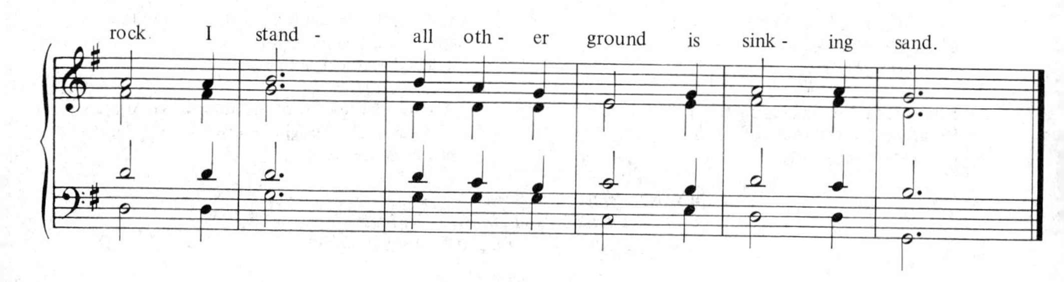

Words: Edward Mote (1797-1874)
Music: First tune - H. F. Hemy (1818-88),
adapted by J. G. Walton (1821-1905)

MY HOPE IS BUILT ON NOTHING LESS

(Second tune: 'Solid rock' 88.88.88.)

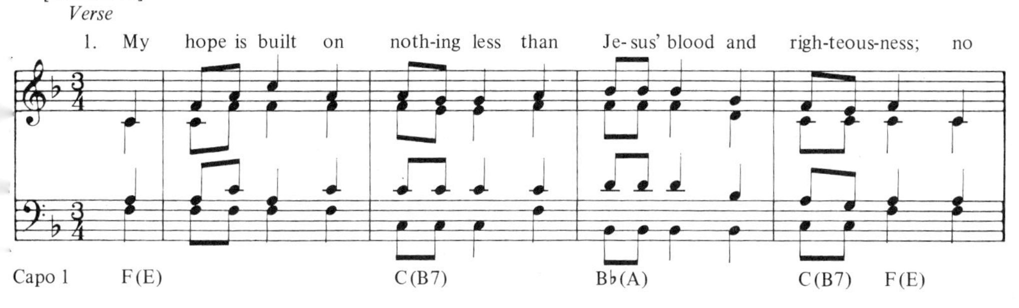

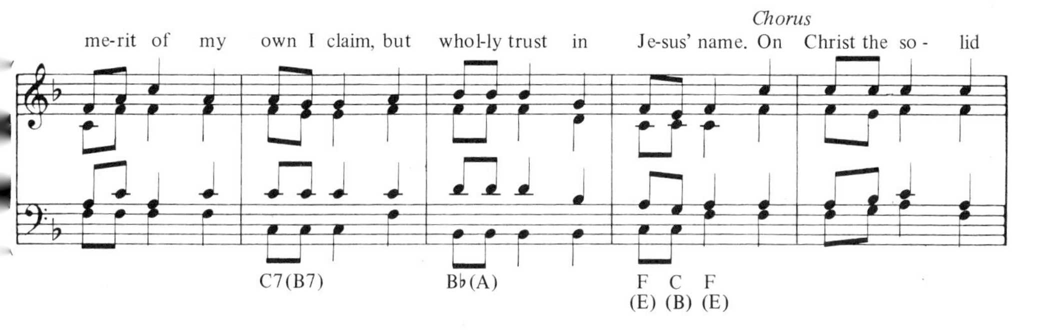

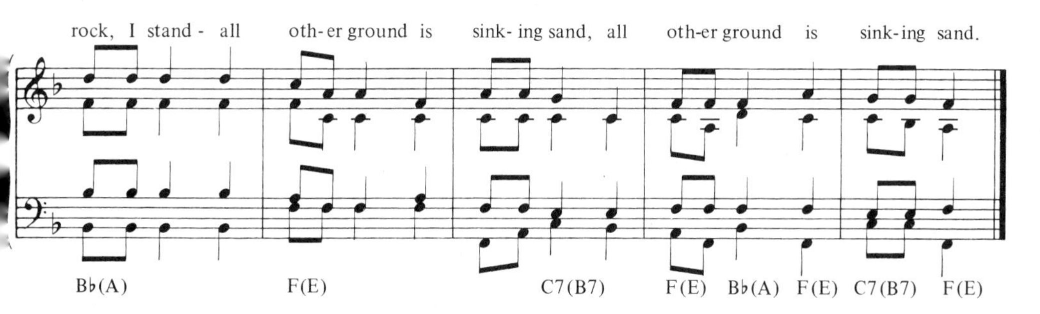

2. When weary in this earthly race,
 I rest on his unchanging grace;
 in every wild and stormy gale
 my anchor holds and will not fail.

3. His vow, his covenant and blood
 are my defence against the flood;
 when earthly hopes are swept away
 he will uphold me on that day.

4. When the last trumpet's voice shall sound,
 O may I then in him be found!
 Clothed in his righteousness alone,
 faultless to stand before his throne.

Words: Edward Mote (1797-1874)
Music: Second tune - William B. Bradbury

336

MY PEOPLE, WHAT HAVE I DONE TO YO

('Reproaches' 98.78.78

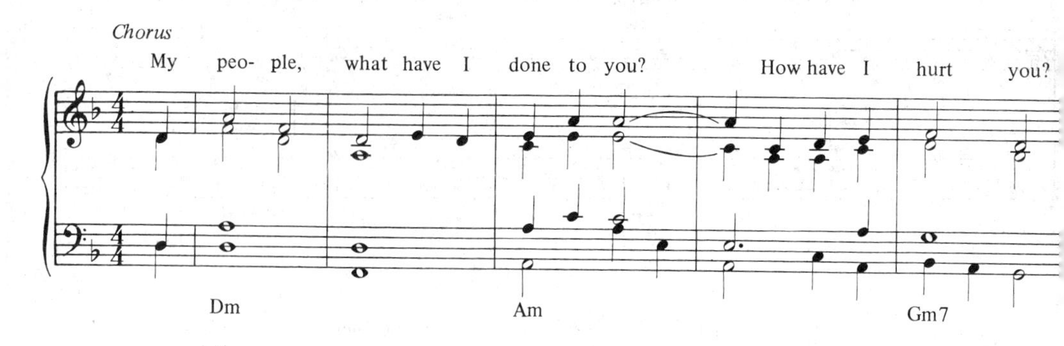

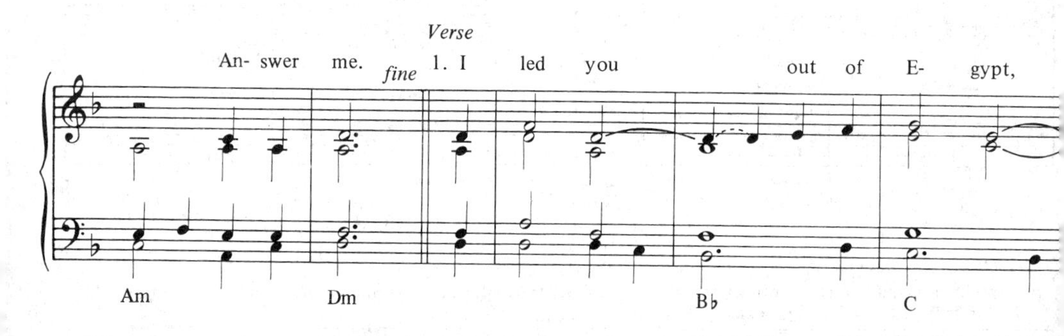

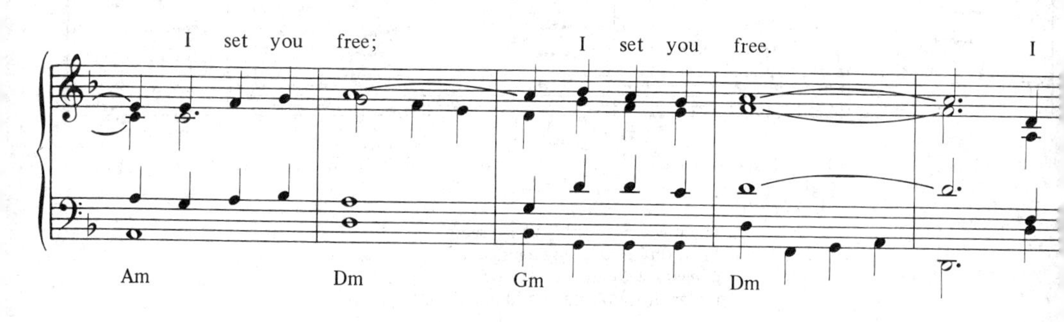

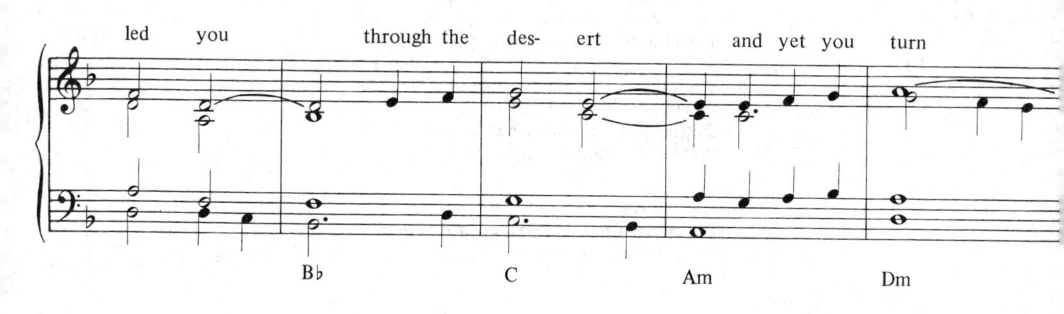

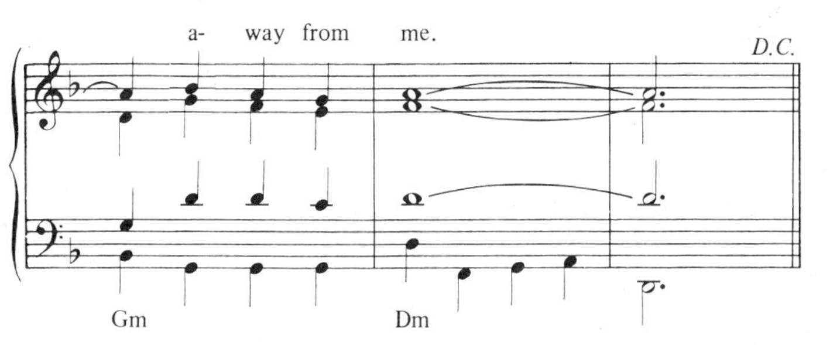

2. I fed you in the desert,
I led you through the raging sea.
I gave you saving water
and yet you found a cross for me.

3. I gave you a royal sceptre;
you offered me a crown of thorns.
I raised you as a nation;
you mocked and treated me with scorn.

Words and Music: Francesca Leftley,
arranged by Frances M. Kelly

337

MY SONG IS LOVE UNKNOWN

('Love unknown' 66.66.44.44.)

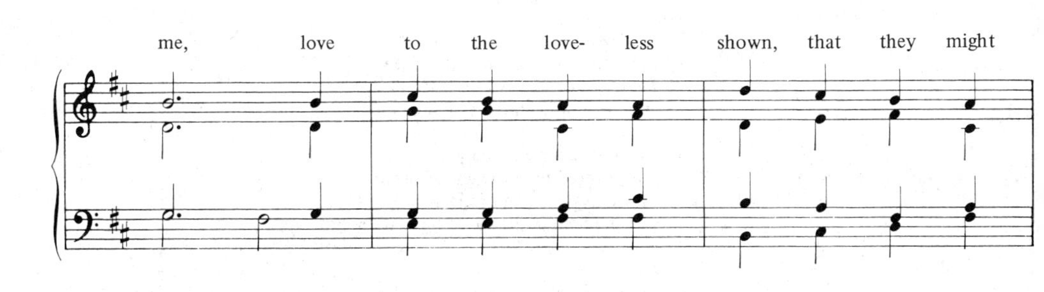

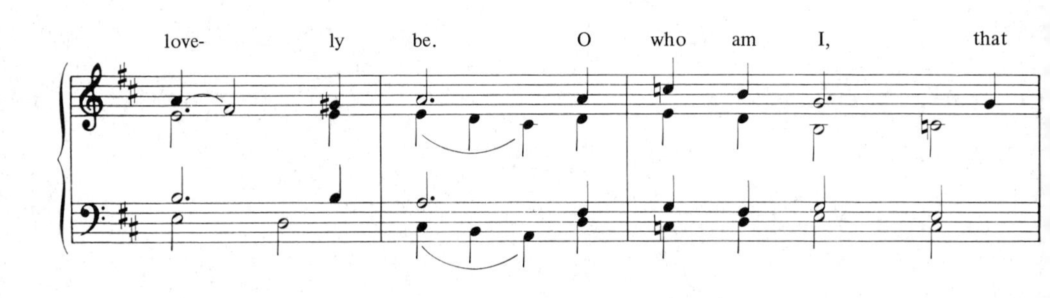

2. He came from his blest throne,
salvation to bestow;
but men made strange, and none
the longed-for Christ would know,
but O, my friend, my friend indeed,
who at my need his life did spend!

3. Sometimes they strew his way,
and his sweet praises sing;
resounding all the day
hosannas to their King;
then 'Crucify!' is all their breath,
and for his death they thirst and cry.

4. Why, what hath my Lord done?
What makes this rage and spite?
He made the lame to run,
he gave the blind their sight.
Sweet injuries! Yet they at these
themselves displease, and 'gainst him rise.

5. They rise, and needs will have
my dear Lord made away;
a murderer they save,
the Prince of Life they slay.
Yet cheerful he to suffering goes,
that he his foes from thence might free.

6. Here might I stay and sing,
no story so divine;
never was love, dear King,
never was grief like thine.
This is my friend in whose sweet praise
I all my days could gladly spend.

Words: Samuel Crossman (c. 1624-84)
Music: John Ireland (1879-1962)

This tune may be found in a higher key at Hymn 148

MY SOUL DOTH MAGNIFY THE LORD

Words: Luke 1:46-47, 49
Music: Unknown, arranged by Betty Pulkingham

NEARER, MY GOD TO THEE

('Horbury' 64.64.664.)

[HARMONY]

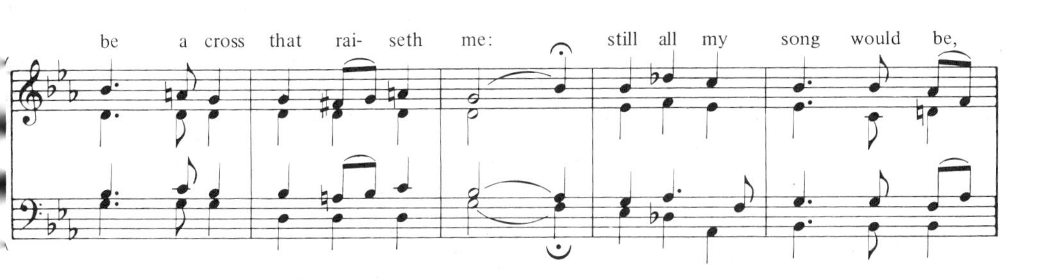

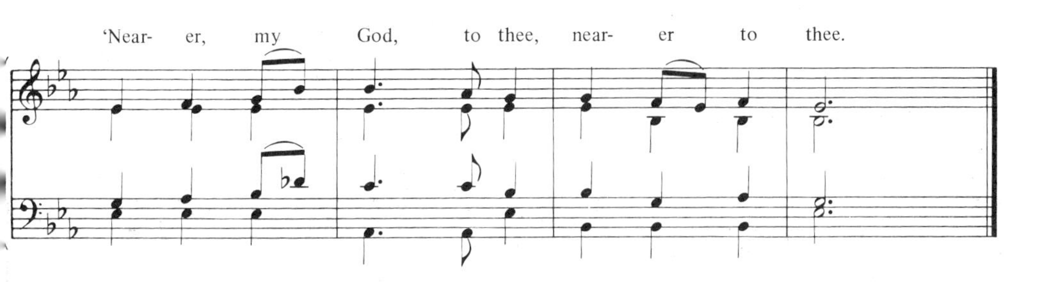

2. Though, like the wanderer
the sun gone down,
darkness be over me,
my rest a stone;
yet in my dreams I'd be
nearer, my God, to thee,
nearer to thee!

3. There let the way appear,
steps unto heaven;
all that thou send'st to me
in mercy given:
angels to beckon me
nearer, my God, to thee,
nearer to thee!

Words: Sarah F. Adams (1805-48)
Music: John B. Dykes (1823-76)

NEAR THE HEART OF JESUS

2. Near the mind of Jesus,
   here we find what Jesus
   wills for the friends of Jesus
   constantly.

3. Near the feet of Jesus,
   here we meet with Jesus,
   guiding the friends of Jesus
   patiently.

4. Near the arms of Jesus,
   here the calm of Jesus
   comforts the friends of Jesus
   ceaselessly.

Words and Music: *Susan Sayers, arranged by Frances M. Kelly*

Alternative keyboard accompaniment.

NEW EVERY MORNING IS THE LOVE
('Melcombe' L.M.)

[HARMONY]

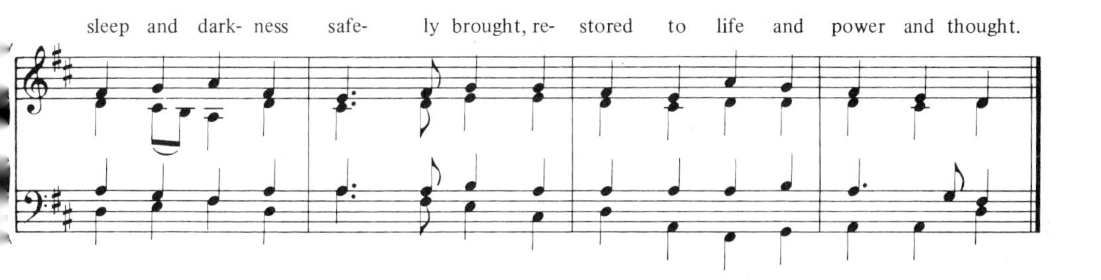

2. New mercies, each returning day,
hover around us while we pray;
new perils past, new sins forgiven,
new thoughts of God, new hopes of heaven.

3. If on our daily course our mind
be set to hallow all we find,
new treasures still, of countless price,
God will provide for sacrifice.

4. Old friends, old scenes, will lovelier be,
as more of heaven in each we see;
some softening gleam of love and prayer
shall dawn on every cross and care.

5. We need not bid, for cloistered cell,
our neighbour and our work farewell,
nor strive to wind ourselves too high
for sinful man beneath the sky.

6. The trivial round, the common task,
will furnish all we need to ask,
room to deny ourselves, a road
to bring us daily nearer God.

7. Only, O Lord, in thy dear love
fit us for perfect rest above;
and help us, this and every day,
to live more nearly as we pray.

Words, based on Lamentations 3:23 : John Keble (1792-1866)
Music: Samuel Webbe (1740-1816)

This song should be acted out by the characters, with everyone joining together for the second part of Verse 3 and the Chorus.

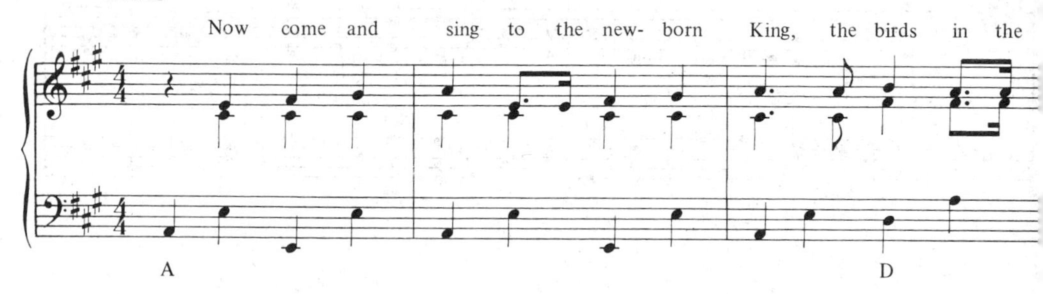

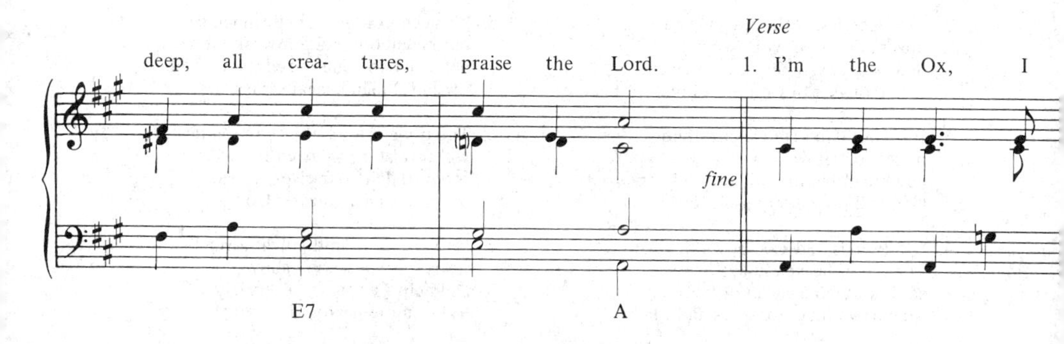

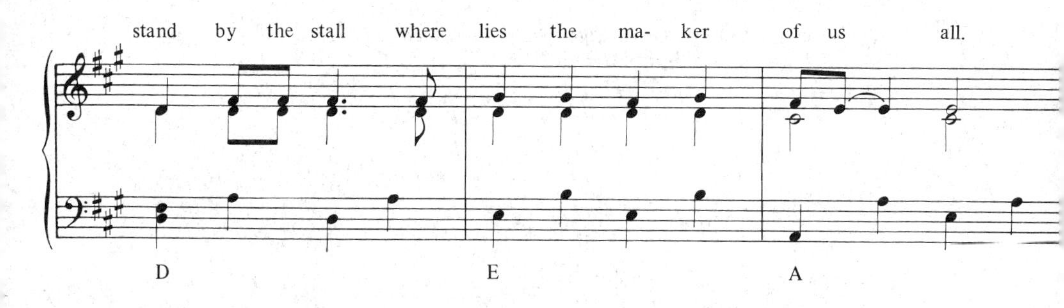

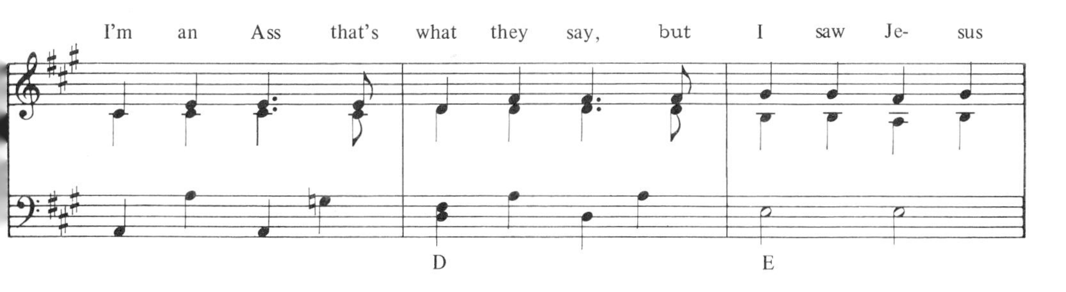

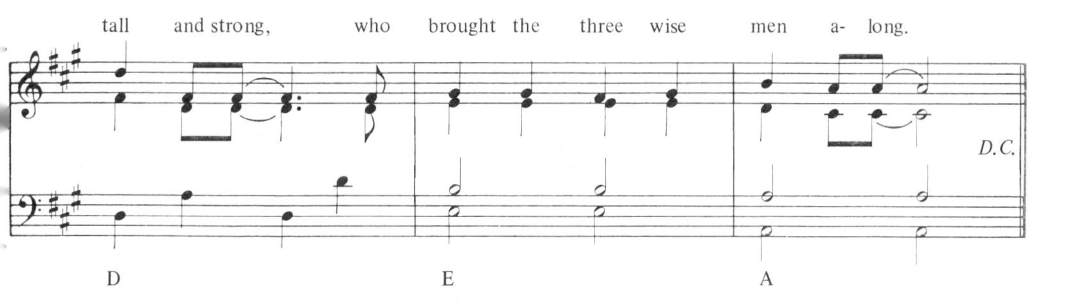

2. I'm a Mouse, so small and grey,
for me this is a happy day.
I'm a Cat all black with fur,
for Jesus I will purr and purr.
I'm a Dog, I jump up high
and praise the Lord of earth and sky.
We, the Monkeys, love to swing;
for Jesus we will clap and sing.

3. I'm a Rabbit, with big long ears,
for Jesus' sake I'll give three cheers.
I'm a Chicken, scratching around,
and I'll adore without a sound.
Silently, without a fuss,
he came to earth as one of us.
May he bless and help us all,
everyone, both great and small.

Words and Music: Kevin Mayhew

NOW LET US FROM THIS TABLE RISE
('Solothurn' L.M.)

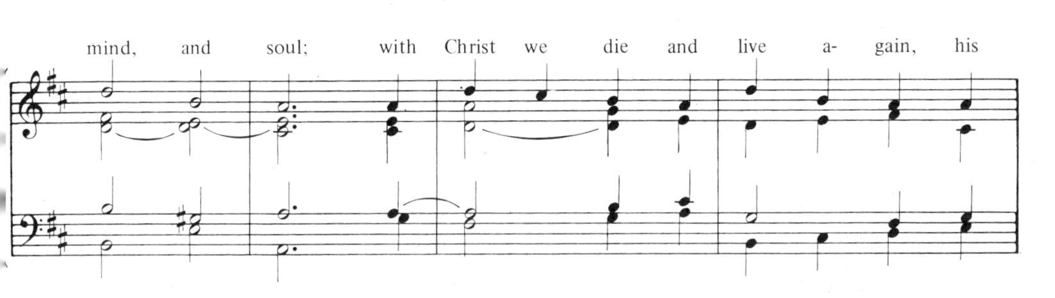

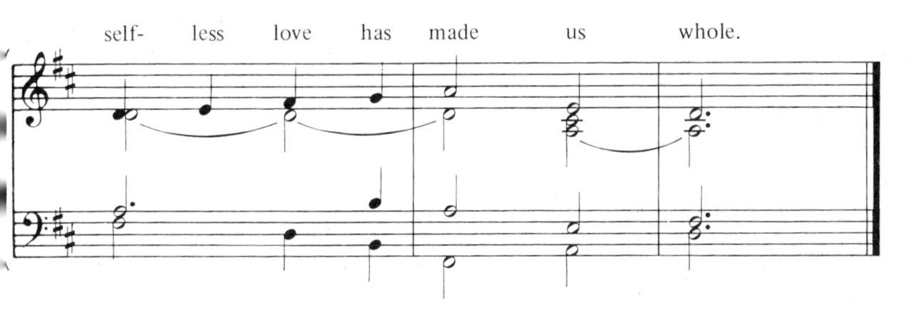

2. With minds alert, upheld by grace,
to spread the Word in speech and deed,
we follow in the steps of Christ,
at one with man in hope and need.

3. To fill each human house with love,
it is the sacrament of care;
the work that Christ began to do
we humbly pledge ourselves to share.

4. Then give us courage, Father God,
to choose again the pilgrim way,
and help us to accept with joy
the challenge of tomorrow's day.

Words: Fred Kaan (b. 1929)
Music: Swiss Traditional Melody

344

NOW, MY TONGUE, THE MYSTERY TELLING

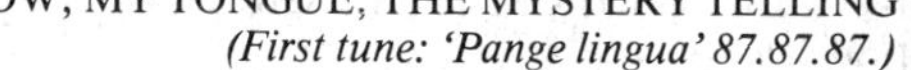

A different version of this tune may be found at Hymn 355

2. That last night, at supper lying,
   'mid the Twelve, his chosen band,
   Jesus, with the law complying,
   keeps the feast its rites demand;
   then, more precious food supplying,
   gives himself with his own hand.

3. Given for us, and condescending
   to be born for us below,
   he, with men in converse blending,
   dwelt the seed of truth to sow,
   till he closed with wondrous ending
   his most patient life of woe.

4. Word-made-flesh, true bread he maketh
   by his word his flesh to be,
   wine his blood; which whoso taketh
   must from carnal thoughts be free:
   faith alone, though sight forsaketh,
   shows true hearts the mystery.

PART TWO

5. Therefore we, before him bending,
   this great sacrament revere:
   types and shadows have their ending,
   for the newer rite is here;
   faith, our outward sense befriending,
   makes our inward vision clear.

6. Glory let us give and blessing
   to the Father and the Son,
   honour, might, and praise addressing,
   while eternal ages run;
   ever too his love confessing,
   who, from both, with both is one.
   Amen.

NOW, MY TONGUE, THE MYSTERY TELLING

(Second tune: 'Tantum ergo (Grafton)' 87.87.87.)

Words: St Thomas Aquinas (1227-74)
tr. E. Caswall, J.M. Neale et al.
Music: First tune – Plainsong mode III
Second tune – French melody (1881)

NOW THANK WE ALL OUR GOD

(First tune: 'Nun danket' 67.67.66.66.)

2. O may this bounteous God
through all our life be near us,
with ever joyful hearts
and blessed peace to cheer us;
and keep us in his grace,
and guide us when perplexed,
and free us from all ills
in this world and the next.

3. All praise and thanks to God
the Father now be given,
the Son and him who reigns
with them in highest heaven,
the one Eternal God,
whom earth and heaven adore;
for thus it was, is now,
and shall be evermore.

Words: Martin Rinkart (1586-1649),
tr. Catherine Winkworth (1827-78)
Music: First tune - J. Cruger (1598-1662)

Second tune overleaf

NOW THANK WE ALL OUR GOD

(Second tune: 'Gracias' 67.67.66.66.)

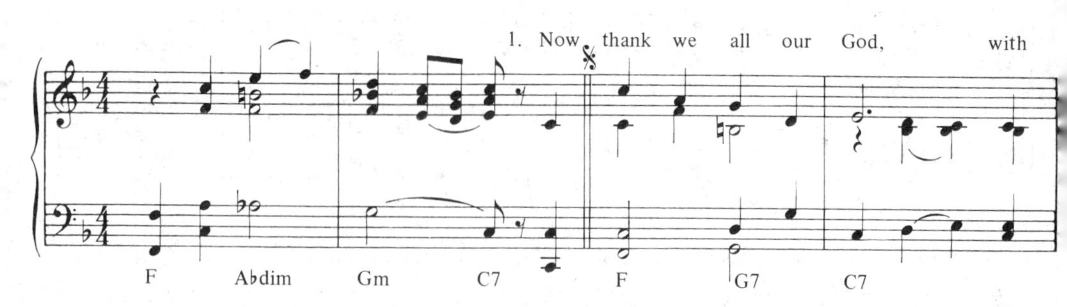

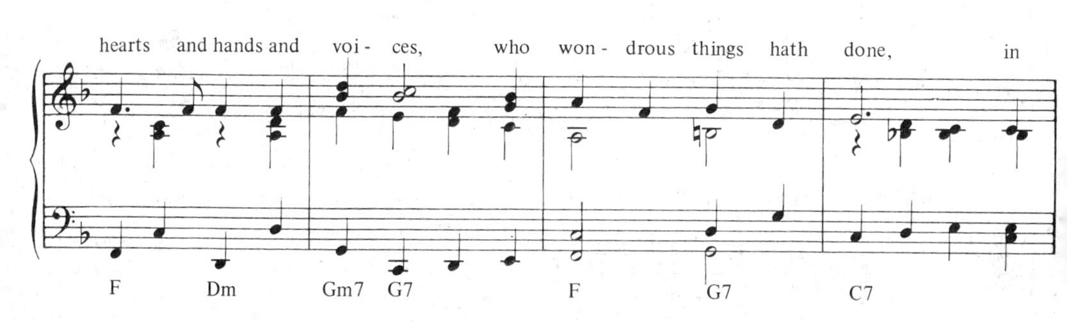

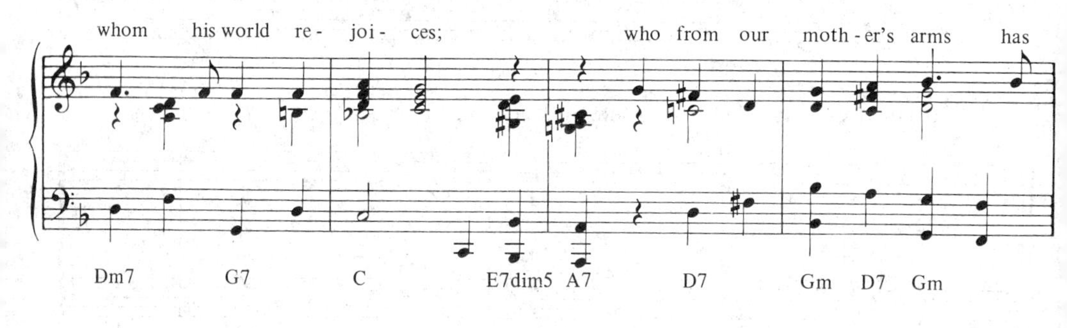

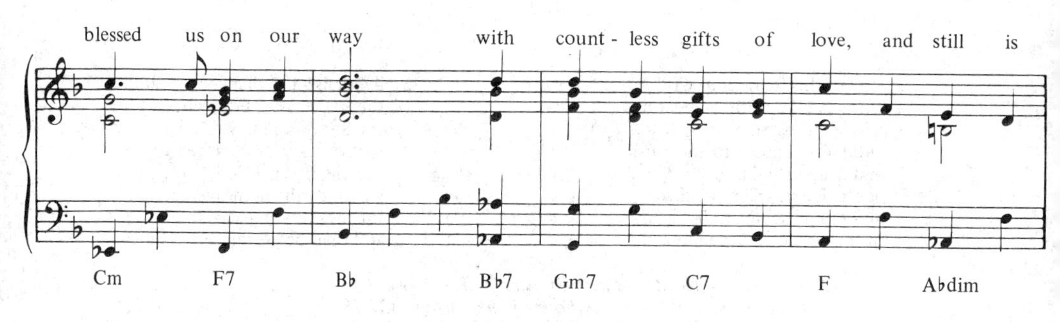

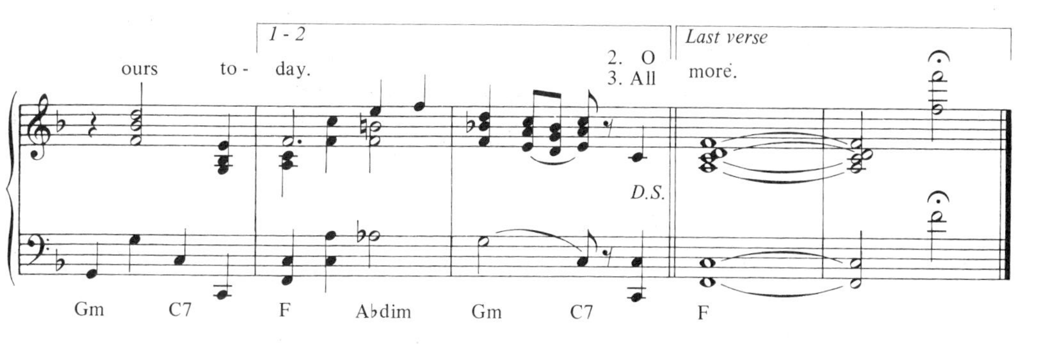

2. O may this bounteous God
through all our life be near us,
with ever joyful hearts
and blessed peace to cheer us;
and keep us in his grace,
and guide us when perplexed,
and free us from all ills
in this world and the next.

3. All praise and thanks to God
the Father now be given,
the Son, and him who reigns
with them in highest heaven,
the one eternal God,
whom earth and heaven adore,
for thus it was, is now,
and shall be evermore.

Words: Martin Rinkart (1586-1649),
tr. Catherine Winkworth (1827-78)
Music: Second tune - Geoffrey Beaumont

346

NOW THE GREEN BLADE RISETH **(Love is come again)**

('Noel nouvelet' 11 10. 10 11.)

2. In the grave they laid him, Love whom men had slain,
thinking that never he would wake again,
laid in the earth like grain that sleeps unseen:
love is come again like wheat that springeth green.

3. Forth he came at Easter, like the risen grain,
he that for three days in the grave had lain,
quick from the dead my risen Lord is seen:
love is come again like wheat that springeth green.

4. When our hearts are wintry, grieving or in pain,
thy touch can call us back to life again,
fields of our heart that dead and bare have been:
love is come again like wheat that springeth green.

Words: J. M. C. Crum (1872-1958)
Music: Traditional French melody, arranged by John Rombaut

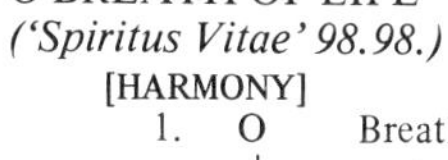

O BREATH OF LIFE

('Spiritus Vitae' 98.98.)

[HARMONY]

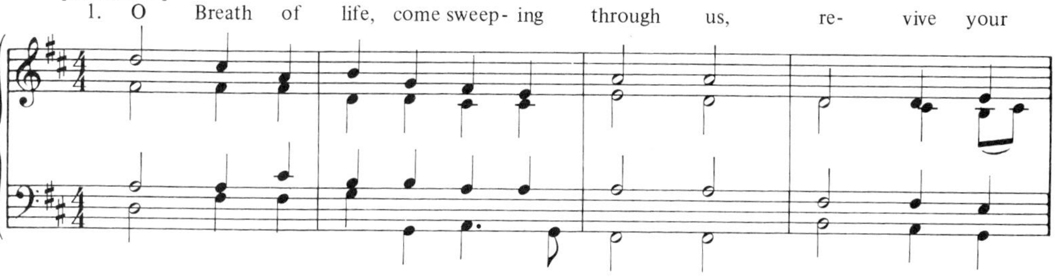

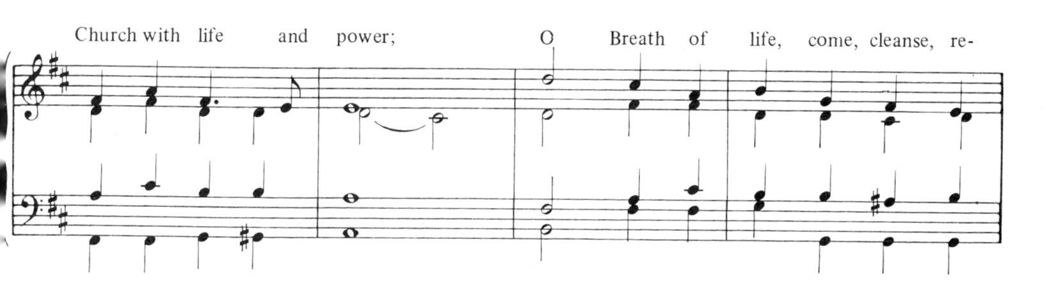

2. O Breath of love, come breathe within us,
   renewing thought and will and heart;
   come, love of Christ, afresh to win us,
   revive your Church in every part!

3. O Wind of God, come bend us, break us
   till humbly we confess our need;
   then, in your tenderness remake us,
   revive, restore - for this we plead.

Words: Elizabeth A.P. Head (1850-1936)
Music: Mary J. Hammond (1878-1964)

O COME, ALL YE FAITHFUL
('Adeste fideles' Irregular)

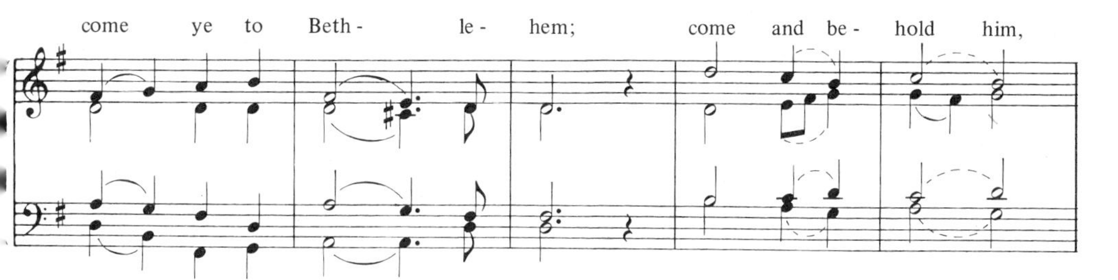

2. God of God,
light of light,
lo! he abhors not the Virgin's womb;
very God,
begotten not created:

3. Sing, choirs of angels,
sing in exultation,
sing all ye citizens of heaven above:
glory to God
in the highest:

4. Yea, Lord, we greet thee,
born this happy morning,
Jesu, to thee be glory given;
Word of the Father,
now in flesh appearing:

Words: John Wade (d. 1786)
tr. Frederick Oakeley (1802-80)
Music: 18th century, probably by J. F. Wade

349

O COME, O COME, EMMANUEL

('Veni, Emmanuel' 88.88.88.)

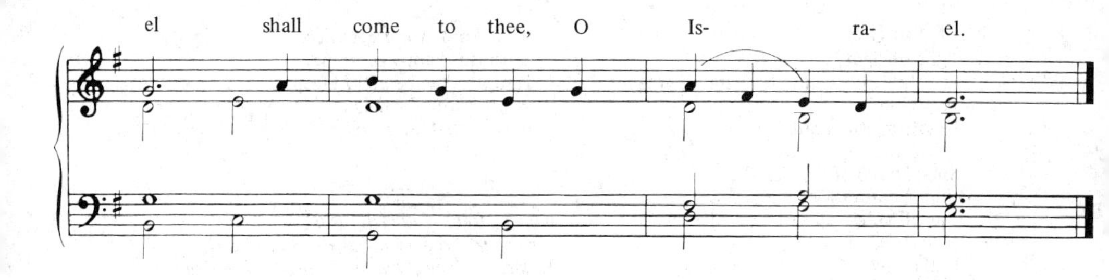

2. O come, thou Rod of Jesse, free
thine own from Satan's tyranny;
from depths of hell thy people save,
and give them vict'ry o'er the grave:

3. O come, thou Dayspring, come and cheer
our spirits by thine advent here;
disperse the gloomy clouds of night,
and death's dark shadows put to flight:

4. O come, thou Key of David, come
and open wide our heavenly home;
make safe the way that leads on high,
and close the path to misery:

5. O come, O come, thou Lord of Might,
who to thy tribes on Sinai's height
in ancient times didst give the Law
in cloud and majesty and awe.

Words: from the 'Great O Antiphons' (12th-13th c.),
translated by J. M. Neale (1818-66)
Music: Adapted by T. Helmore from a French Missal,
arranged by Dom Gregory Murray

OH COME TO THE WATER
('Isaiah 55')

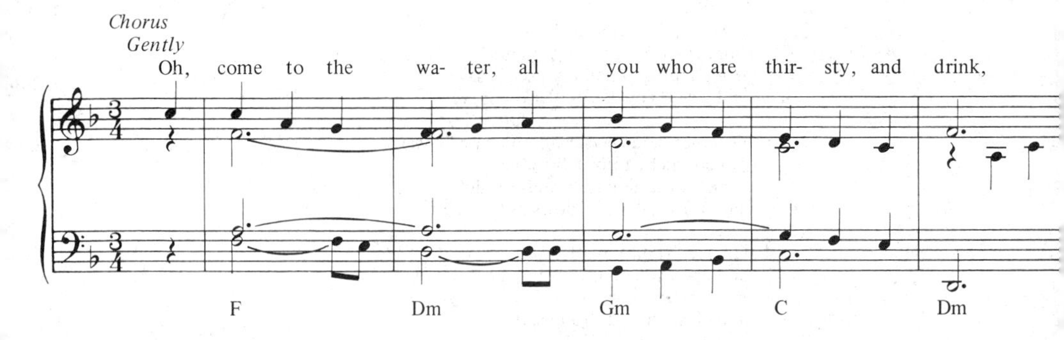

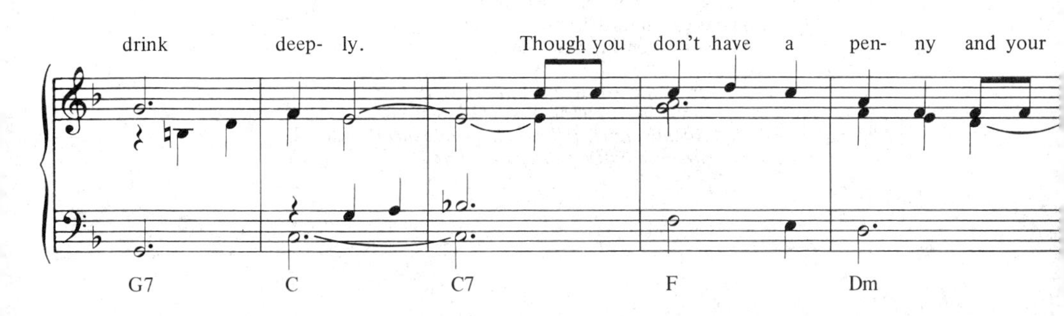

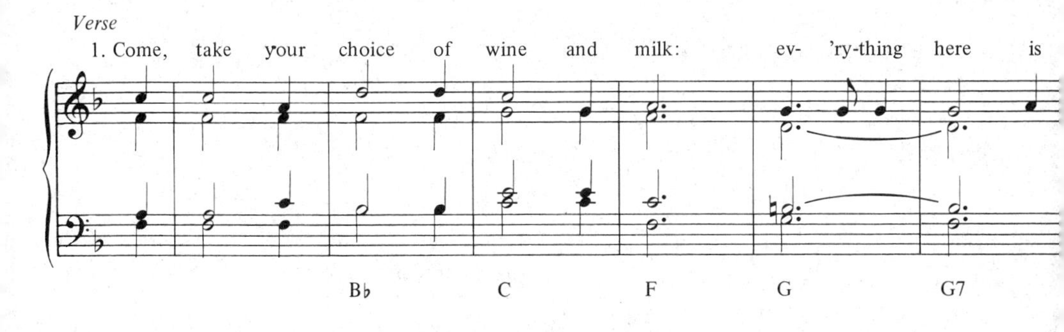

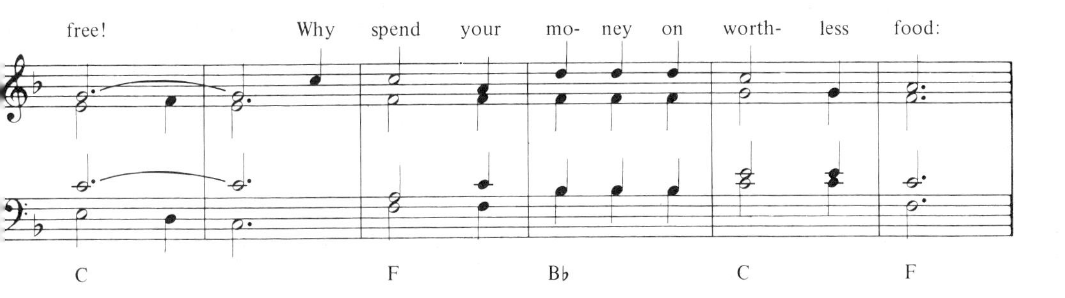

2. Now, listen well and you will find
   food that will feed your soul.
   Just come to me to receive your share,
   food that will feed your soul.

3. I promise you good things to come;
   you are my chosen ones.
   I name you witnesses to my world;
   you are my chosen ones.

Words, based on Isaiah 55: 1-4, and Music: Kevin Mayhew

O FOR A CLOSER WALK WITH GOD

('Stracathro' C.M.)

[HARMONY]

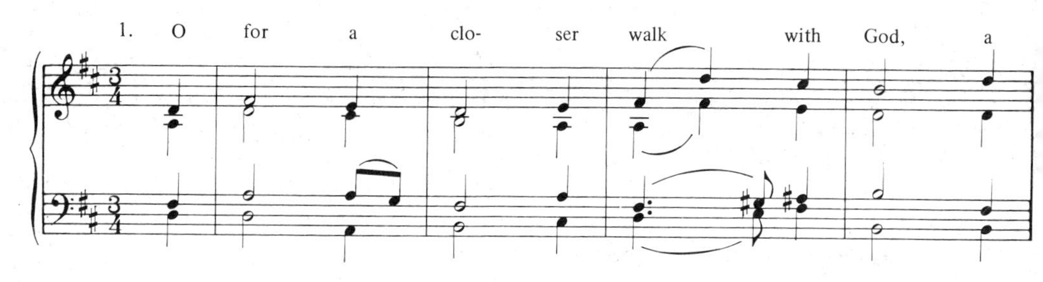

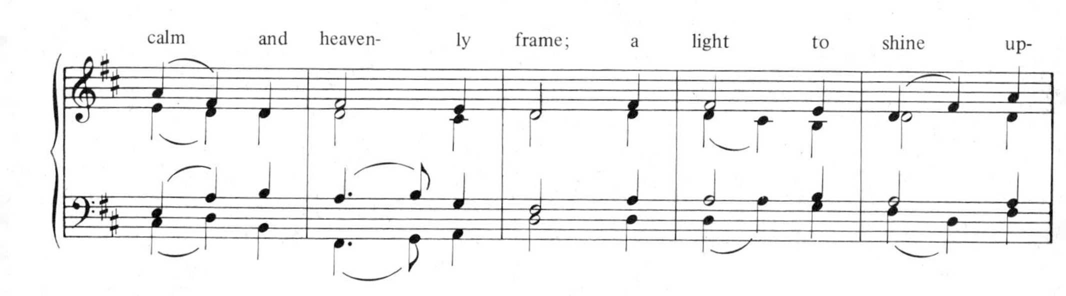

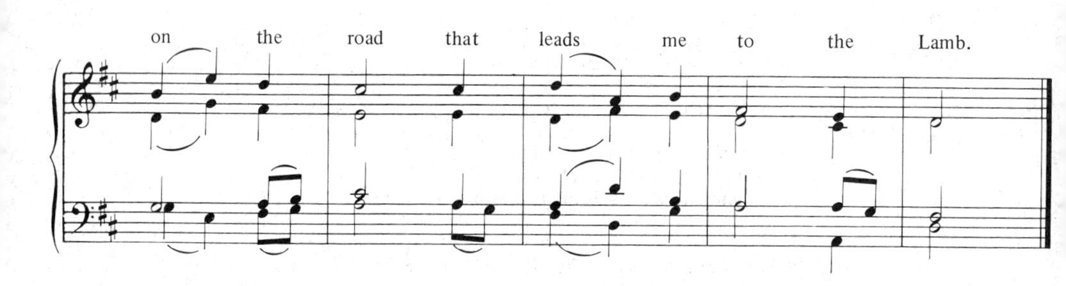

2. Return, O holy Dove, return,
   sweet messenger of rest:
   I hate the sins that made thee mourn,
   and drove thee from my breast.

3. The dearest idol I have known,
   whate'er that idol be,
   help me to tear it from thy throne,
   and worship only thee.

4. So shall my walk be close with God,
   calm and serene my frame;
   so purer light shall mark the road
   that leads me to the Lamb.

Words: William Cowper (1731-1800)
Music: melody by Charles Hutcheson (1792-1860), harmonised by David Evans ('Scottish Hymnary' 1927)

O FOR A HEART TO PRAISE MY GOD
('Stockton' C.M.)

[HARMONY]

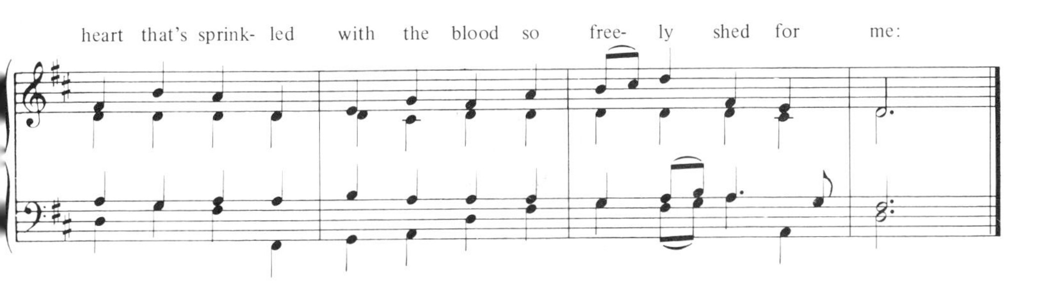

2. A heart resigned, submissive, meek,
my great Redeemer's throne;
where only Christ is heard to speak,
where Jesus reigns alone:

3. A humble, lowly, contrite heart,
believing, true, and clean,
which neither life nor death can part
from him that dwells within:

4. A heart in every thought renewed,
and full of love divine;
perfect and right and pure and good -
a copy, Lord, of thine.

5. My heart, thou know'st, can never rest
till thou create my peace;
till of mine Eden repossest,
from self, and sin, I cease.

6. Thy nature, gracious Lord, impart,
come quickly from above;
write thy new name upon my heart,
thy new best name of love.

Words: Charles Wesley (1707-88)
Music: Thomas Wright (1763-1829)

O FOR A THOUSAND TONGUES TO SING

('Richmond' C.M.)

353

[HARMONY]

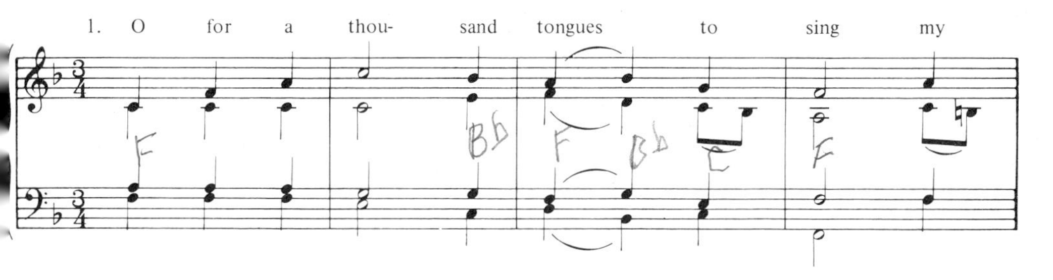

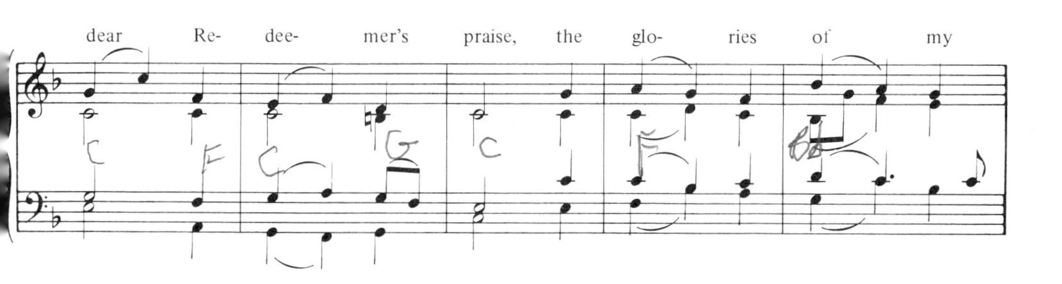

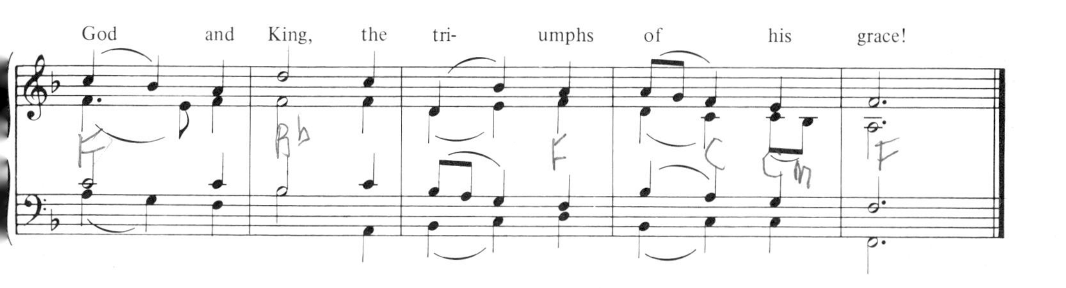

2. Jesus! the name that charms our fears,
   that bids our sorrows cease;
   'tis music in the sinner's ears,
   'tis life and health and peace.

3. He breaks the power of cancelled sin,
   he sets the prisoner free;
   his blood can make the foulest clean;
   his blood availed for me.

4. He speaks; and, listening to his voice,
   new life the dead receive,
   the mournful broken hearts rejoice,
   the humble poor believe.

5. Hear him, ye deaf; his praise, ye dumb,
   your loosened tongues employ;
   ye blind, behold your Saviour come;
   and leap, ye lame, for joy!

6. My gracious Master and my God,
   assist me to proclaim
   and spread through all the earth abroad
   the honours of thy name.

Words: Charles Wesley (1707-88)
Music: adapted from Thomas Haweis (1734-1820)

354 OF THE FATHER'S LOVE BEGOTTEN

('Corde natus' 87.87.877.)

2. By his word was all created;
he commanded, it was done:
heav'n and earth and depth of ocean,
universe of three in one,
all that grows beneath the shining
of the light of moon and sun:
evermore and evermore.

3. Blessed was that day for ever
when the Virgin, full of grace,
by the Spirit's pow'r conceiving,
bore the Saviour of our race,
and the child, the world's Redeemer,
first revealed his sacred face:
evermore and evermore.

4. O, ye heights of heav'n, adore him,
angels and archangels sing!
Every creature bow before him
singing praise to God our King;
let no earthly tongue be silent,
all the world with homage ring:
evermore and evermore.

5. He, by prophets sung, is here now,
promised since the world began,
now on earth in flesh descended
to atone for sins of man.
All creation praise its Master,
see fulfilment of his plan:
evermore and evermore.

6. Glory be to God the Father,
glory be to God the Son,
glory to the Holy Spirit,
persons three, yet Godhead one.
Glory be from all creation
while eternal ages run:
evermore and evermore.

Words: *Aurelius C. Prudentius (348-413),*
tr. J. M. Neale, H. W. Baker and others
Music: *Plainsong Melody, adapted by*
Theodoricus Petrus in 'Piae Cantiones' (1582)

355

OF THE GLORIOUS BODY TELLING
(First tune: 'Pange lingua' 87.87.87.)

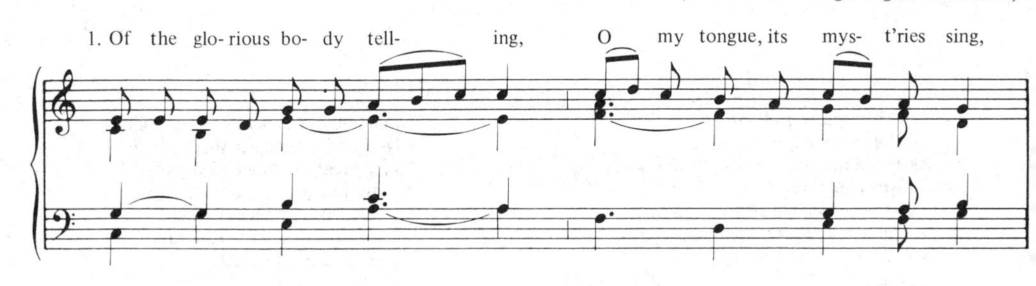

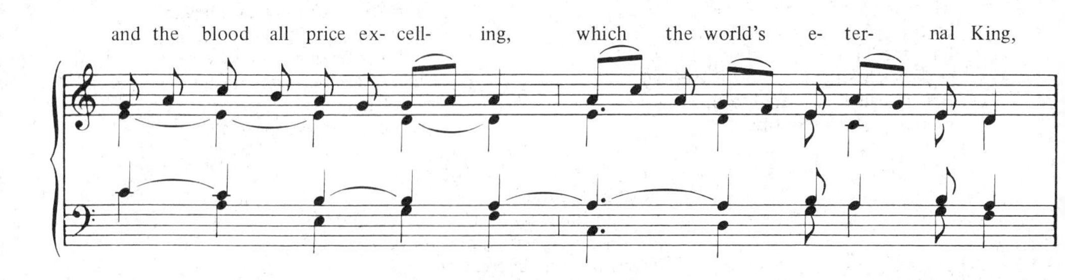

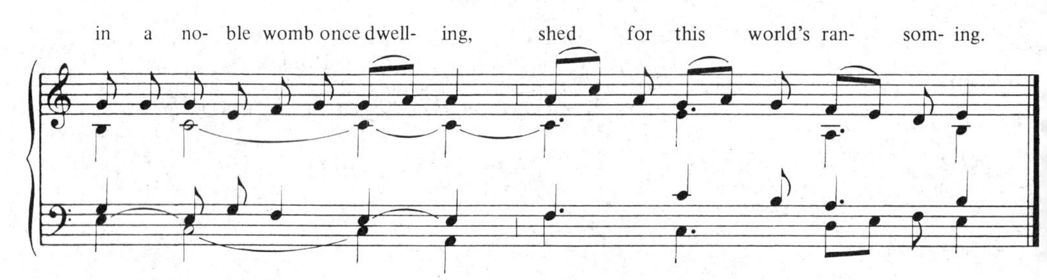

A different version of this tune may be found at Hymn 344

2. Giv'n for us, for us descending,
   of a virgin to proceed,
   man with man in converse blending,
   scattered he the gospel seed,
   till his sojourn drew to ending,
   which he closed in wondrous deed.

3. At the last great supper lying,
   circled by his brethren's band,
   meekly with the law complying,
   first, he finished its command.
   Then, immortal food supplying,
   gave himself with his own hand.

4. Word made flesh, by word he maketh
   very bread his flesh to be;
   man in wine Christ's blood partaketh,
   and if senses fail to see,
   faith alone the true heart waketh,
   to behold the mystery.

5. Therefore, we before him bending,
   this great sacrament revere;
   types and shadows have their ending,
   for the newer rite is here;
   faith, our outward sense befriending,
   makes the inward vision clear.

6. Glory let us give, and blessing,
   to the Father and the Son,
   honour, might and praise addressing,
   while eternal ages run;
   ever too his love confessing,
   who from both, with both is one.

Words: St Thomas Aquinas (1227-74)
tr. J. M. Neale, E. Caswall, et al.
Music: First tune - Proper Sarum melody

OF THE GLORIOUS BODY TELLING

(Second tune: 'St Thomas' 87.87.87.)

2. Giv'n for us, for us descending,
of a virgin to proceed,
man with man in converse blending,
scattered he the gospel seed,
till his sojourn drew to ending,
which he closed in wondrous deed.

3. At the last great supper lying,
circled by his brethren's band,
meekly with the law complying,
first, he finished its command.
Then, immortal food supplying,
gave himself with his own hand.

4. Word made flesh, by word he maketh
very bread his flesh to be;
man in wine Christ's blood partaketh,
and if senses fail to see,
faith alone the true heart waketh,
to behold the mystery.

5. Therefore, we before him bending,
this great sacrament revere;
types and shadows have their ending,
for the newer rite is here;
faith, our outward sense befriending,
makes the inward vision clear.

6. Glory let us give, and blessing,
to the Father and the Son,
honour, might and praise addressing,
while eternal ages run;
ever too his love confessing,
who from both, with both is one.

Words: St Thomas Aquinas (1227-74),
tr. J. M. Neale, E. Caswall et al.
Music: Second tune - Samuel Webbe (1740-1816)

OFT IN DANGER, OFT IN WOE

('University College' 77.77.)

[HARMONY]

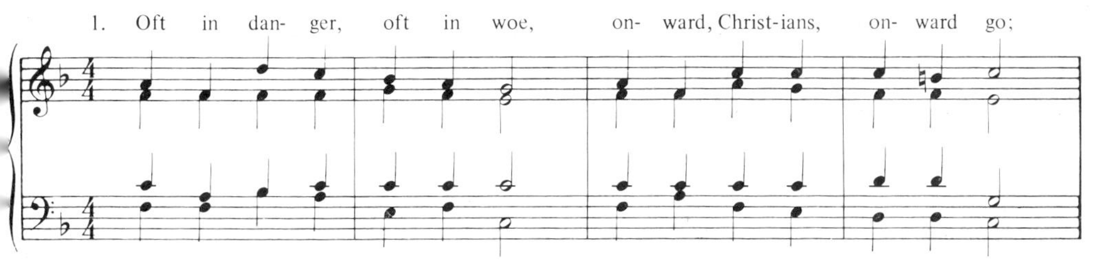

2. Onward, Christians, onward go,
join the war, and face the foe;
will ye flee in danger's hour?
know ye not your Captain's power?

3. Let your drooping hearts be glad;
march in heavenly armour clad;
fight, nor think the battle long,
victory soon shall tune your song.

4. Let not sorrow dim your eye,
soon shall every tear be dry;
let not fears your course impede,
great your strength, if great your need.

5. Onward then in battle move;
more than conquerors ye shall prove;
though opposed by many a foe,
Christian soldiers, onward go.

Words: Henry Kirke White (1785-1806), and others
Music: Henry J. Gauntlett (1805-76)

357

O GOD BEYOND ALL PRAISING

('Thaxted' 13 13.13 13.13 13.)

2. Then hear, O gracious Saviour,
accept the love we bring,
that we who know your favour
may serve you as our king;
and whether our tomorrows
be filled with good or ill,
we'll triumph through our sorrows
and rise to bless you still:
to marvel at your beauty
and glory in your ways,
and make a joyful duty
our sacrifice of praise.

Words: Michael Perry (b. 1942)
Music: Gustav Holst (1874-1934)

O GOD OF BETHEL, BY WHOSE HAND
('Burford' C.M.)

[HARMONY]

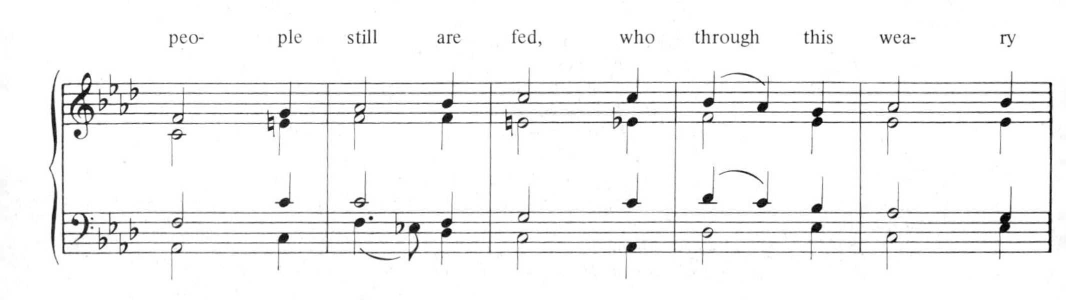

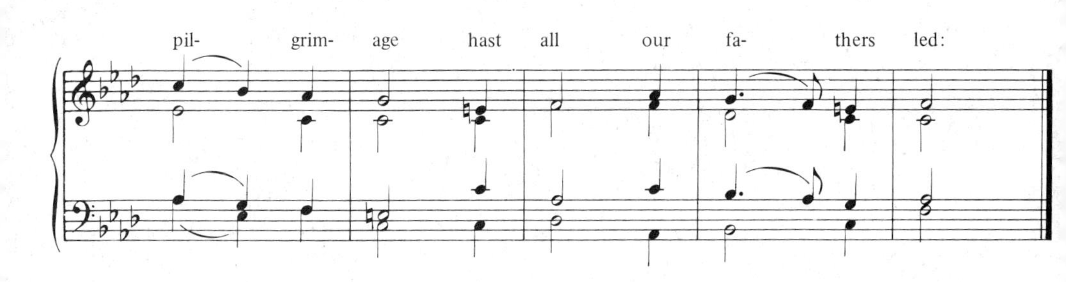

2. Our vows, our prayers, we now present
   before thy throne of grace;
   God of our fathers, be the God
   of their succeeding race.

3. Through each perplexing path of life
   our wandering footsteps guide;
   give us each day our daily bread,
   and raiment fit provide.

4. O spread thy covering wings around,
   till all our wanderings cease,
   and at our Father's loved abode
   our souls arrive in peace.

Words: Philip Doddridge (1702-51)
and John Logan (1748-88)
Music: from 'Chetham's Psalmody' (1718)

O GOD OF EARTH AND ALTAR

('King's Lynn' 76.76.D.)

2. From all that terror teaches,
from lies of tongue and pen,
from all the easy speeches
that comfort cruel men,
from sale and profanation
of honour and the sword,
from sleep and from damnation,
deliver us, good Lord.

3. Tie in a living tether
the prince and priest and thrall,
bind all our lives together,
smite us and save us all;
in ire and exultation
aflame with faith, and free,
lift up a living nation,
a single sword to thee.

Words: G. K. Chesterton (1874-1936)
Music: English traditional melody,
arranged by Ralph Vaughan Williams (1872-1958)

O GOD, OUR HELP IN AGES PAST

('St Anne' C.M.)

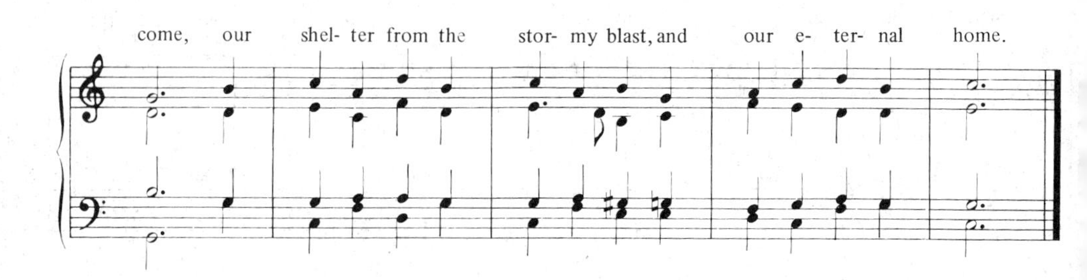

2. Beneath the shadow of thy throne,
   thy saints have dwelt secure;
   sufficient is thine arm alone,
   and our defence is sure.

3. Before the hills in order stood,
   or earth received her frame,
   from everlasting thou art God,
   to endless years the same.

4. A thousand ages in thy sight,
   are like an evening gone;
   short as the watch that ends the night
   before the rising sun.

5. Time, like an ever-rolling stream,
   bears all its sons away;
   they fly forgotten, as a dream
   dies at the opening day.

6. O God, our help in ages past,
   our hope for years to come,
   be thou our guard while troubles last,
   and our eternal home.

Words, based on Psalm 90:
Isaac Watts (1674-1748)
Music: William Croft (1678-1727)

O HAPPY BAND OF PILGRIMS
('Knecht' 76.76.)

[HARMONY]

2. O happy if ye labour
as Jesus did for men;
O happy if ye hunger
as Jesus hungered then.

3. The cross that Jesus carried
he carried as your due:
the crown that Jesus weareth
he weareth it for you.

4. The faith by which ye see him,
the hope in which ye yearn,
the love that through all troubles
to him alone will turn,

5. What are they but forerunners
to lead you to his sight?
What are they save the effluence
of uncreated light?

6. The trials that beset you,
the sorrows ye endure,
the manifold temptations
that death alone can cure,

7. What are they but his jewels
of right celestial worth?
what are they but the ladder
set up to heaven on earth?

8. O happy band of pilgrims,
look upward to the skies,
where such a light affliction
shall win so great a prize.

Words: John M. Neale (1818-66)
Music: Justin H. Knecht (1752-1817)

O HAPPY DAY! THAT FIXED MY CHOICE

[HARMONY]

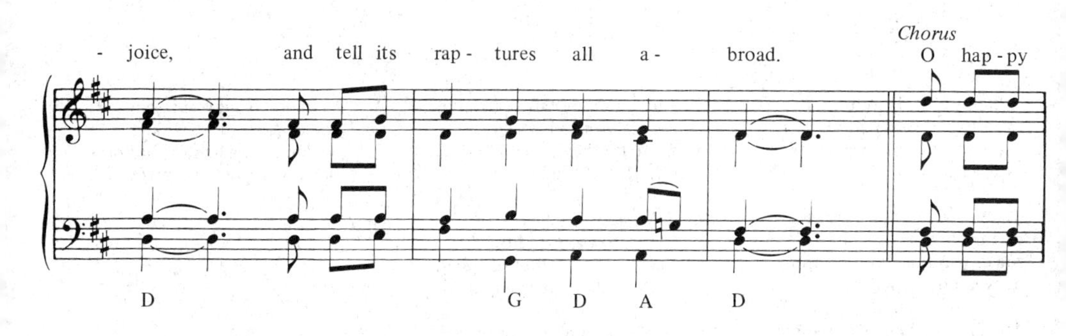

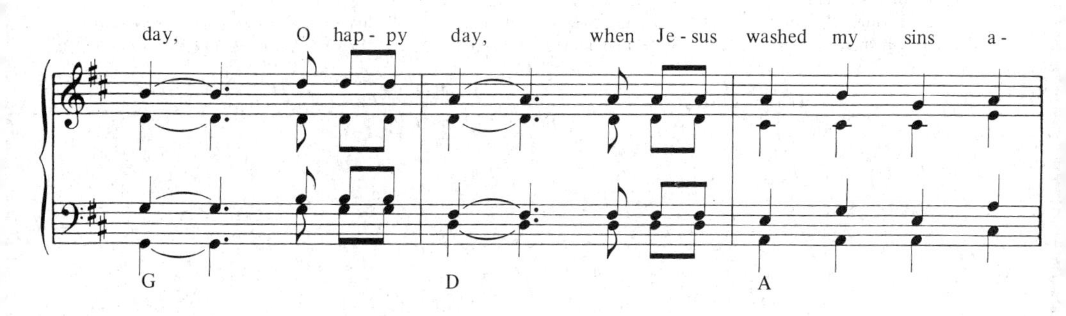

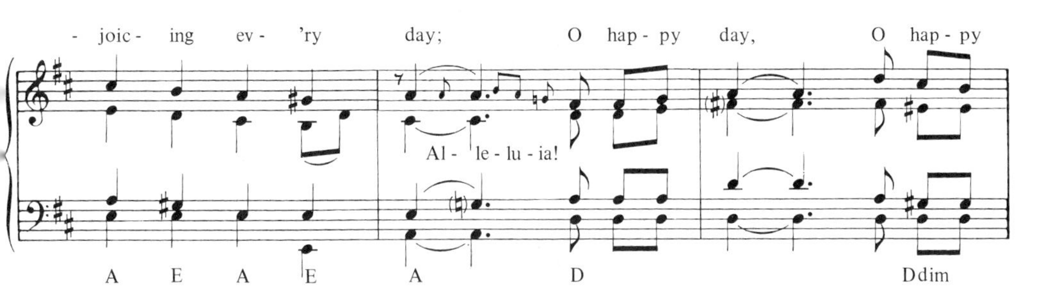

2. 'Tis done, the great transaction's done!
I am my Lord's, and he is mine!
He drew me, and I followed on,
charmed to confess the voice divine.

3. Now rest, my long divided heart,
fixed on this blissful centre, rest;
nor ever from thy Lord depart,
with him of ev'ry good possessed.

4. High heav'n, that heard the solemn vow,
that vow renewed shall daily hear;
till in life's latest hour I bow,
and bless in death a bond so dear.

Words: Philip Doddridge (1702-51)
Music: Ron Jones

O HOLY SPIRIT, LORD OF GRACE
('Tallis' Ordinal' C.M.)

[HARMONY]

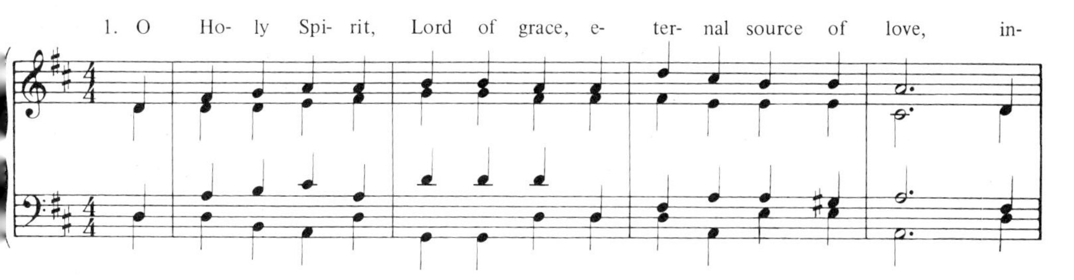

2. As thou dost join with holiest bonds
the Father and the Son,
so fill thy saints with mutual love
and link their hearts in one.

3. To God the Father, God the Son,
and God the Holy Ghost,
eternal glory be from man,
and from the angel-host.

Words: Charles Coffin (1676-1749),
tr. J. Chandler
Music: Thomas Tallis (c. 1505-85)

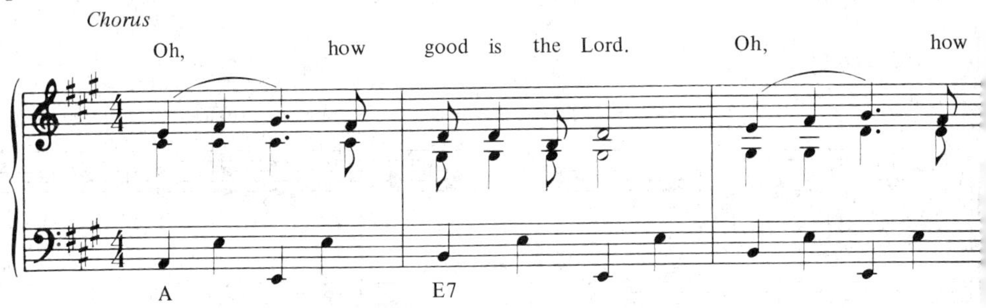
Chorus
Oh, how good is the Lord. Oh, how
A
E7

good is the Lord. Oh, how good is the Lord! I
A
A7
D

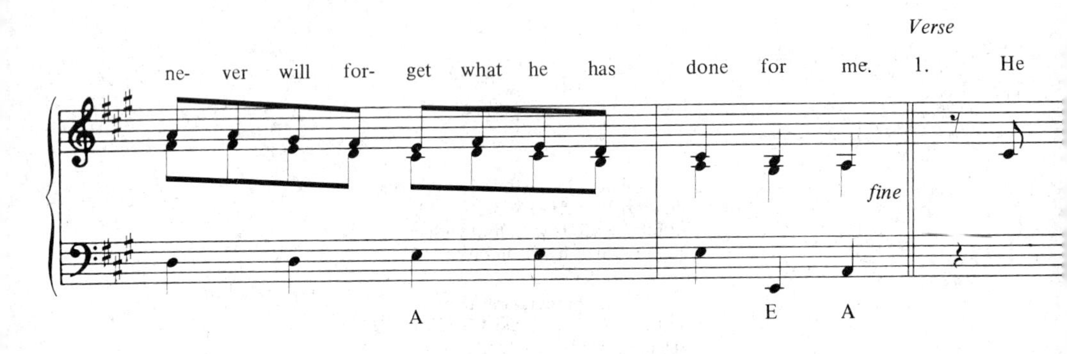
Verse
ne- ver will for- get what he has done for me. 1. He
fine
A
E A

gives us sal- va- tion, how good is the Lord. He
E7

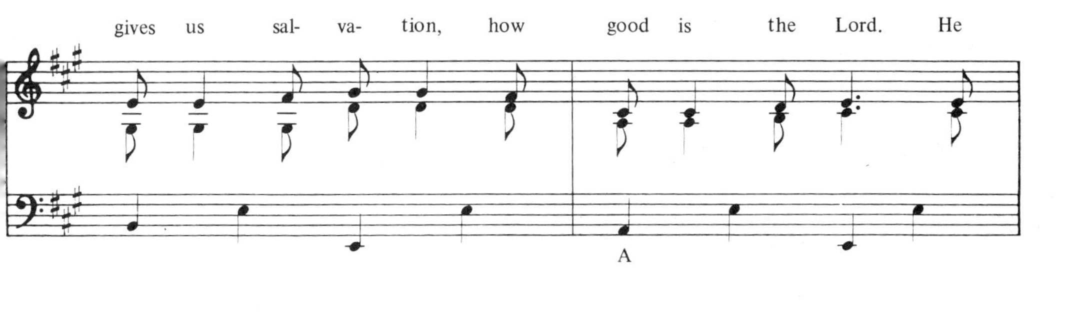

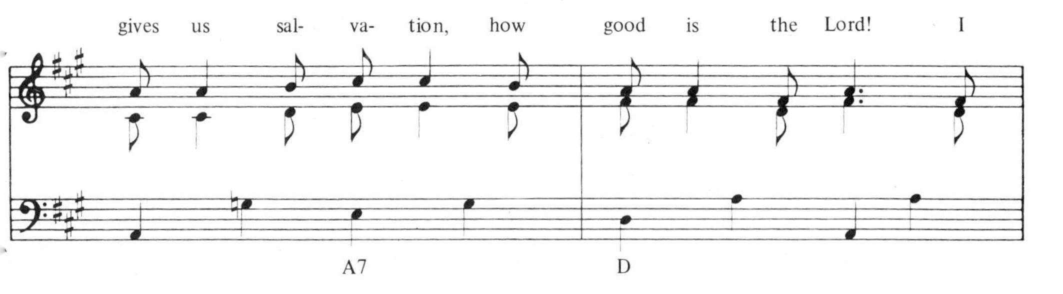

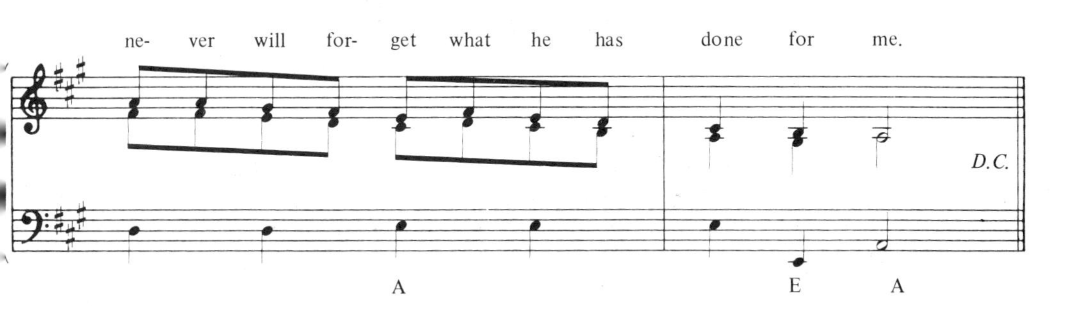

2. He gives us his Spirit . . .

3. He gives us his healing . . .

4. He gives us his body . . .

5. He gives us his freedom . . .

6. He gives us each other . . .

7. He gives us his glory . . .

Words and Music: Traditional, arranged by Elaine Irwin

O JESUS, I HAVE PROMISED

('Hatherop Castle' 76.76.D.)

Gently but firmly

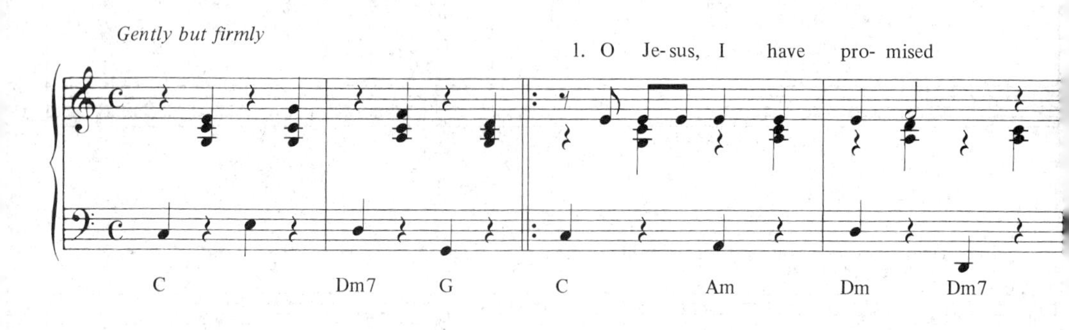

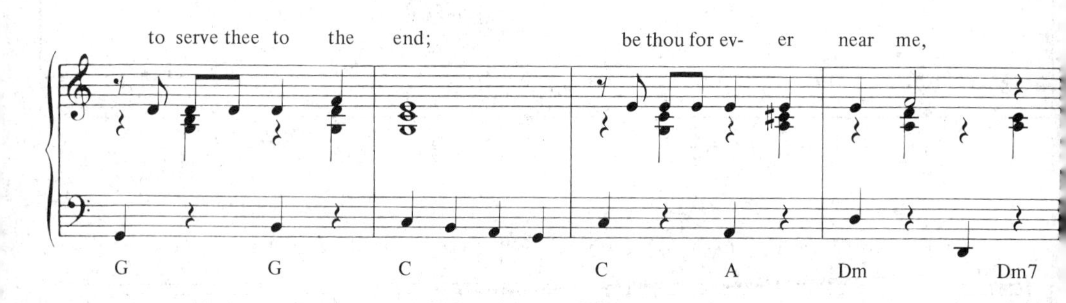

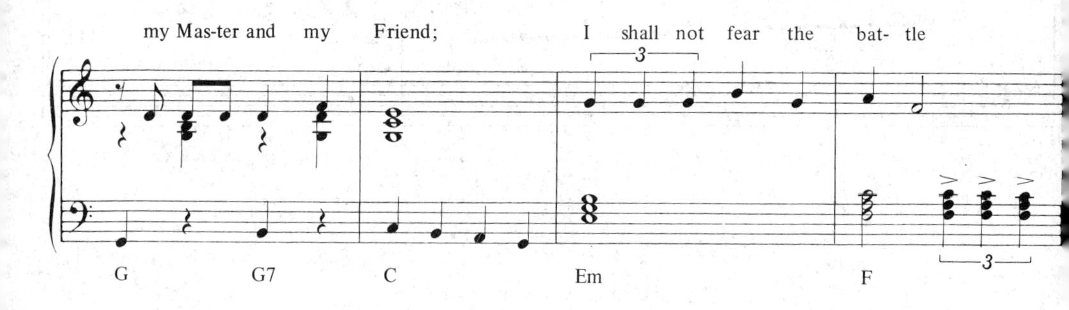

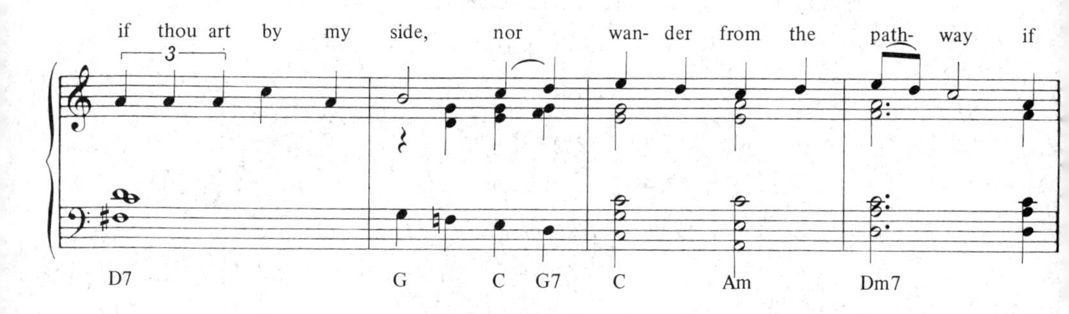

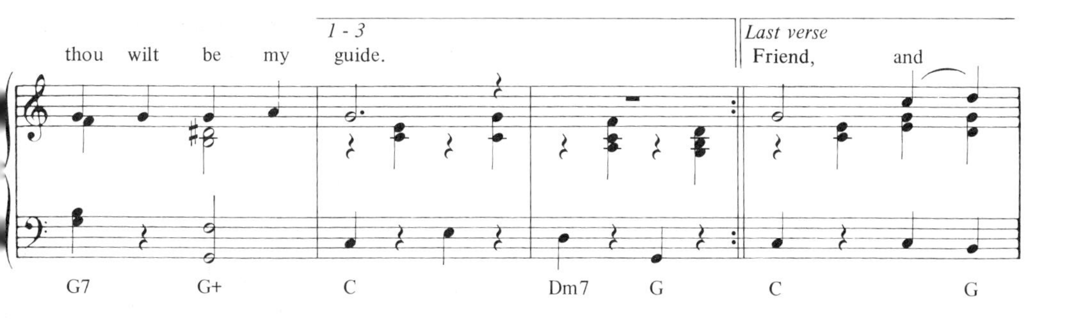

2. O let me feel thee near me:
   the world is ever near;
   I see the sights that dazzle,
   the tempting sounds I hear;
   my foes are ever near me,
   around me and within;
   but, Jesus, draw thou nearer,
   and shield my soul from sin.

3. O let me hear thee speaking
   in accents clear and still,
   above the storms of passion,
   the murmurs of self-will;
   O speak to reassure me,
   to hasten or control;
   O speak, and make me listen,
   thou guardian of my soul.

4. O Jesus, thou hast promised
   to all who follow thee,
   that where thou art in glory
   there shall thy servant be;
   and, Jesus, I have promised
   to serve thee to the end:
   O give me grace to follow,
   my Master and my Friend.

5. O let me see thy foot-marks,
   and in them plant mine own;
   my hope to follow duly
   is in thy strength alone:
   O guide me, call me, draw me,
   uphold me to the end;
   and then in heaven receive me,
   my Saviour and my Friend.

Words: John E. Bode (1816-74)
Music: Geoffrey Beaumont

366

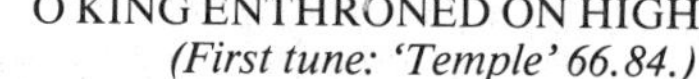

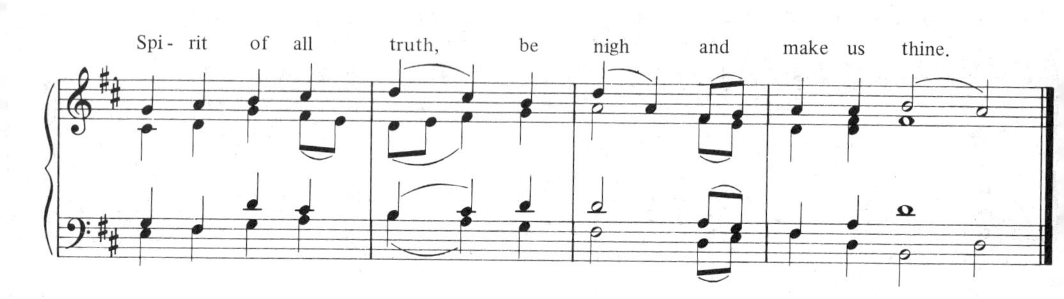

O KING ENTHRONED ON HIGH
(Second tune: 'Amen Court' 66.84.)

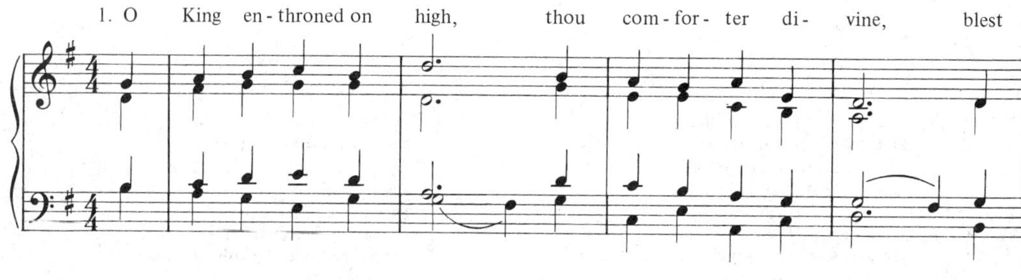

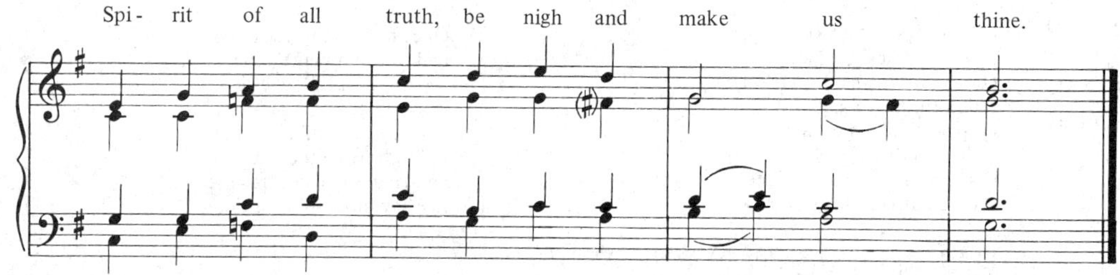

2. Thou art the source of life,
   thou art our treasure-store;
   give us thy peace, and end our strife
   for evermore.

3. Descend, O heavenly Dove,
   abide with us alway;
   and in the fulness of thy love
   cleanse us, we pray.

Words: Greek hymn (8th century)
tr. J. Brownlie (1857-1925)
Music: First tune – Walford Davies (1869-1941)
Second tune – J. Dykes Bower (1905-81)

367

O LITTLE TOWN OF BETHLEHEM

('Forest Green' D.C.M.) [HARMONY]

2. O morning stars, together
 proclaim the holy birth,
 and praises sing to God the King,
 and peace to men on earth;
 for Christ is born of Mary;
 and, gathered all above,
 while mortals sleep, the angels keep
 their watch of wondering love.

3. How silently, how silently
 the wondrous gift is giv'n!
 So God imparts to human hearts
 the blessings of his heaven.
 No ear may hear his coming;
 but in this world of sin,
 where meek souls will receive him, still
 the dear Christ enters in.

4. Where children pure and happy
 pray to the blessed Child,
 where misery cries out to thee,
 Son of the mother mild;
 where charity stands watching
 and faith holds wide the door,
 the dark night wakes, the glory breaks,
 and Christmas comes once more.

Words: Phillips Brooks (1835-93)
Music: Traditional English melody, collected, adapted and arranged by Ralph Vaughan Williams (1872-1958)

368

OH LORD, ALL THE WORLD (Turning the world upside down)
('All things new')

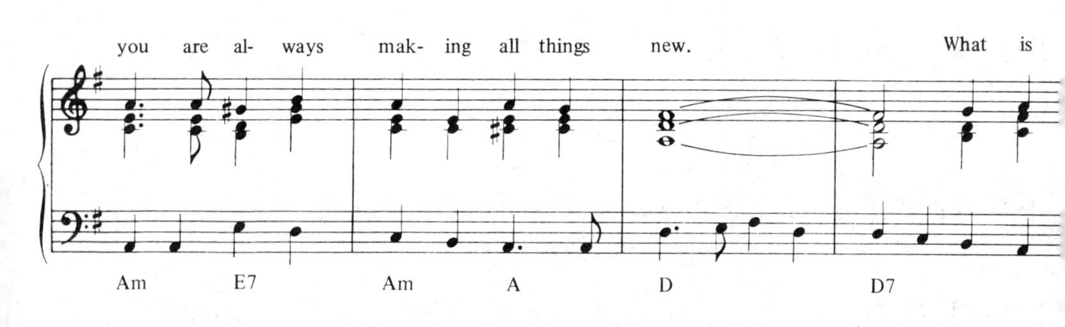

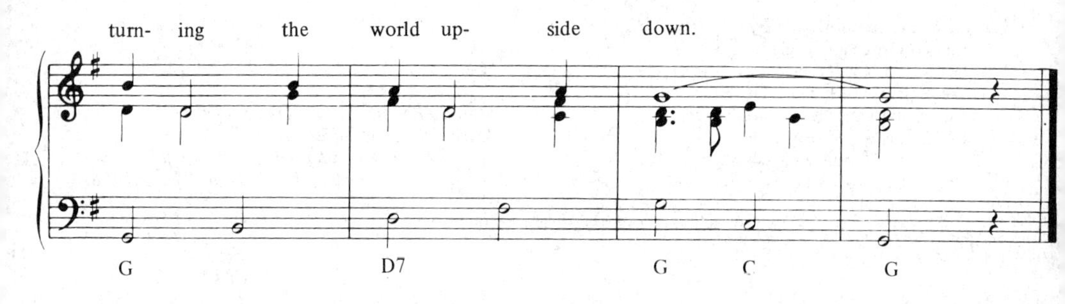

2. The world's only loving to its friends,
but you have brought us love that never ends;
loving enemies too, and this loving with you
is what's turning the world upside down.

3. This world lives divided and apart.
You draw all men together and we start
in your body to see that in fellowship we
can be turning the world upside down.

4. The world wants the wealth to live in state,
but you show us a new way to be great:
like a servant you came, and if we do the same,
we'll be turning the world upside down.

5. Oh Lord, all the world belongs to you,
and you are always making all things new.
Send your Spirit on all in your Church whom you call
to be turning the world upside down.

Words and Music: Patrick Appleford

O LORD, FURNACE OF LOVE
('Assisi')

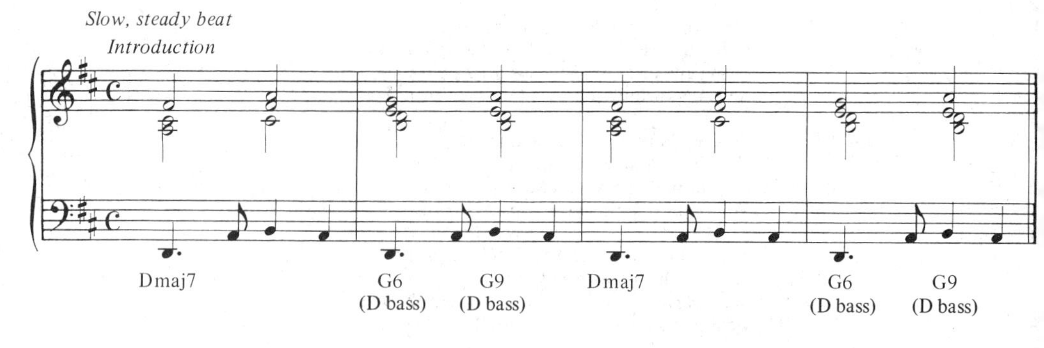

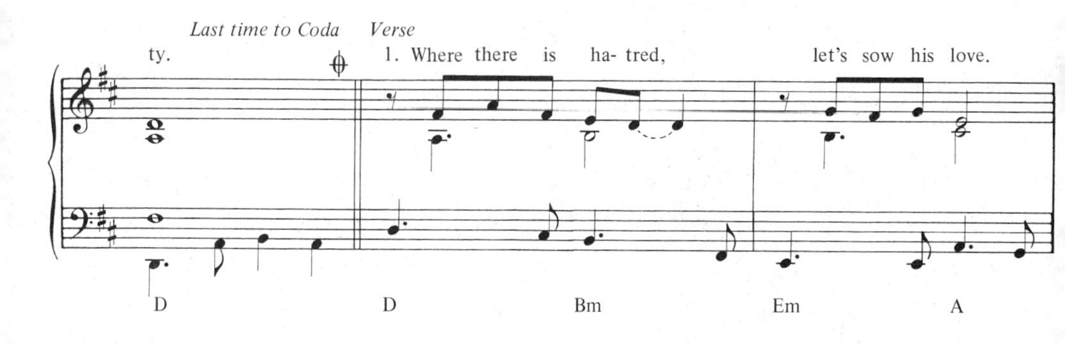

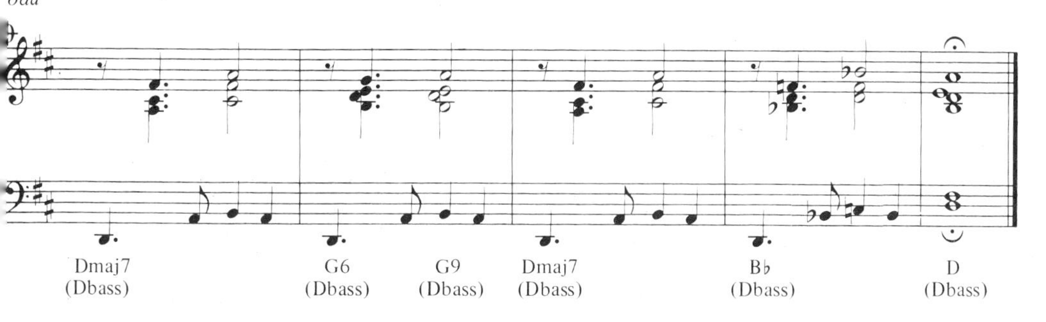

2. Where there is doubt, let's kindle faith.
   Where there's discouragement, let's bring assurance.
   Where there is grief, let's awaken joy.
   Where there is darkness, light.

Words, based on the Prayer of Francis of Assisi, and Music: Aniceto Nazareth

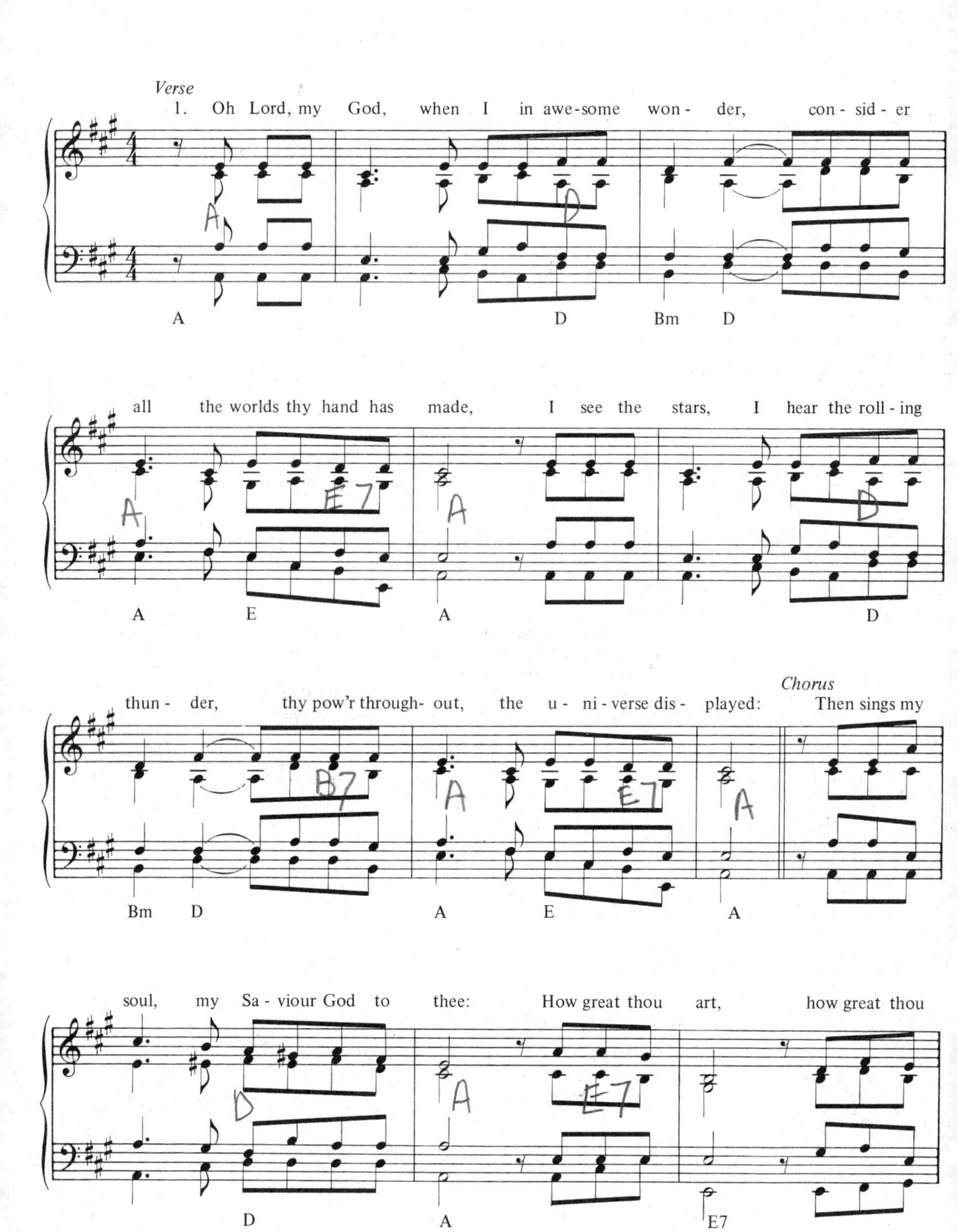
Verse
1. Oh Lord, my God, when I in awe-some won - der, con - sid - er
A D Bm D
all the worlds thy hand has made, I see the stars, I hear the roll - ing
A E A D
thun - der, thy pow'r through- out, the u - ni - verse dis - played:
Chorus
Then sings my
Bm D A E A
soul, my Sa - viour God to thee: How great thou art, how great thou
D A E7

2. When through the woods
    and forest glades I wander
and hear the birds
    sing sweetly in the trees;
when I look down
    from lofty mountain grandeur,
and hear the brook,
    and feel the gentle breeze:

3. And when I think
    that God, his Son not sparing,
sent him to die, I
    scarce can take it in
that on the cross,
    my burden gladly bearing,
he bled and died
    to take away my sin.

4. When Christ shall come
    with shout of acclamation
and take me home,
    what joy shall fill my heart;
when I shall bow
    in humble adoration,
and there proclaim:
    my God, how great thou art.

Words: Carl Boberg, translated by Stuart Hine
Music: Swedish Folk Melody, arranged by Stuart Hine

371

O LOVE, HOW DEEP
('Eisenach' L.M.)

[HARMONY]

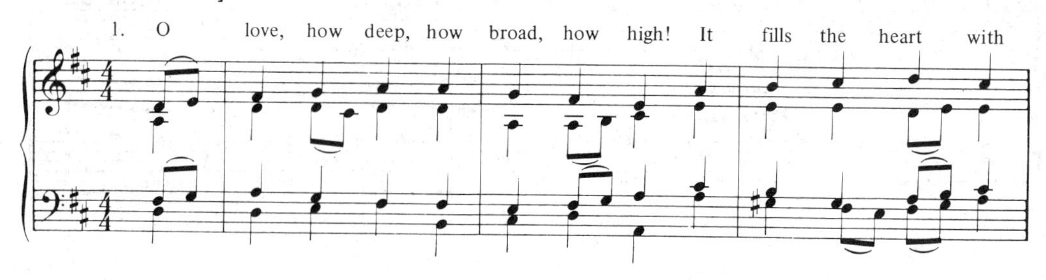

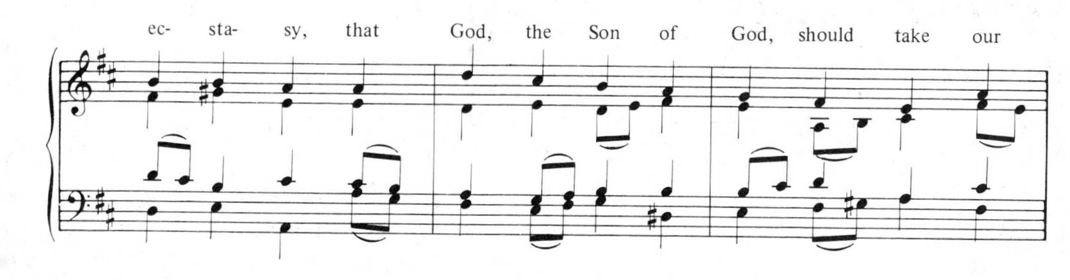

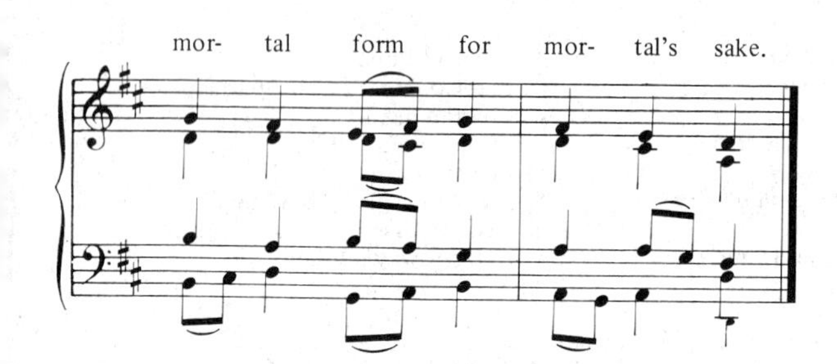

A different harmonisation of this tune may be found at Hymn 512

2. He sent no angel to our race
of higher or of lower place,
but wore the robe of human frame,
and he himself to this world came.

3. For us baptized, for us he bore
his holy fast, and hungered sore;
for us temptations sharp he knew;
for us the tempter overthrew.

4. For us to wicked men betrayed,
scourged, mocked, in crown of thorns arrayed,
for us he bore the cross's death;
for us at length gave up his breath.

5. For us he rose from death again,
for us he went on high to reign,
for us he sent his Spirit here
to guide, to strengthen, and to cheer.

6. All honour, laud and glory be,
O Jesu, Virgin-born, to thee,
all glory, as is ever meet,
to Father and to Paraclete.

Words: B. Webb, from Thomas à Kempis
Music: Johann H. Schein (1586-1630), harmony from J. S. Bach

O LOVE, THAT WILT NOT LET ME GO

('St Margaret' 88.88 6.)

[HARMONY]

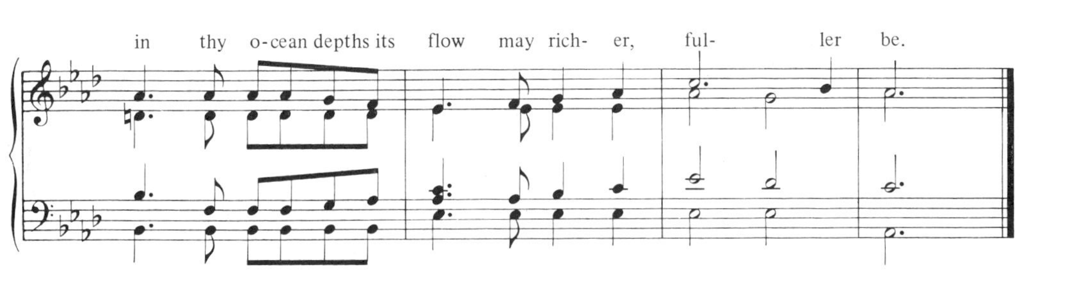

2. O Light that followest all my way,
   I yield my flickering torch to thee:
   my heart restores its borrowed ray,
   that in thy sunshine's blaze its day
   may brighter, fairer be.

3. O Joy that seekest me through pain,
   I cannot close my heart to thee:
   I trace the rainbow through the rain,
   and feel the promise is not vain
   that morn shall tearless be.

4. O Cross that liftest up my head,
   I dare not ask to fly from thee:
   I lay in dust life's glory dead,
   and from the ground there blossoms red
   life that shall endless be.

Words: George Matheson (1842-1906)
Music: A.L. Peace (1844-1912)

O LOVE, WHO FORMEDST ME TO WEAR

(First tune: 'St Matthias' 88.88.88.)

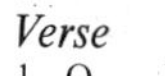

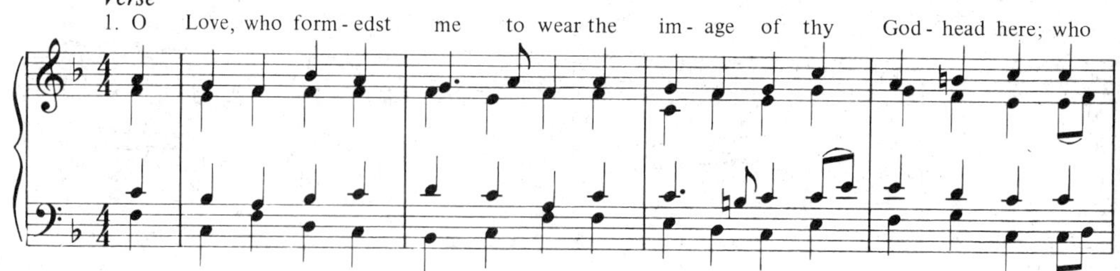

2. O Love, who ere life's earliest dawn
on me thy choice hast gently laid;
O Love, who here as man wast born,
and wholly like to us wast made:

3. O Love, who once in time wast slain,
pierced through and through with bitter woe;
O Love, who wrestling thus didst gain
that we eternal joy might know:

4. O Love, who once shalt bid me rise
from out this dying life of ours;
O Love, who once o'er yonder skies
shalt set me in the fadeless bowers:

Words: Johann Scheffler (1624-77), tr. C. Winkworth
Music: First tune – William H. Monk (1823-89)
Second tune – from 'Easy Hymns for Catholic Schools' (1851)

O LOVE, WHO FORMEDST ME TO WEAR
(Second tune: 'Stella' 88.88.88.)

Words and Music: Mimi Farra

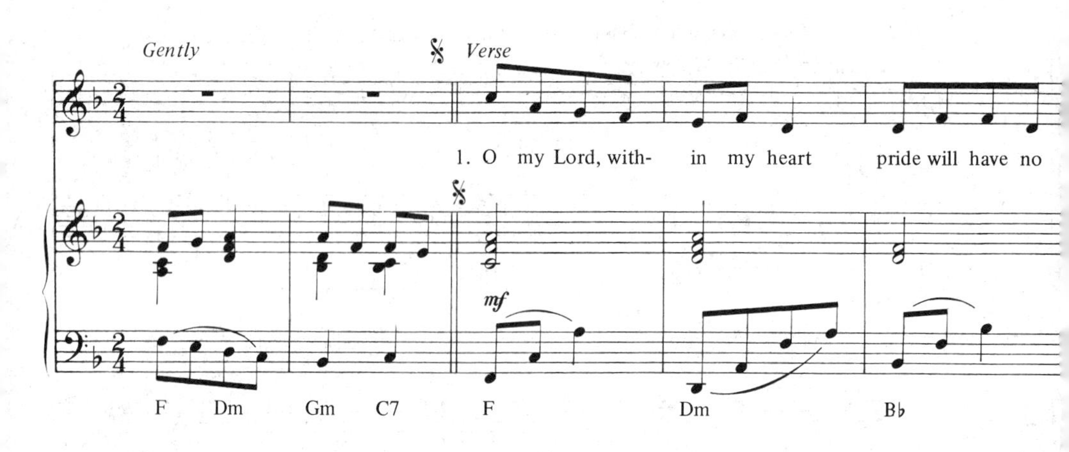
Gently
Verse
1. O my Lord, with- in my heart pride will have no
mf
F Dm Gm C7 F Dm B♭

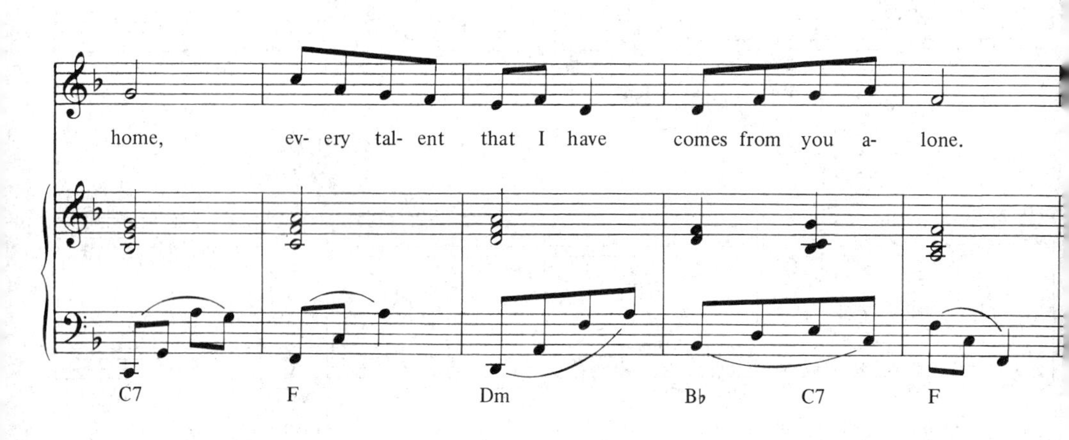
home, ev- ery tal- ent that I have comes from you a- lone.
C7 F Dm B♭ C7 F

Chorus
And, like a child at rest, close to it's mo- ther's breast,
Am Dm Am Dm

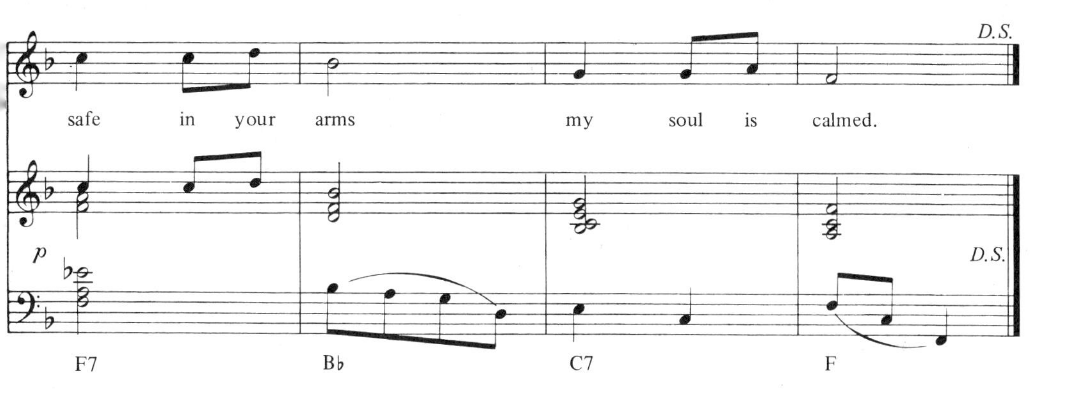

2. Lord, my eyes do not look high,
nor my thoughts take wings,
for I can find treasures in
ordinary things.

3. Great affairs are not for me,
deeds beyond my scope.
In the simple things I do
I find joy and hope.

Words, based on Psalm 131, and Music: Estelle White

O MY SAVIOUR LIFTED FROM THE EARTH
('North Coates' 65.65.)

[HARMONY]

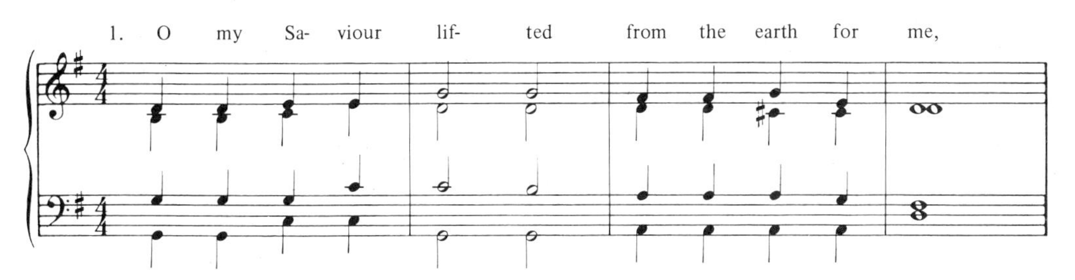

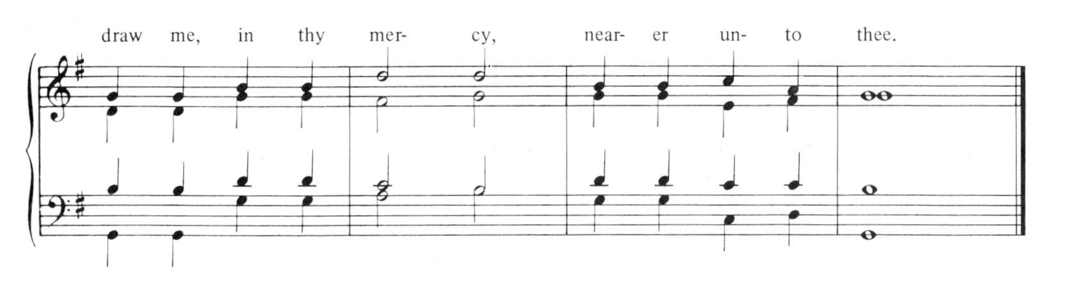

2. Lift my earth-bound longings,
   fix them, Lord, above;
   draw me with the magnet
   of thy mighty love.

3. Lord, thine arms are stretching
   ever far and wide,
   to enfold thy children
   to thy loving side.

4. And I come, O Jesus:
   dare I turn away?
   No, thy love hath conquered,
   and I come today,

5. Bringing all my burdens,
   sorrow, sin, and care;
   at thy feet I lay them,
   and I leave them there.

Words: William Walsham How (1823-97)
Music: Timothy R. Matthews (1826-1910)

377 ON A HILL FAR AWAY (The old rugged cross)

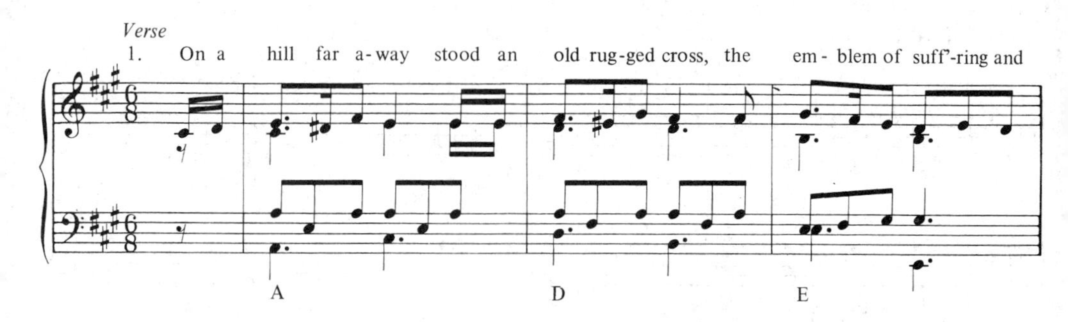

2. Oh that old rugged cross, so despised by the world,
   has a wondrous attraction for me:
   for the dear Lamb of God left his glory above
   to bear it to dark Calvary.

3. In the old rugged cross, stained with blood so divine,
   a wondrous beauty I see.
   For 'twas on that old cross Jesus suffered and died
   to pardon and sanctify me.

4. To the old rugged cross I will ever be true,
   its shame and reproach gladly bear.
   Then he'll call me some day to my home faraway,
   there his glory for ever I'll share.

Words and Music: George Bennard

ONCE IN ROYAL DAVID'S CITY
('Irby' 87.87.77.)

[HARMONY]

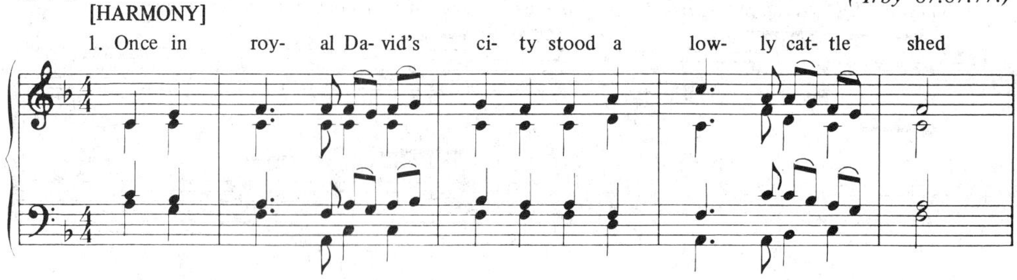

2. He came down to earth from heaven,
who is God and Lord of all,
and his shelter was a stable
and his cradle was a stall;
with the poor, and mean, and lowly,
lived on earth our Saviour holy.

3. And through all his wondrous childhood
he would honour and obey,
love, and watch the lowly maiden
in whose gentle arms he lay;
Christian children, all must be
mild, obedient, good as he.

4. For he is our childhood's pattern,
day by day like us he grew;
he was little, weak and helpless,
tears and smiles like us he knew;
and he feeleth for our sadness,
and he shareth in our gladness.

5. And our eyes at last shall see him
through his own redeeming love,
for that child so dear and gentle
is our Lord in heaven above;
and he leads his children on
to the place where he is gone.

6. Not in that poor lowly stable,
with the oxen standing by,
we shall see him; but in heaven,
set at God's right hand on high;
when like stars his children crowned
all in white shall wait around.

Words: Cecil Francis Alexander (1818-95)
Music: Henry J. Gauntlett (1805-76)

ONCE, ONLY ONCE AND ONCE FOR ALL
('Albano' C.M.)

[HARMONY]

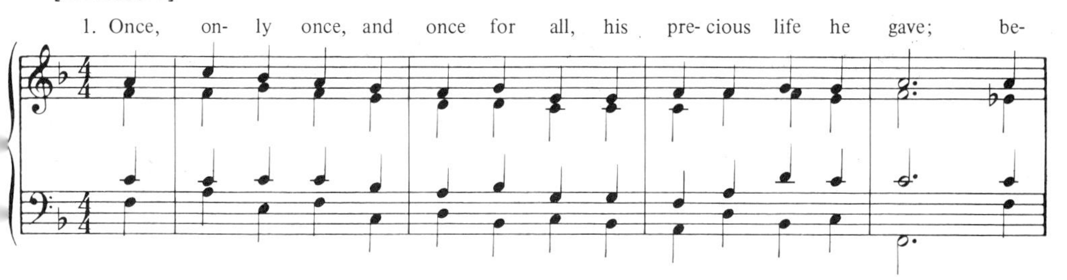

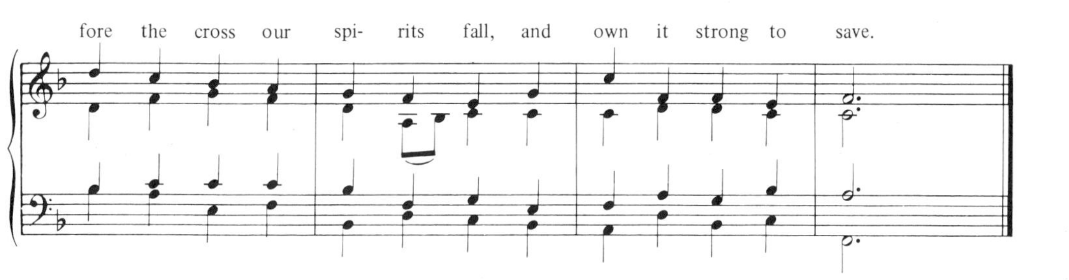

2. 'One offering, single and complete,'
with lips and heart we say;
but what he never can repeat
he shows forth day by day.

3. For, as the priest of Aaron's line
within the holiest stood,
and sprinkled all the mercy-shrine
with sacrificial blood;

4. so he who once atonement wrought,
our Priest of endless power,
presents himself for those he bought
in that dark noontide hour.

5. His manhood pleads where now it lives
on heaven's eternal throne,
and where in mystic rite he gives
its presence to his own.

6. And so we show thy death, O Lord,
till thou again appear;
and feel, when we approach thy board,
we have an altar here.

7. All glory to the Father be,
all glory to the Son,
all glory, Holy Ghost, to thee,
while endless ages run.

Words: William Bright (1824-1901)
Music: Vincent Novello (1781-1861)

380

ON CHRISTMAS NIGHT ALL CHRISTIANS SING
('Sussex carol' 88.88.88.)

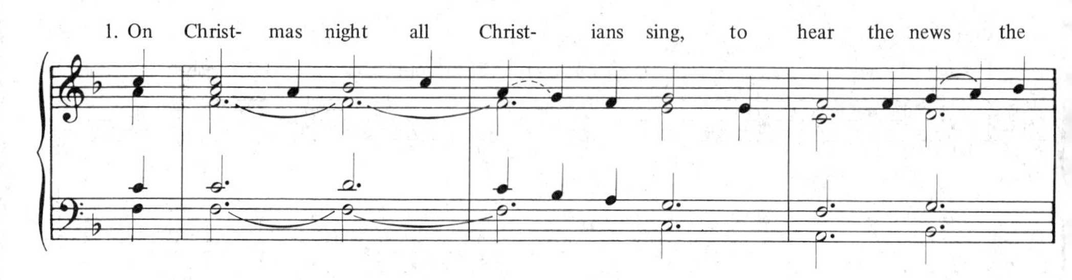

2. Then why should men on earth be so sad, *(2)*
since our Redeemer made us glad,
when from our sin he set us free,
all for to gain our liberty?

3. When sin departs before his grace, *(2)*
then life and health come in its place,
angels and men with joy may sing,
all for to see the new-born King.

4. All out of darkness we have light, *(2)*
which made the angels sing this night:
'Glory to God and peace to men,
now and for evermore. Amen.'

Words and Music: Traditional English (Sussex) Carol, harmonised by Frances M. Kelly

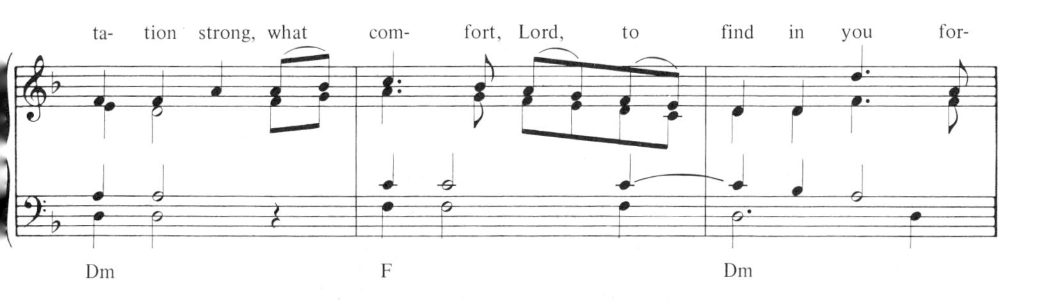

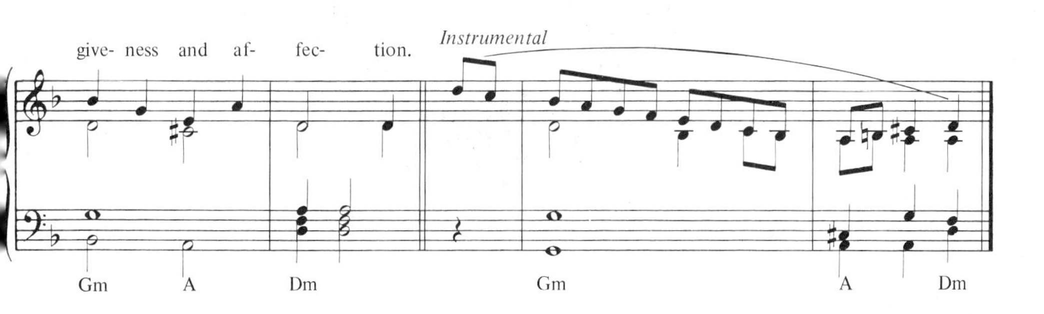

2. When beauty takes us by surprise
to challenge undiscerning eyes,
what joy to find reflected there
the splendour of your glory.

3. In times of loneliness or grief,
or constant pain with no relief,
what strength to find the caring Christ
within and right beside us.

4. The love of Jesus never ends,
it only deepens and extends.
So, Lord, to whom else could we go,
for you give life its meaning.

Words and Music: Susan Sayers,
arranged by John Rombaut

ON JORDAN'S BANK THE BAPTIST'S CRY

('Winchester New' L.M.)

[HARMONY]

2. Then cleansed be every Christian breast,
and furnished for so great a guest!
Yea, let us each our hearts prepare
for Christ to come and enter there.

3. For thou art our salvation, Lord,
our refuge and our great reward;
without thy grace our souls must fade,
and wither like a flower decayed.

4. Stretch forth thy hand, to heal our sore,
and make us rise, to fall no more;
once more upon thy people shine,
and fill the world with love divine.

5. All praise, eternal Son, to thee
whose advent sets thy people free,
whom, with the Father, we adore,
and Holy Ghost, for evermore.

Words: Charles Coffin (1676-1749),
tr. John Chandler (1806-76)
Music: from 'Musikalisches Handbuch' (1690)

 [HARMONY]

ONWARD CHRISTIAN SOLDIERS

('St Gertrude' 65.65. Triple)

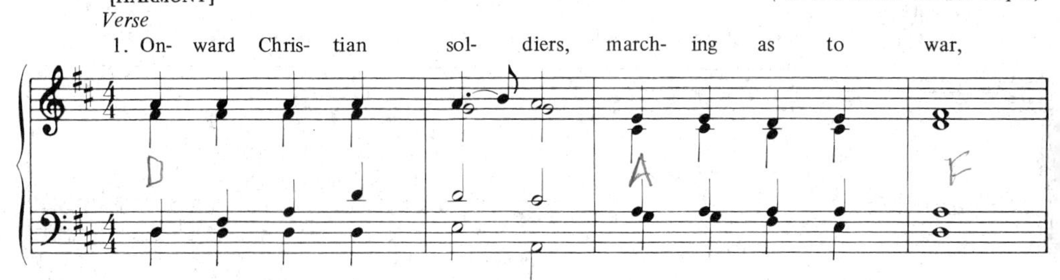

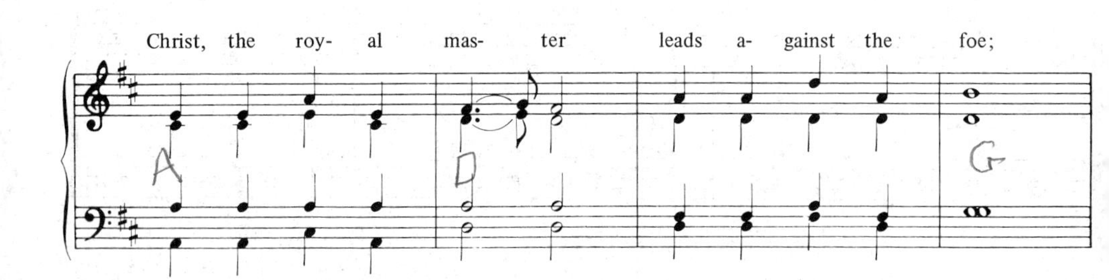

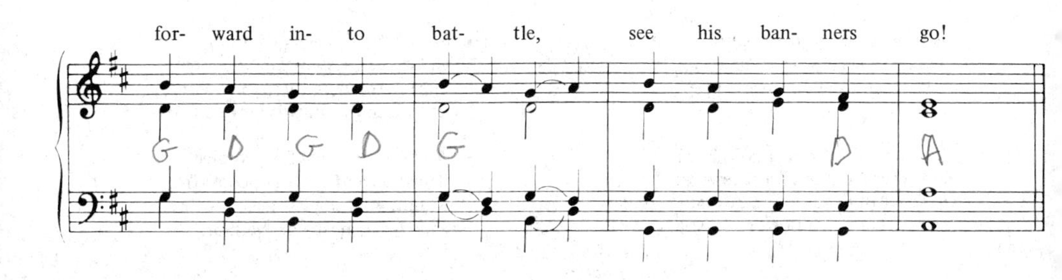

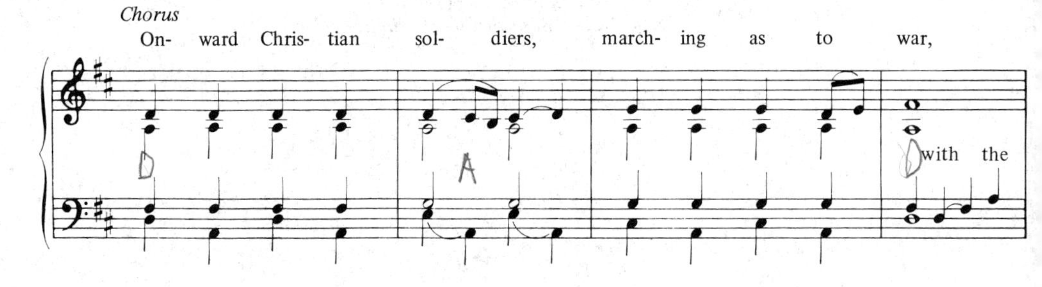

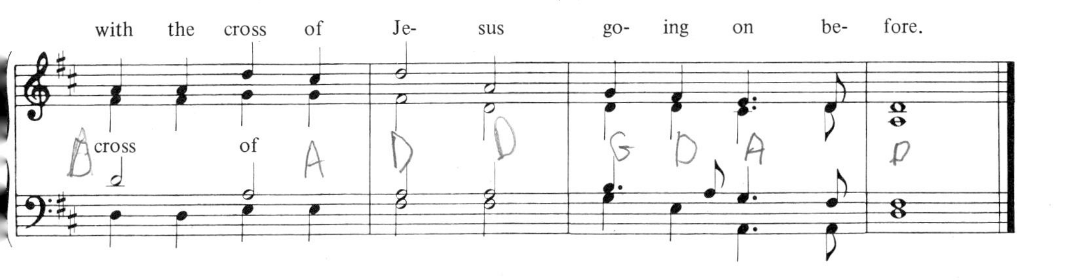

2. At the sign of triumph Satan's legions flee;
 on then, Christian soldiers, on to victory.
 Hell's foundations quiver at the shout of praise;
 brothers, lift your voices, loud your anthem raise.

3. Like a mighty army moves the Church of God.
 Brothers, we are treading where the saints have trod;
 we are not divided, all one body we,
 one in hope and doctrine, one in charity.

4. Crowns and thrones may perish, kingdoms rise and wane,
 but the Church of Jesus constant will remain;
 gates of hell can never 'gainst that Church prevail;
 we have Christ's own promise, and that cannot fail.

5. Onward, then, ye people, join our happy throng,
 blend with ours your voices in the triumph song;
 glory, laud and honour unto Christ our King;
 this through countless ages men and angels sing.

Words: Sabine Baring-Gould (1834-1924)
Music: Arthur Sullivan (1842-1900)

2. Peace he promised to our fathers
in the ancient desert-land;
peace he offers in abundance
to his faithful pilgrim-band.

3. All we have is offered to him
as we come to sing his praise.
Blessed is the Lord of heaven,
mighty God of all our days.

Words, based on Psalm 122, and Music: Kevin Mayhew,
arranged by Frances M. Kelly

1. Op - en my eyes that I may see,
C G C G7
Lord, you are pre - sent here with me;
C F D G
make me a - ware in life and in pray'r
G7 C F G
your Spi - rit hov - ers ev - 'ry - where.
C Dm G7 C
fine

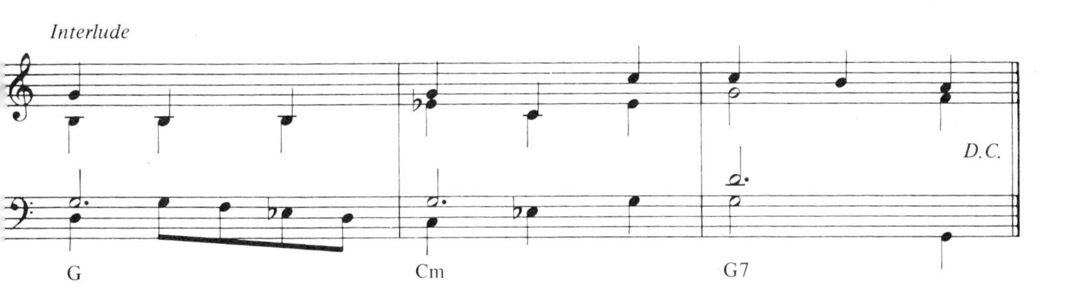

2. Open my ears that I may hear
   Lord, let me find your meaning clear;
   may I be stirred
   to ponder your Word
   till, Lord, your still small voice is heard.

3. Open my mind that I may learn;
   your will for me may I discern.
   Help me explore
   the wonders galore
   Father, you give us evermore.

4. Open my heart that I may love;
   though I am weak, let your great love
   flow out through me
   to others, for we
   share in your love eternally.

5. Open our lips that we may sing
   our thanks to you for everything:
   bind us in one
   till your will is done
   here as in heaven by everyone.

Words: Patrick Appleford
Music: Melody adapted from Edward Elgar by Patrick Appleford, arranged by Frances M. Kelly

Words and Music: Robert Cure,
arranged by David Peacock

387

OPEN YOUR EARS, O CHRISTIAN PEOPLE

('God has spoken')

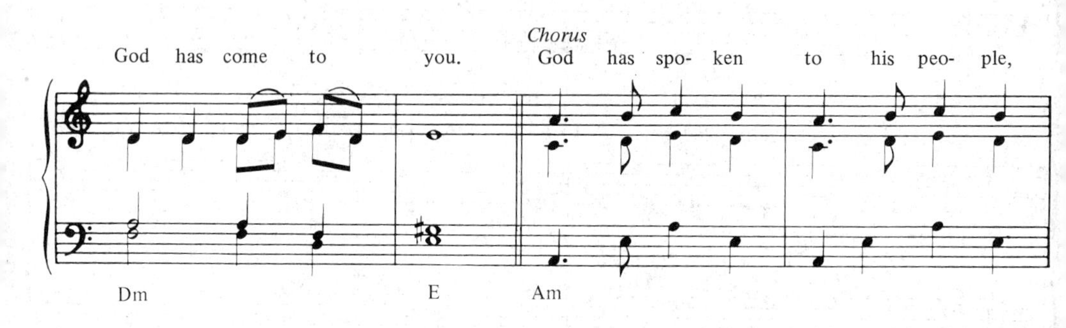

2. Israel comes to greet the Saviour,
   Judah is glad to see his day.
   From east and west the peoples travel,
   he will show the way.

3. He who has ears to hear his message,
   he who has ears, then let him hear.
   He who would learn the way of wisdom,
   let him hear God's words.

Words: Willard F. Jabusch
Music: Israeli Folk Song Melody,
arranged by John Rombaut

388

O PERFECT LOVE

('Strength and stay' 11 10.11 10.)

[HARMONY]

1. O per- fect love, all hu- man thought tran- scen- ding,

low- ly we kneel in prayer be- fore thy throne,

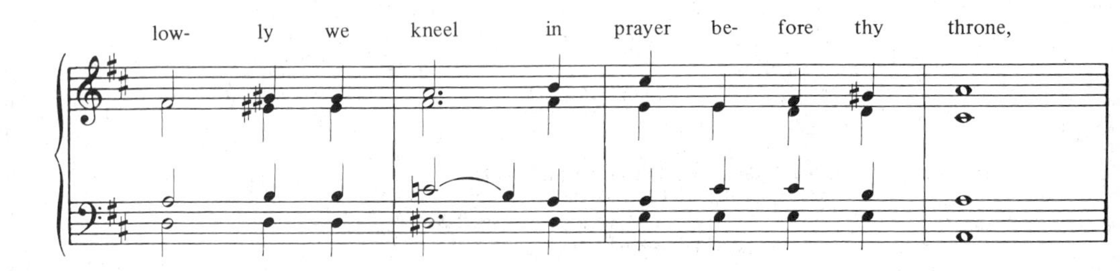

that theirs may be the love which knows no end- ing

whom thou for ev- er- more dost join in one.

An alternative harmonisation is at Hymn 393

2. O perfect life, be thou their full assurance
   of tender charity, and steadfast faith,
   of patient hope, and quiet, brave endurance,
   with childlike trust that fears not pain nor death.

3. Grant them the joy which brightens earthly sorrow,
   grant them the peace which calms all earthly strife;
   and to life's day the glorious unknown morrow
   that dawns upon eternal love and life.

Words: Dorothy F. Gurney (1858-1932)
Music: John B. Dykes (1823-76)

O PRAISE YE THE LORD
('Laudate Dominum' 10 10.11 11.)

2. O praise ye the Lord!
praise him upon earth
in tuneful accord,
ye sons of new birth.
Praise him who hath brought you
his grace from above,
praise him who hath taught you
to sing of his love.

3. O praise ye the Lord!
all things that give sound;
each jubilant chord
re-echo around;
loud organs, his glory
forth tell in deep tone,
and, sweet harp, the story
of what he hath done.

4. O praise ye the Lord!
thanksgiving and song
to him be outpoured
all ages along;
for love in creation,
for heaven restored,
for grace of salvation,
O praise ye the Lord!

Words: Henry Williams Baker (1821-77), based on Psalms 148 and 150
Music: C. Hubert H. Parry (1848-1918)

390 O SACRED HEAD SORE WOUNDED

('Passion Chorale' 76.76.D.)

2. Thy beauty, long-desirèd,
   hath vanished from our sight;
   thy power is all expirèd,
   and quenched the light of light.
   Ah me! for whom thou diest,
   hide not so far thy grace:
   show me, O Love most highest,
   the brightness of thy face.

3. I pray thee, Jesus, own me,
   me, Shepherd good, for thine;
   who to thy fold hast won me,
   and fed with truth divine.
   Me guilty, me refuse not,
   incline thy face to me,
   this comfort that I lose not,
   on earth to comfort thee.

4. In thy most bitter passion
   my heart to share doth cry,
   with thee for my salvation
   upon the cross to die.
   Ah, keep my heart thus movèd
   to stand thy cross beneath,
   to mourn thee, well-belovèd,
   yet thank thee for thy death.

5. My days are few, O fail not,
   with thine immortal power,
   to hold me that I quail not
   in death's most fearful hour:
   that I may fight befriended,
   and see in my last strife
   to me thine arms extended
   upon the cross of life.

Words: tr. Paul Gerhardt (1607-76)
Music: Hans Leo Hassler (1564-1612)
arranged by J.S. Bach

391

2. Run to the moon, moon won't you hide me?
   Run to the sea, sea won't you hide me?
   Run to the sun, sun won't you hide me,
   all on that day?

3. Lord said: 'Sinner man, the moon'll be a-bleeding.'
   Lord said: 'Sinner man, the sea'll be a-sinking.'
   Lord said: 'Sinner man, the sun'll be a-freezing,
   all on that day.'

4. Run to the Lord: 'Lord, won't you hide me?' *(3)*
   all on that day.

5. Lord said: 'Sinner man, you should have been a-praying!' *(3)*
   all on that day.

Words and Music: Traditional Spiritual

O SOUL, ARE YOU WEARY AND TROUBLED **(Turn your eyes upon Jesus)**

[HARMONY]

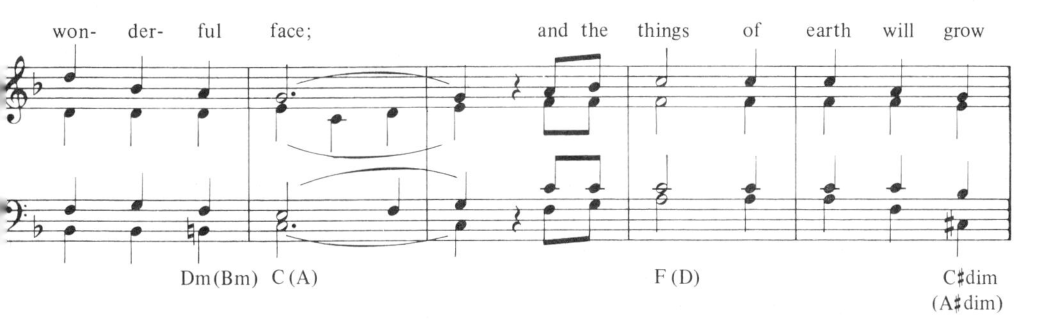

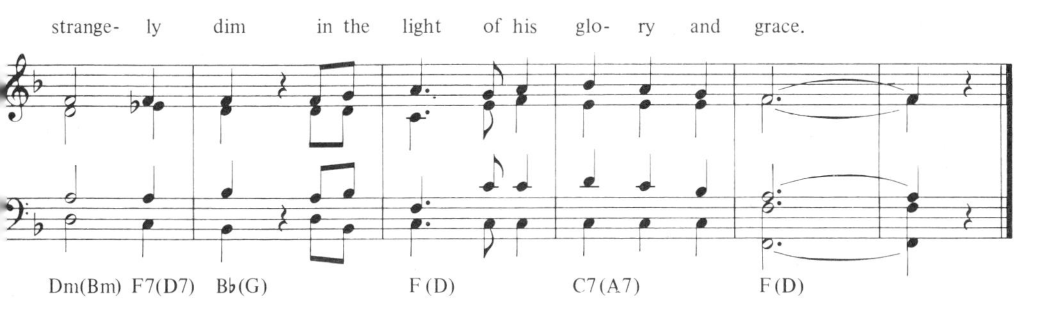

2. Through death into life everlasting
he passed, and we follow him there;
over us sin no more hath dominion
for more than conqu'rors we are!

3. His word shall not fail you he promised;
believe him, and all will be well:
then go to a world that is dying,
his perfect salvation to tell!

Words and Music: Helen H. Lemmel

393

O STRENGTH AND STAY UPHOLDING ALL CREATION

('Strength and stay' 11 10.11 10.)

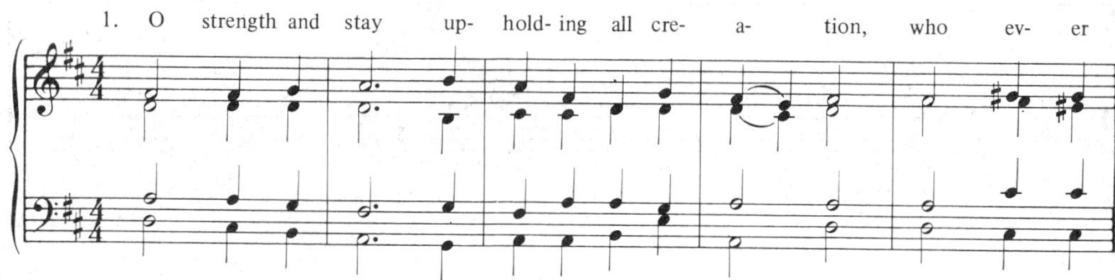

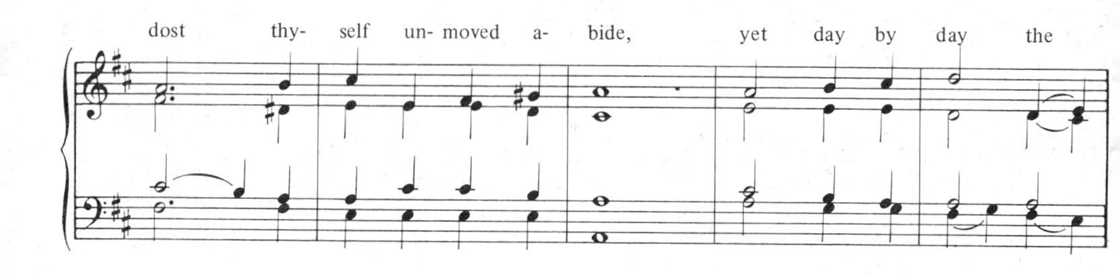

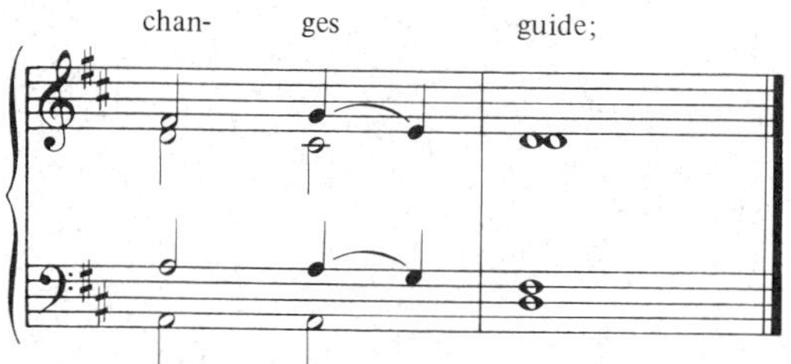

An alternative harmonisation is at Hymn 388

2. Grant to life's day a calm unclouded ending,
   an eve untouched by shadows of decay,
   the brightness of a holy death-bed blending
   with dawning glories of the eternal day.

3. Hear us, O Father, gracious and forgiving,
   through Jesus Christ thy co-eternal Word,
   who with the Holy Ghost by all things living
   now and to endless ages art adored.

Words: St Ambrose (c. 340-97),
tr. J. Ellerton and F. J. A. Hort
Music: John B. Dykes (1823-76

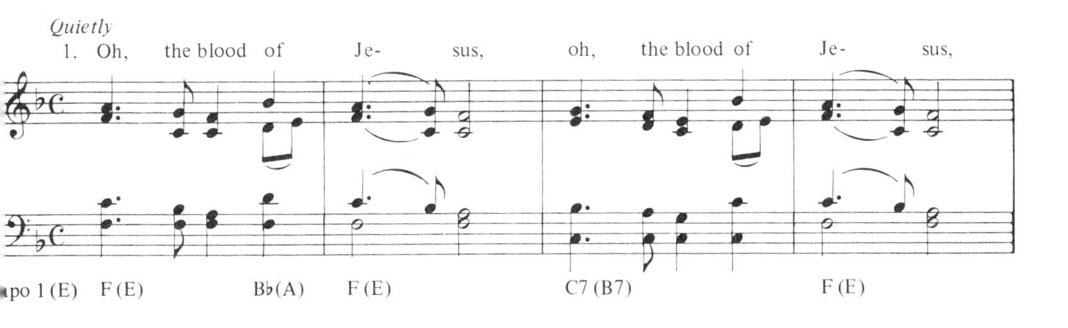

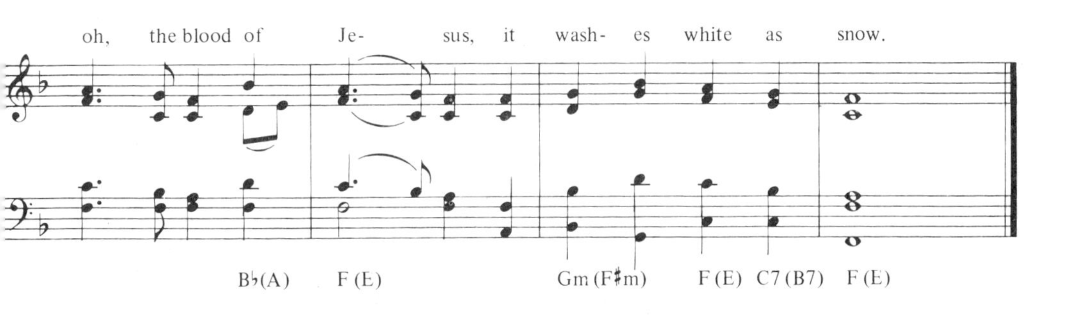

2. Oh, the word of Jesus, *(3)*
it cleanses white as snow.

3. Oh, the love of Jesus, *(3)*
it makes his body whole.

Words and Music: Unknown,
arranged by Betty Pulkingham

OH THE LOVE OF MY LORD **(As gentle as silence)**

2. Every day, every hour, every moment
have been blessed by the strength of his love.
At the turn of each tide
he is there at my side,
and his touch is as gentle as silence.

3. There've been times when I've turned from his presence,
and I've walked other paths, other ways.
But I've called on his name
in the dark of my shame,
and his mercy was gentle as silence.

Words and Music: Estelle White

OH THE WORD OF MY LORD
(Song of a Young Prophet)

Only the final chorus ends on the note of D; the others end on F♯.

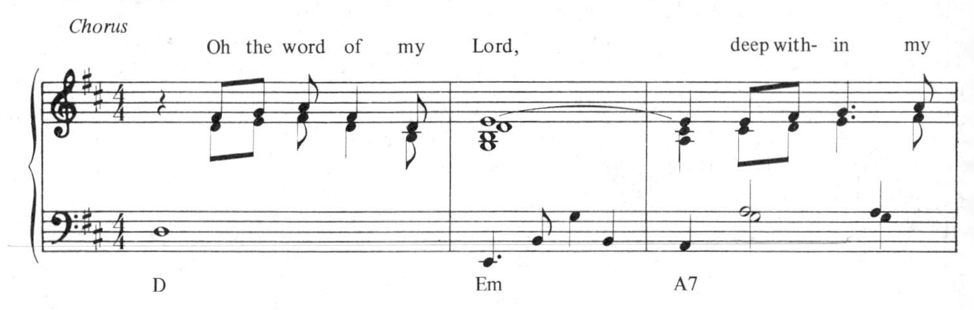

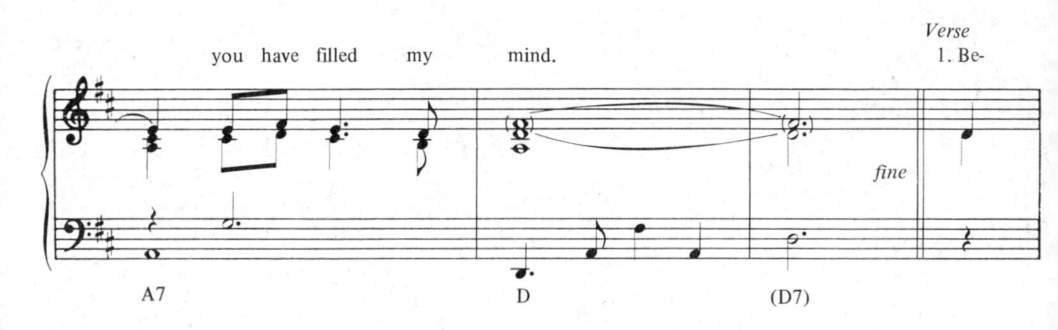

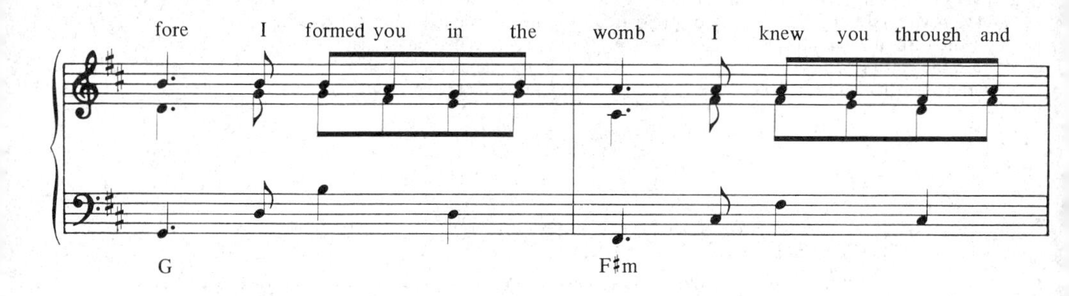

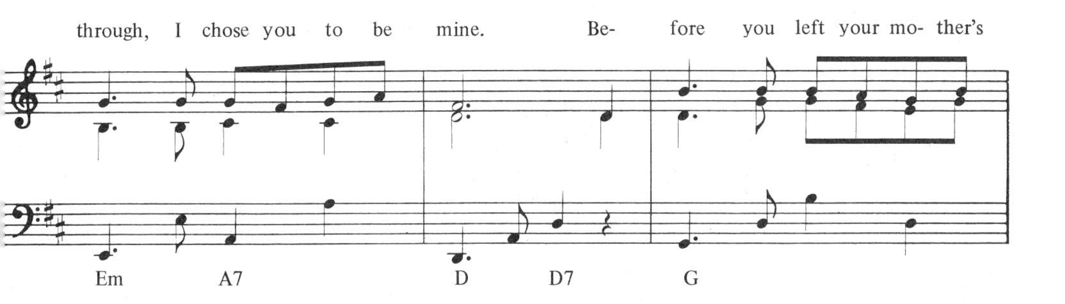

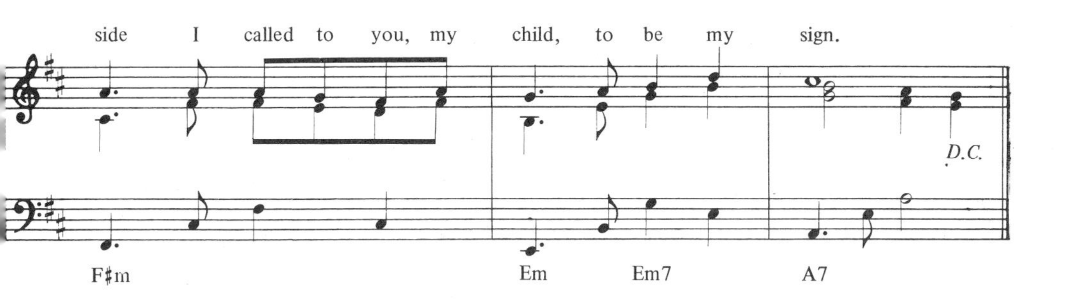

2. I know that you are very young,
but I will make you strong
– I'll fill you with my word;
and you will travel through the land,
fulfilling my command
which you have heard.

3. And everywhere you are to go
my hand will follow you;
you will not be alone.
In all the danger that you fear
you'll find me very near,
your words my own.

4. With all my strength you will be filled:
you will destroy and build,
for that is my design.
You will create and overthrow,
reap harvests I will sow
– your word is mine.

Words, based on Jeremiah 1, and Music: Damian Lundy

397

O THOU WHO AT THY EUCHARIST

('Song 1' 10 10.10 10.10 10.)

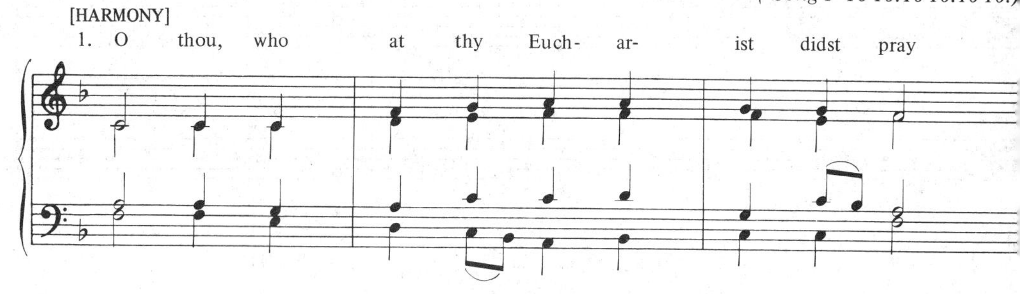

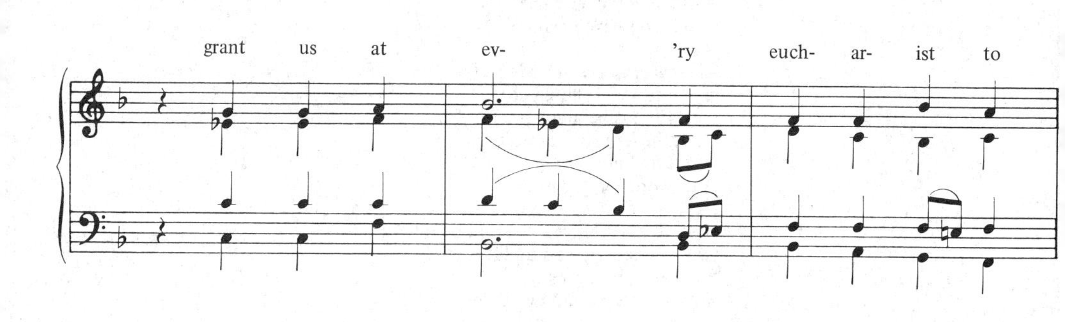

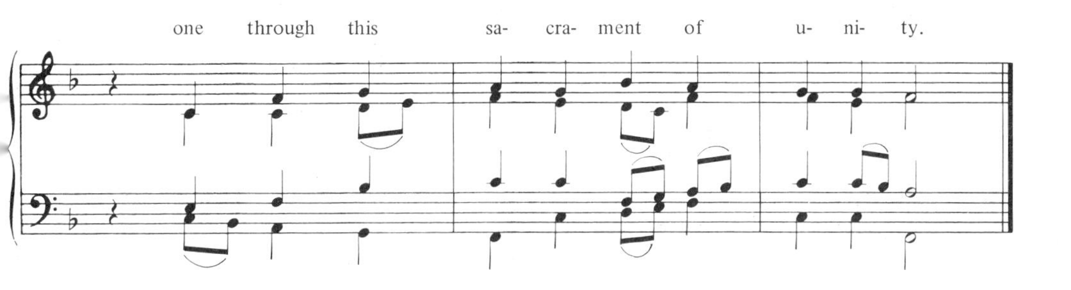

2. For all thy Church, O Lord, we intercede;
make thou our sad divisions soon to cease;
draw us the nearer each to each, we plead,
by drawing all to thee, O Prince of Peace:
thus may we all one bread, one body be,
one through this sacrament of unity.

3. We pray thee too for wanderers from thy fold;
O bring them back good Shepherd of the sheep,
back to the faith which saints believed of old,
back to the Church which still that faith doth keep:
soon may we all one bread, one body be,
one through this sacrament of unity.

4. So, Lord, at length when sacraments shall cease,
we may be one with all thy Church above,
one with thy saints in one unbroken peace,
one with thy saints in one unbounded love:
more blessèd still, in peace and love to be
one with the Trinity in unity.

Words, based on John 17: William Harry Turton (1856-1938)
Music: Orlando Gibbons (1583-1625)

398 O THOU WHO CAMEST FROM ABOVE

(First tune: 'Hereford' L.M.)

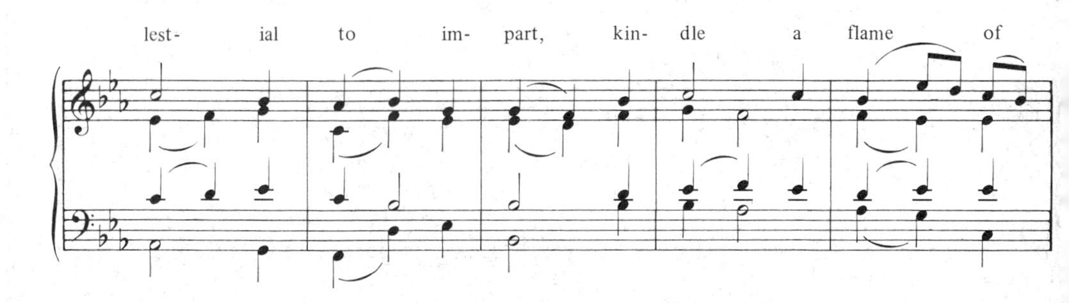

2. There let it for thy glory burn
   with inextinguishable blaze.
   And trembling to its source return
   in humble prayer, and fervent praise.

3. Jesus, confirm my heart's desire
   to work, and speak, and think for thee;
   still let me guard the holy fire,
   and still stir up thy gift in me.

4. Ready for all thy perfect will,
   my acts of faith and love repeat,
   till death thy endless mercies seal,
   and make my sacrifice complete.

Words: Charles Wesley (1707-88)
Music: First tune - Samuel S. Wesley (1810-76)

O THOU WHO CAMEST FROM ABOVE
(Second tune: 'Affection' L.M.)

[HARMONY]

2. There let it for thy glory burn
with inextinguishable blaze,
and trembling to its source return
in humble prayer and fervent praise.

3. Jesus, confirm my heart's desire
to work and speak and think for thee;
still let me guard the holy fire
and still stir up the gift in me.

4. Ready for all thy perfect will,
my acts of faith and love repeat;
till death thy endless mercies seal,
and make the sacrifice complete.

Words: Charles Wesley (1707-88)
Music: Second tune - 'Greenwood's Psalmody', Halifax (1838)

OUR BLEST REDEEMER
('St Cuthbert' 86.84.)

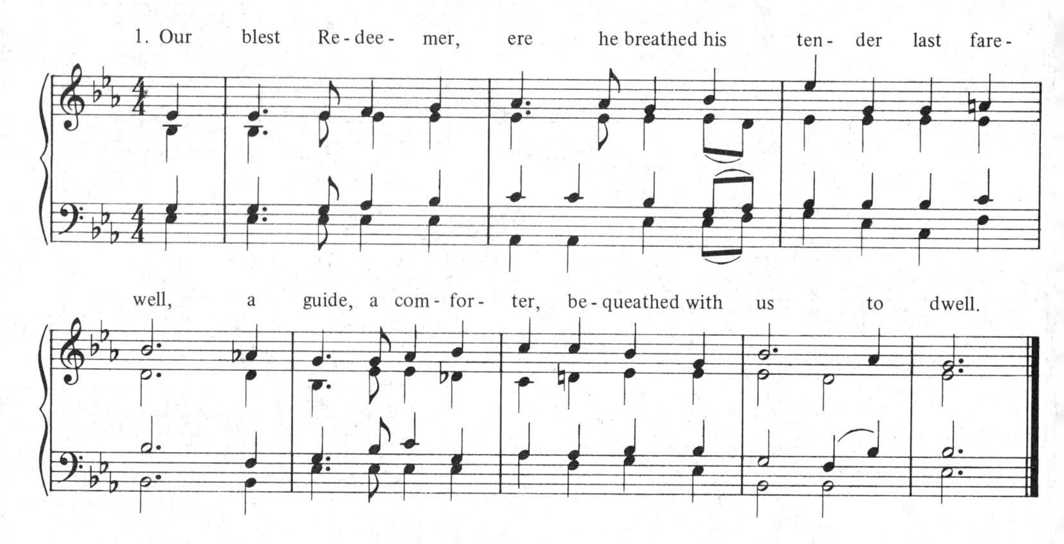

2. He came in tongues of living flame,
to teach, convince, subdue;
all-powerful as the wind he came,
as viewless too.

3. He came sweet influence to impart,
a gracious, willing guest,
while he can find one humble heart
wherein to rest.

4. And his that gentle voice we hear,
soft as the breath of even,
that checks each fault, that calms each fear,
and speaks of heaven.

5. And every virtue we possess,
and every victory won,
and every thought of holiness,
are his alone.

6. Spirit of purity and grace,
our weakness, pitying, see;
O make our hearts thy dwelling-place,
and worthier thee.

Words: Harriet Auber (1773-1862)
Music: John Bacchus Dykes (1823-76)

OUR FATHER (Caribbean Lord's Prayer)

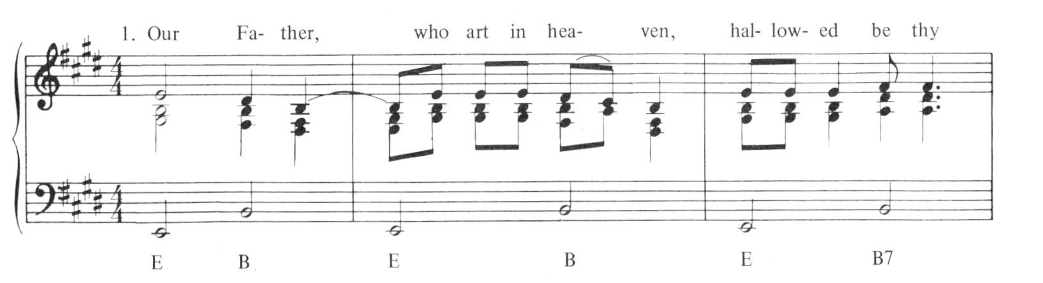

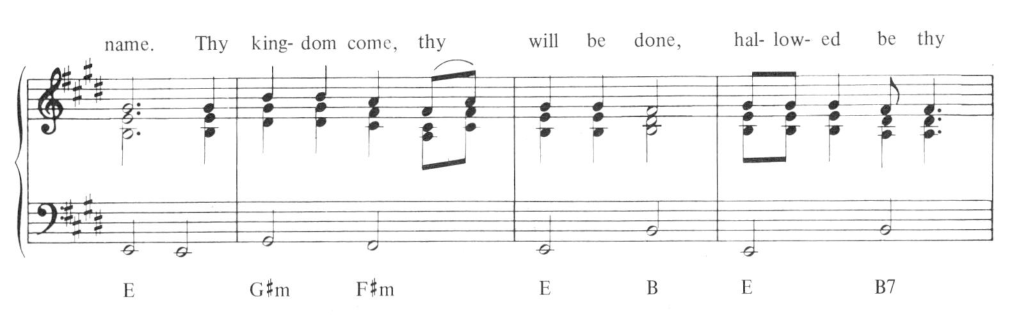

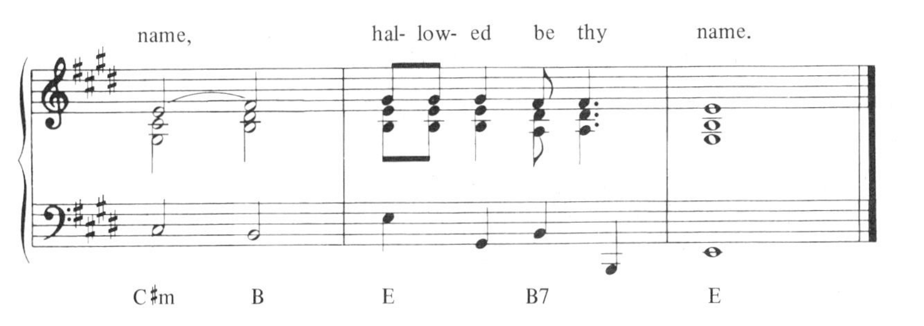

2. On earth as it is in heaven,
 hallowed be thy name.
 Give us this day our daily bread,
 hallowed be thy name.

3. Forgive us our trespasses,
 hallowed be thy name.
 As we forgive those who trespass against us,
 hallowed be thy name.

4. And lead us not into temptation,
 hallowed be thy name.
 But deliver us from all that is evil,
 hallowed be thy name.

5. For thine is the kingdom, the power and the glory,
 hallowed be thy name.
 For ever, and ever, and ever,
 hallowed be thy name.

6. Amen, amen, it shall be so,
 hallowed be thy name.
 Amen, amen, it shall be so,
 hallowed be thy name.

Words, based on Matthew 6: 9-13; Luke 11: 2-4, and Music: Traditional Caribbean, arranged by Michael Irwin

OUR HEARTS WERE MADE FOR YOU

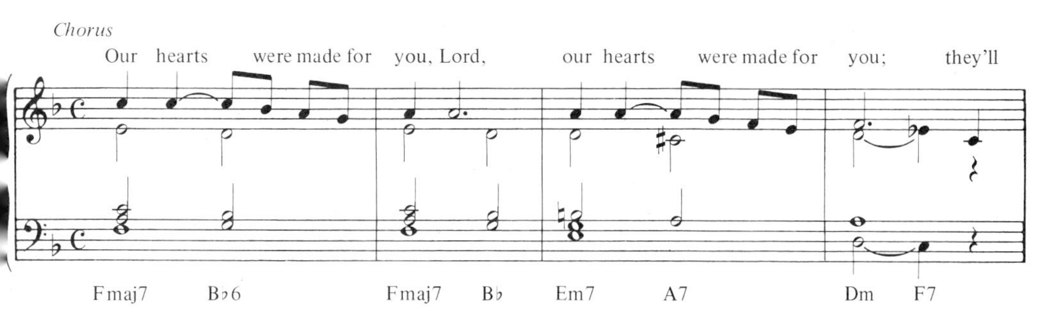

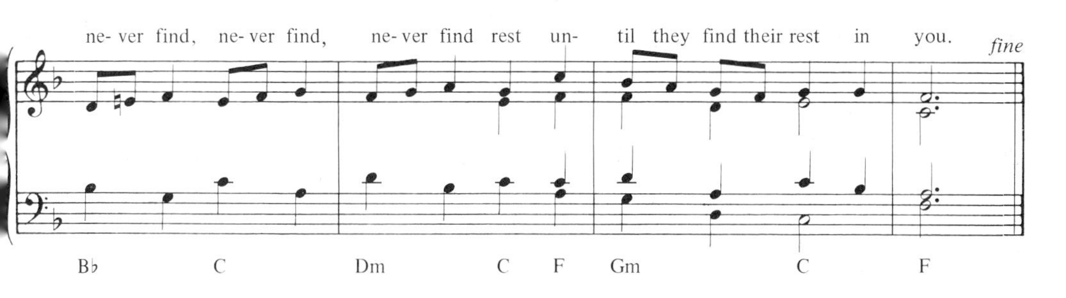

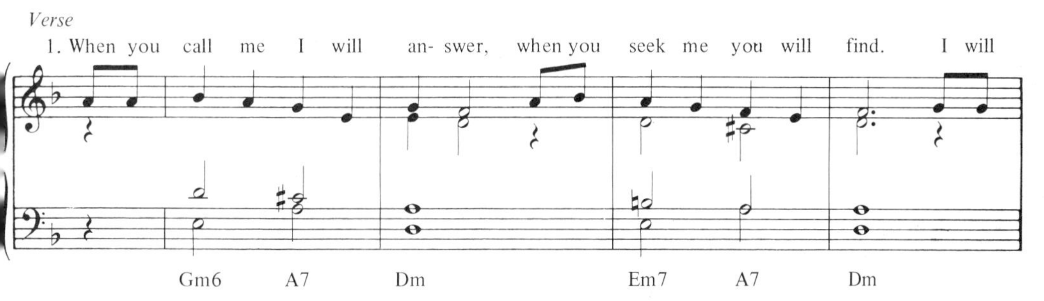

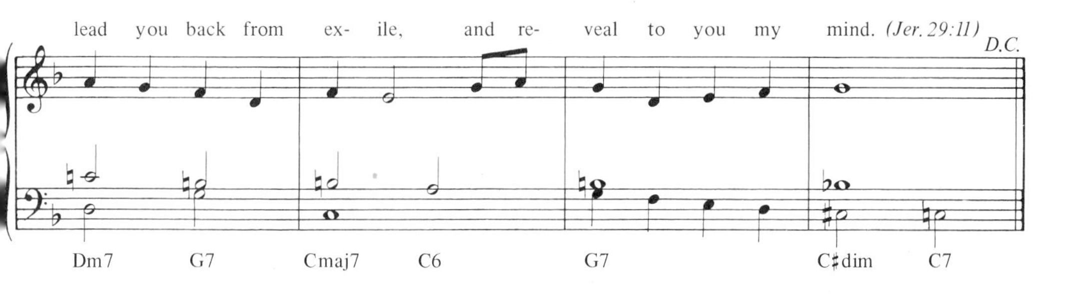

2. I will take you from the nations,
and will bring you to your land.
From your idols I will cleanse you.
and you'll cherish my command. *(Ezek. 36: 24-27)*

3. I will put my law within you,
I will write it on your heart;
I will be your God and Saviour,
you, my people set apart. *(Jer. 31: 33)*

Words, based on Scripture, and Music: Aniceto Nazareth

Chorus
O what a gift! What a won-der-ful gift! Who can tell the won-ders of the Lord? Let us op-en our eyes, our ears, and our hearts; it is Christ the Lord, it is he!
fine
Verse
1. In the still-ness of the night when the world was a-sleep, the al-migh-ty word leapt out.
2. On the night be-fore he died it was Pass-ov-er night, and he gath-ered his friends to-geth-er.
3. On the hill of Cal-va-ry the world held its breath, for there for the world to see,
4. Ear-ly on that morn-ing when the guards were sleep-ing, back to life came he!
5. Some-day with the saints we will come be-fore our Fa-ther and then we will shout and dance and sing.
Bm A Bm Em
Bm A Bm
A Bm Bm
A G A Bm

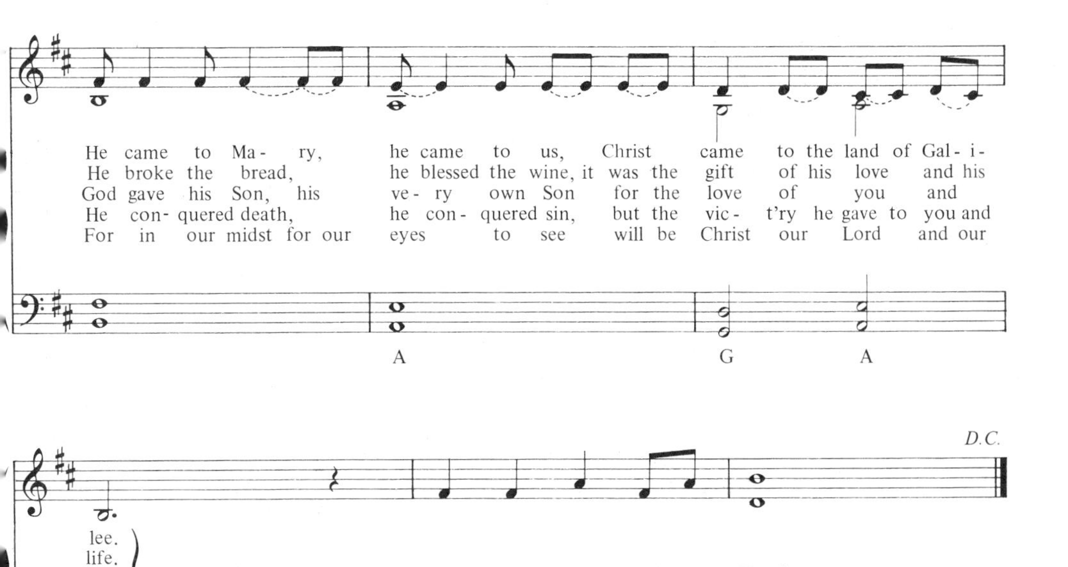

D.C.

lee.
life.
me.
me!
King.

Christ our Lord and our King!

Bm F♯m Bm

Words and Music: Pat Uhl Howard arranged by Betty Pulkingham

2. Oh when the drums begin to bang . . .

3. Oh when the stars fall from the skies . . .

4. Oh when the moon turns into blood . . .

5. Oh when the sun turns into fire . . .

6. Oh when the fires begin to blaze. . .

7. Oh when the Lord calls out the names . . .

Words and Music: Traditional,
arranged by Frances M. Kelly

O WORD OF GOD ABOVE
('St Edmund' S.M.)

2. Grace in this font is stored
to cleanse each guilty child;
the Spirit's blest anointing poured
brightens the once defiled.

3. Here Christ of his own blood
himself the chalice gives,
and feeds his own with angels' food,
on which the spirit lives.

4. For guilty souls that pine
sure mercies here abound,
and healing grace with oil and wine
for every secret wound.

5. God from his throne afar,
comes in this house to dwell;
and prayer, beyond the evening star,
builds here her citadel.

6. All might, all praise be thine,
the God whom all adore;
the Father, Son, and Spirit divine,
both now and evermore.

Words: C. Guiet (1601-64) tr. I. Williams
Music: Edmund Gilding (†1782)

405

O WORSHIP THE KING
('Hanover' 10 10.11 11.)

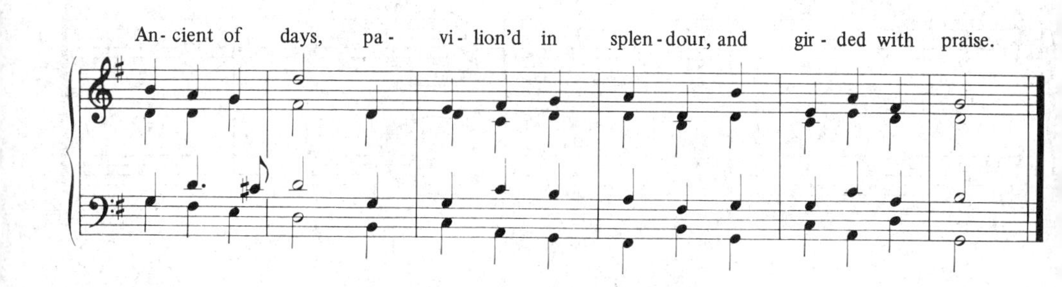

2. O tell of his might, O sing of his grace,
whose robe is the light, whose canopy space:
his chariots of wrath the deep thunder-clouds form,
and dark is his path on the wings of the storm.

3. The earth with its store of wonders untold,
almighty, thy power hath founded of old,
hath stablished it fast by a changeless decree,
and round it hath cast, like a mantle, the sea.

4. Thy bountiful care what tongue can recite?
It breathes in the air; it shines in the light;
it streams from the hills, it descends to the plain,
and sweetly distils in the dew and the rain.

5. Frail children of dust and feeble as frail,
in thee do we trust, nor find thee to fail;
thy mercies how tender, how firm to the end,
our maker, defender, redeemer, and friend.

6. O measureless might, ineffable love,
while angels delight to hymn thee above,
thy humbler creation, though feeble their lays,
with true adoration shall sing to thy praise.

Words, based on Psalm 104:
Robert Grant (1779-1838)
Music: William Croft (1678-1727)

O WORSHIP THE LORD
('Was lebet' 13 10.13 10.)

2. Low at his feet lay thy burden of carefulness:
high on his heart he will bear it for thee,
comfort thy sorrows, and answer thy prayerfulness,
guiding thy steps as may best for thee be.

3. Fear not to enter his courts in the slenderness
of the poor wealth thou wouldst reckon as thine:
truth in its beauty, and love in its tenderness,
these are the offerings to lay on his shrine.

4. These, though we bring them in trembling and fearfulness,
he will accept for the name that is dear;
mornings of joy give for evenings of tearfulness,
trust for our trembling and hope for our fear.

Words: John Samuel Bewley Monsell (1811-75)
Music: Melody from MS by J.H. Rheinhardt, Üttingen (1754)

407 PEACE I LEAVE WITH YOU

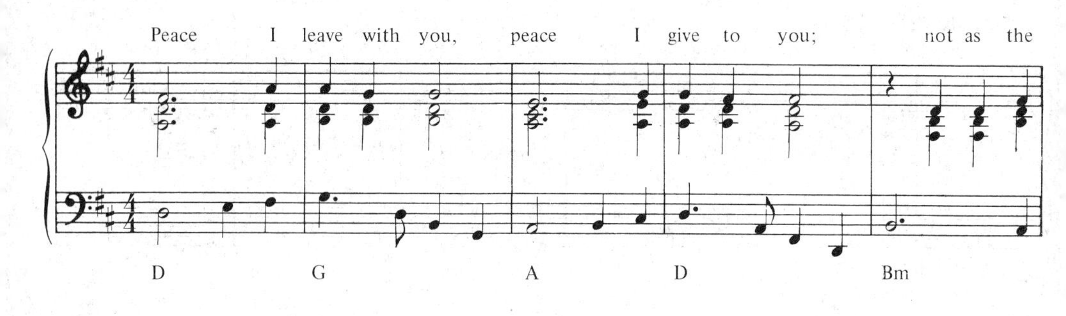

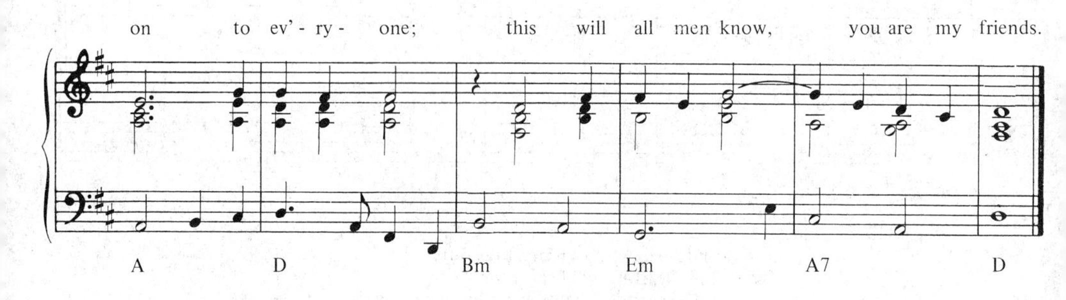

Words, based on John 14, and Music: Peter Madden

PEACE IS FLOWING LIKE A RIVER

2. Love is flowing like a river . . .

3. Joy is flowing like a river . . .

4. Hope is flowing like a river . . .

Words and Music: Unknown, arranged by John Rombaut

2. Peace is the gift of Christ to his Church,
wound of the lance of his love.
Love is the pain he suffered for man,
offered to us:
Oh, to accept the wound that brings us peace!

3. Joy is the gift the Spirit imparts,
born of the heavens and earth.
We are his children, children of joy,
people of God:
He is our Lord, our peace, our love, our joy!

Words and Music: John Glynn,
arranged by Frances M. Kelly

PEACE, PERFECT PEACE

('Song 46' 10 10.)

[HARMONY]

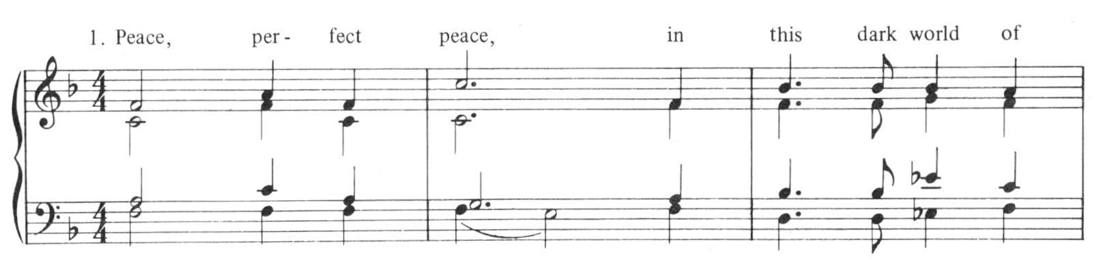

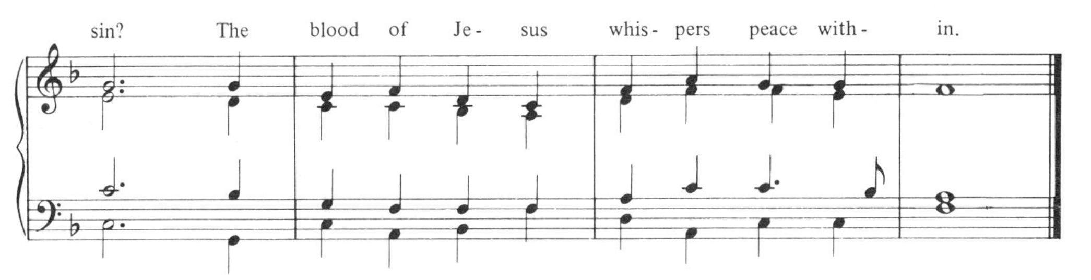

2. Peace, perfect peace, by thronging duties pressed?
   To do the will of Jesus, this is rest.

3. Peace, perfect peace, with sorrows surging round?
   On Jesus' bosom nought but calm is found.

4. Peace, perfect peace, with loved ones far away?
   In Jesus' keeping we are safe and they.

5. Peace, perfect peace, our future all unknown?
   Jesus we know, and he is on the throne.

6. Peace, perfect peace, death shadowing us and ours?
   Jesus has vanquished death and all its powers.

7. It is enough: earth's struggles soon shall cease,
   and Jesus call us to heaven's perfect peace.

Words: Edward Henry Bickersteth (1825-1906)
Music: Orlando Gibbons (1583-1625)

PEACE, PERFECT PEACE IS THE GIFT

2. Love, perfect love . . .

3. Faith, perfect faith . . .

4. Hope, perfect hope . . .

5. Joy, perfect joy . . .

Words and Music: Kevin Mayhew

PETER AND JOHN WENT TO PRAY **(Silver and gold)**

Words, based on Acts 3: Unknown
Music: Unknown, arranged by Betty Pulkingham

413

POUR OUT THY SPIRIT

('Duke Street' L.M.)

[HARMONY]

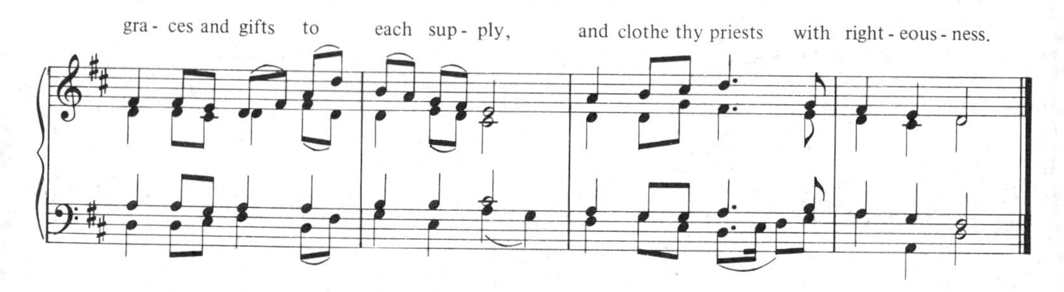

A different harmonisation of this tune may be found at Hymn 120

2. Within the temple when they stand,
to teach the truth, as taught by thee,
Saviour, like stars in thy right hand
may all thy Church's pastors be.

3. Wisdom, and zeal, and faith impart,
firmness with meekness, from above,
to bear thy people in their heart,
and love the souls whom thou dost love:

4. To watch, and pray, and never faint,
by day and night, strict guard to keep,
to warn the sinner, cheer the saint,
nourish thy lambs, and feed thy sheep.

5. Then, when their work is finished here,
may they in hope their charge resign;
when the Chief Shepherd shall appear,
O God, may they and we be thine.

Words: James Montgomery (1771-1854)
Music: John Hatton (†1793)

('Bunessan' 55.54.D.)

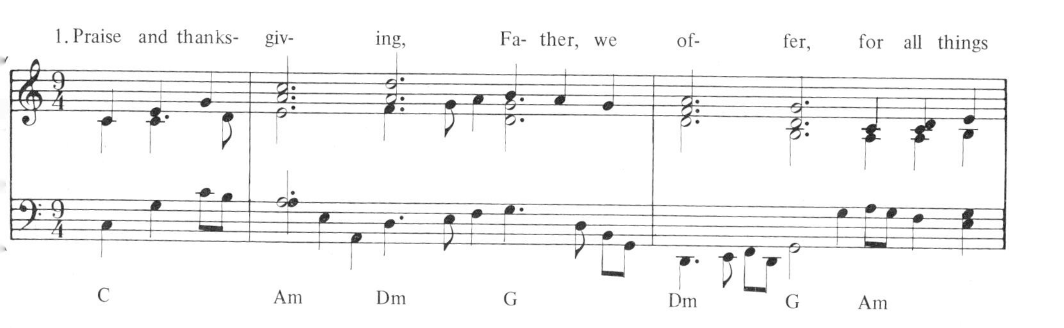

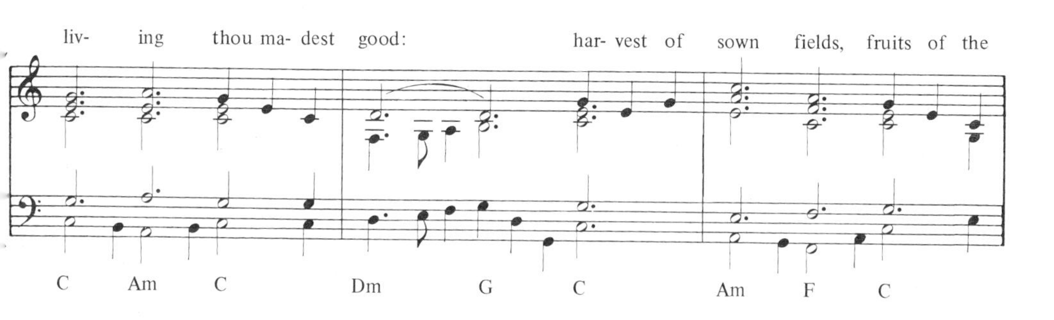

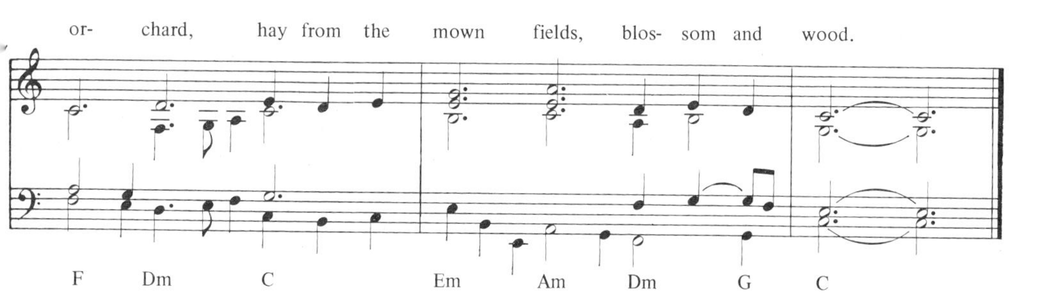

A different arrangement of this tune is at Hymn 326

2. Bless thou the labour
we bring to serve thee,
that with our neighbour
we may be fed.
Sowing or tilling,
we would work with thee;
harvesting, milling,
for daily bread.

3. Father, providing
food for thy children,
thy wisdom guiding
teaches us share
one with another,
so that rejoicing
with us, our brother
may know thy care.

4. Then will thy blessing
reach every people;
all men confessing
thy gracious hand.
Where thy will reigneth
no man will hunger:
thy love sustaineth;
fruitful the land.

Words: Albert F. Bayly (1901-84)
Music: Traditional Gaelic melody,
arranged by Una Macdonald

PRAISE, GLORY, TO YOU (**Speak of my love)**

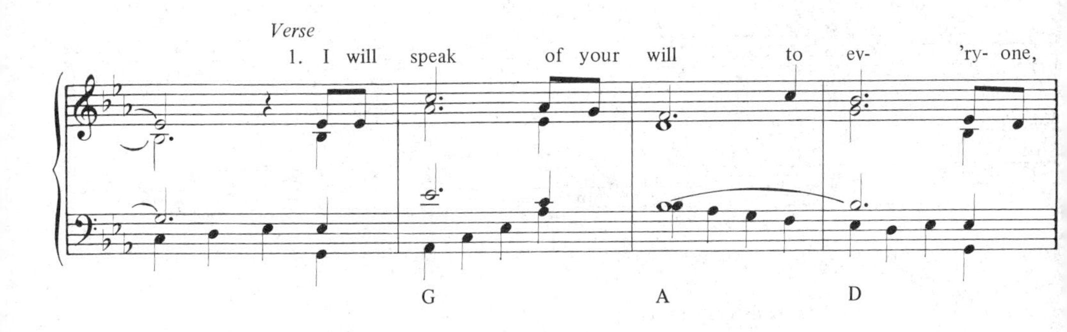

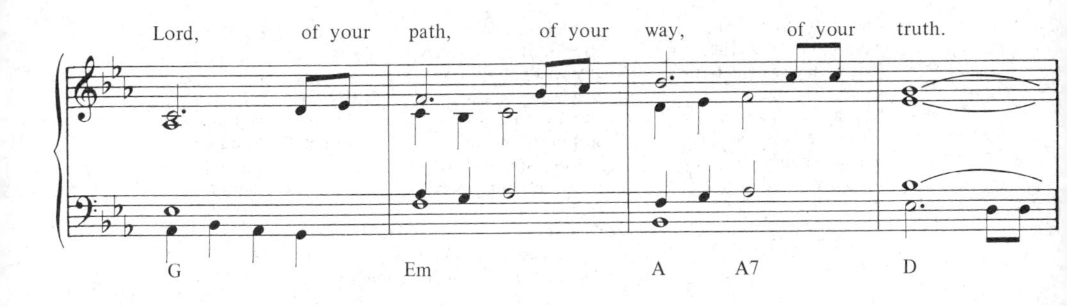

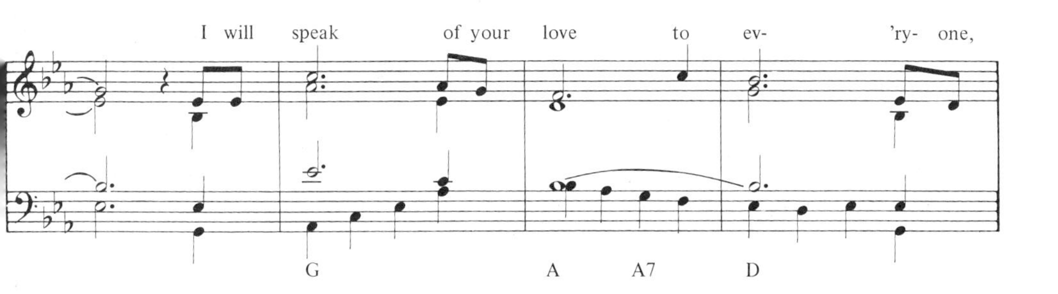

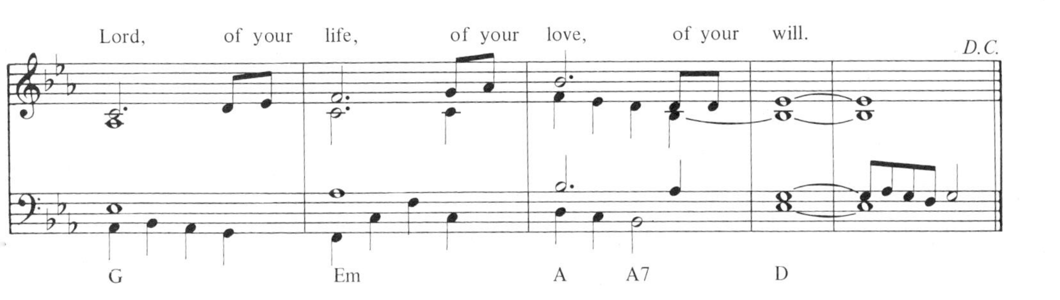

2. They are blessed who hear the Word of the Lord;
they are blessed who keep to God's word.
They are blest who obey what God may command,
for the glory of God they shall see.

3. I will worship and praise you, Lord God of might,
you are life, you are love, you are truth.
Praise to you, alleluia, alleluia!
Praise to you, Lord our God, evermore.

Words and Music: Alfred Camilleri,
arranged by Frances M. Kelly

416

PRAISE GOD FROM WHOM ALL BLESSINGS FLOW
('Doxology' L.M.)

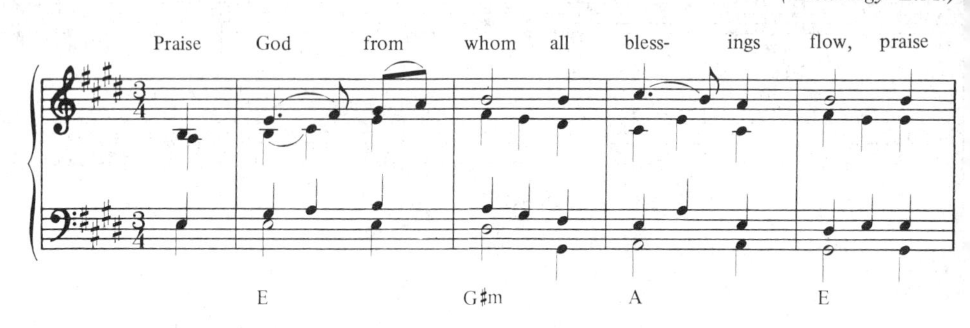

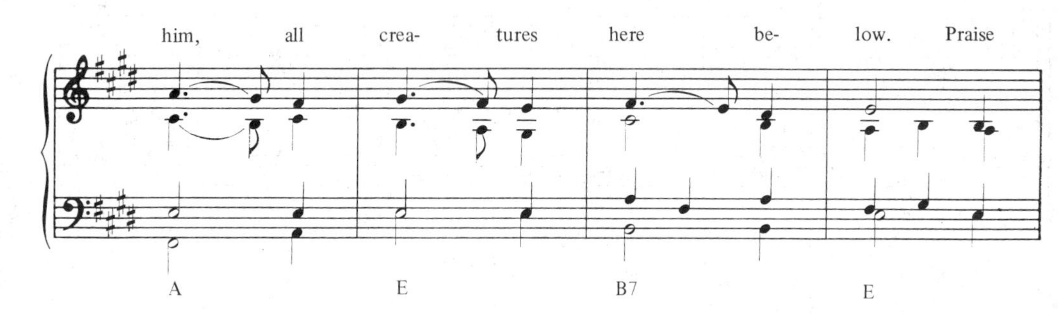

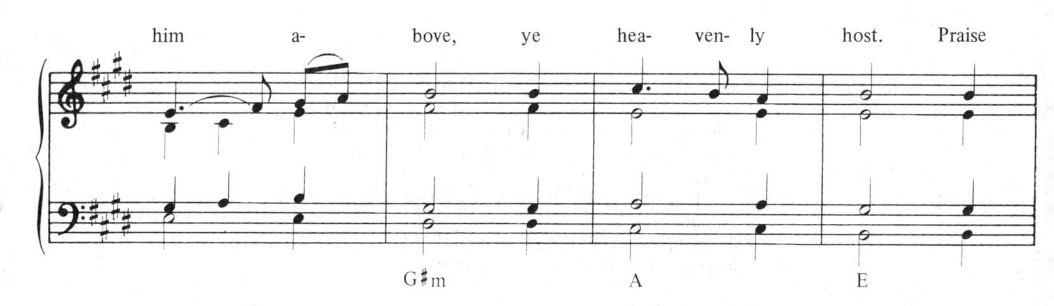

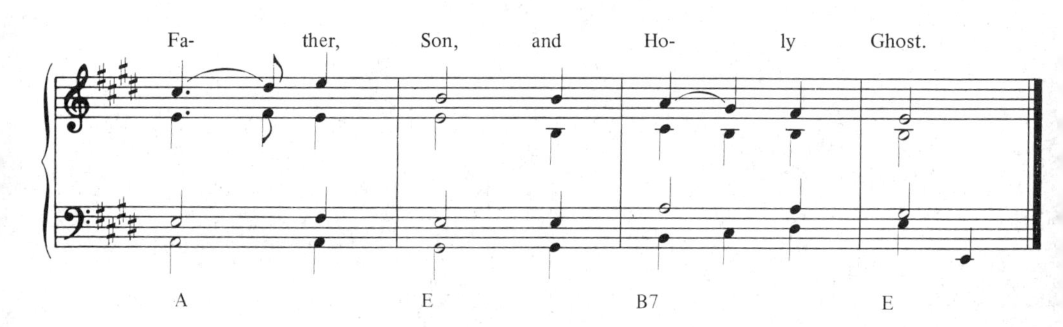

Words: Thomas Ken (1637-1710)
Music: from 'Come Together' by Jimmy and Carol Owens

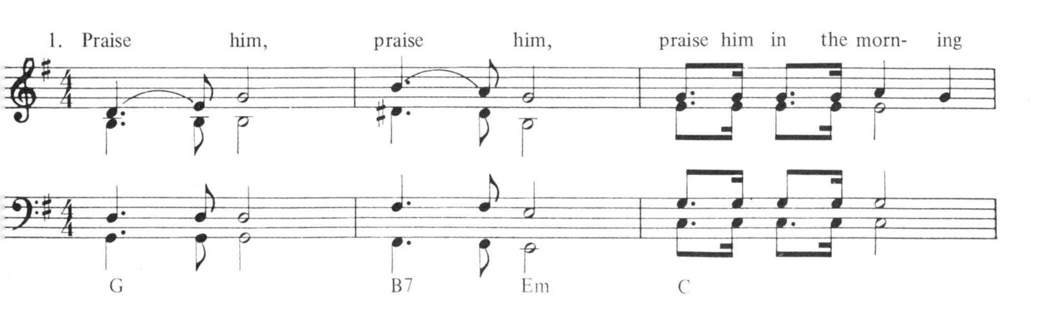

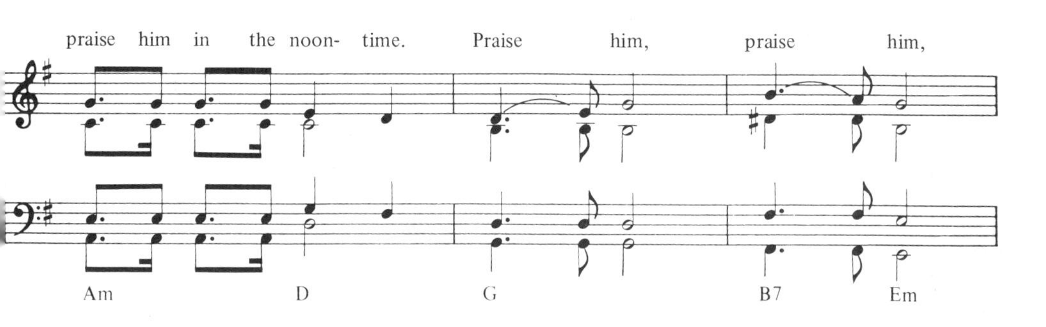

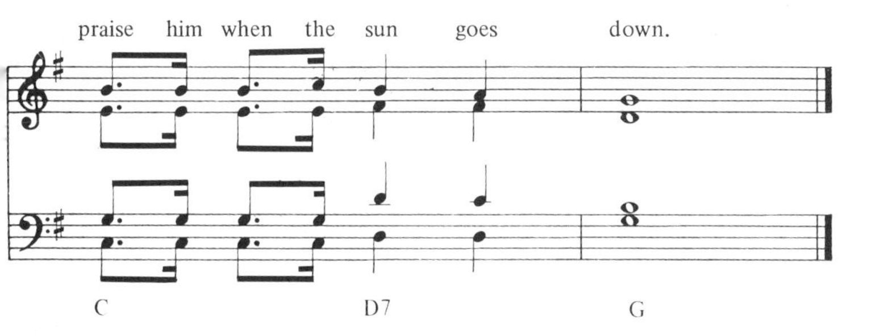

2. Love him . . .

3. Trust him . . .

4. Serve him . . .

5. Jesus . . .

Words and Music: Unknown, arranged by Michael Irwin

418

PRAISE, MY SOUL, THE KING OF HEAVEN

('Praise, my soul' 87.87.87.)

praise him still the same as e- ver, slow to chide, and swift to bless.
Praise him! Praise him! Praise him! Praise him! Glo - rious in his faith - ful - ness.
3. Fa - ther - like, he tends and spares us; well our fee - ble frame he knows;
in his hands he gent - ly bears us, res - cues us from all our foes.

Words: Henry Francis Lyte (1793-1847)
Music: John Goss (1800-80)

PRAISE, O PRAISE, OUR GOD AND KING

419

('Monkland' 77.77.)

[HARMONY]

2. Praise him that he made the sun
   day by day his course to run:

3. And the silver moon by night,
   shining with her gentle light:

4. Praise him that he gave the rain
   to mature the swelling grain:

5. And hath bid the fruitful field
   crops of precious increase yield:

6. Praise him for our harvest-store;
   he hath filled the garner-floor:

7. And for richer food than this,
   pledge of everlasting bliss:

8. Glory to our bounteous King;
   glory let creation sing:
      glory to the Father, Son,
      and blest Spirit, Three in One.

Words: Henry Williams Baker (1821-77)
Music: John Antes (1740-1811) arranged by J.B. Wilkes.

PRAISE THE LORD IN HIS HOLY HOUSE

('Praise the Lord')

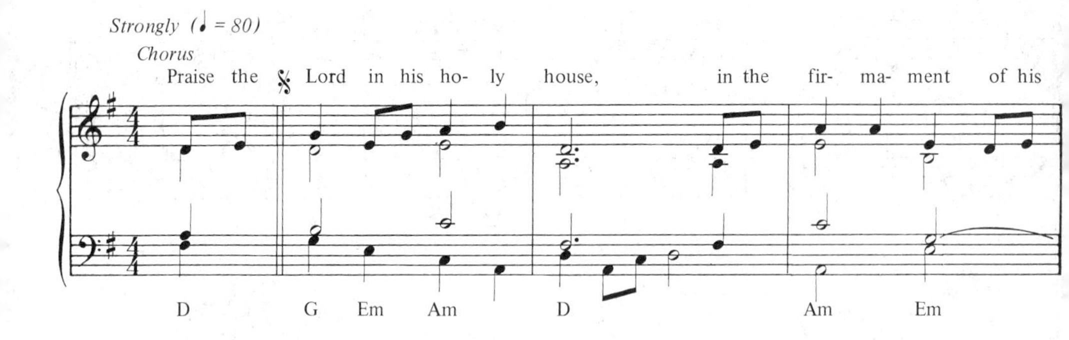

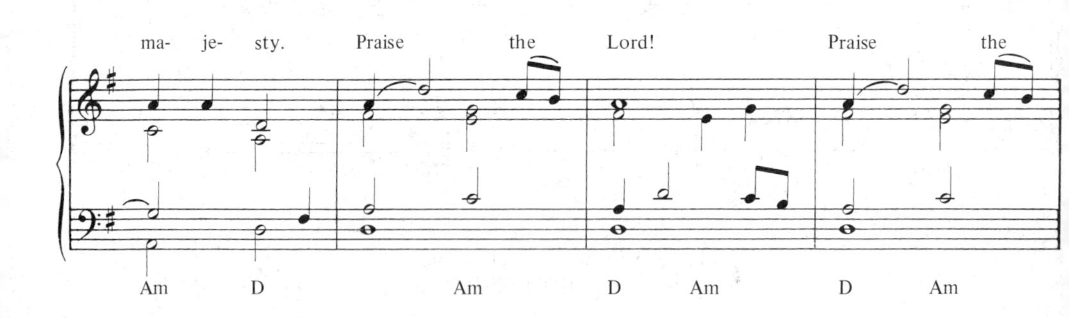

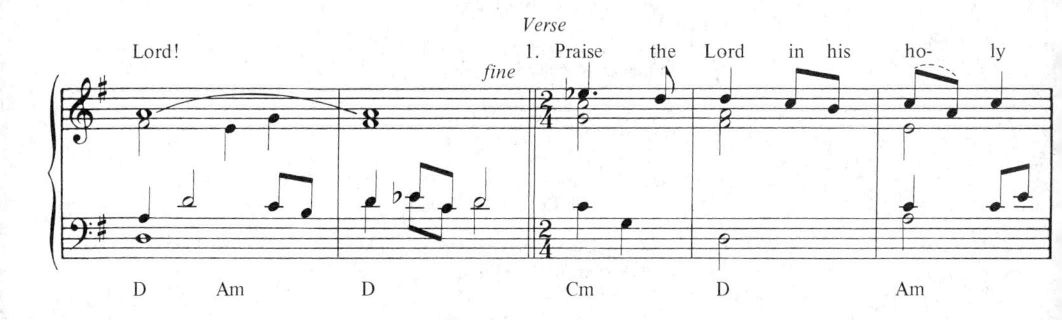

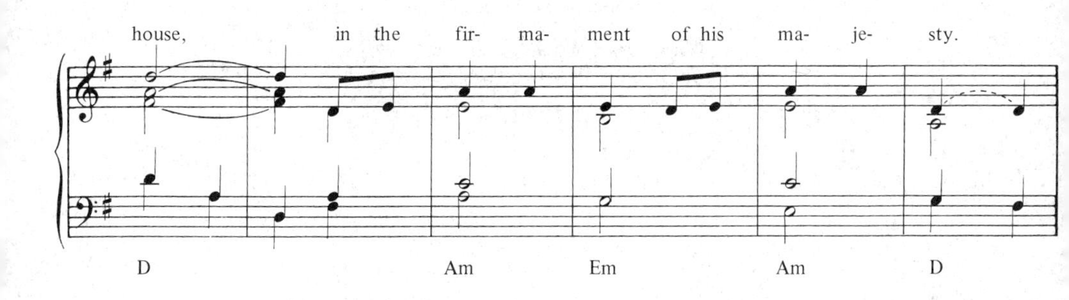

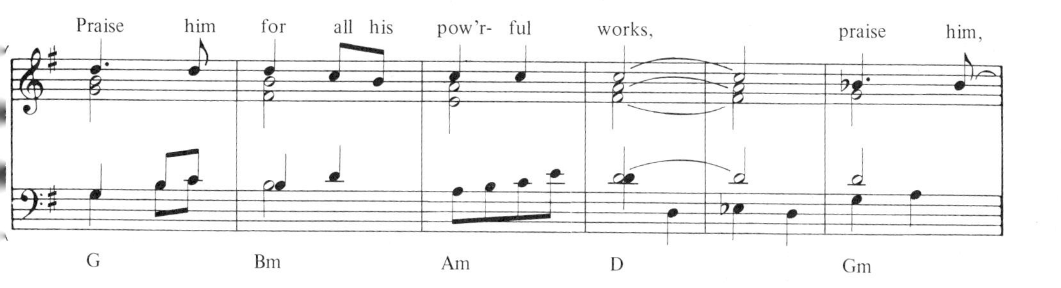

2. Praise him with your resounding horns,
praise him with your lutes, your guitars and harps.
Praise with dancing and tambourines,
tune your strings and play the flute!

3. Praise the Lord with your cymbals and drums,
praise him, brass and woodwind, a choir of voices.
Alleluia, alleluia!
All living, sing praise to God!

Words, based on Huub Oosterhuis' version of Psalm 150, and Music: Frances M. Kelly

PRAISE THE LORD! YE HEAV'NS ADORE HIM

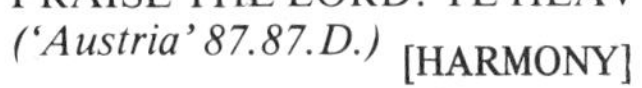

('Austria' 87.87.D.) [HARMONY]

1. Praise the Lord! Ye heav'ns a- dore him, praise him, an- gels in the height;

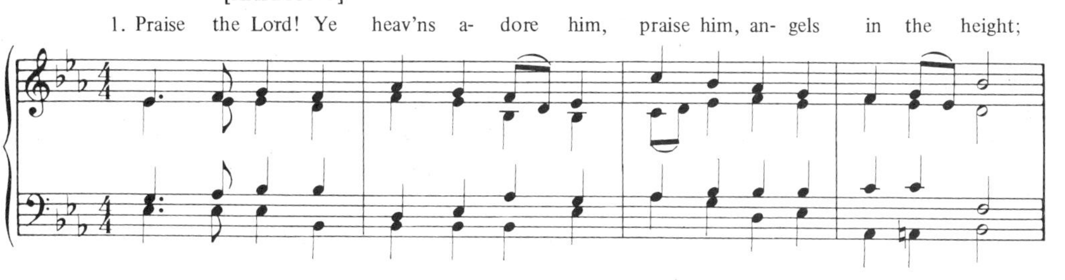

sun and moon, re- joice be- fore him, praise him, all ye stars and light.

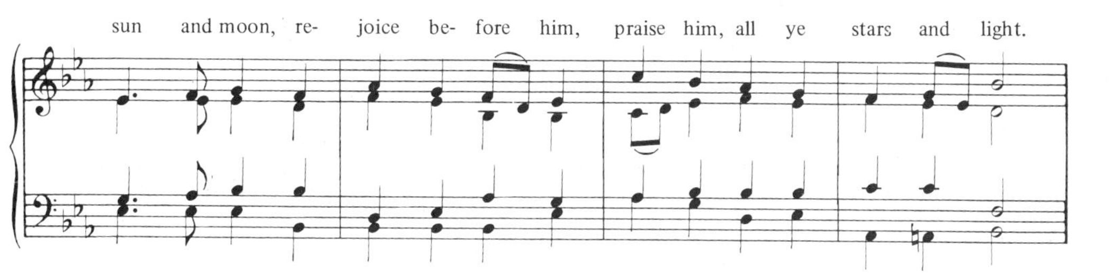

Praise the Lord, for he is glo- rious; worlds his migh- ty voice o- beyed:

laws, which nev- er shall be bro- ken, for their gui- dance he hath made.

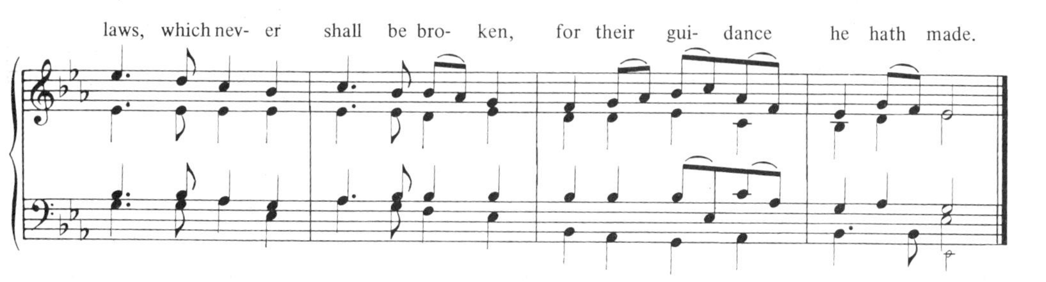

2. Praise the Lord! for he is glorious;
never shall his promise fail;
God hath made his saints victorious;
sin and death shall not prevail.
Praise the God of our salvation,
hosts on high, his power proclaim,
heaven and earth and all creation,
laud and magnify his name!

3. Worship, honour, glory, blessing,
Lord, we offer to thy name;
young and old, thy praise expressing,
join their Saviour to proclaim.
As the saints in heaven adore thee,
we would bow before thy throne;
as thine angels serve before thee,
so on earth thy will be done.

Words: Vv. 1-2 Foundling Hospital (1796);
V.3 E. Osler (1798-1863)
Music: Croation folk melody, adapted by F. J. Haydn (1732-1809)

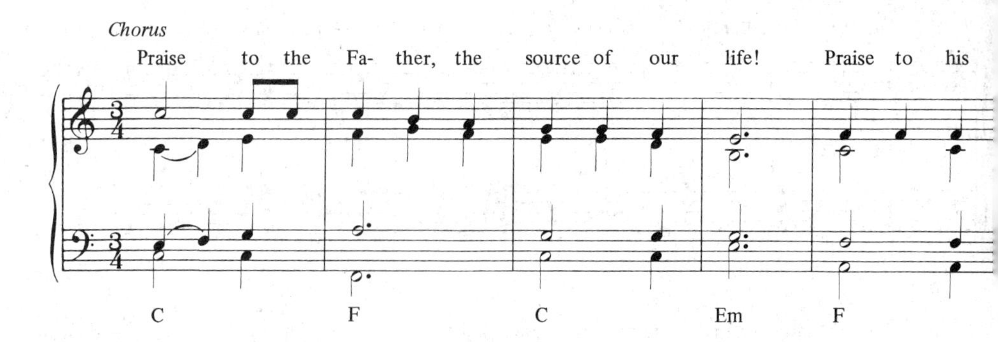
Chorus
Praise to the Fa- ther, the source of our life! Praise to his
C F C Em F

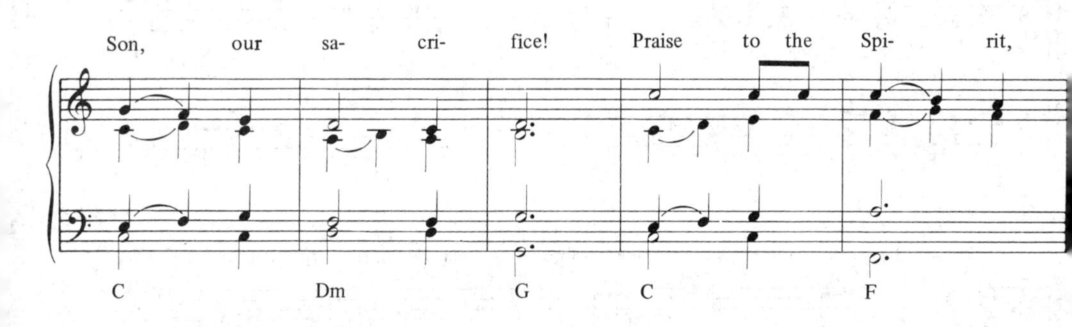
Son, our sa- cri- fice! Praise to the Spi- rit,
C Dm G C F

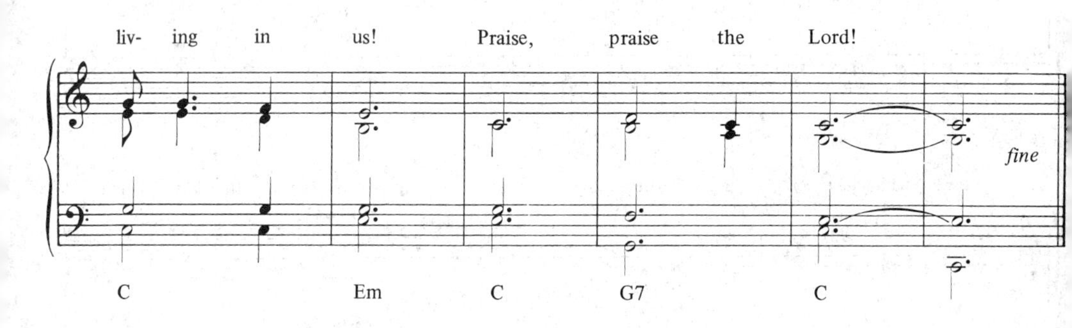
liv- ing in us! Praise, praise the Lord!
fine
C Em C G7 C

Verse
1. In serv- ing, we of- fer our- selves as wit- ness to
Am G F

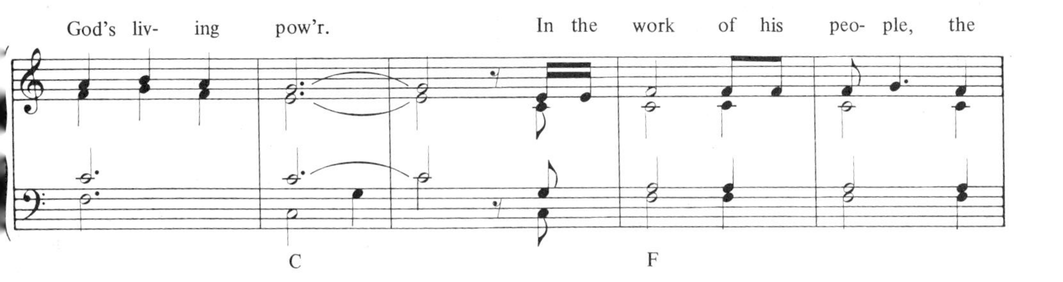

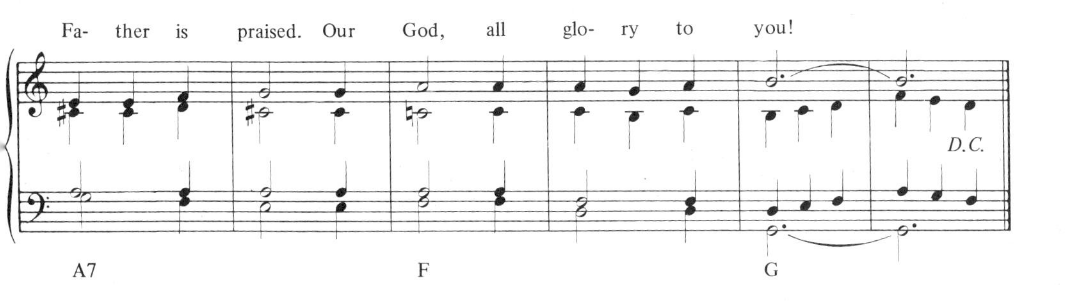

2. Through Jesus, our service of love;
   with him, our strength and our joy;
   in him, the source of all healing power!
   Jesus, all glory to you!

3. The strength of the Spirit is ours,
   living in us as we work:
   the healing touch of the Father and Son.
   Spirit, all glory to you!

Words and Music: Christine McCann

423

PRAISE TO THE HOLIEST IN THE HEIGHT

(First tune: 'Richmond' C.M.)

[HARMONY]

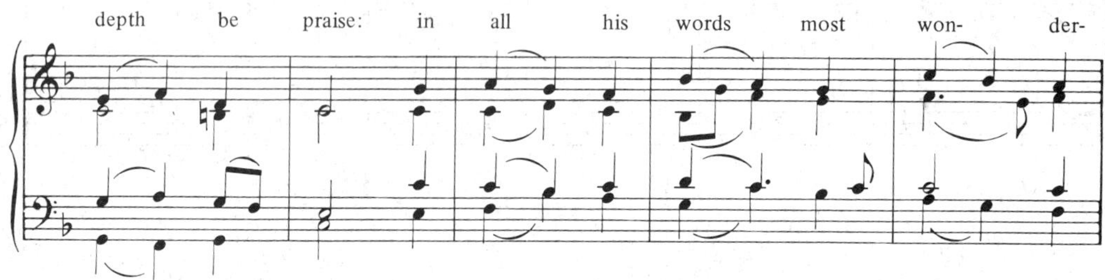

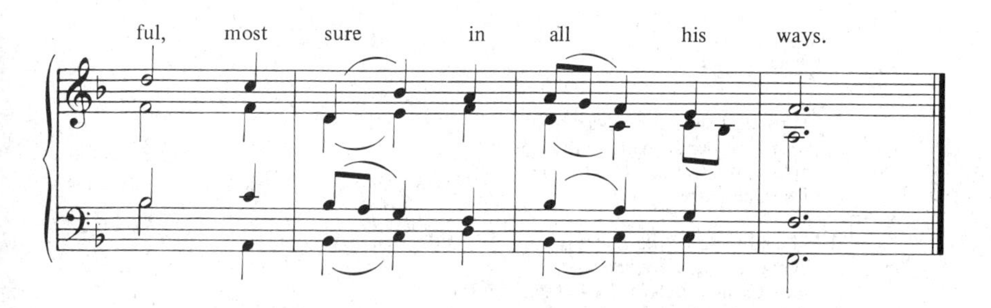

2. O loving wisdom of our God!
when all was sin and shame,
a second Adam to the fight
and to the rescue came.

3. O wisest love! that flesh and blood,
which did in Adam fail,
should strive afresh against the foe,
should strive and should prevail.

4. And that a higher gift than grace
should flesh and blood refine,
God's presence and his very self,
and essence all-divine.

5. O generous love! that he, who smote
in Man for man the foe,
the double agony in Man
for man should undergo.

6. And in the garden secretly,
and on the cross on high,
should teach his brethren, and inspire
to suffer and to die.

7. Praise to the Holiest in the height,
and in the depth be praise:
in all his words most wonderful,
most sure in all his ways.

Words: John Henry Newman (1801-90)
Music: First tune - Thomas Haweis (1734-1820)

PRAISE TO THE HOLIEST IN THE HEIGHT
(Second tune: 'Gerontius' C.M.)

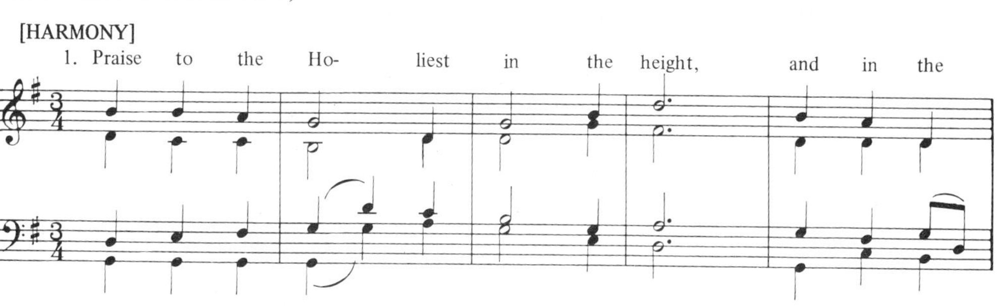

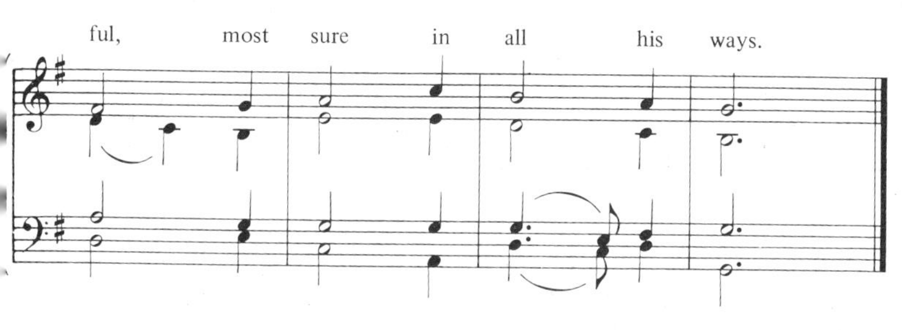

2. O loving wisdom of our God!
when all was sin and shame,
a second Adam to the fight
and to the rescue came.

3. O wisest love! that flesh and blood,
which did in Adam fail,
should strive afresh against the foe,
should strive and should prevail.

4. And that a higher gift than grace
should flesh and blood refine,
God's presence and his very self,
and essence all-divine.

5. O generous love! that he, who smote
in Man for man the foe,
the double agony in Man
for man should undergo.

6. And in the garden secretly,
and on the cross on high,
should teach his brethren, and inspire
to suffer and to die.

7. Praise to the Holiest in the height,
and in the depth be praise:
in all his words most wonderful,
most sure in all his ways.

Words: John Henry Newman (1801-90)
Music: Second tune - John B. Dykes (1823-76)

424

PRAISE TO THE LORD, THE ALMIGHTY
('Lobe den Herren' 14 14.4.7.8.)

2. Praise to the Lord, who o'er all things
so wondrously reigneth,
shieldeth thee gently from harm,
or when fainting sustaineth:
hast thou not seen
how thy heart's wishes have been
granted in what he ordaineth?

3. Praise to the Lord, who doth prosper
thy work and defend thee,
surely his goodness and mercy
shall daily attend thee:
ponder anew
what the Almighty can do,
if to the end he befriend thee.

4. Praise to the Lord, oh, let all that
is in us adore him!
All that has life and breath,
come now in praises before him.
Let the Amen
sound from his people again,
now as we worship before him.

Words: Joachim Neander (1650-80),
tr. C. Winkworth
Music: from 'Stralsund Gesangbuch' (1665)

PRAISE WE NOW THE WORD OF GRACE

('Savannah' 77.77.)

[HARMONY]

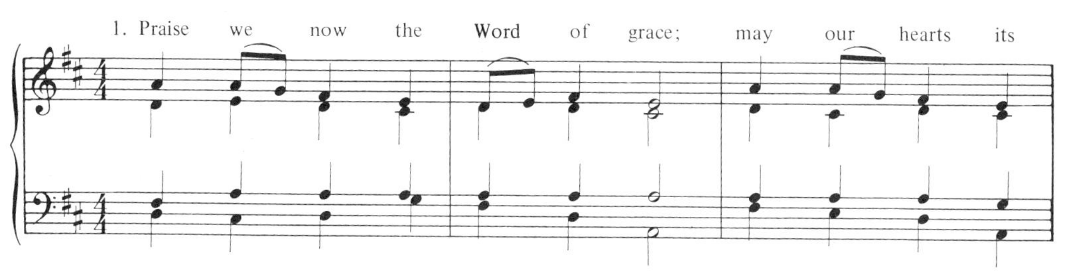

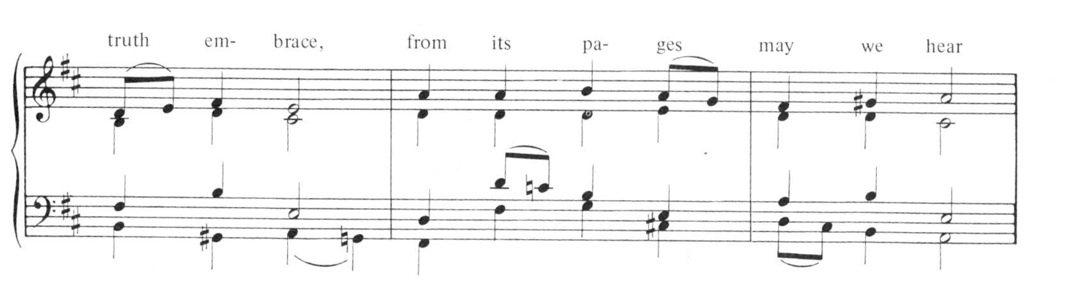

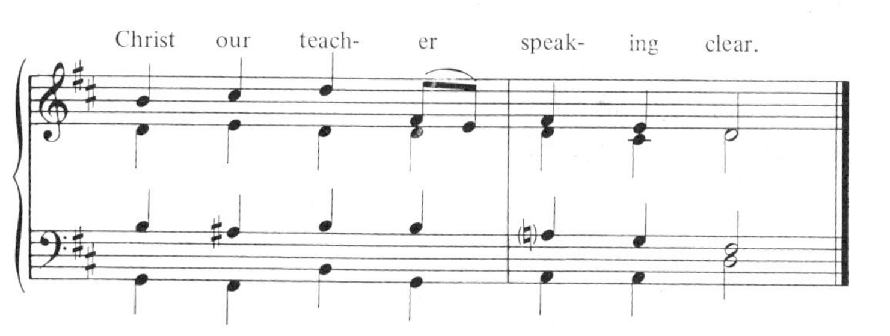

This tune may be found in a higher key at Hymn 315

2. May the Gospel of the Lord
 everywhere be spread abroad,
 that the world around may own
 Christ as King, and Christ alone.

Words: S. N. Sedgwick (1872-1941)
Music: John Wesley's 'Foundery Collection' (1742)

PRAY WHEN THE MORN IS BREAKING
('Meirionydd' 76.76.D.)

2. Remember all who love thee,
all who are loved by thee,
and next for those that hate thee
pray thou, if such there be:
last for thyself in meekness
a blessing humbly claim,
and link with each petition
thy great Redeemer's name.

3. But if 'tis e'er denied thee
in solitude to pray,
should holy thoughts come o'er thee
upon life's crowded way,
e'en then the silent breathing
that lifts thy soul above
shall reach the thronèd Presence
of mercy, truth and love.

Words: Jane Cross Simpson (1811-86), and others
Music: William Lloyd (1785-1852)

PUT ON THE ARMOUR OF JESUS CHRIST

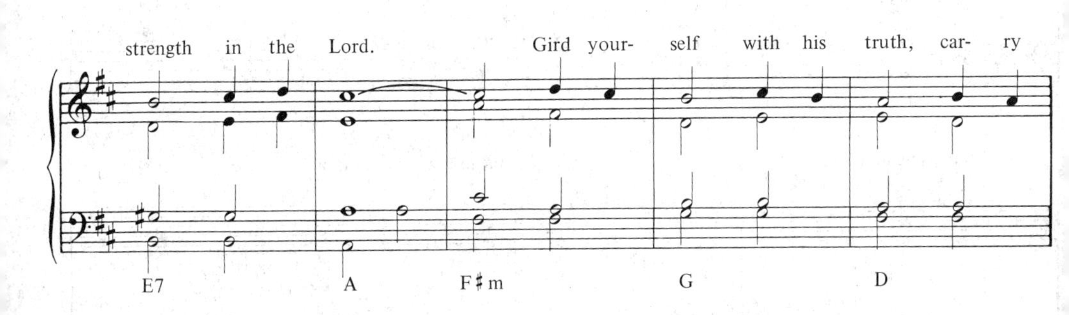

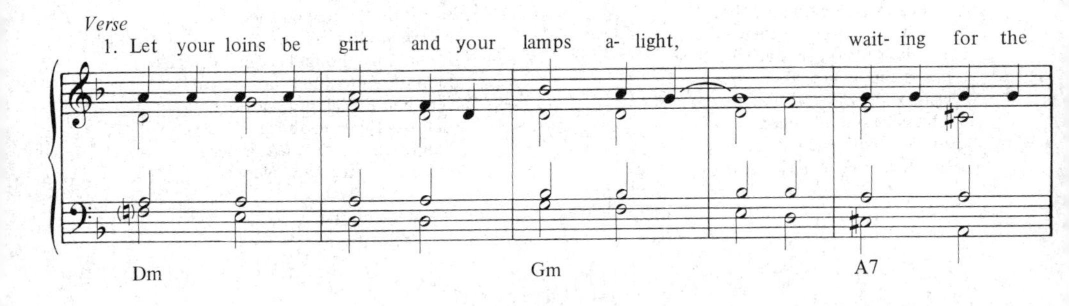

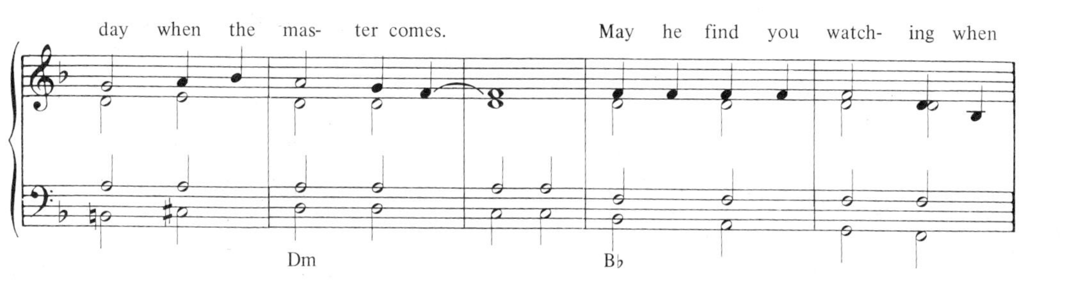

2. If we die with him we shall live with him.
   If we now endure, we shall reign with him.
   If we are not faithful, he'll still keep faith,
   he cannot be false to himself. *(2 Timothy 2: 11)*

Words, from Scripture, and Music: Aniceto Nazareth,
arranged by John Rombaut

PUT THOU THY TRUST IN GOD
('Carlisle' S.M.)

[HARMONY]

This tune can be found in a higher key at Hymn 433, and in a different harmonisation at Hymn 54.

2. Commit thy ways to him,
   thy work into his hands,
   and rest on his unchanging Word,
   who heaven and earth commands.

3. Though years on years roll on,
   his covenant shall endure;
   though clouds and darkness hide his path,
   the promised grace is sure.

4. Give to the winds thy fears;
   hope, and be undismayed:
   God hears thy sighs and counts thy tears;
   God shall lift up thy head.

5. Through waves and clouds and storms
   his power will clear thy way:
   wait thou this time; the darkest night
   shall end in brightest day.

6. Leave to his sovereign sway
   to choose and to command;
   so shalt thou, wondering, own his way,
   how wise, how strong his hand.

Words: Paul Gerhardt (1607-76),
tr. J. Wesley and others
Music: C. Lockhart (1745-1815)

REACH OUT AND TOUCH THE LORD

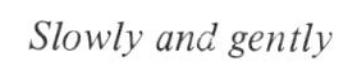

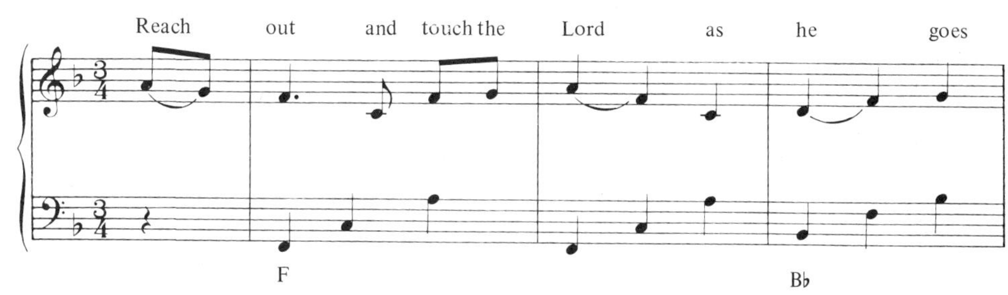

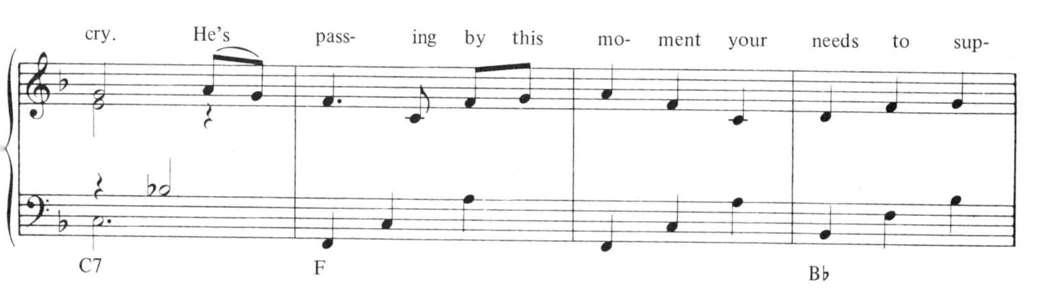

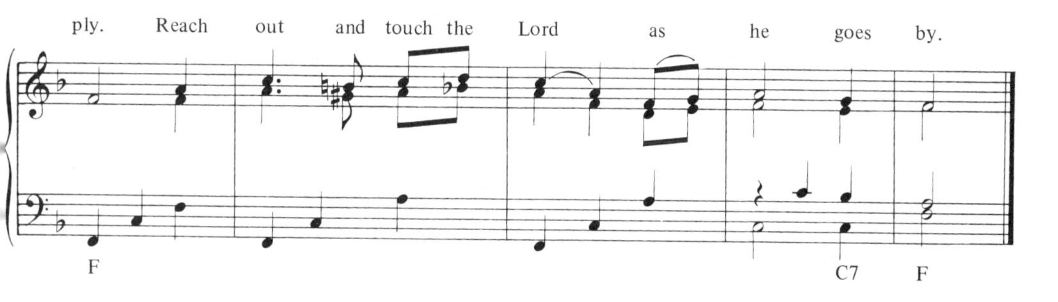

Words and Music: Bill Harmon

430 REJOICE IN THE LORD ALWAYS

This may be sung as a round; successive entries are numbered

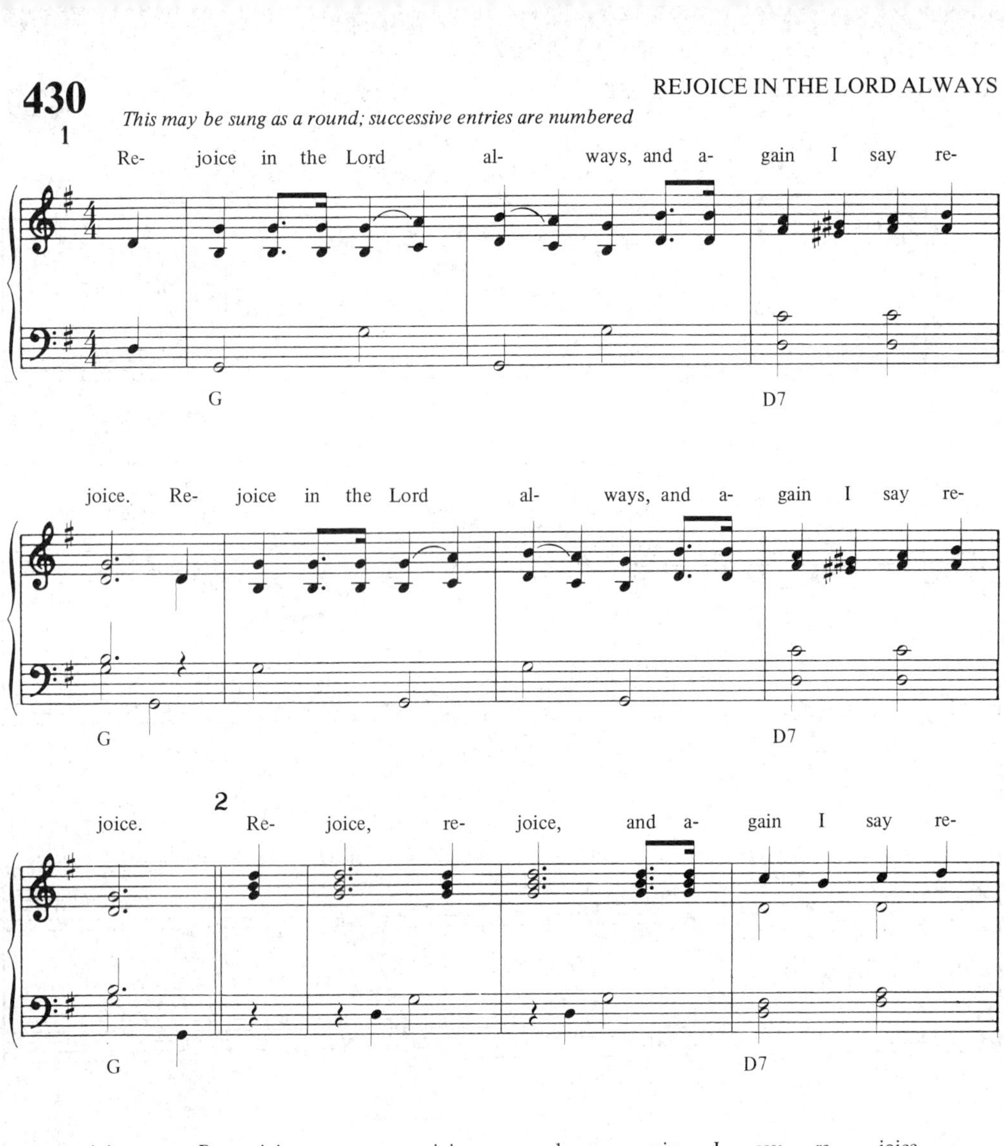

Words, based on Philippians 4: 4, and Music: Unknown, arranged by Michael Irwin

REJOICE, O LAND, IN GOD THY MIGHT
('Wareham' L.M.)

2. Glad shalt thou be, with blessing crowned,
with joy and peace thou shalt abound;
yea, love with thee shall make his home
until thou see God's Kingdom come.

3. He shall forgive thy sins untold:
remember thou his love of old;
walk in his way, his Word adore.
and keep his truth for evermore.

Words: Robert Bridges (1844-1930)
Music: William Knapp (1698-1768)

432 [HARMONY]

REJOICE! THE LORD IS KING
('Gopsal' 66.66.88.)

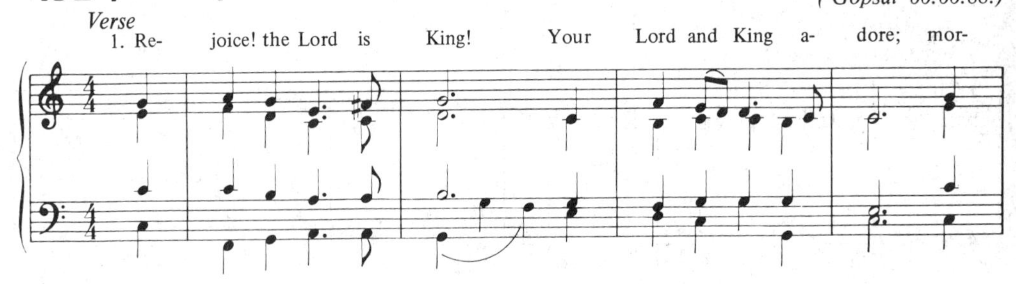

2. Jesus the Saviour reigns,
   the God of truth and love;
   when he had purged our stains,
   he took his seat above:

3. His Kingdom cannot fail;
   he rules o'er earth and heaven;
   the keys of death and hell
   are to our Jesus given:

4. He sits at God's right hand
   till all his foes submit,
   and bow to his command,
   and fall beneath his feet:

Words: Charles Wesley (1707-88)
Music: G. F. Handel (1685-1759)

REVIVE THY WORK, O LORD

('Carlisle' S.M.)

This tune can be found in a lower key at Hymn 428, and in a different harmonisation at Hymn 54

2. Revive thy work, O Lord!
   disturb this sleep of death;
   quicken the smouldering embers now
   by thine almighty breath.

3. Revive thy work, O Lord!
   create soul-thirst for thee:
   and hungering for the Bread of Life
   O may our spirits be.

4. Revive thy work, O Lord!
   exalt thy precious name;
   and by the Holy Ghost our love
   for thee and thine inflame.

5. Revive thy work, O Lord!
   give Pentecostal showers;
   the glory shall be all thine own,
   the blessing, Lord, be ours.

Words: Albert Midlane (1825-1909)
Music: Charles Lockhart (1745-1815)

RIDE ON! RIDE ON IN MAJESTY
('Winchester New' L.M.)

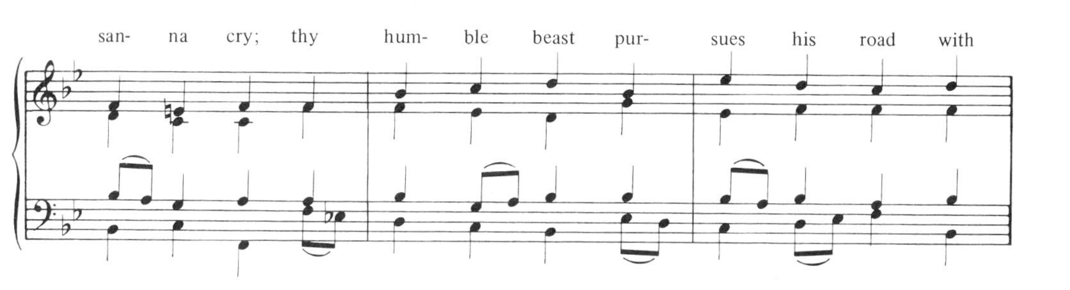

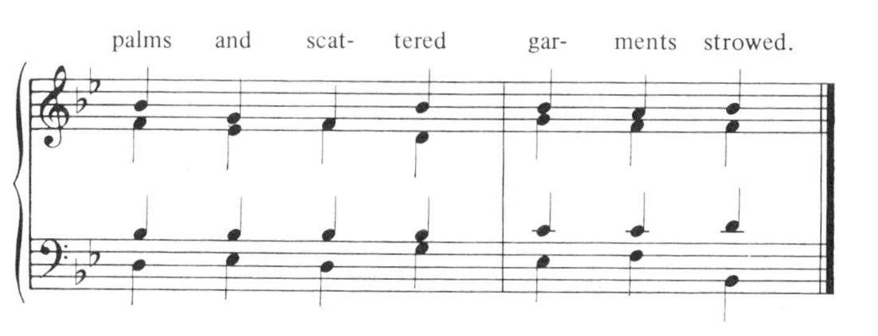

2. Ride on! Ride on in majesty!
In lowly pomp ride on to die:
O Christ, thy triumphs now begin
o'er captive death and conquered sin.

3. Ride on! Ride on in majesty!
The wingèd squadrons of the sky
look down with sad and wondering eyes
to see the approaching sacrifice.

4. Ride on! Ride on in majesty!
Thy last and fiercest strife is nigh;
the Father, on his sapphire throne,
expects his own anointed Son.

5. Ride on! Ride on in majesty!
In lowly pomp ride on to die;
bow thy meek head to mortal pain,
then take, O God, thy power, and reign.

Words: Henry Hart Milman (1791-1868)
Music: adapted from a chorale in the 'Musikalisches Handbuch', Hamburg (1690)

435

RING OUT YOUR JOY
('Joy')

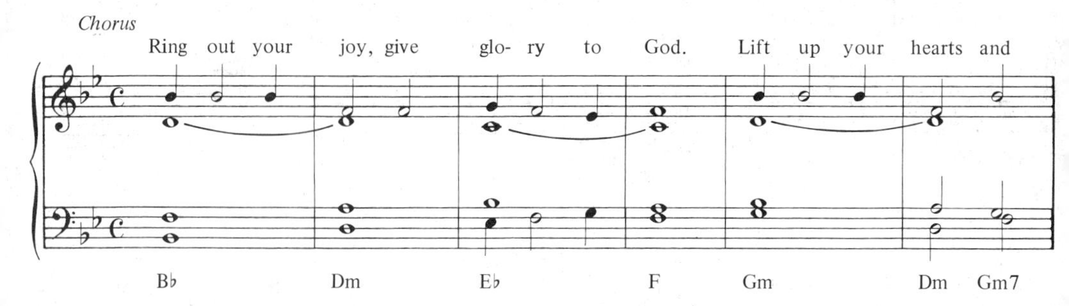

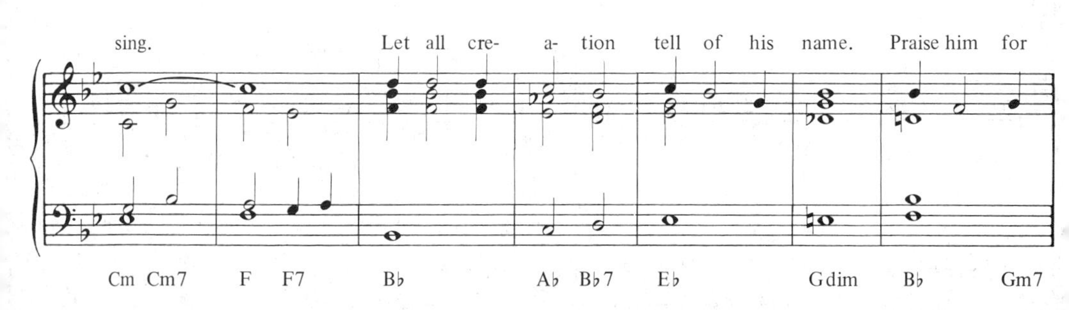

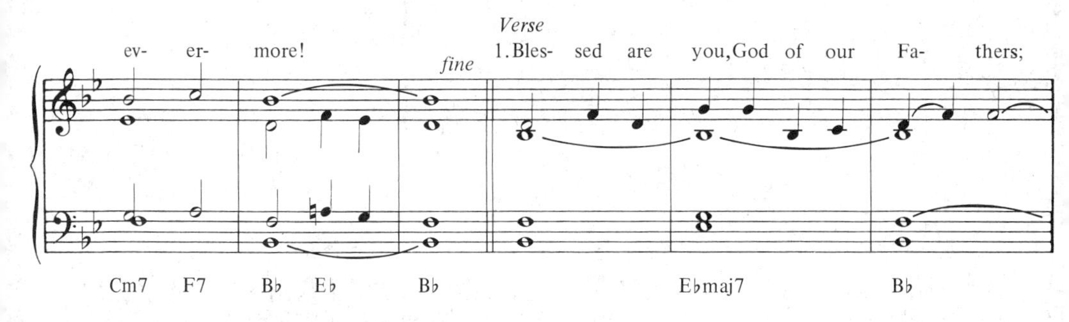

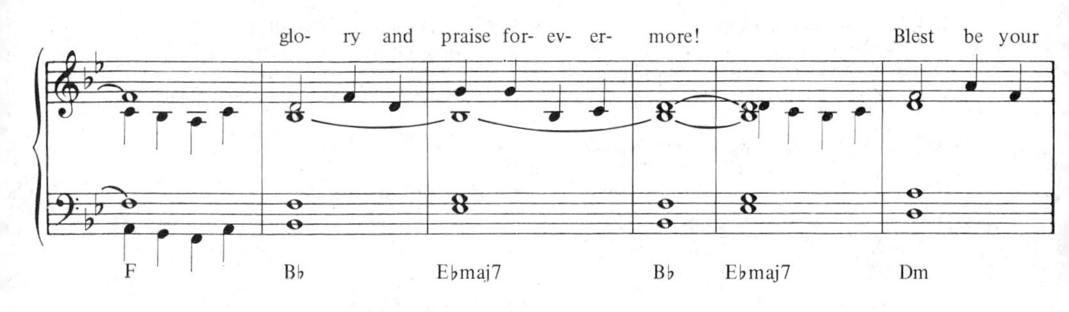

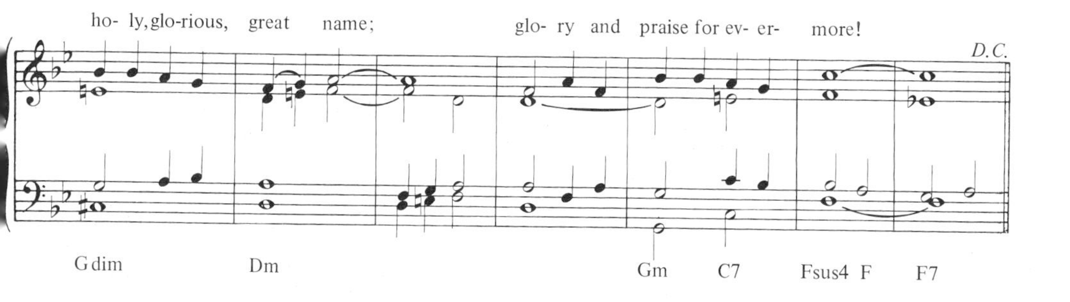

2. Blest in the temple of your glory;
   glory and praise for evermore!
   Blessèd, enthroned over your Kingdom;
   glory and praise for evermore!

3. Blest, you who know the deeps and highest;
   glory and praise for evermore!
   Blest in the firmament of heaven;
   glory and praise for evermore!

4. All things the Lord has made, now bless him;
   glory and praise for evermore!
   Angels and saints, now bless and praise him;
   glory and praise for evermore!

Words, based on the Canticle of Daniel, and Music: Aniceto Nazareth

RISE AND SHINE, AND GIVE GOD HIS GLORY

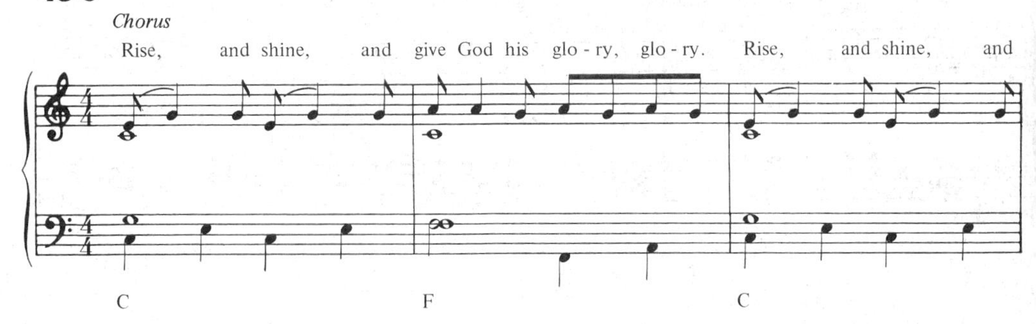

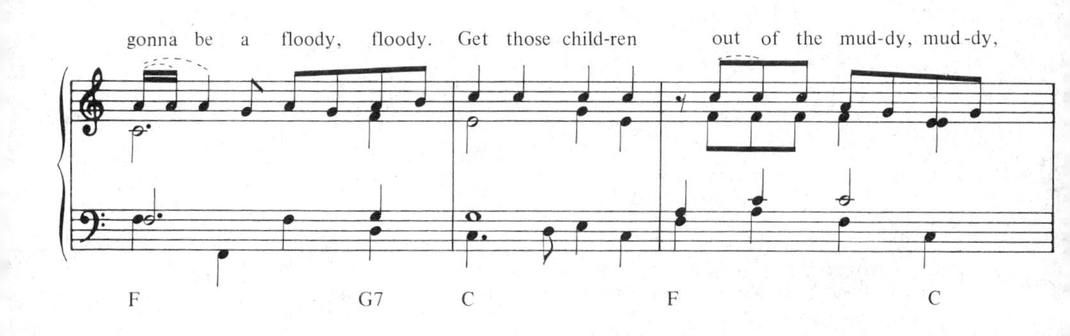

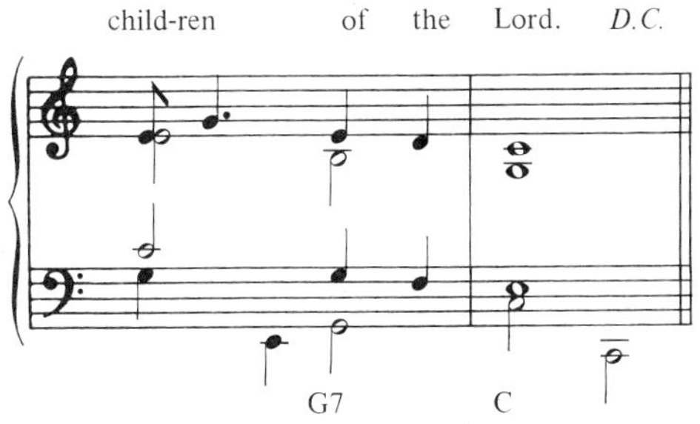

child-ren of the Lord. *D.C.*

G7 C

2. So Noah, he built him, he built him an arky, arky,
   Noah, he built him, he built him an arky, arky,
   built it out of hickory barky, barky,
   children of the Lord.

3. The animals, they came on, they came on, by twosies, twosies,
   animals, they came on, they came on, by twosies, twosies,
   elephants and kangaroosies, roosies,
   children of the Lord.

4. It rained and poured for forty daysies, daysies,
   rained and poured for forty daysies, daysies,
   nearly drove those animals crazyies, crazyies,
   children of the Lord.

5. The sun came out and dried up the landy, landy,
   sun came out and dried up the landy, landy,
   everything was fine and dandy, dandy,
   children of the Lord.

6. If you get to heaven before I do-sies, do-sies,
   you get to heaven before I do-sies, do-sies,
   tell those angels, I'm comin' too-sies, too-sies,
   children of the Lord.

Words, based on Genesis 6: 4, and Music: Traditional, arranged by Michael Irwin

RISE UP, O MEN OF GOD
('Falcon Street (Silver Street)' S.M.)

[HARMONY]

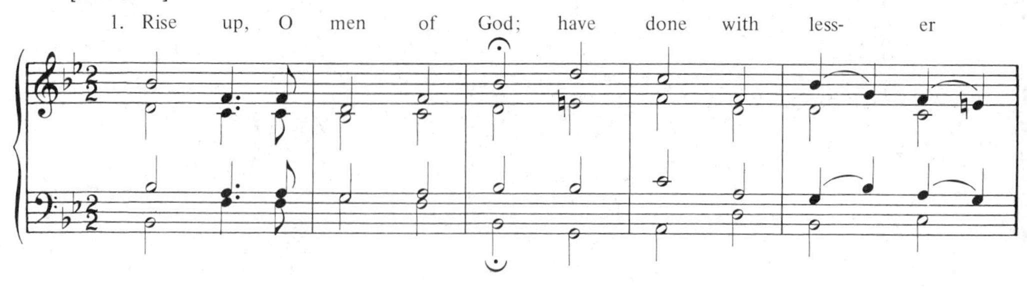

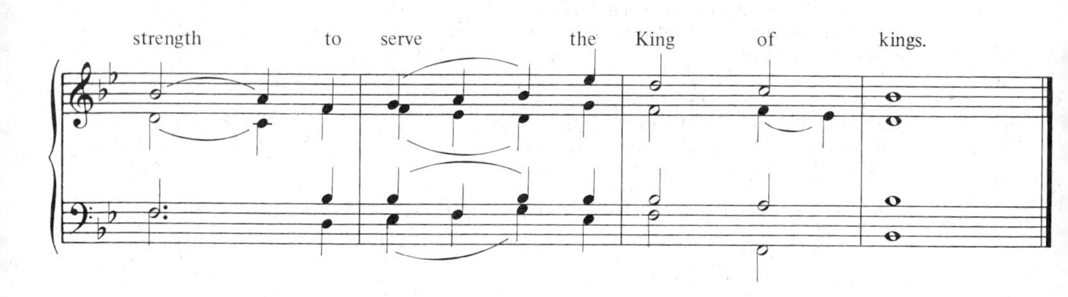

2. Rise up, O men of God;
his Kingdom tarries long;
bring in the day of brotherhood,
and end the night of wrong.

3. Rise up, O men of God;
the Church for you doth wait:
her strength unequal to her task;
rise up, and make her great.

4. Lift high the cross of Christ;
tread where his feet have trod;
as brothers of the Son of Man
rise up, O men of God.

Words: William Pierson Merrill (1867-1954)
Music: late form of melody by
Isaac Smith (c. 1730-1800)

ROCK OF AGES, CLEFT FOR ME
('Petra' 77.77.77.)

2. Not the labours of my hands
can fulfil thy law's demands;
could my zeal no respite know,
could my tears for ever flow,
all for sin could not atone:
thou must save, and thou alone.

3. Nothing in my hands I bring,
simply to thy cross I cling;
naked, come to thee for dress;
helpless, look to thee for grace;
foul, I to the fountain fly;
wash me, Saviour, or I die.

4. While I draw this fleeting breath,
when mine eyes are closed in death,
when I soar through tracts unknown,
see thee on thy judgement throne;
rock of ages, cleft for me,
let me hide myself in thee.

Words: Augustus Montague Toplady (1740-78)
Music: Richard Redhead (1820-1901)

ROUND ME FALLS THE NIGHT

('Seelenbrautigam' 55.88.55.)

439

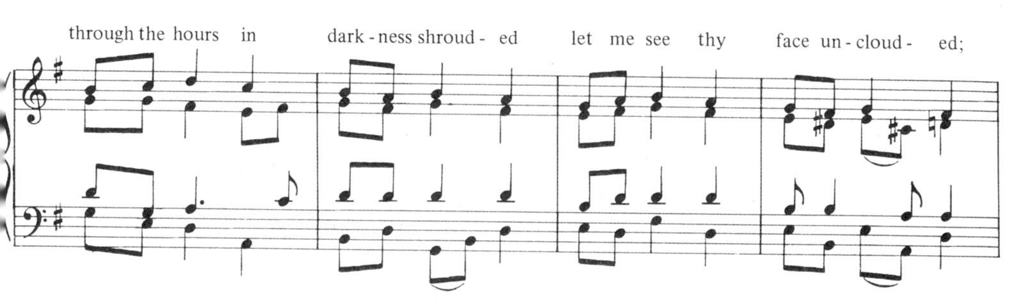

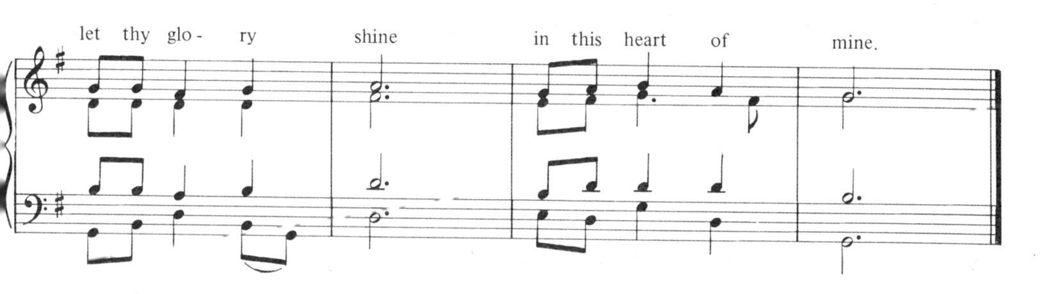

2. Earthly work is done,
earthly sounds are none;
rest in sleep and silence seeking,
let me hear thee softly speaking;
in my spirit's ear
whisper, 'I am near.'

3. Blessèd, heavenly Light,
shining through earth's night;
voice, that oft of love hast told me;
arms, so strong to clasp and hold me;
thou thy watch wilt keep,
Saviour, o'er my sleep.

Words: William Romanis (1824-99)
Music: Adam Drese (1620-1701), harmonised by F. Layriz

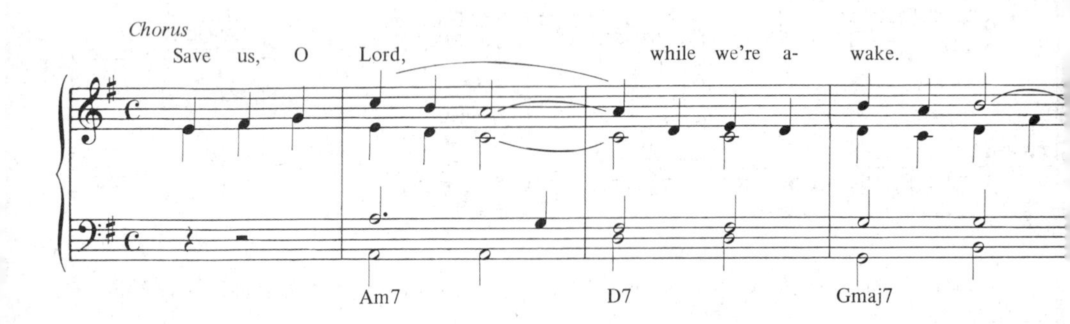
Chorus
Save us, O Lord, while we're a- wake.
Am7
D7
Gmaj7

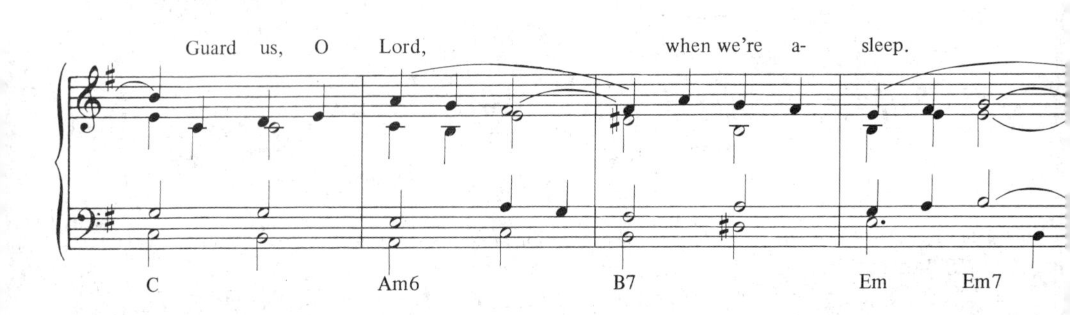
Guard us, O Lord, when we're a- sleep.
C
Am6
B7
Em
Em7

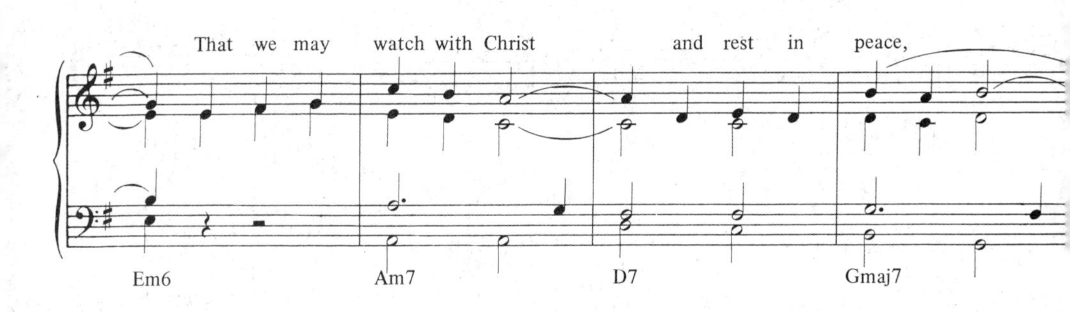
That we may watch with Christ and rest in peace,
Em6
Am7
D7
Gmaj7

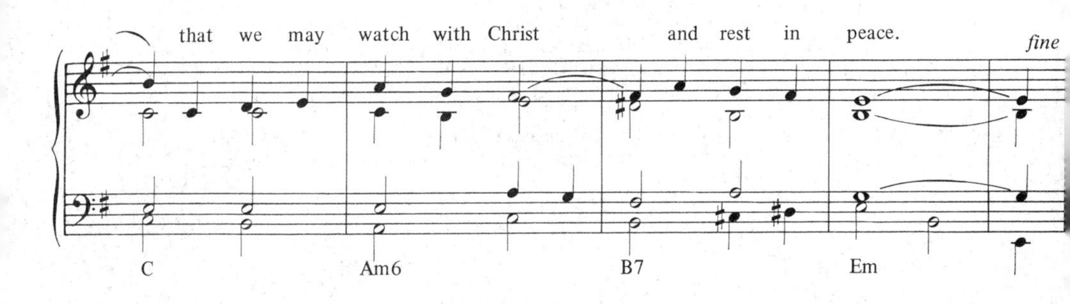
that we may watch with Christ and rest in peace.
fine
C
Am6
B7
Em

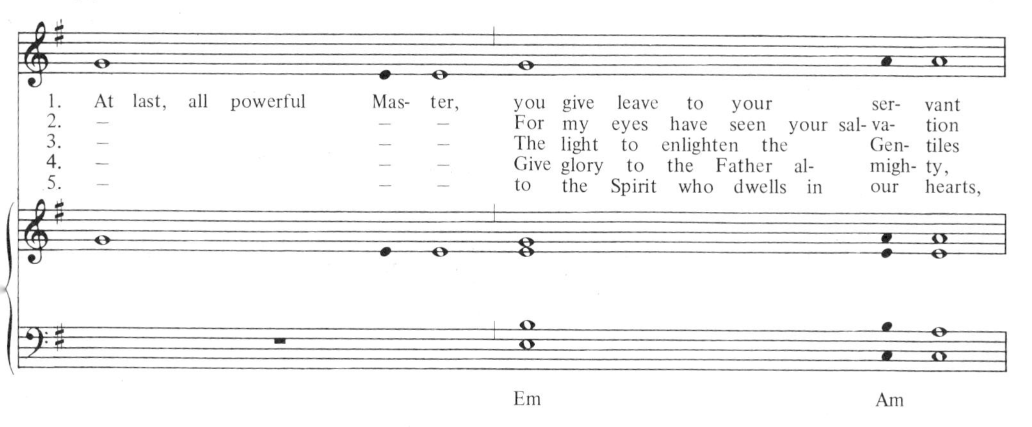

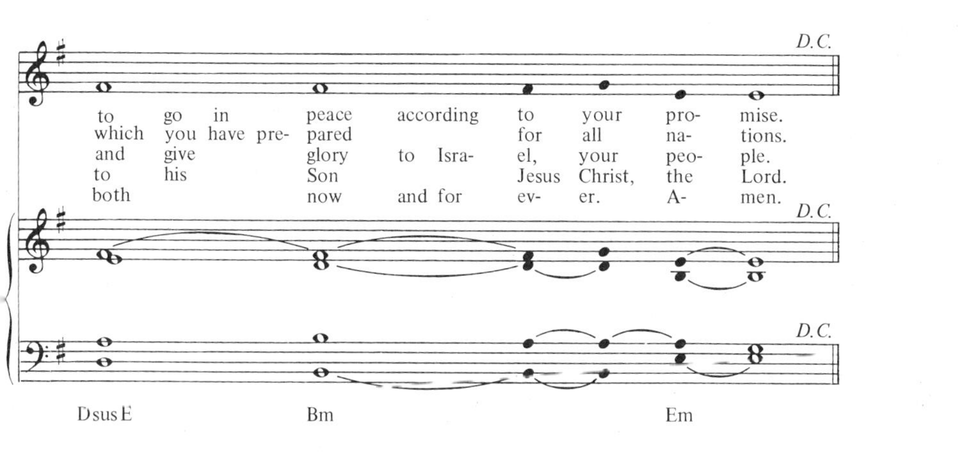

Words: Luke 2:29-32 (Grail translation)
Music: Aniceto Nazareth,
arranged by John Rombaut

441

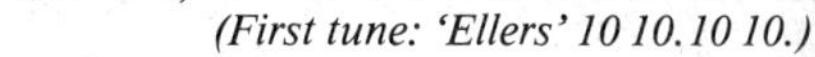

SAVIOUR, AGAIN TO THY DEAR NAME
(First tune: 'Ellers' 10 10.10 10.)

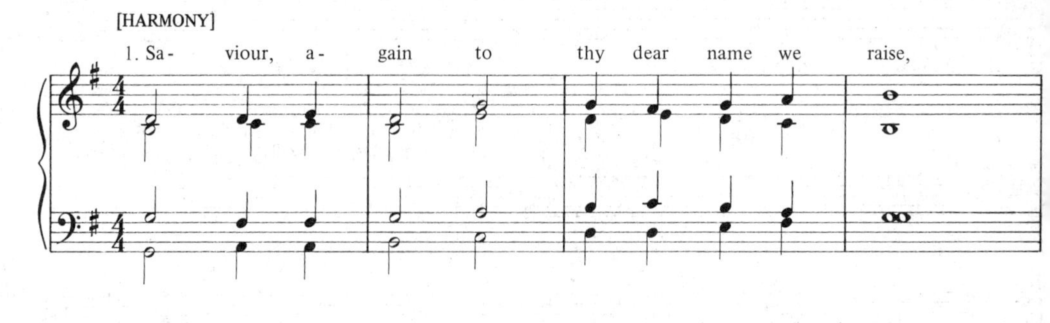

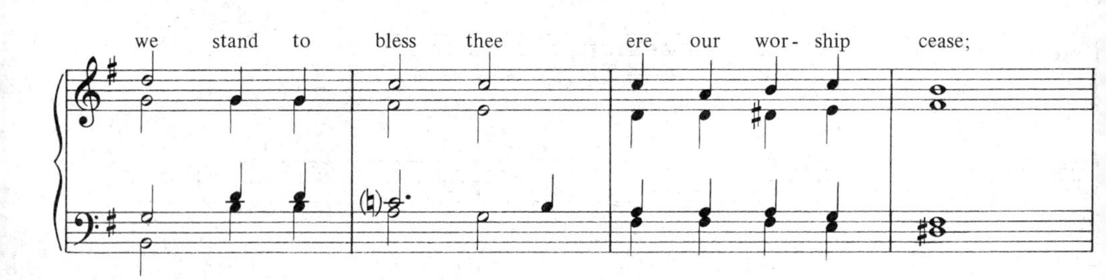

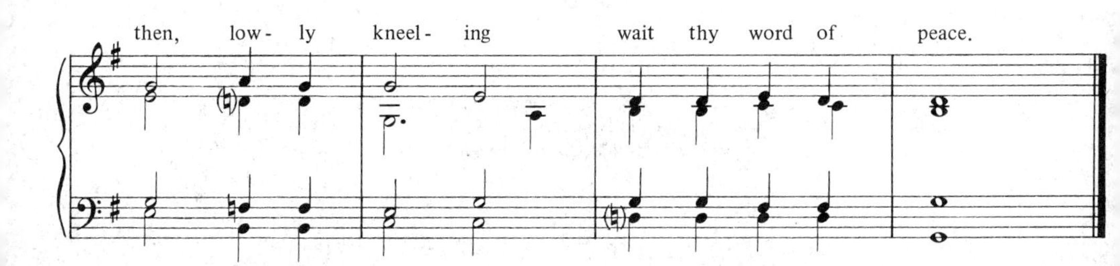

2. Grant us thy peace upon our homeward way;
with thee began, with thee shall end, the day:
guard thou the lips from sin, the hearts from shame,
that in this house have called upon thy name.

3. Grant us thy peace, Lord, through the coming night;
turn thou for us its darkness into light;
from harm and danger keep thy children free,
for dark and light are both alike to thee.

4. Grant us thy peace throughout our earthly life,
our balm in sorrow, and our stay in strife;
then, when thy voice shall bid our conflict cease,
call us, O Lord, to thine eternal peace.

Words: John Ellerton (1826-93)
Music: First tune – Edward J. Hopkins (1818-1901)

SAVIOUR, AGAIN TO THY DEAR NAME
(Second tune: 'Woodlands' 10 10.10 10.)

2. Grant us thy peace upon our homeward way;
with thee began, with thee shall end, the day:
guard thou the lips from sin, the hearts from shame,
that in this house have called upon thy name.

3. Grant us thy peace, Lord, through the coming night;
turn thou for us its darkness into light;
from harm and danger keep thy children free,
for dark and light are both alike to thee.

4. Grant us thy peace throughout our earthly life,
our balm in sorrow, and our stay in strife;
then, when thy voice shall bid our conflict cease,
call us, O Lord, to thine eternal peace.

Words: John Ellerton (1826-93)
Music: Second tune – Walter Greatorex (1877-1949)

Words, based on Psalm 139: 2-3: J. Edwin Orr
Music: Traditional Maori melody, arranged by Christopher Dunne

SEE AMID THE WINTER'S SNOW
('Oxford' 77.77. & Chorus)

443

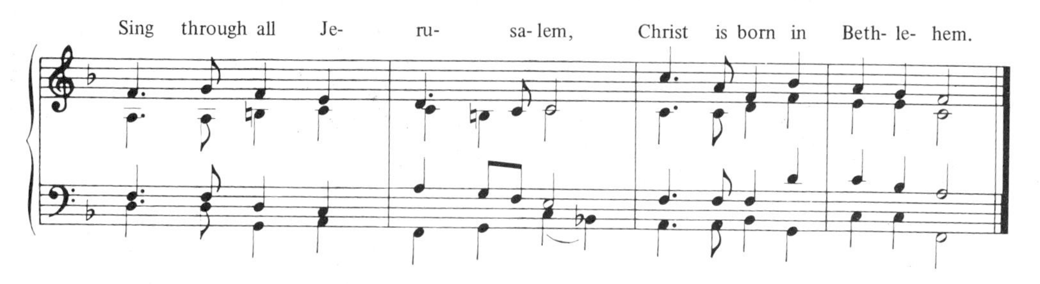

2. Lo, within a manger lies
he who built the starry skies;
he who, throned in heights sublime,
sits amid the cherubim.

3. Say, ye holy shepherds, say,
what your joyful news today?
Wherefore have ye left your sheep
on the lonely mountain steep?

4. 'As we watched at dead of night,
lo, we saw a wondrous light;
angels, singing peace on earth,
told us of the Saviour's birth.'

5. Sacred infant, all divine,
what a tender love was thine,
thus to come from highest bliss,
down to such a world as this!

6. Virgin mother, Mary blest,
by the joys that fill thy breast,
pray for us, that we may prove
worthy of the Saviour's love.

Words: Edward Caswall (1814-78)
Music: John Goss (1800-80)

SEE HIM A-LYING **(Calypso Carol)**

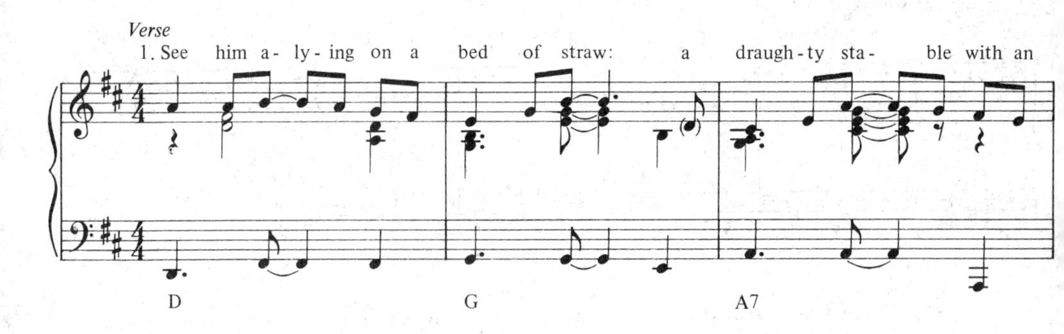

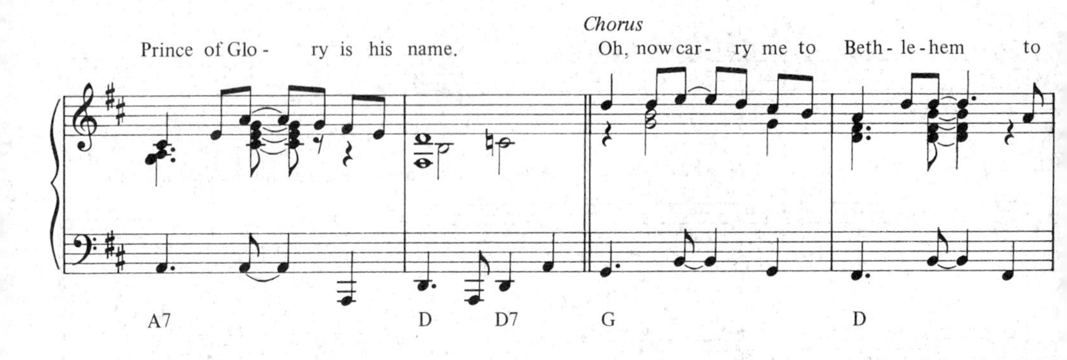

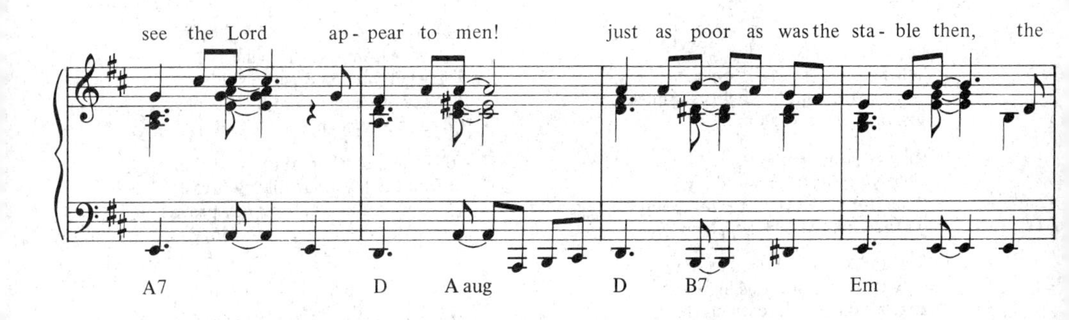

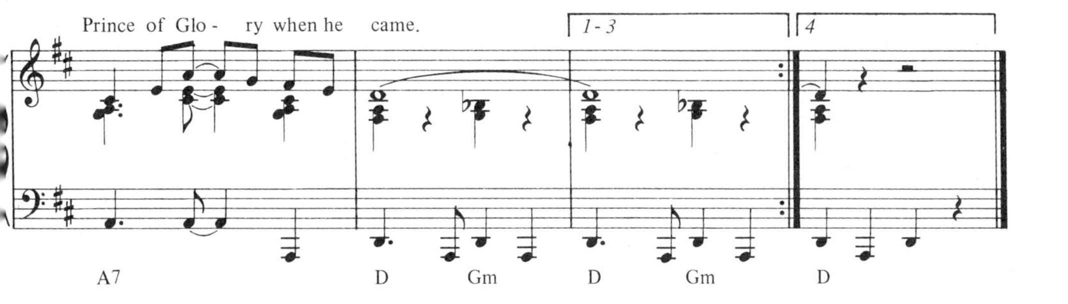

2. Star of silver, sweep across the skies,
   show where Jesus in the manger lies;
   shepherds swiftly from your stupor rise
   to see the Saviour of the world!

3. Angels, sing again the song you sang,
   bring God's glory to the heart of man;
   sing that Bethl'em's little baby can
   be salvation to the soul.

4. Mine are riches, from your poverty;
   from your innocence, eternity;
   mine, forgiveness by your death for me,
   child of sorrow for my joy.

Words and Music: Michael Perry, arranged by Stephen Coates.

This may be sung as a round.

2. Ask and it shall be given unto you,
seek and ye shall find;
knock, and it shall be opened unto you;
allelu, alleluia.

This second verse is not part of the song as originally written. The origin is unknown.

Words, based on Matthew 6: 33; 7: 7 and Music: Karen Lafferty

SEE THE CONQUEROR MOUNTS IN TRIUMPH

('Rex Gloriae' 87.87.D.)

[HARMONY]

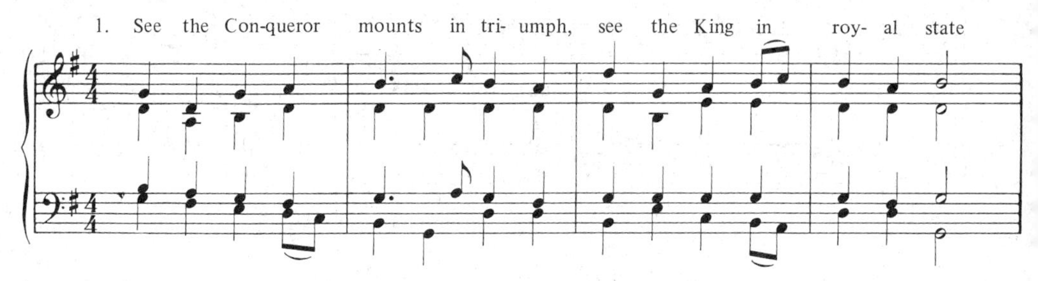

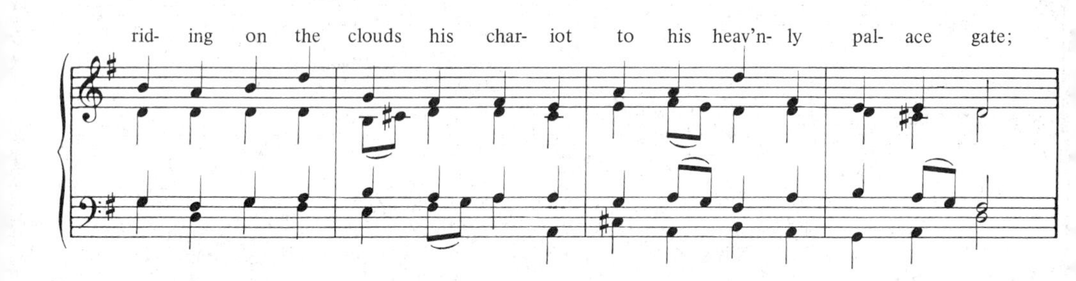

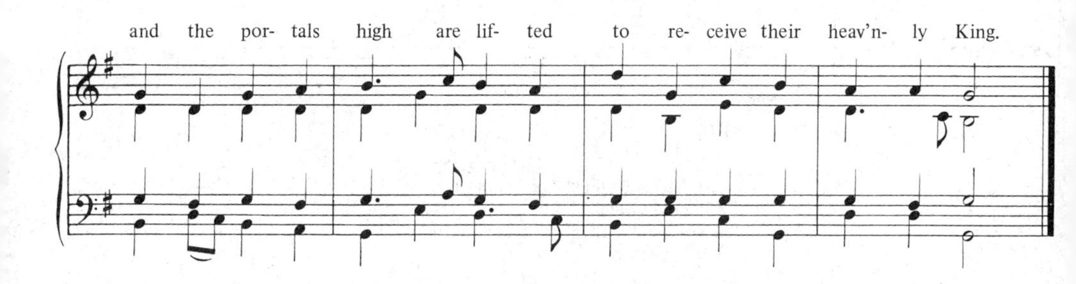

2. Who is this that comes in glory,
with the trump of jubilee?
Lord of battles, God of armies,
he has gained the victory;
he who on the cross did suffer,
he who from the grave arose,
he has vanquished sin and Satan,
he by death has spoiled his foes.

3. Thou hast raised our human nature
in the clouds of God's right hand;
there we sit in heavenly places,
there with thee in glory stand;
Jesus reigns, adored by angels;
man with God is on the throne;
mighty Lord, in thine ascension,
we by faith behold our own.

4. Glory be to God the Father;
glory be to God the Son,
dying, risen, ascending for us,
who the heavenly realm has won;
glory to the Holy Spirit;
to one God in persons Three;
glory both in earth and heaven,
glory, endless glory, be.

Part Two

5. Holy Ghost, illuminator,
shed thy beams upon our eyes,
help us to look up with Stephen,
and to see beyond the skies,
where the Son of Man in glory
standing is at God's right hand,
beckoning on his Martyr army,
succouring his faithful band.

6. See him, who is gone before us,
heavenly mansions to prepare,
see him, who is ever pleading
for us with prevailing prayer,
see him, who with sound of trumpet
and with his angelic train,
summoning the world to judgement,
on the clouds will come again.

7. Glory be to God the Father;
glory be to God the Son,
dying, risen, ascending for us,
who the heavenly realm has won;
glory to the Holy Spirit;
to one God in persons Three;
glory both in earth and heaven,
glory, endless glory, be.

Words: Christopher Wordsworth (1807-85)
Music: Henry Smart (1813-79)

SEND FORTH YOUR SPIRIT, O LORD

('Renew')

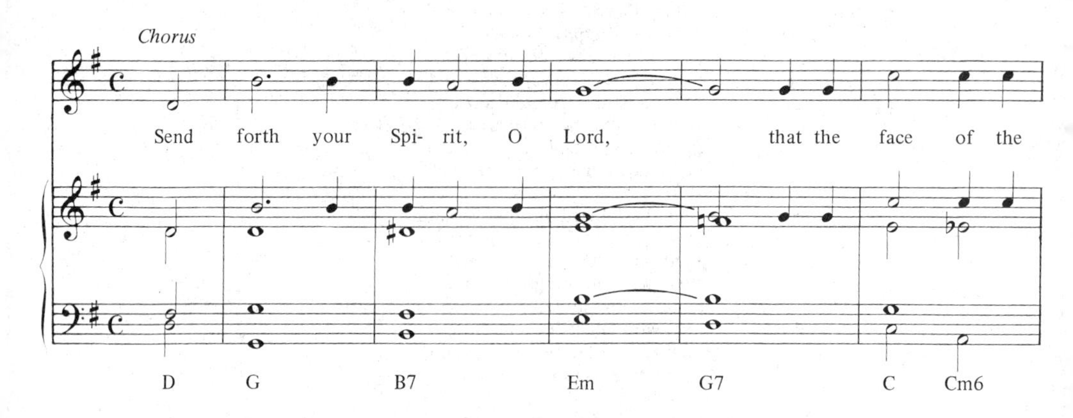

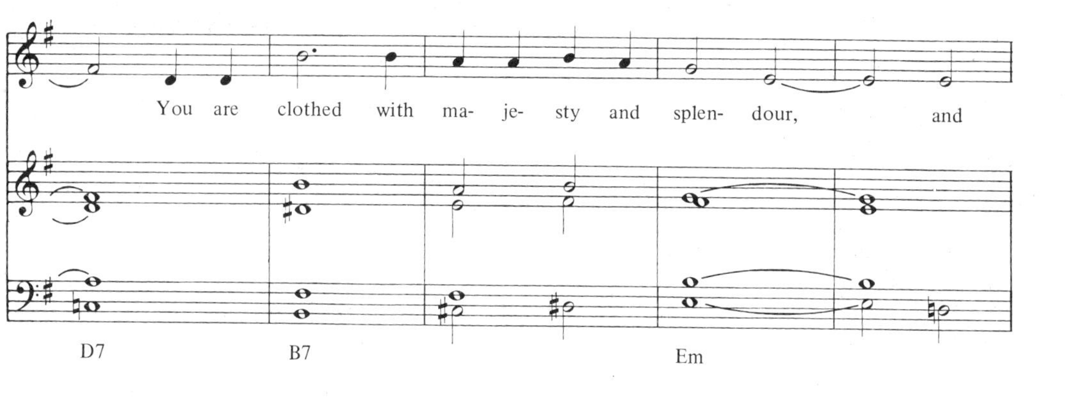

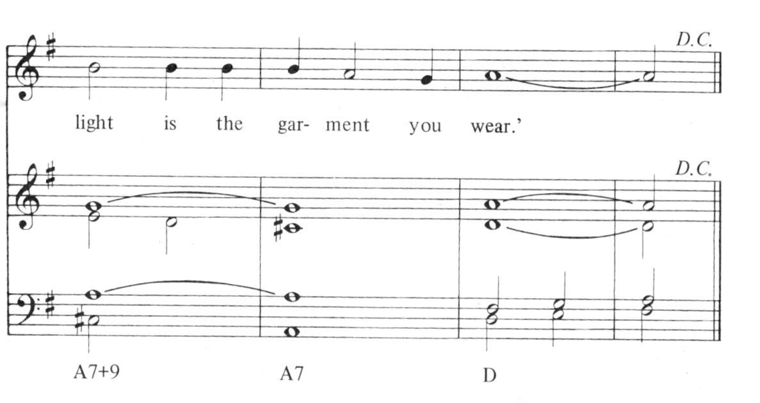

2. You have built your palace on the waters.
   Like the winds, the angels do your word.
   You have set the earth on its foundations,
   so firm, to be shaken no more.

3. All your creatures look to you for comfort;
   from your open hand they have their fill.
   You send forth your Spirit and revive them,
   the face of the earth you renew.

4. While I live, I sing the Lord God's praises;
   I will thank the author of these marvels.
   Praise to God, the Father, Son and Spirit,
   both now and for ever. Amen.

Words, based on Psalm 104, and Music: Aniceto Nazareth

448

SHALOM, MY FRIEND **(Shalom)**

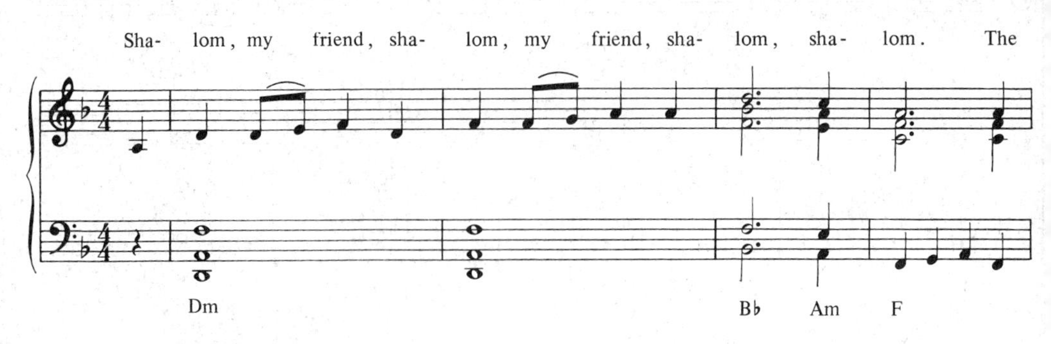

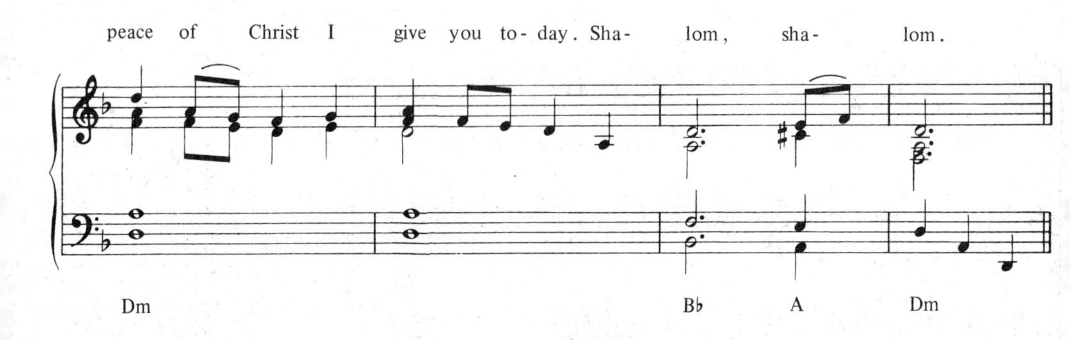

Words and Music: Traditional Israeli folk song, arranged by Sandra Joan Billington

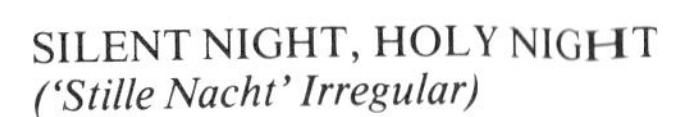

SILENT NIGHT, HOLY NIGHT
('Stille Nacht' Irregular)

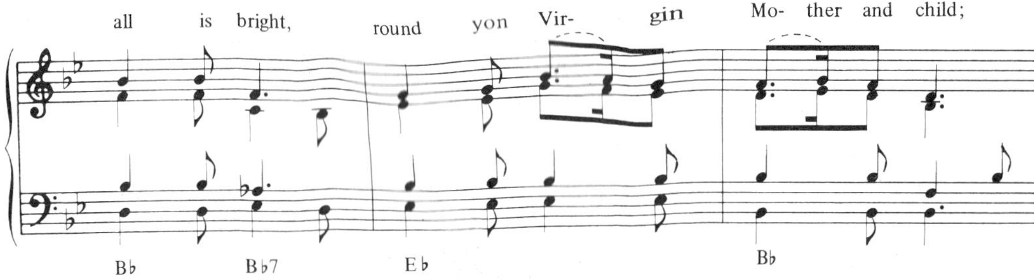

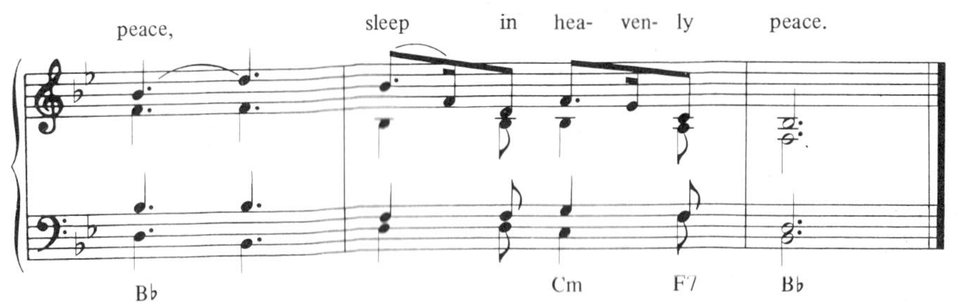

2. Silent night, holy night.
Shepherds quake at the sight,
glories stream from heaven afar,
heavenly hosts sing alleluia:
Christ, the Saviour is born. (2)

3. Silent night, holy night.
Son of God, love's pure light
radiant beams from thy holy face,
with the dawn of redeeming grace:
Jesus, Lord, at thy birth. (2)

Words: Joseph Mohr (1792-1848), tr. J. Young
Music: Franz Gruber (1787-1863), arranged by John Rombaut

SING A NEW SONG TO THE LORD

('Onslow Square' 77.11.8.)

2. Now to the ends of the earth
   see his salvation is shown;
   and still he remembers his mercy and truth
   unchanging in love to his own.

3. Sing a new song and rejoice,
   publish his praises abroad;
   let voices in chorus, with trumpet and horn,
   resound for the joy of the Lord!

4. Join with the hills and the sea
   thunders of praise to prolong;
   in judgement and justice he comes to the earth -
   O sing to the Lord a new song!

Words, based on Psalm 98: Timothy Dudley-Smith (b.1926)
Music: David G. Wilson (b.1940)

SING HALLELUJAH TO THE LORD

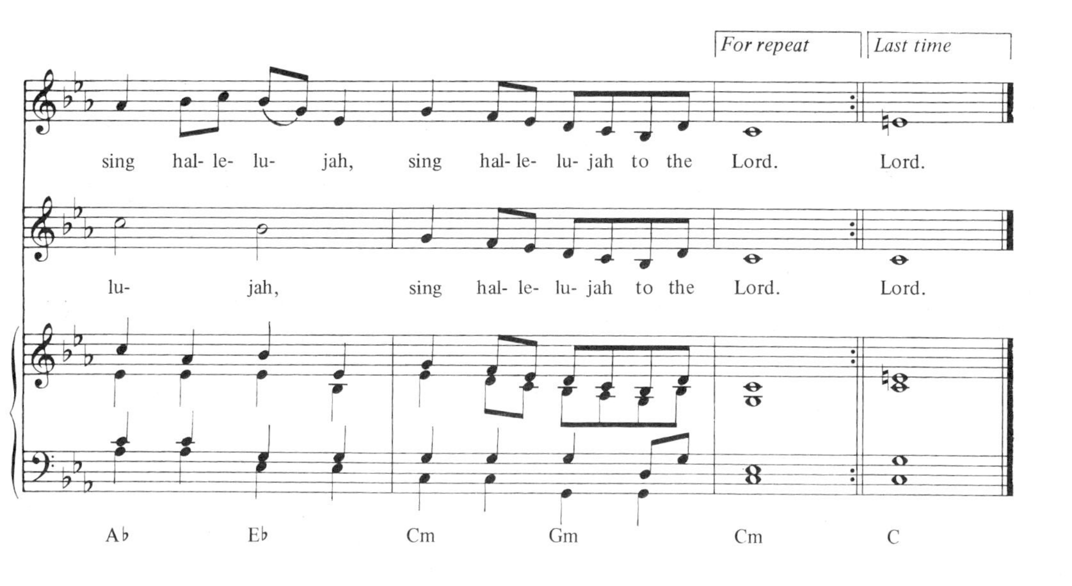

Words and Music: Linda Stassen-Benjamin

SING MY TONGUE, THE GLORIOUS BATTLE
(First tune: 'Pange Lingua' 87.87.87.)

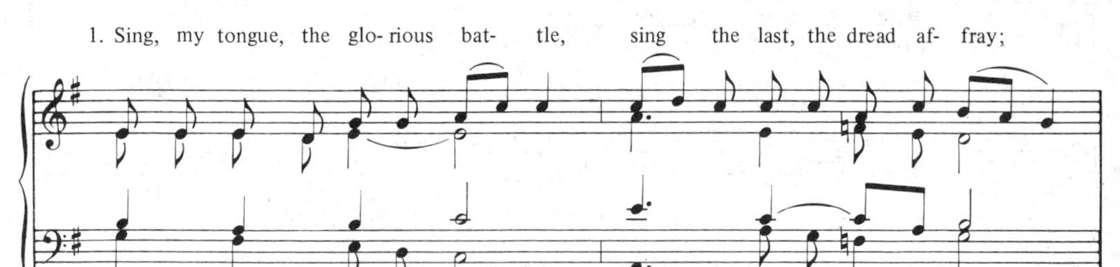

A different version of this tune may be found at Hymn 355

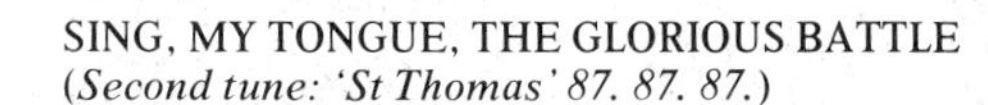

[HARMONY]

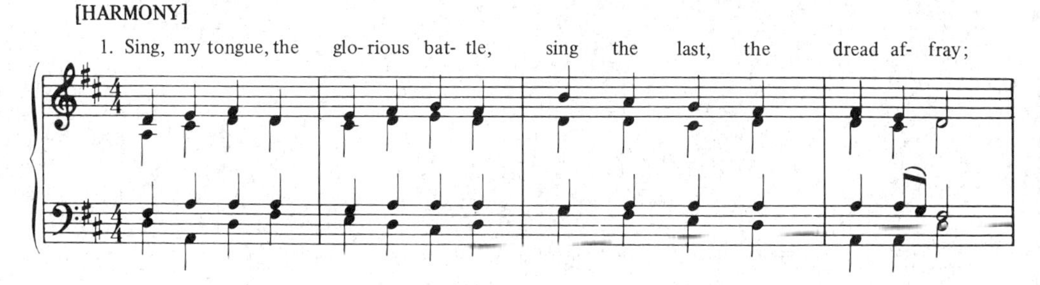

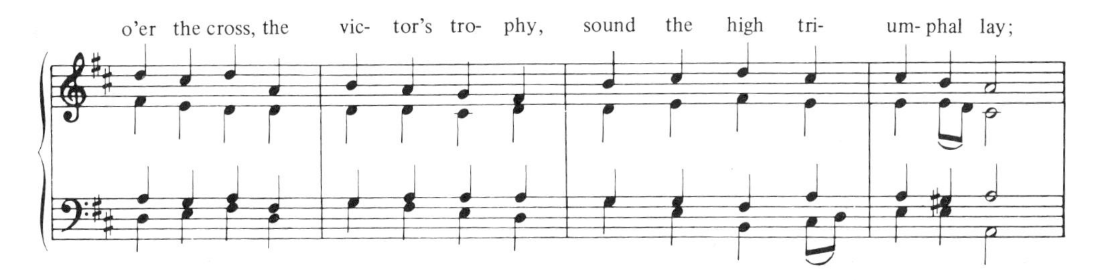

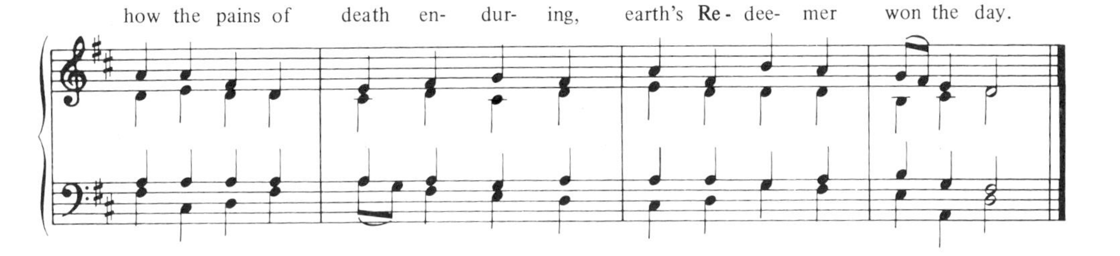

PART 1

2. When at length th'appointed fulness
   of the sacred time was come,
   he was sent, the world's creator,
   from the Father's heav'nly home,
   and was found in human fashion,
   offspring of the Virgin's womb.

3. Now the thirty years are ended
   which on earth he willed to see,
   willingly he meets his Passion,
   born to set his people free;
   on the cross the Lamb is lifted,
   there the sacrifice to be.

4. There the nails and spear he suffers,
   vinegar and gall and reed;
   from his sacred body piercèd
   blood and water both proceed:
   precious flood, which all creation
   from the stain of sin hath freed.

PART 2

5. Faithful cross, above all other,
   one and only noble tree,
   none in foliage, none in blossom,
   none in fruit thy peer may be;
   sweet the wood, and sweet the iron,
   and thy load, most sweet is he.

6. Bend, O lofty tree, thy branches,
   thy too rigid sinews bend;
   and awhile the stubborn hardness,
   which thy birth bestowed, suspend;
   and the limbs of heaven's high Monarch
   gently on thine arms extend.

7. Thou alone wast counted worthy
   this world's ransom to sustain,
   that a shipwrecked race for ever
   might a port of refuge gain,
   with the sacred blood anointed
   of the Lamb for sinners slain.

This Doxology is sung after either part:

8. Praise and honour to the Father,
   praise and honour to the Son,
   praise and honour to the Spirit,
   ever Three and ever One:
   One in might, and One in glory,
   while eternal ages run.

Words: Venantius Fortunatus (c. 530-609),
tr. J. M. Neale
Music: First tune - Plainsong Mode iii
Second tune - Samuel Webbe (1740-1816)

SING PRAISE TO THE LORD (Jacob's Song)

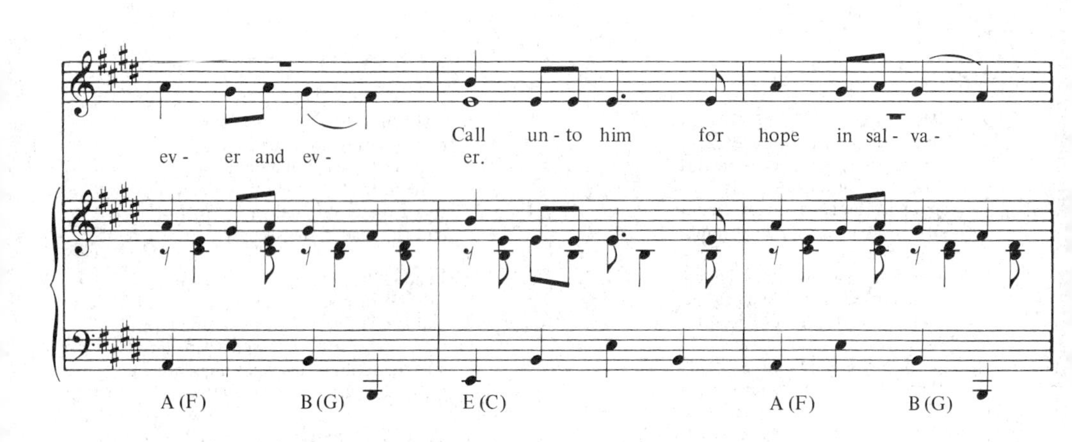

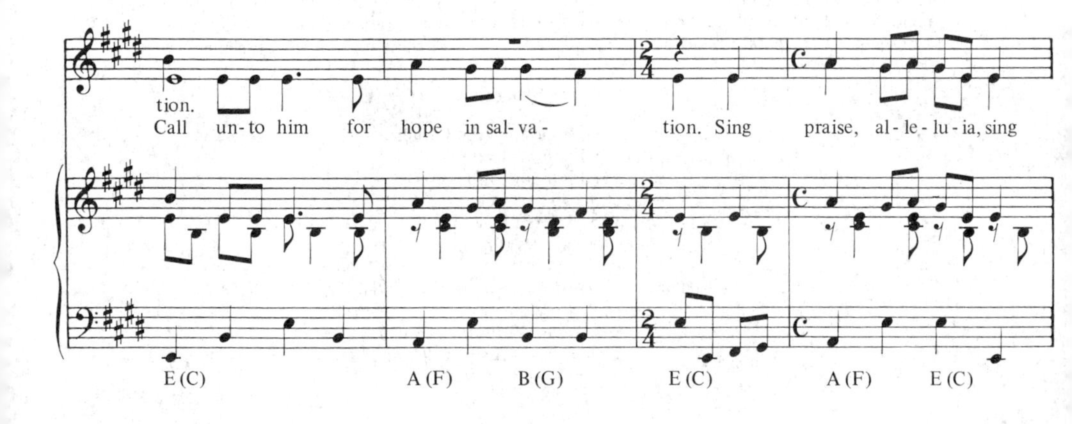

CODA overleaf

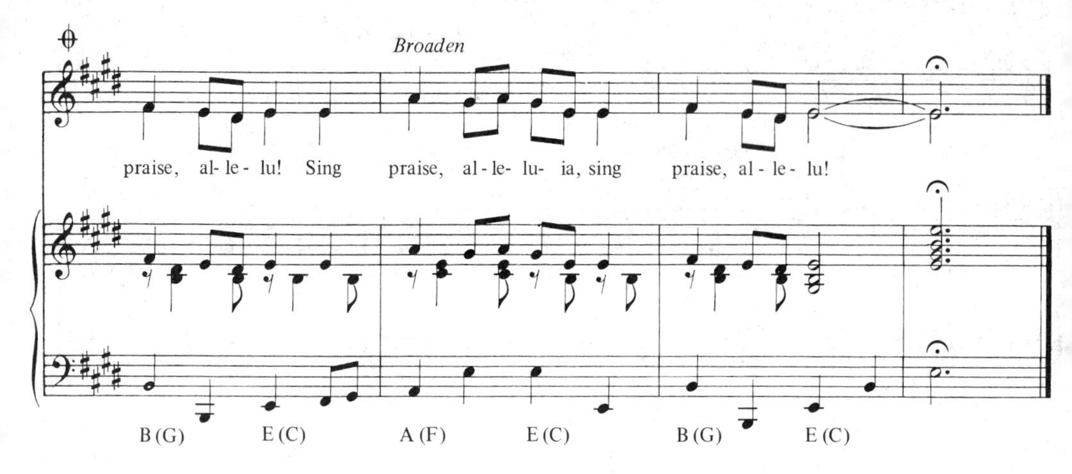

Words: Jacob Krieger
Music: Jacob Krieger, adapted by Mikel Kennedy

454

SOLDIERS OF CHRIST ARISE
('St Ethelwald' S.M.)

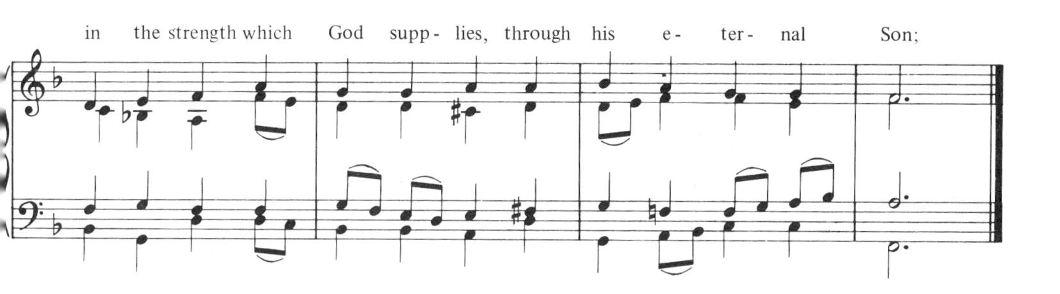

2. Strong in the Lord of Hosts,
and in his mighty power:
who in the strength of Jesus trusts
is more than conqueror.

3. Stand then in his great might,
with all his strength endued;
and take, to arm you for the fight,
the panoply of God.

4. From strength to strength go on,
wrestle and fight and pray;
tread all the powers of darkness down,
and win the well-fought day;

5. That, having all things done,
and all your conflicts past,
ye may o'ercome, through Christ alone,
and stand entire at last.

Words, based on Ephesians 6:
Charles Wesley (1707-88)
Music: William Henry Monk (1823-89)

455

SOLDIERS, WHO ARE CHRIST'S BELOW

('Orientis partibus' 77.77.)

[HARMONY]

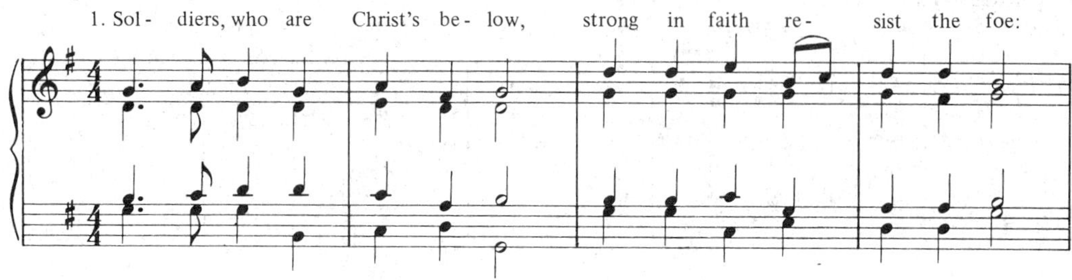

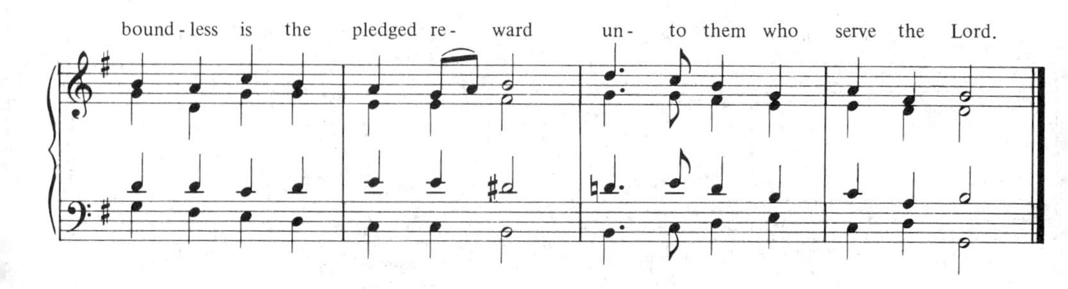

2. 'Tis no palm of fading leaves
that the conqueror's hand receives;
joys are his, serene and pure,
light that ever shall endure.

3. For the souls that overcome
waits the beauteous heavenly home,
where the blessèd evermore
tread on high the starry floor.

4. Passing soon and little worth
are the things that tempt on earth;
heavenward lift thy soul's regard:
God himself is thy reward.

5. Father, who the crown dost give,
Saviour, by whose death we live,
Spirit, who our hearts dost raise,
Three in One, thy name we praise.

Words: Latin hymn (18th century) tr. J.H. Clark
Music: Pierre de Corbeil (†1222)

456

2. Some days there are smiles all around,
some days there are tears,
but with both we know we can grow up
just like our Lord Jesus.

Words and Music: Estelle White

SONGS OF PRAISE THE ANGELS SANG

('St Edmund' 77.77.D.)

2. Heaven and earth must pass away;
songs of praise shall crown that day:
God will make new heavens and earth;
songs of praise shall hail their birth.
And will man alone be dumb
till that glorious Kingdom come?
No, the Church delights to raise
psalms and hymns and songs of praise.

3. Saints below, with heart and voice,
still in songs of praise rejoice;
learning here, by faith and love,
songs of praise to sing above.
Hymns of glory, songs of praise,
Father, unto thee we raise,
Jesu, glory unto thee,
with the Spirit, ever be.

Words: James Montgomery (1771-1854) and others
Music: Charles Steggall (1826-1905)

('Salzburg' 77.77.D.) [HARMONY]

2. Manifest at Jordan's stream,
Prophet, Priest, and King supreme;
and at Cana wedding-guest
in thy Godhead manifest;
manifest in power divine,
changing water into wine:
anthems be to thee addressed;
God in man made manifest.

3. Manifest in making whole
palsied limbs and fainting soul;
manifest in valiant fight;
quelling all the devil's might;
manifest in gracious will,
ever bringing good from ill:
anthems be to thee addressed;
God in man made manifest.

4. Sun and moon shall darkened be,
stars shall fall, the heavens shall flee;
Christ will then like lightning shine,
all will see his glorious sign;
all will then the trumpet hear,
all will see the Judge appear·
thou by all will be confessed;
God in man made manifest.

5. Grant us grace to see thee, Lord,
mirrored in thy holy word;
may we imitate thee now,
and be pure, as pure art thou;
that we like to thee may be
at thy great Epiphany;
and may praise thee, ever blest,
God in man made manifest.

Words: Christopher Wordsworth (1807-85)
Music: melody by J. Hintze (1622-1702), harmonised by J. S. Bach

459

SPIRIT OF MERCY, TRUTH, AND LOVE
(First tune: 'Melcombe' L.M.)

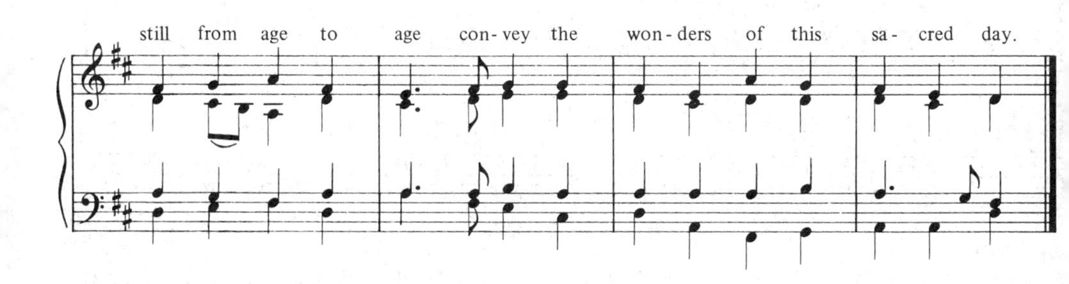

2. In every clime, by every tongue,
be God's surpassing glory sung;
let all the listening earth be taught
the acts our great Redeemer wrought.

3. Unfailing comfort, heavenly guide,
still o'er thy holy Church preside;
still let mankind thy blessings prove,
Spirit of mercy, truth, and love.

Words: 'Foundling Hospital Collection' (1774)
Music: First tune – Samuel Webbe (1740-1816)

SPIRIT OF MERCY, TRUTH, AND LOVE
(Second tune: 'Warrington' L.M.)

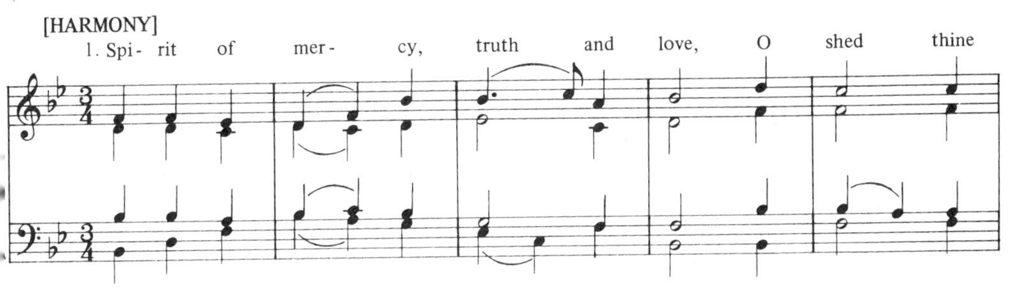

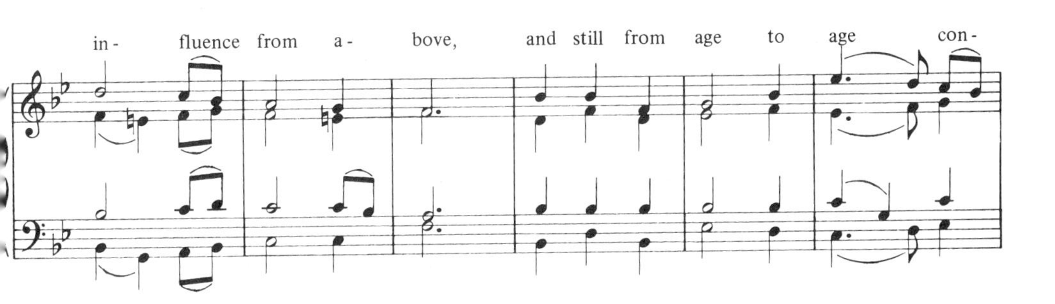

2. In every clime, by every tongue,
be God's surpassing glory sung;
let all the listening earth be taught
the acts our great Redeemer wrought.

3. Unfailing comfort, heavenly guide,
still o'er thy holy Church preside;
still let mankind thy blessings prove,
Spirit of mercy, truth, and love.

Words: 'Foundling Hospital Collection' (1774)
Music: Second tune – Ralph Harrison (1748-1810)

460 SPIRIT OF THE LIVING GOD

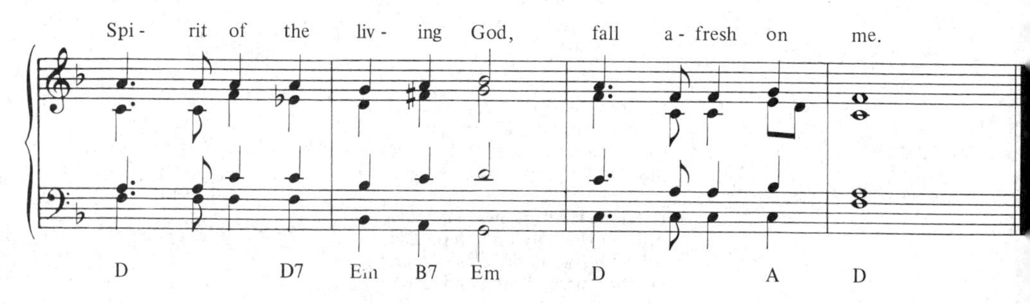

2. *Repeat Verse 1 singing* 'us' *instead of* 'me'.

When appropriate, a third verse may be added, singing 'on them' *– for example, before Confirmation, or at a service for the sick.*

Words and Music: Michael Iverson

SPIRIT... COME AND MAKE US NEW (Spirit, whose name is love)

461

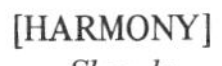

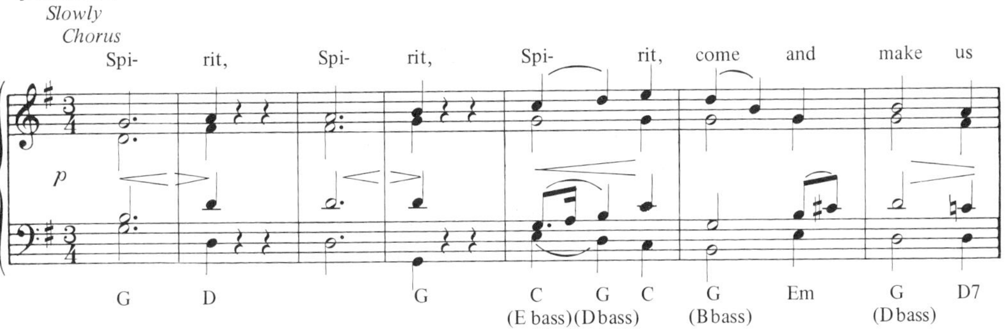

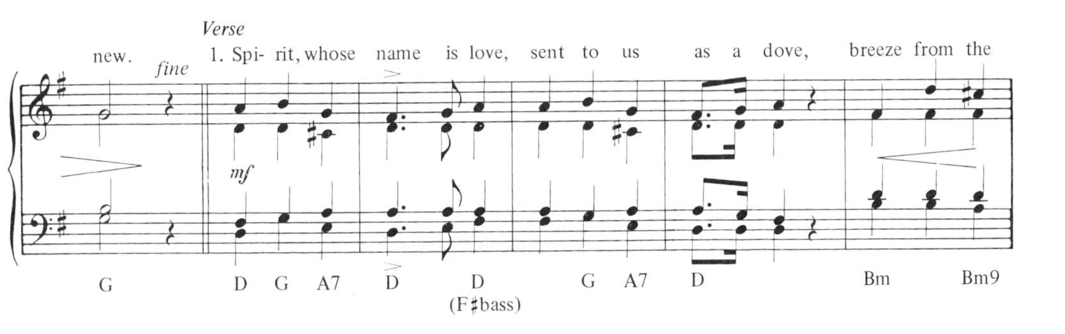

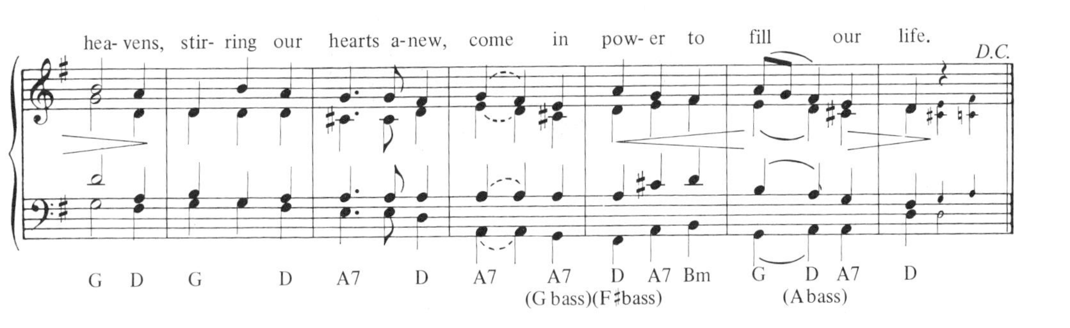

2. Spirit, with healing wings,
   whose name creation sings,
   comfort our sorrow,
   bind up the broken heart,
   bless and gladden each chosen soul.

3. Spirit, eternal truth,
   both source and living proof,
   sent from the Father,
   through his beloved Son,
   loosen our bonds, set your people free.

Words: Kevin Mayhew
Music: Georg Vogler (1749-1814), adapted by Kevin Mayhew

STAND UP AND BLESS THE LORD
('Carlisle' S.M.)

462

This tune can be found in a lower key at Hymn 428, and in a different harmonisation at Hymn 54

2. Though high above all praise,
above all blessing high,
who would not fear his holy name,
and laud and magnify?

3. O for the living flame
from his own altar brought,
to touch our lips, our mind inspire,
and wing to heaven our thought.

4. God is our strength and song,
and his salvation ours;
then be his love in Christ proclaimed
with all our ransomed powers.

5. Stand up, and bless the Lord,
the Lord your God adore;
stand up, and bless his glorious name
henceforth for evermore.

Words: James Montgomery (1771-1854)
Music: Charles Lockhart (1745-1815)

STAND UP, STAND UP FOR JESUS
('Morning light' 76.76.D.

[HARMONY]

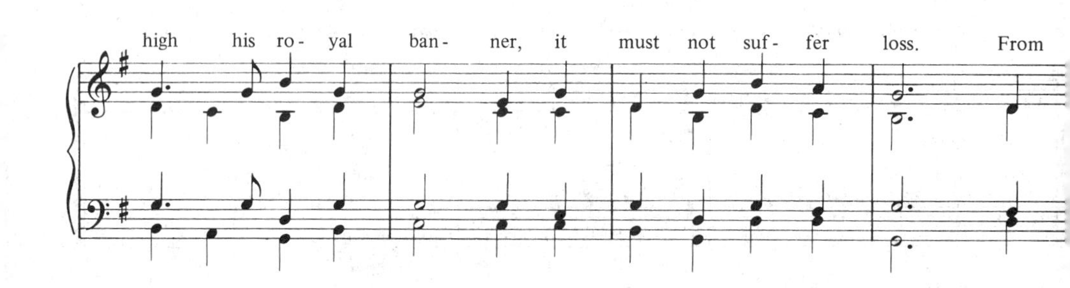

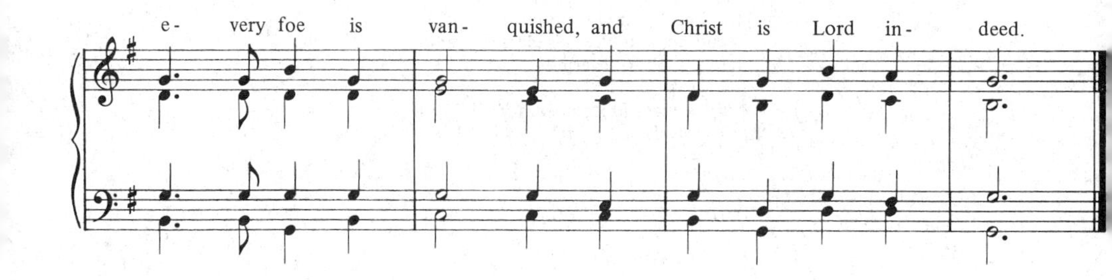

2. Stand up, stand up for Jesus,
the solemn watchword hear:
if while ye sleep he suffers,
away with shame and fear.
Where'er ye meet with evil,
within you or without,
charge for the God of battles,
and put the foe to rout.

3. Stand up, stand up for Jesus,
the trumpet call obey;
forth to the mighty conflict
in this his glorious day.
Ye that are men now serve him
against unnumbered foes;
let courage rise with danger
and strength to strength oppose.

4. Stand up, stand up for Jesus,
stand in his strength alone;
the arm of flesh will fail you,
ye dare not trust your own.
Put on the Gospel armour,
each piece put on with prayer;
when duty calls or danger
be never wanting there.

5. Stand up, stand up for Jesus,
the strife will not be long;
this day the noise of battle,
the next the victor's song.
To him that overcometh
a crown of life shall be;
he with the King of Glory
shall reign eternally.

Words, based on Ephesians 6:
George Duffield (1818-88)
Music: George James Webb (1803-87)

464

STARS OF THE MORNING
(First tune: 'Trisagion' 10 10.10 10.)

[HARMONY]

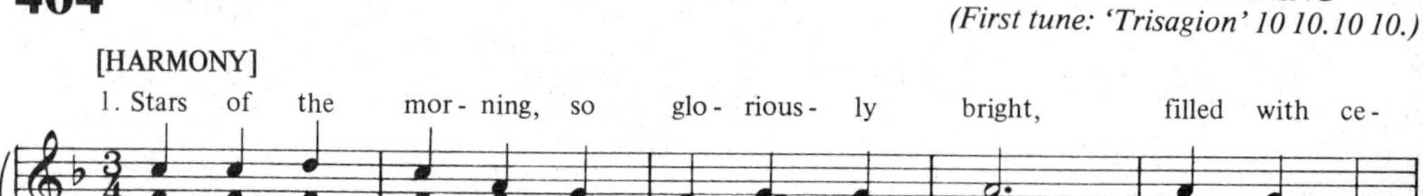

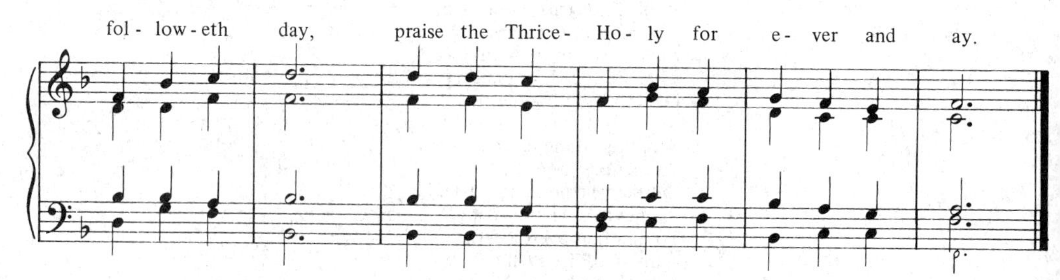

2. These are thy ministers,
these dost thou own,
Lord God of Sabaoth,
nearest thy throne;
these are thy messengers,
these dost thou send,
help of the helpless ones,
man to defend.

3. These keep the guard
amidst Salem's dear bowers,
thrones, principalities,
virtues and powers,
where, with the living ones,
mystical four,
cherubim, seraphim,
bow and adore.

4. Then, when the earth
was first poised in mid space,
then, when the planets
first sped on their race,
then, when was ended
the six days' employ,
then all the sons of God
shouted for joy.

5. Still let them succour us;
still let them fight,
Lord of angelic hosts,
battling for right;
till, where their anthems
they ceaselessly pour,
we with the angels
may bow and adore.

Words: from the Greek of St. Joseph the Hymnographer,
tr. John M. Neale (1818-66)
Music: Henry Smart (1813-79)

STARS OF THE MORNING

(Second tune: 'Quedlinburg' 10 10.10 10.)

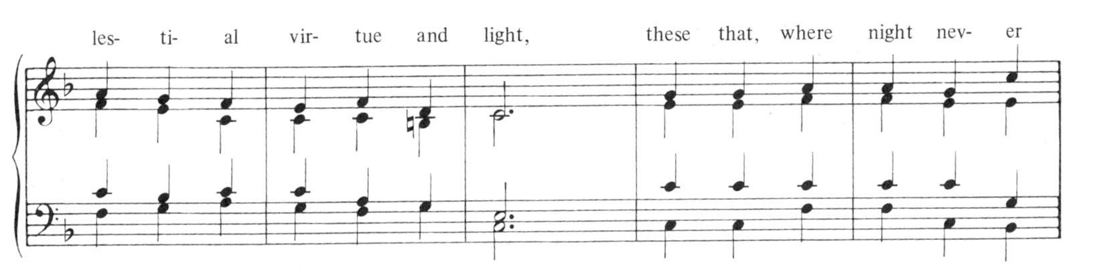

2. These are thy ministers,
these dost thou own,
Lord God of Sabaoth,
nearest thy throne;
these are thy messengers,
these dost thou send,
help of the helpless ones,
man to defend.

3. These keep the guard
amidst Salem's dear bowers,
thrones, principalities,
virtues and powers,
where, with the living ones,
mystical four,
cherubim, seraphim,
bow and adore.

4. Then, when the earth
was first poised in mid space,
then, when the planets
first sped on their race,
then, when was ended
the six days' employ,
then all the sons of God
shouted for joy.

5. Still let them succour us;
still let them fight,
Lord of angelic hosts,
battling for right;
till, where their anthems
they ceaselessly pour,
we with the angels
may bow and adore.

Words: from the Greek of St. Joseph the Hymnographer,
tr. John M. Neale (1818-66)
Music: from a chorale by J. C. Kittel (1732-1809)

STEAL AWAY

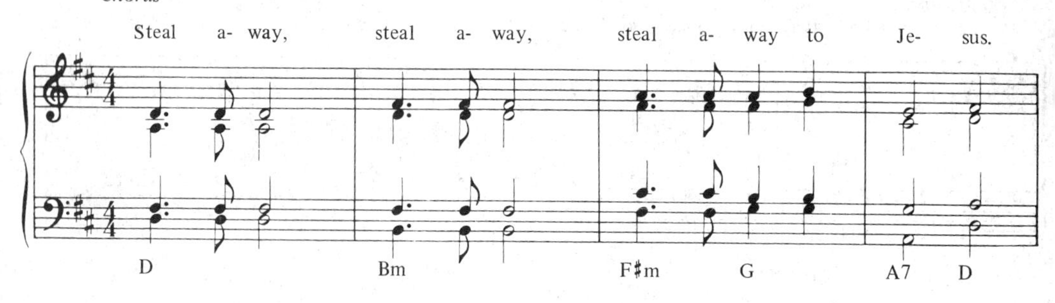

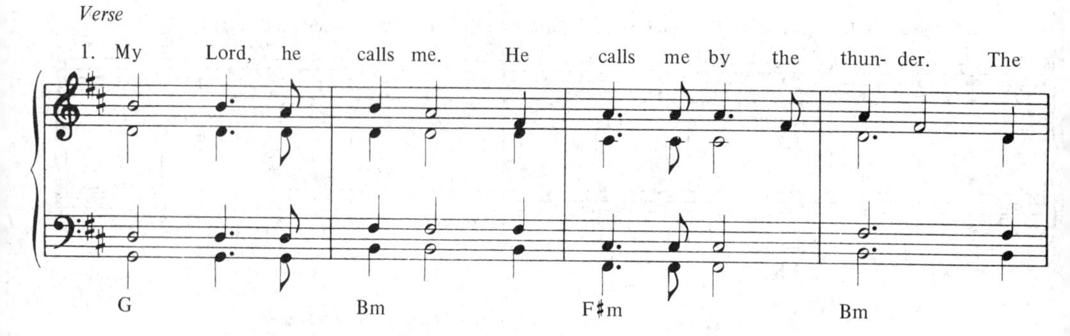

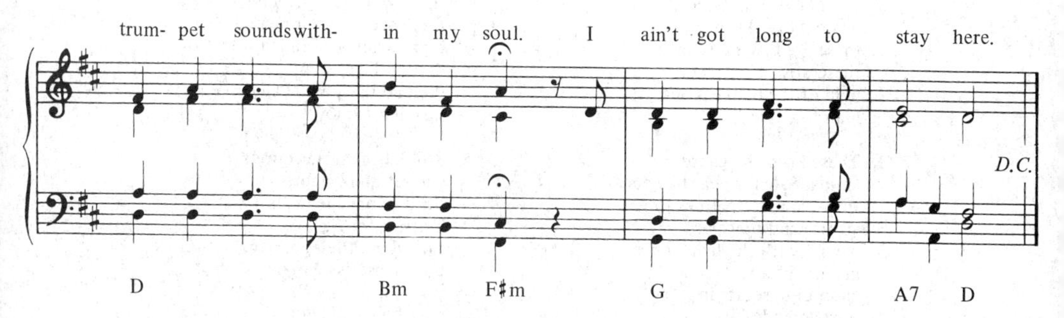

2. Green trees are bending,
   the sinner stands a-trembling.
   The trumpet sounds within my soul;
   I ain't got long to stay here.

3. My Lord, he calls me,
   he calls me by the lightning.
   The trumpet sounds within my soul;
   I ain't got long to stay here.

Words and Music: Traditional Spiritual, arranged by Michael Irwin

466

STRENGTHEN FOR SERVICE, LORD

('Acht Gott und Herr' 87.87.)

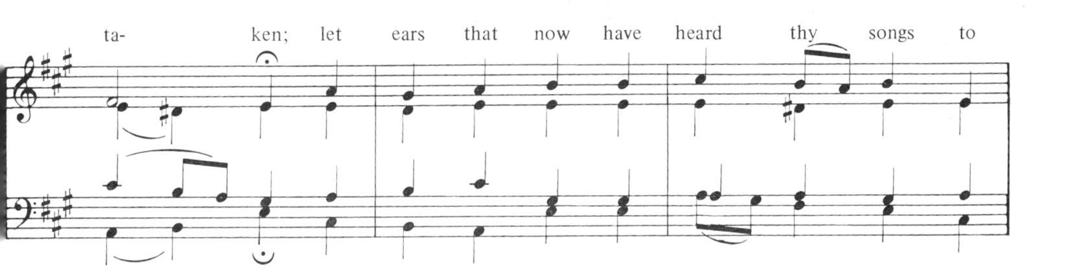

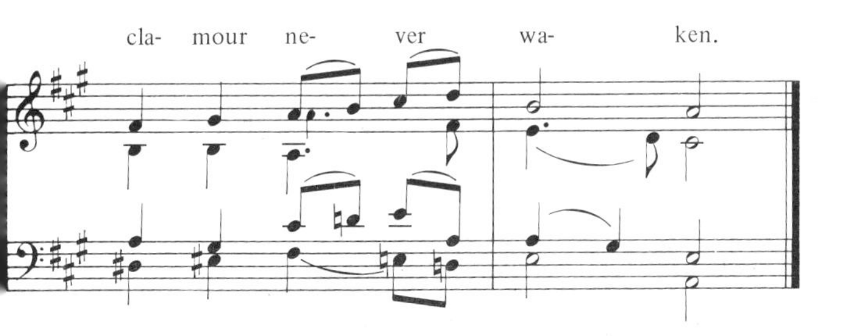

2. Lord, may the tongues which 'Holy' sang
   keep free from all deceiving;
   the eyes which saw thy love be bright,
   thy blessed hope perceiving.

3. The feet that tread thy holy courts
   from light do thou not banish;
   the bodies by thy Body fed
   with thy new life replenish.

Words: *Syriac Liturgy,*
perhaps by Ephraim the Syrian (c. 306-373),
tr. C. W. Humphreys and Percy Dearmer
Music: *from 'Neu-Leipziger Gesangbuch' (1682),*
arranged by J. S. Bach

467

SUN OF MY SOUL, THOU SAVIOUR DEAR

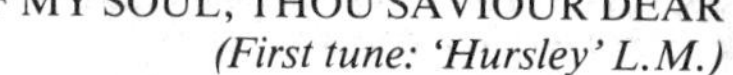
(First tune: 'Hursley' L.M.)

[HARMONY]

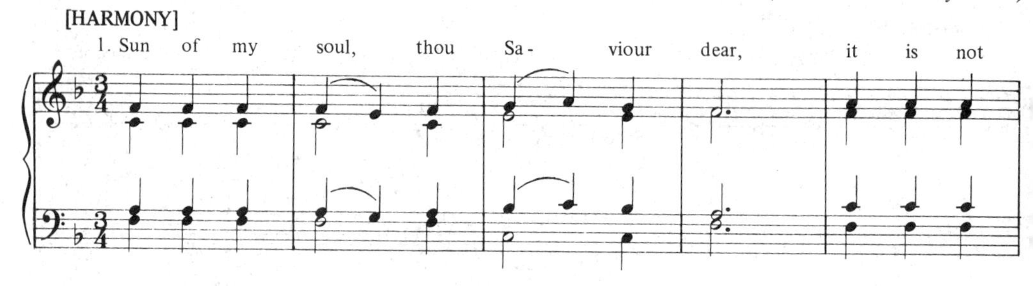

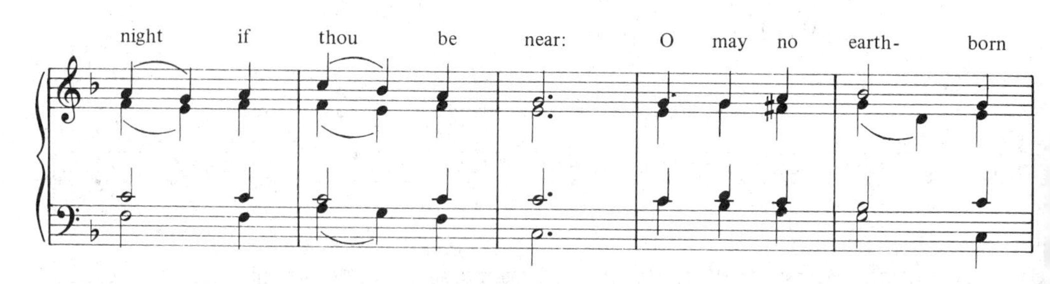

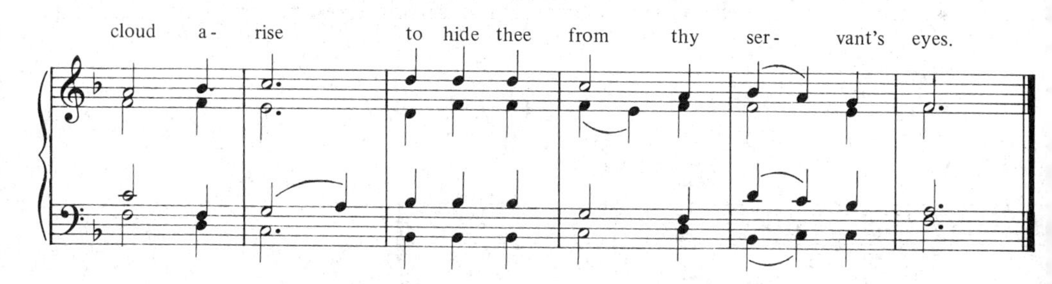

2. When the soft dews of kindly sleep
my wearied eyelids gently steep,
be my last thought, how sweet to rest
for ever on my Saviour's breast.

3. Abide with me from morn till eve,
for without thee I cannot live;
abide with me when night is nigh,
for without thee I dare not die.

4. If some poor wandering child of thine
have spurned today the voice divine,
now, Lord, the gracious work begin;
let him no more lie down in sin.

5. Watch by the sick; enrich the poor
with blessings from thy boundless store;
be every mourner's sleep tonight
like infant's slumbers, pure and light.

6. Come near and bless us when we wake,
ere through the world our way we take;
till in the ocean of thy love
we lose ourselves in heaven above.

Words: John Keble (1792-1866)
Music: First tune - 'Katholisches Gesangbuch' (c. 1775)

SUN OF MY SOUL, THOU SAVIOUR DEAR
(Second tune: 'Abends' L.M.)

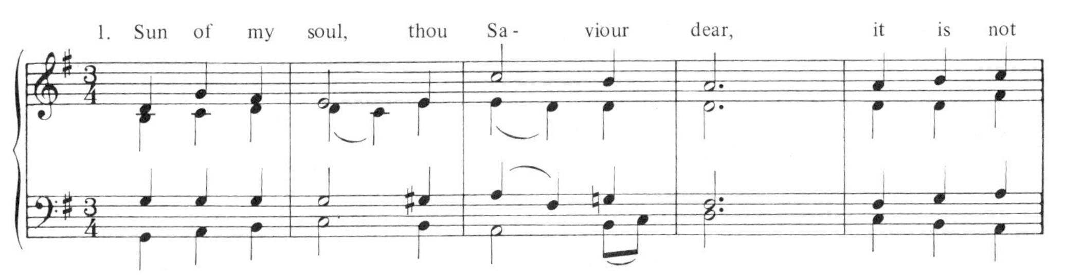

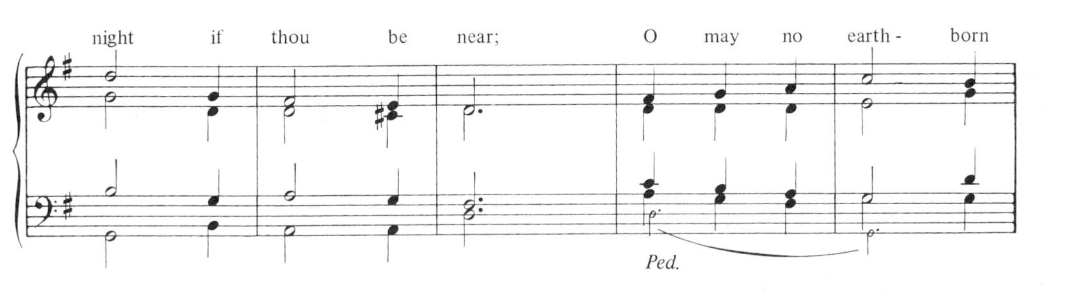

2. When the soft dews of kindly sleep
   my wearied eyelids gently steep,
   be my last thought, how sweet to rest
   for ever on my Saviour's breast.

3. Abide with me from morn till eve,
   for without thee I cannot live;
   abide with me when night is nigh,
   for without thee I dare not die.

4. If some poor wandering child of thine
   have spurned today the voice divine,
   now, Lord, the gracious work begin;
   let him no more lie down in sin.

5. Watch by the sick; enrich the poor
   with blessings from thy boundless store;
   be every mourner's sleep tonight
   like infant's slumbers, pure and light.

6. Come near and bless us when we wake,
   ere through the world our way we take;
   till in the ocean of thy love
   we lose ourselves in heaven above.

Words: John Keble (1792-1866)
Music: Second tune - H. S. Oakeley (1830-1903)

TAKE ME, LORD

2. Lord, I pray that each day I will listen to your will.
Many times I have failed but I know you love me still.
Teach me now, guide me, Lord. Keep me close to you always.

3. I am weak. Fill me now with your strength and set me free.
Make me whole. Fashion me so that you will live in me.
Hold me now in your hands. Form me now with your Spirit.

Words and Music: *Francesca Leftley,*
arranged by Frances M. Kelly

2. Take my hands.
They speak now for my heart,
and by their actions
they will show their love.
Guard them on their daily course,
be their strength and guiding force
to ever serve the Trinity above.

3. Take my hands.
I give them to you, Lord.
Prepare them for the
service of your name.
Open them to human need
and by their love they'll sow your seed
so all may know the love and hope you give.

Words and Music: Sebastian Temple

470

TAKE MY LIFE AND LET IT BE
(First tune: 'Hollingside' 77.77.D.)

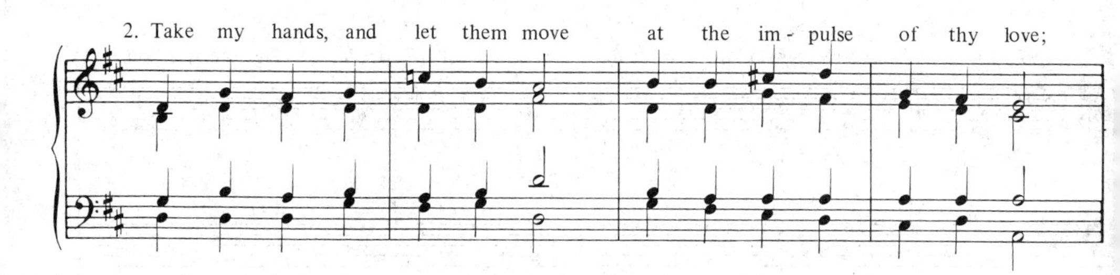

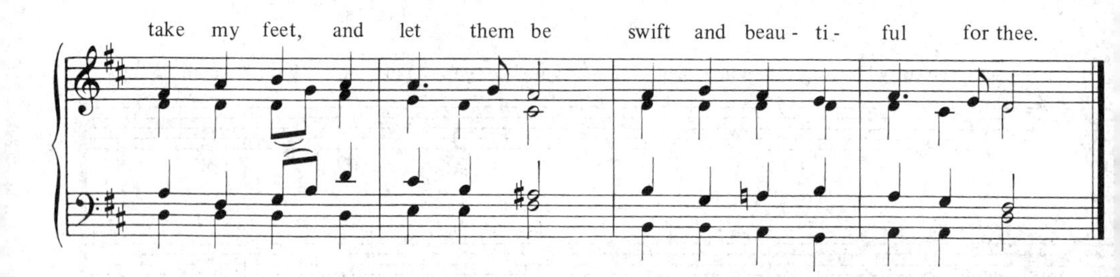

3. Take my voice, and let me sing
always, only, for my King;
take my lips, and let them be
filled with messages from thee.

4. Take my silver and my gold;
not a mite would I withhold;
take my intellect, and use
every power as thou shalt choose.

5. Take my will, and make it thine,
it shall be no longer mine;
take my heart: it is thine own;
it shall be thy royal throne.

6. Take my love; my Lord, I pour
at thy feet its treasure-store;
take myself, and I will be
ever, only, all for thee.

Words: Frances Havergal (1793-1870)
Music: First tune - John B. Dykes (1823-76)

TAKE MY LIFE AND LET IT BE
(Second tune: 'Nottingham' 77.77.D.)

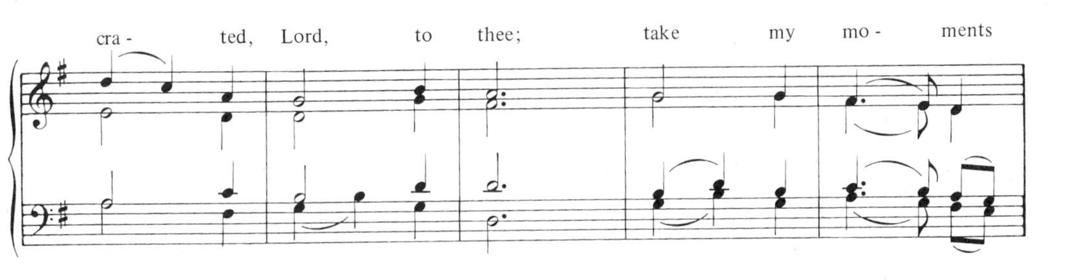

2. Take my hands, and let them move
at the impulse of thy love;
take my feet, and let them be
swift and beautiful for thee.

3. Take my voice, and let me sing
always, only, for my King;
take my lips, and let them be
filled with messages from thee.

4. Take my silver and my gold;
not a mite would I withhold;
take my intellect, and use
every power as thou shalt choose.

5. Take my will, and make it thine,
it shall be no longer mine;
take my heart: it is thine own;
it shall be thy royal throne.

6. Take my love; my Lord, I pour
at thy feet its treasure-store;
take myself, and I will be
ever, only, all for thee.

Words: Frances Hevergal (1793-1870)
Music: Second tune - W. A. Mozart (1756-91)

Gently
Introduction
C F G C

Chorus
Take this bread: it is my body. Take this cup: it is my
F G C F G

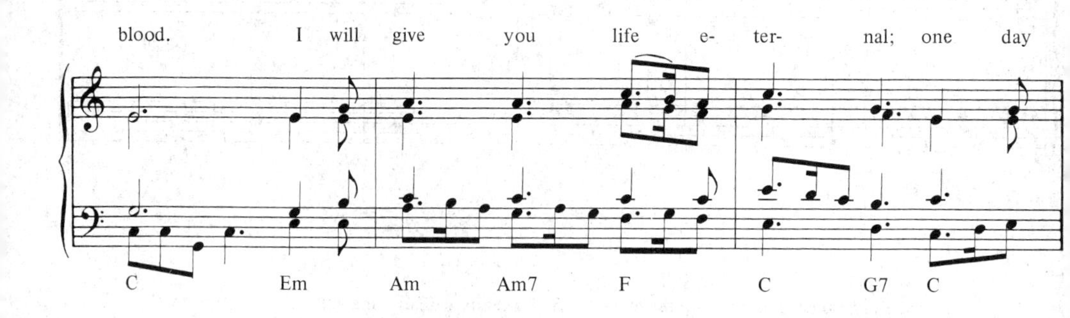
blood. I will give you life e- ter- nal; one day
C Em Am Am7 F C G7 C

I will raise you up.
Verse
1. You are the bread come down from
fine
F Dm G C Cmaj7 Am F

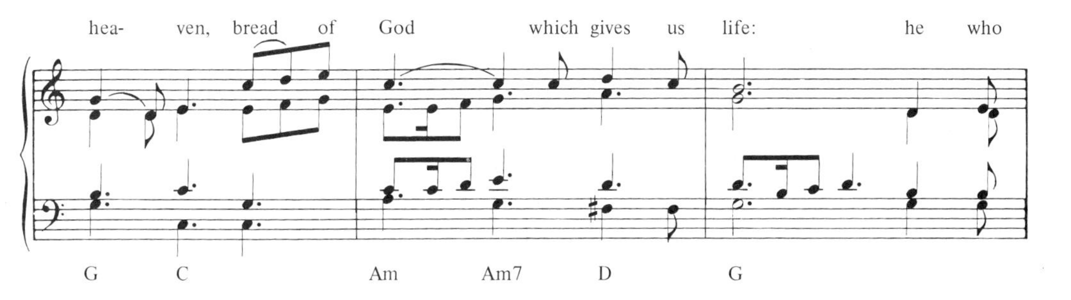

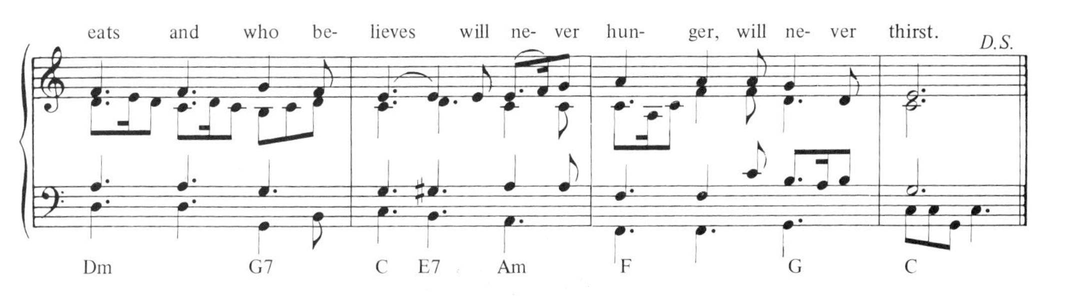

2. Whoever comes to you believing,
   never will be turned away:
   you have come to do the will
   of him who sent you with life for all.

3. Well may we hear the words you give us,
   words of God and Word of life;
   build our faith and teach us how
   to follow you and be one with God.

4. Where else to go in search of purpose?
   Where to go to find the truth?
   You present the Way to life,
   and we believe you, the Son of God.

Words, based on John 6: Stephen Smyth
Music: Gerry Fitzpatrick

TAKE UP THY CROSS
('Breslau' L.M.)

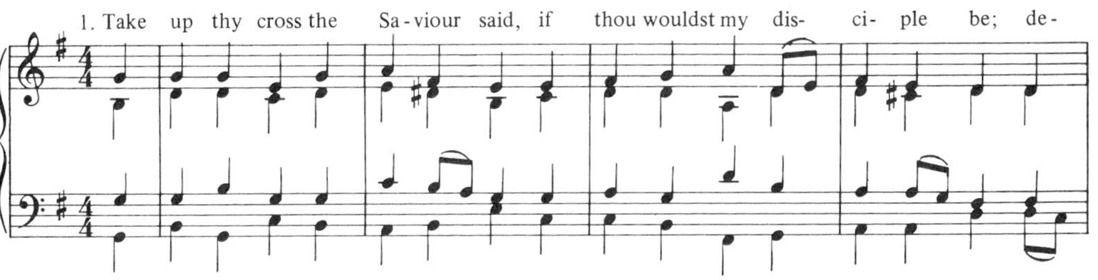

2. Take up thy cross – let not its weight
fill thy weak spirit with alarm:
his strength shall bear thy spirit up,
and brace thy heart, and nerve thine arm.

3. Take up thy cross, nor heed the shame,
nor let thy foolish pride rebel:
thy Lord for thee the cross endured,
to save thy soul from death and hell.

4. Take up thy cross then in his strength,
and calmly every danger brave;
'twill guide thee to a better home,
and lead to victory o'er the grave.

5. Take up thy cross, and follow Christ,
nor think till death to lay it down;
for only he who bears the cross
may hope to wear the glorious crown.

6. To thee, great Lord, the One in Three,
all praise for evermore ascend:
O grant us in our home to see
the heavenly life that knows no end.

Words, based on Mark 8: Charles William Everest (1814-77)
Music: 'As Hymnodus Sacer' (1625), arr. F. Mendelssohn

Steadily
Chorus
'Take up your cross', he says, 'and fol- low me, and in my love and
F
Dm
C

com- fort you shall hide. I am the Way,' he says, 'so fol- low me; do not
Dm
A
F
Dm

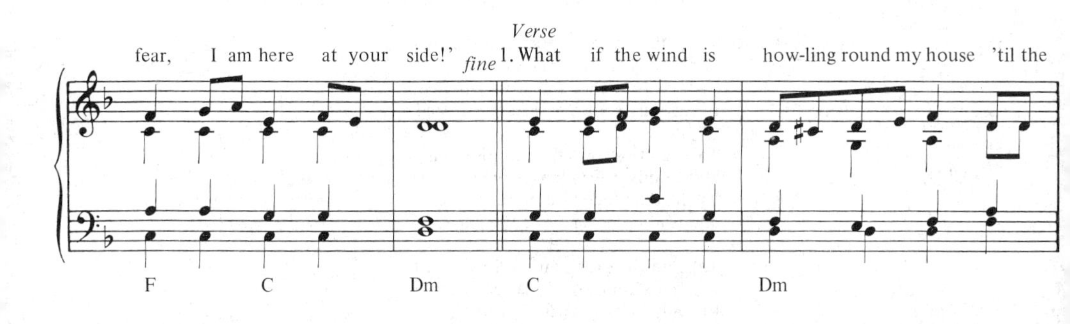
Verse
fear, I am here at your side!' fine 1. What if the wind is how-ling round my house 'til the
F
C
Dm
C
Dm

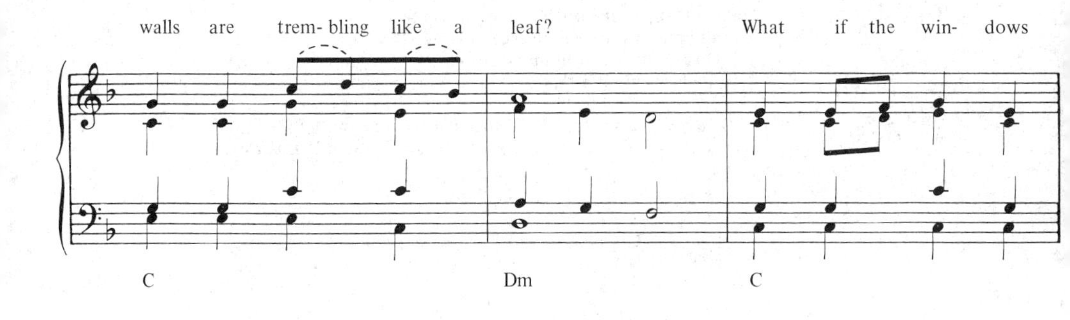
walls are trem- bling like a leaf? What if the win- dows
C
Dm
C

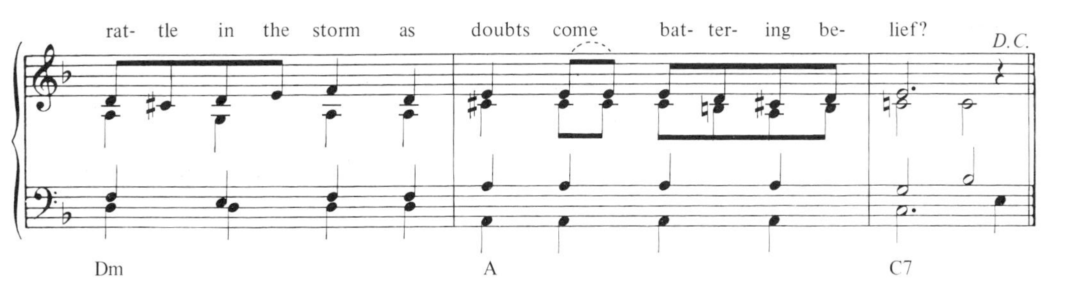

2. What if the rocks are blistering my feet,
 and the sun's heat beats upon my head?
 Near me a grass path beckons with its flowers,
 I'm tempted to go that way instead.

3. What if the tiredness aches behind my eyes
 and my boat is impossible to steer?
 Out on an ocean, drifting and alone,
 am I still, even then, to persevere?

4. Strangest of wonders, wonderfully strange,
 that the cross can set me free.
 Nothing is stronger than the love of God:
 I know very well that he loves me.

Words, based on Mark 8 and John 14,
and Music: Susan Sayers,
arranged by John Rombaut

474

TEACH ME MY GOD AND KING
('Sandys' S.M.)

[HARMONY]

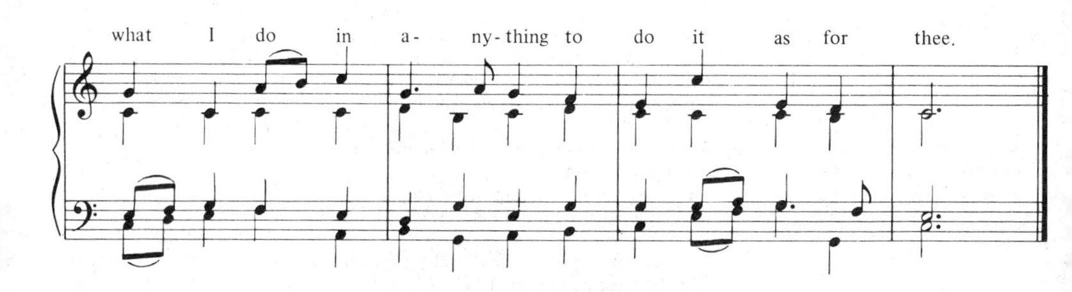

2. A man that looks on glass,
   on it may stay his eye;
   or, if he pleaseth, through it pass,
   and then the heaven espy.

3. All may of thee partake;
   nothing can be so mean
   which, with this tincture, 'for thy sake',
   will not grow bright and clean.

4. A servant with this clause
   makes drudgery divine;
   who sweeps a room, as for thy laws,
   makes that and the action fine.

5. This is the famous stone
   that turneth all to gold;
   for that which God doth touch and own
   cannot for less be told.

Words: George Herbert (1593-1632)
Music: English traditional carol from
W. Sandys' 'Christmas Carols' (1833)

TELL OUT, MY SOUL
('Woodlands' 10 10.10 10.)

2. Tell out, my soul, the greatness of his name!
Make known his might, the deeds his arm has done;
his mercy sure, from age to age the same;
his holy name - the Lord, the Mighty One.

3. Tell out, my soul, the greatness of his might!
Powers and dominions lay their glory by.
Proud hearts and stubborn wills are put to flight,
the hungry fed, the humble lifted high.

4. Tell out, my soul, the glories of his Word!
Firm is his promise, and his mercy sure.
Tell out, my soul, the greatness of the Lord
to children's children and for evermore!

Words, based on Luke 1:46-55: Timothy Dudley-Smith (b.1926)
Music: Walter Greatorex (1877-1949)

476

TEN THOUSAND TIMES TEN THOUSAND

('Komm, Seele' 76.86.D.)

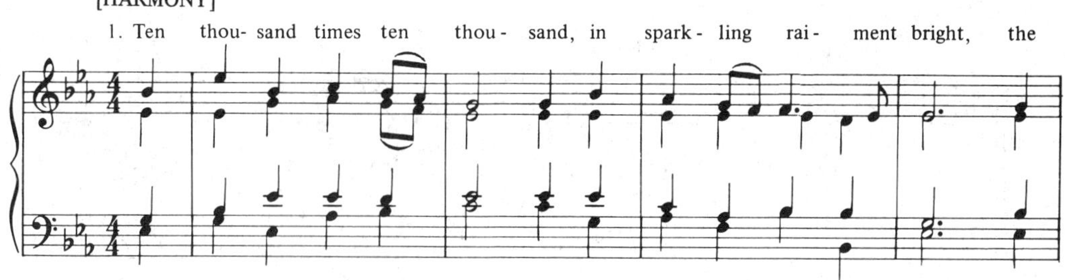

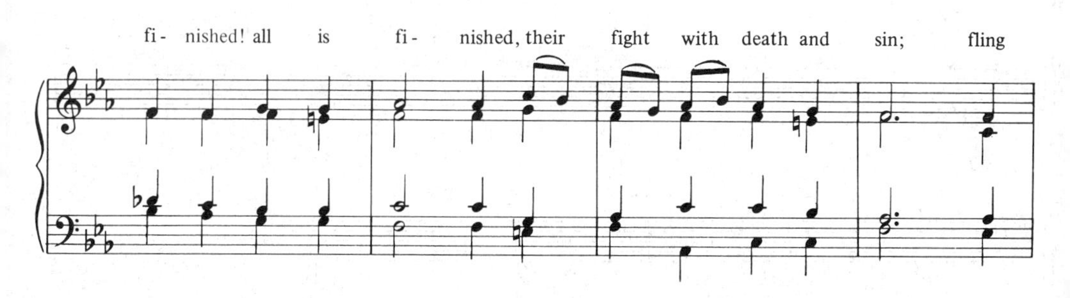

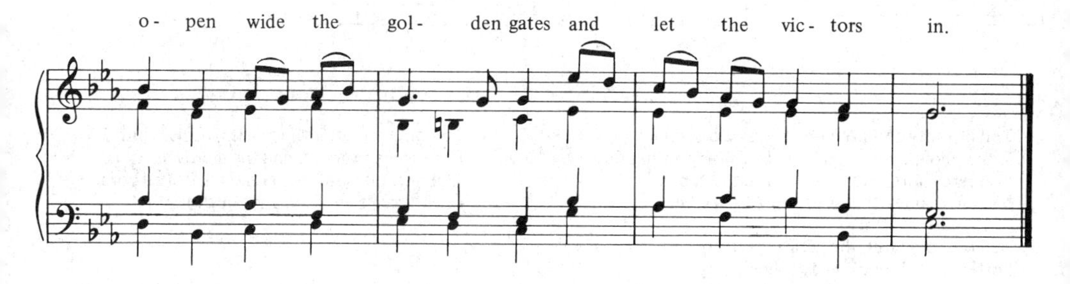

2. What rush of alleluias
fills all the earth and sky,
what ringing of a thousand harps
bespeaks the triumph nigh!
O day, for which creation
and all its tribes were made!
O joy, for all its former woes
a thousand-fold repaid!

3. O then what raptured greetings
on Canaan's happy shore,
what knitting severed friendships up,
where partings are no more!
Then eyes with joy shall sparkle
that brimmed with tears of late:
orphans no longer fatherless,
nor widows desolate.

4. Bring near thy great salvation,
thou Lamb for sinners slain,
fill up the roll of thine elect,
then take thy power and reign:
appear, Desire of Nations;
thine exiles long for home;
show in the heavens thy promised sign;
thou Prince and Saviour, come.

Words: Henry Alford (1810-71)
Music: Johann Wolfgang Franck (1641-88)

2. Thank you for all my friends and brothers.
Thank you for all the men that live.
Thank you, for even greatest enemies
I can forgive.

3. Thank you for many little sorrows.
Thank you for every kindly word,
Thank you, for everywhere your guidance
reaches every land.

4. Thank you, I see your Word has meaning.
Thank you, I know your Spirit here.
Thank you, because you love all people,
those both far and near.

5. Thank you, O Lord, you spoke unto us.
Thank you, that for our words you care.
Thank you, O Lord, you came among us,
bread and wine to share.

6. Thank you, O Lord, your love is boundless.
Thank you that I am full of you.
Thank you, you make me feel so glad and
thankful as I do.

Words: Walter van der Haas and Peter-Paul van Lelyveld
Music: Martin G. Schneider

THANK YOU, LORD, FOR GIVING US LIFE

Verse

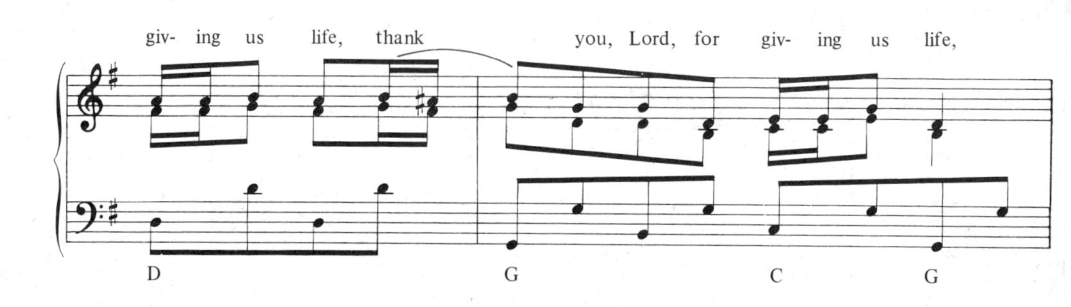

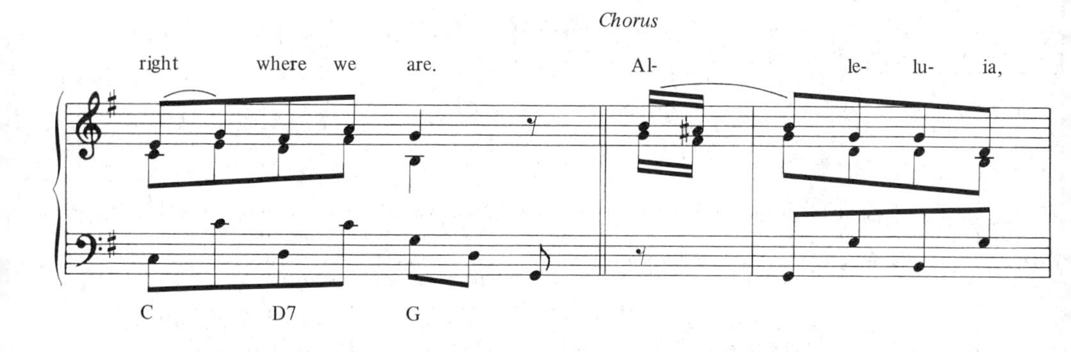

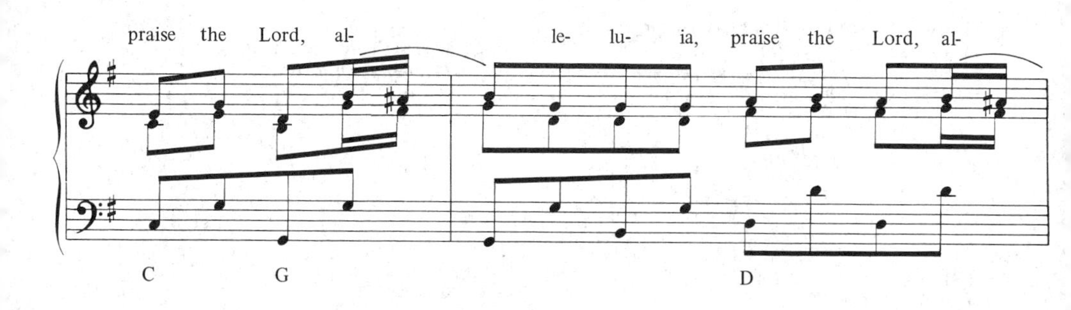

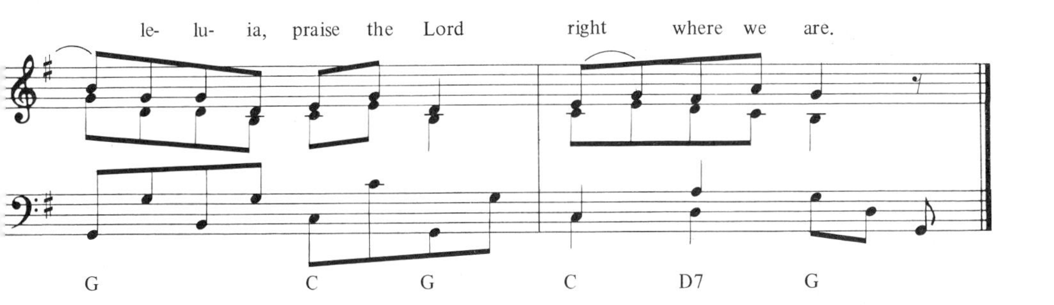

2. Thank you, Lord, for giving us love . . .

3. Thank you, Lord, for giving us joy . . .

4. Thank you, Lord, for giving us peace . . .

5. Thank you, Lord, for giving us friends . . .

Words and Music: Diane Davis

THE ADVENT OF OUR KING
('St Thomas' S.M.)

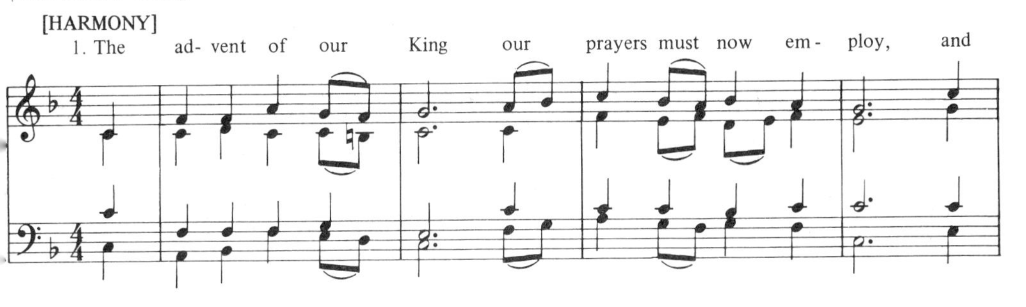

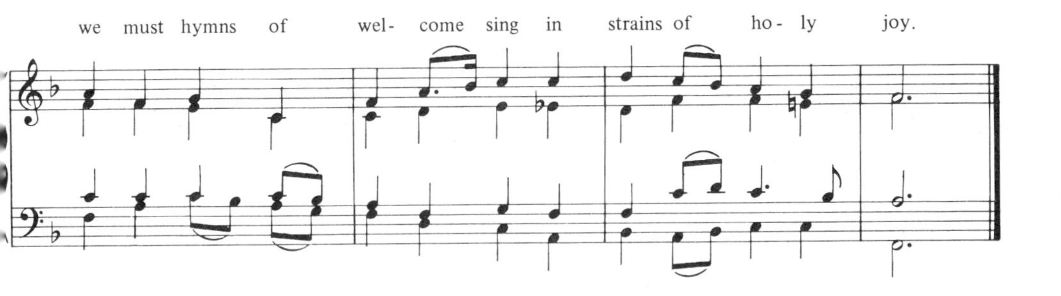

2. The everlasting Son
incarnate deigns to be;
himself a servant's form puts on,
to set his servants free.

3. Daughter of Zion, rise
to meet thy lowly King;
nor let thy faithless heart despise
the peace he comes to bring.

4. As Judge, on clouds of light,
he soon will come again,
and his true members all unite
with him in heaven to reign.

5. All glory to the Son
who comes to set us free,
with Father, Spirit, ever One,
through all eternity.

Words: Charles Coffin (1676-1749)
Music: from Aaron William's 'New Universal Psalmodist' (1770)

480

THE ANGEL, GABRIEL **(Annunciation caro**
('Birjina gaztettobat zegoen' 10 10.12 7 6

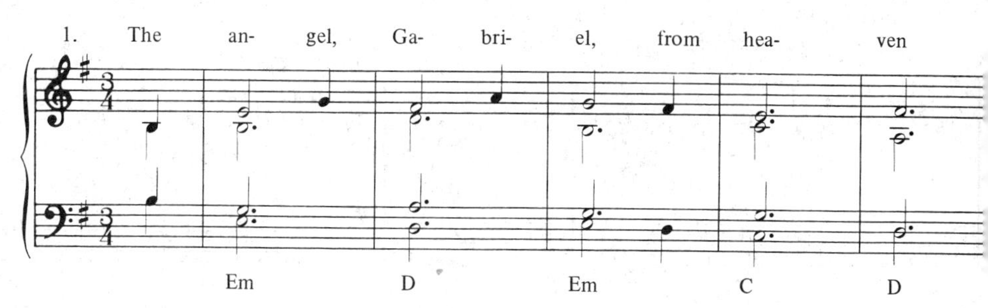

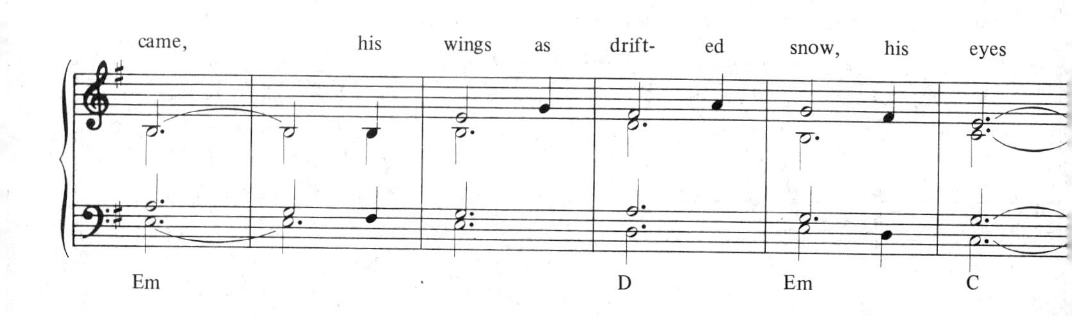

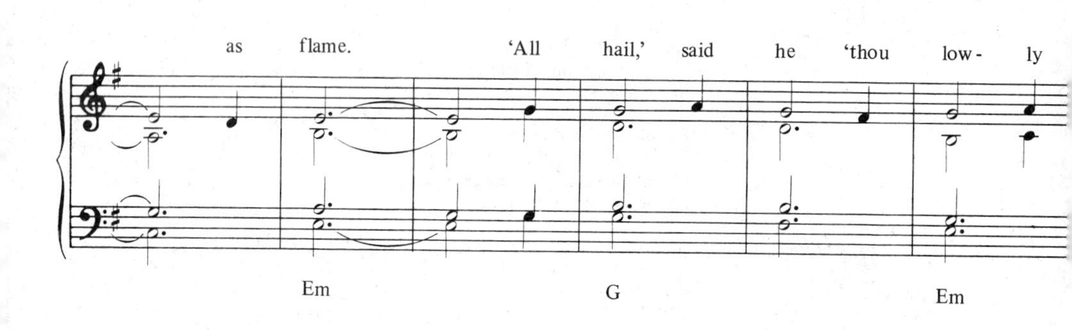

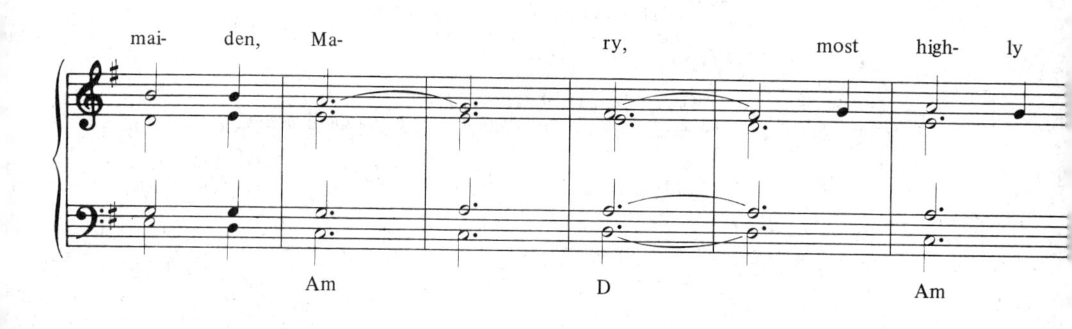

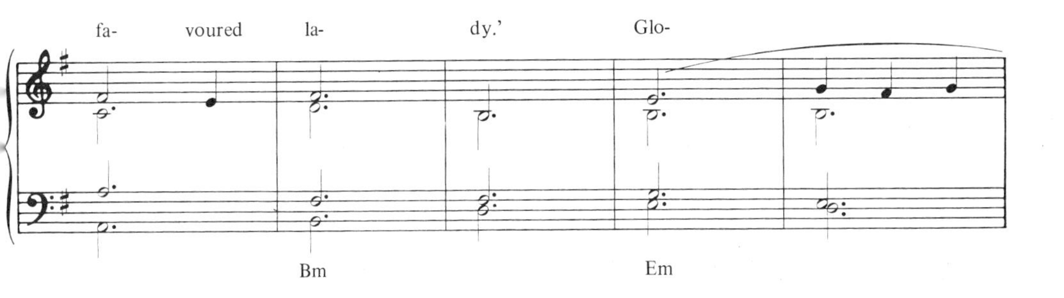

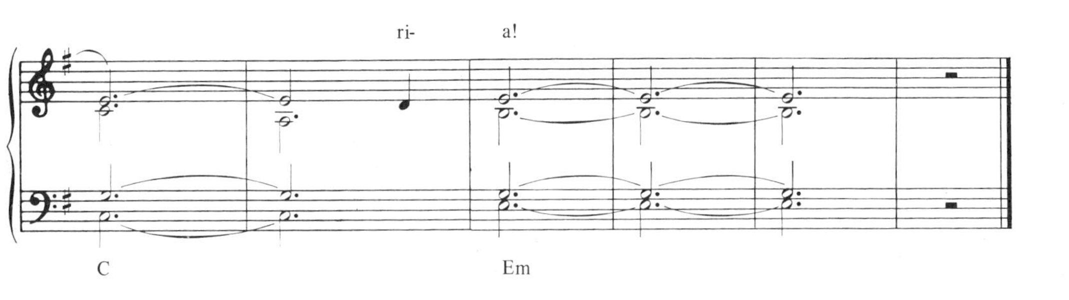

2. 'For know, a blessed Mother thou shalt be.'
   All generations laud and honour thee.
   Thy Son shall be Emmanuel,
      by seers foretold,
   most highly favoured lady.' Gloria!

3. Then gentle Mary meekly bowed her head.
   'To me be, as it pleaseth God,' she said.
   'My soul shall laud and magnify
      his holy name!'
   Most highly favoured lady. Gloria!

4. Of her Emmanuel, the Christ, was born
   in Bethlehem, all on a Christmas morn;
   and Christian folk thoughout the world
      will ever say:
   'Most highly favoured lady!' Gloria!

Words: Sabine Baring-Gould (1834-1924)
Music: Traditional Basque melody,
arranged by John Rombaut

481 THE BODY OF CHRIST NEEDS EYES (Wanted - good hands)

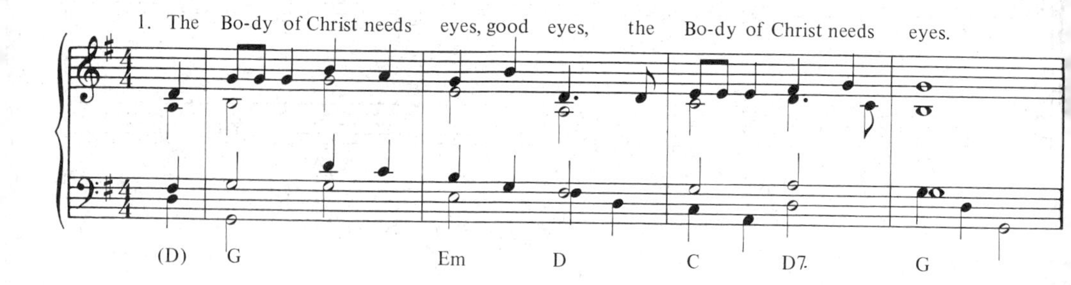

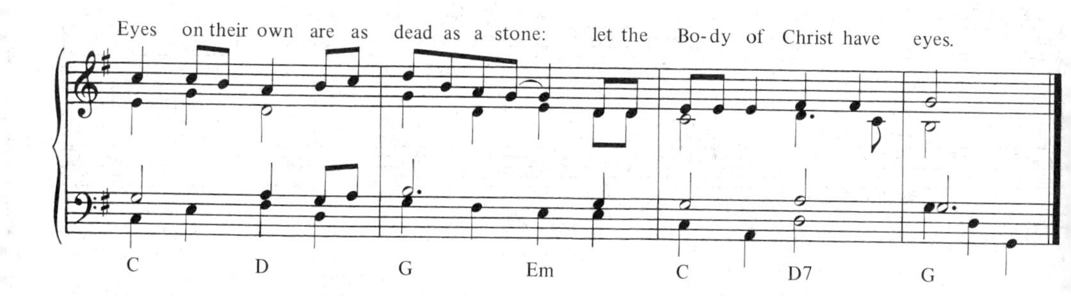

2. The Body of Christ needs hands . . .

3. The Body of Christ needs feet . . .

4. 'Now you are my Body,' Jesus says,
   'my Body has work to do.
   All of you, come then
   and live in me now,
   and you'll find that I live in you.'

Words and Music: Susan Sayers,
arranged by Frances M. Kelly

THE CHURCH OF GOD A KINGDOM IS
('Capel' C.M.)

[HARMONY]

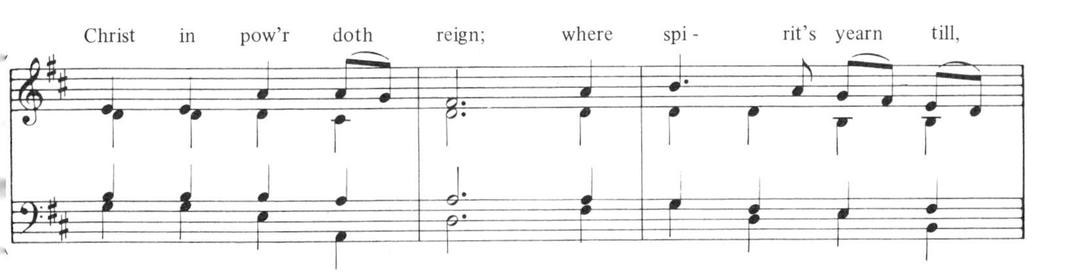

2. Glad companies of saints possess
this Church below, above;
and God's perpetual calm doth bless
their paradise of love.

3. An altar stands within the shrine
whereon, once sacrificed,
is set, immaculate, divine,
the Lamb of God, the Christ.

4. There rich and poor, from countless lands,
praise Christ on mystic rood;
there nations reach forth holy hands
to take God's holy food.

5. There pure life-giving streams o'erflow
the sower's garden-ground;
and faith and hope fair blossoms show,
and fruits of love abound.

6. O King, O Christ, this endless grace
to us and all men bring,
to see the vision of thy face
in joy, O Christ, our King.

Words: L.B.C.L. Muirhead (1845-1925)
Music: Traditional English carol melody

483

THE CHURCH'S ONE FOUNDATION

('Aurelia' 76.76.D.)

[HARMONY]

2. Elect from every nation,
yet one o'er all the earth,
her charter of salvation,
one Lord, one faith, one birth;
one holy name she blesses,
partakes one holy food,
and to one hope she presses,
with every grace endued.

3. 'Mid toil, and tribulation,
and tumult of her war,
she waits the consummation
of peace for evermore;
till with the vision glorious
her longing eyes are blest,
and the great Church victorious
shall be the Church at rest.

4. Yet she on earth hath union
with God the Three in One,
and mystic sweet communion
with those whose rest is won:
O happy ones and holy!
Lord, give us grace that we
like them, the meek and lowly
on high may dwell with thee.

Words: S. J. Stone (1830-1900)
Music: Samuel Sebastian Wesley (1810-1876)

THE CHURCH TRIUMPHANT IN THY LOVE

('Eatington' C.M.)

2. Thee in thy glorious realm they praise,
and bow before thy throne;
we in the kingdom of thy grace:
the kingdoms are but one.

3. The holy to the Holiest leads:
from hence our spirits rise,
and he that in thy statutes treads
shall meet thee in the skies.

Words: Charles Wesley (1707-88)
Music: William Croft (1678-1727)

485

THE DAY IS PAST AND OVER
('St Anatolius (Brown)' 76.76.88.)

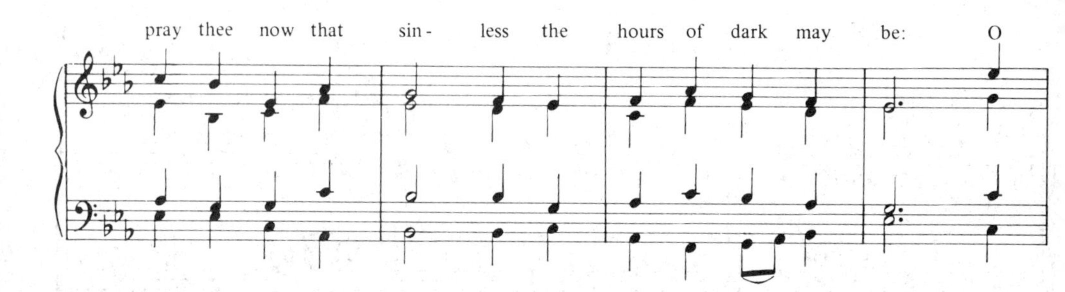

2. The joys of day are over;
I lift my heart to thee,
and ask thee that offenceless
the hours of dark may be:
O Jesu, keep me in thy sight,
and guard me through the coming night.

3. The toils of day are over;
I raise the hymn to thee,
and ask that free from peril
the hours of dark may be:
O Jesu, keep me in thy sight,
and guard me through the coming night.

4. Be thou my soul's preserver,
for thou alone dost know
how many are the perils
through which I have to go:
O loving Jesu, hear my call,
and guard and save me from them all.

Words: Greek (6th century) tr. J.M. Neale
Music: Arthur Henry Brown (1830-1926)

2. Our hearts be pure from evil,
that we may see aright
the Lord in rays eternal
of resurrection-light;
and listening to his accents,
may hear so calm and plain
his own 'All hail' and, hearing,
may raise the victor strain.

3. Now let the heavens be joyful,
and earth her song begin,
the round world keep high triumph,
and all that is therein;
let all things seen and unseen
their notes of gladness blend,
for Christ the Lord hath risen,
our joy that hath no end.

Words: St John Damascene (c. 750),
tr. J. M. Neale (1818-66)
Music: 'Wurtemburg Gesangbuch' (1784)

THE DAY THOU GAVEST

('St Clement' 98.98.)

[HARMONY]

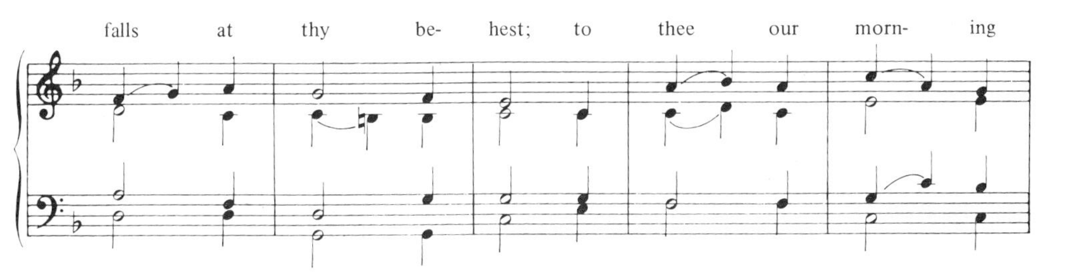

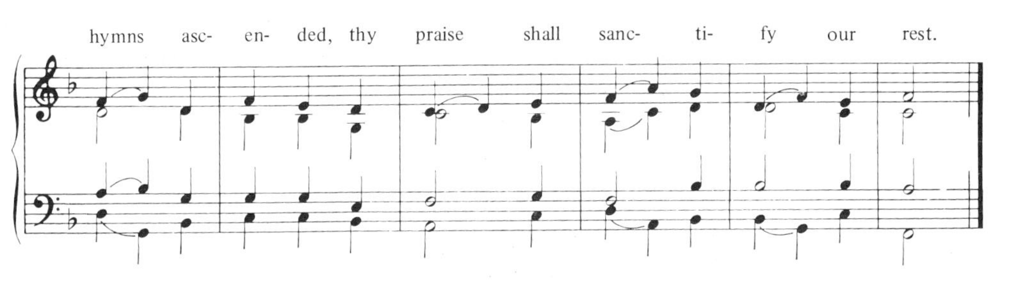

2. We thank thee that thy Church unsleeping,
while earth rolls onward into light,
through all the world her watch is keeping,
and rests not now by day or night.

3. As o'er each continent and island
the dawn leads on another day,
the voice of prayer is never silent,
nor dies the strain of praise away.

4. The sun that bids us rest is waking
our brethren 'neath the western sky
and hour by hour fresh lips are making
thy wondrous doings heard on high.

5. So be it, Lord; thy throne shall never,
like earth's proud empire, pass away;
thy kingdom stands, and grows for ever,
till all thy creatures own thy sway.

Words: John Ellerton (1826-93)
Music: Charles C. Scholefield (1839-1904)

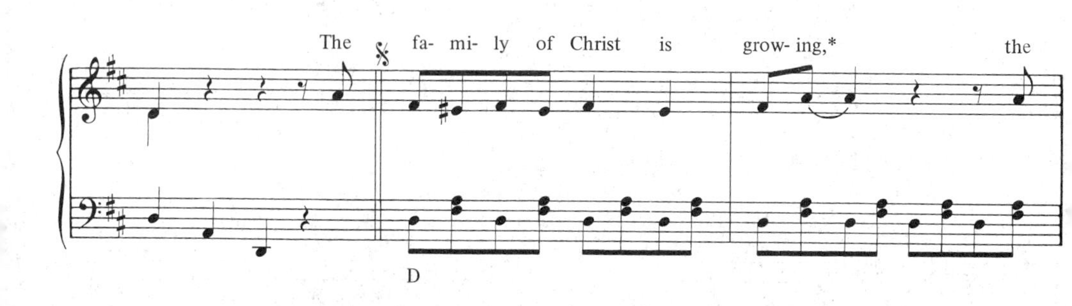

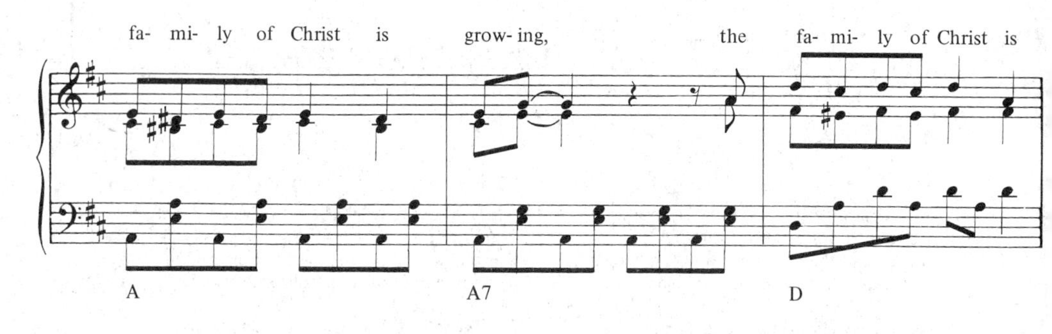

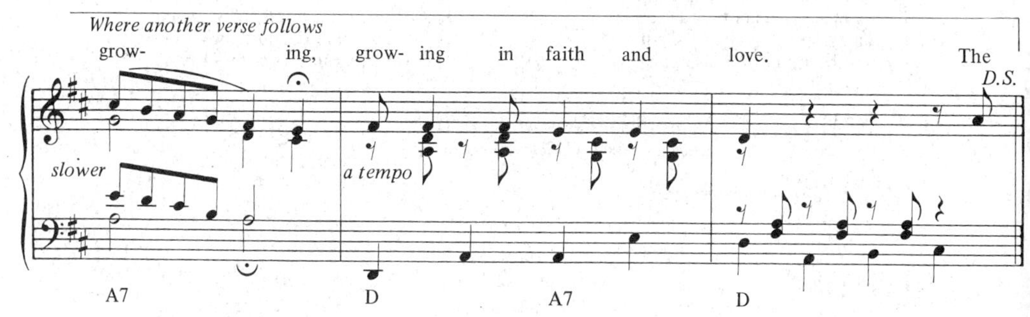

* praying, living, singing, etc.

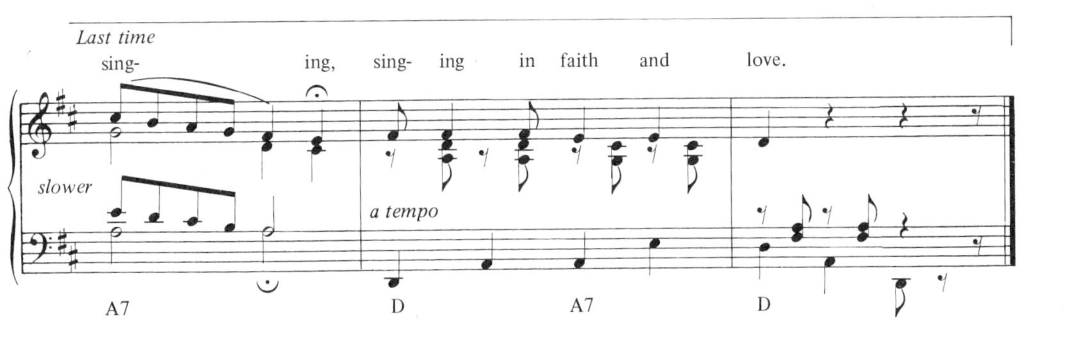

Words: Graham Jeffery
Music: Kevin Mayhew

THE FIRST NOWELL

('The first Nowell' Irregular) [HARMONY]

2. They lookèd up and saw a star,
   shining in the east, beyond them far,
   and to the earth it gave great light,
   and so it continued both day and night.

3. And by the light of that same star,
   three wise men came from country far.
   To seek for a king was their intent,
   and to follow the star wherever it went.

4. The star drew nigh to the north-west,
   o'er Bethlehem it took its rest
   and there it did both stop and stay
   right over the place where Jesus lay.

5. Then entered in those wise men three,
   full reverently upon their knee,
   and offered there in his presence,
   their gold and myrrh and frankincense.

6. Then let us all with one accord
   sing praises to our heav'nly Lord,
   that hath made heaven and earth of nought,
   and with his blood mankind hath bought.

Words: Traditional English carol
Music: Traditional melody, harmonised by John Stainer

490

THE GOD OF ABRAHAM PRAISE

('Leoni' 66.84.D.)

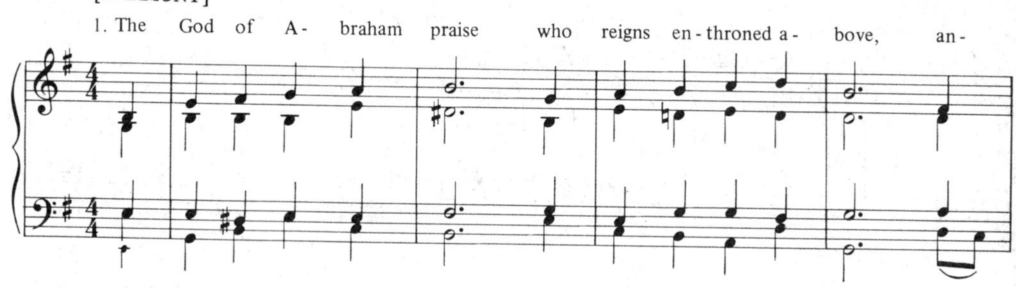

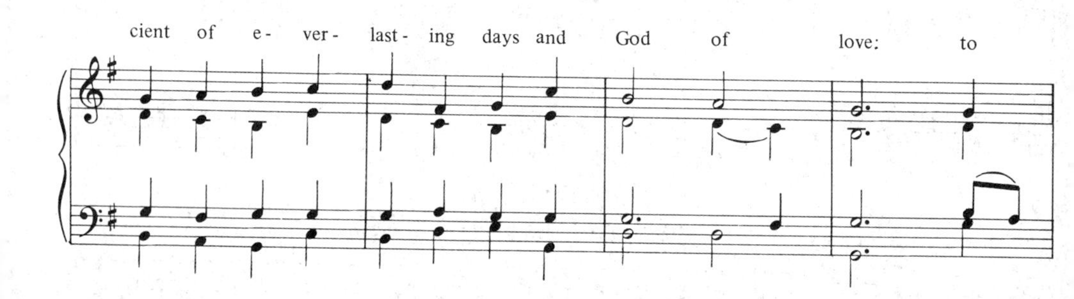

2. Though nature's strength decay,
and earth and hell withstand,
to Canaan's bounds we urge our way
at his command:
the watery deep we pass,
with Jesus in our view;
and through the howling wilderness
our way pursue.

3. The goodly land we see,
with peace and plenty blest:
a land of sacred liberty
and endless rest;
there milk and honey flow,
and oil and wine abound,
and trees of life for ever grow,
with mercy crowned.

4. There dwells the Lord our King,
the Lord our Righteousness,
triumphant o'er the world of sin,
the Prince of peace:
on Zion's sacred height
his kingdom he maintains,
and glorious with his saints in light
for ever reigns.

5. Before the great Three-One
they all exulting stand,
and tell the wonders he hath done
through all their land:
the listening spheres attend,
and swell the growing fame,
and sing in songs which never end
the wondrous name.

6. The God who reigns on high
the great archangels sing,
and 'Holy, Holy, Holy,' cry,
'almighty King!
who was, and is the same,
and evermore shall be:
eternal Father, great I AM,
we worship thee.'

7. Before the Saviour's face
the ransomed nations bow,
o'erwhelmed at his almighty grace
for ever new;
he shows his prints of love –
they kindle to a flame,
and sound through all the worlds above
the slaughtered Lamb.

8. The whole triumphant host
give thanks to God on high;
'hail, Father, Son, and Holy Ghost',
they ever cry.
Hail, Abraham's God, and mine,
(I join the heavenly lays)
all might and majesty are thine,
and endless praise.

Words: Thomas Olivers (1725-99)
Music: Traditional Hebrew melody

491

THE GOD OF LOVE MY SHEPHERD IS

('University' C.M.)

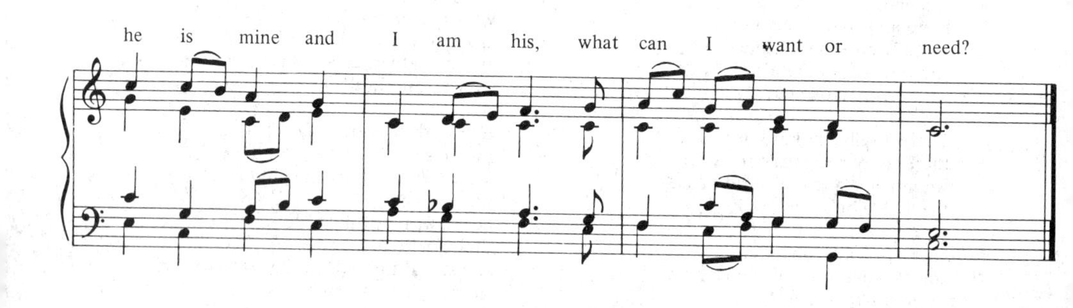

2. He leads me to the tender grass,
where I both feed and rest;
then to the streams that gently pass:
in both I have the best.

3. Or if I stray, he doth convert,
and bring my mind in frame,
and all this not for my desert,
but for his holy name.

4. Yea, in death's shady black abode
well may I walk, not fear;
for thou art with me, and thy rod
to guide, thy staff to bear.

5. Surely thy sweet and wondrous love
shall measure all my days;
and, as it never shall remove,
so neither shall my praise.

Words, based on Psalm 23: George Herbert (1593-1632)
Music: Charles Collignon (1725-85)

THE GOD WHOM EARTH AND SEA AND SKY

('Puer Nobis Nascitur' L.M.)

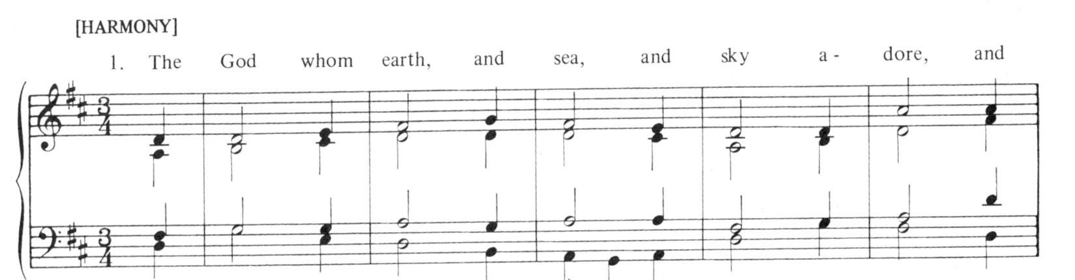

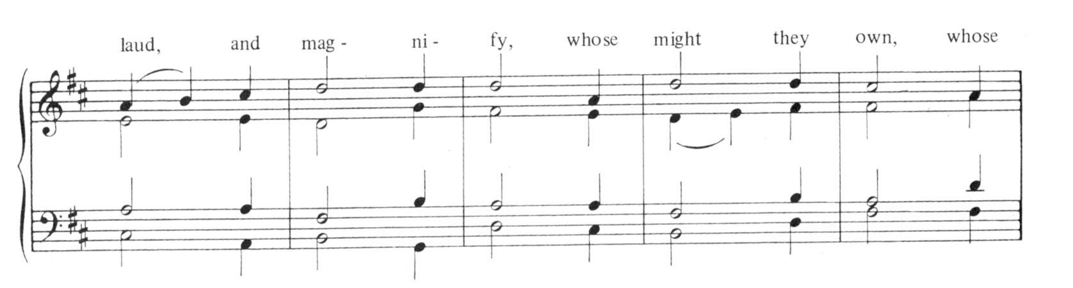

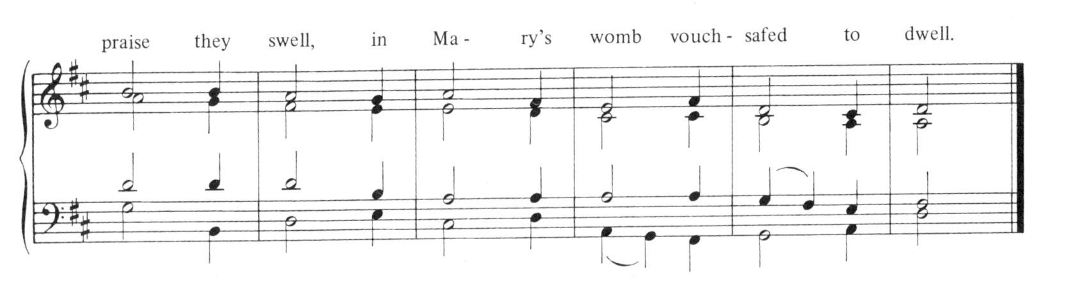

2. The Lord, whom sun and moon obey,
whom all things serve from day to day,
was by the Holy Ghost conceived
of her who through his grace believed.

3. How blest that Mother, in whose shrine
the world's Creator, Lord divine,
whose hand contains the earth and sky,
once deign'd, as in his ark, to lie;

4. Blest in the message Gabriel brought,
blest by the work the Spirit wrought;
from whom the great desire of earth
took human flesh and human birth.

5. O Lord, the Virgin-born, to thee
eternal praise and glory be,
whom with the Father we adore
and Holy Ghost for evermore.

Words: Venantius Fortunatus,(c. 535-609),
translated by J. M. Neale
Music: Melody by M. Praetorius (1571-1621)

493

THE HEAD THAT ONCE WAS CROWNED WITH THORNS
('St Magnus' C.M.)

[HARMONY]

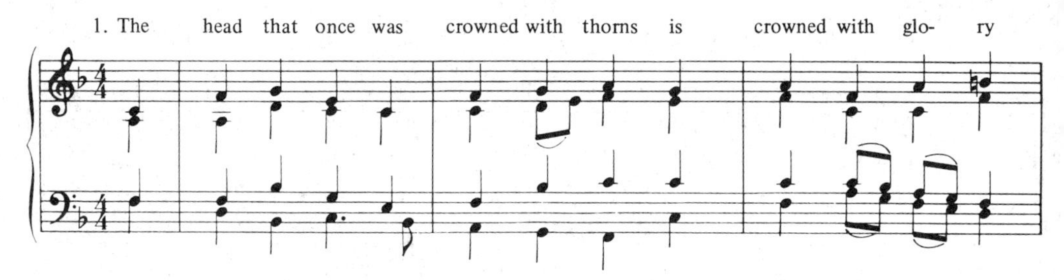

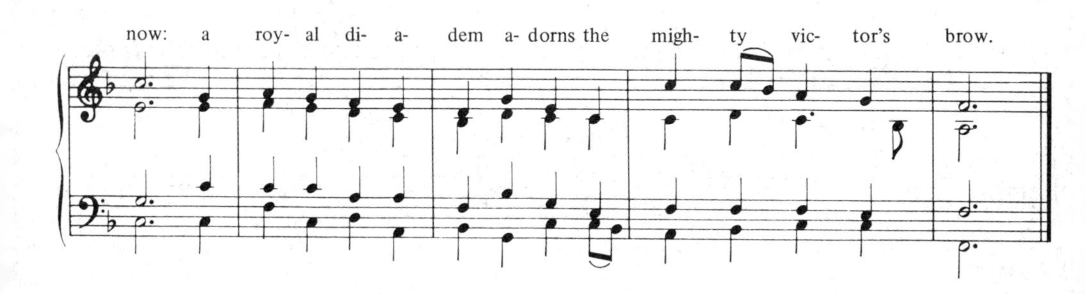

2. The highest place that heaven affords
is his, is his by right.
The King of kings and Lord of lords,
and heaven's eternal light;

3. The joy of all who dwell above,
the joy of all below,
to whom he manifests his love,
and grants his name to know.

4. To them the cross, with all its shame
with all its grace is given;
their name an everlasting name,
their joy the joy of heaven.

5. They suffer with their Lord below,
they reign with him above,
their profit and their joy to know
the mystery of his love.

6. The cross he bore is life and health,
though shame and death to him;
his people's hope, his people's wealth,
their everlasting theme.

Words: Thomas Kelly (1769-1854)
Music: Jeremiah Clark (1670-1707)

THE HEAVENLY CHILD IN STATURE GROWS

('Tallis' Ordinal' C.M.)

[HARMONY]

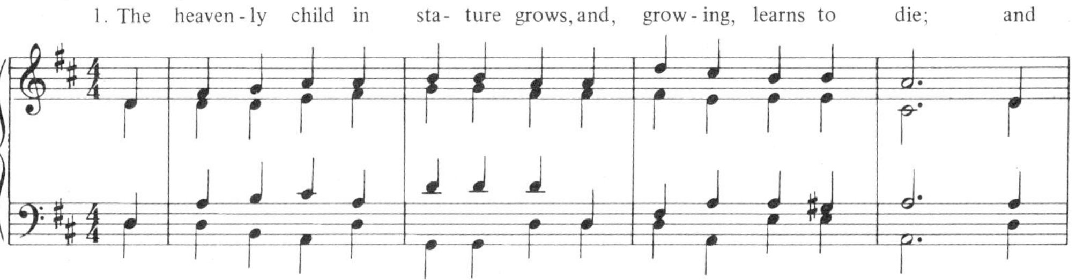

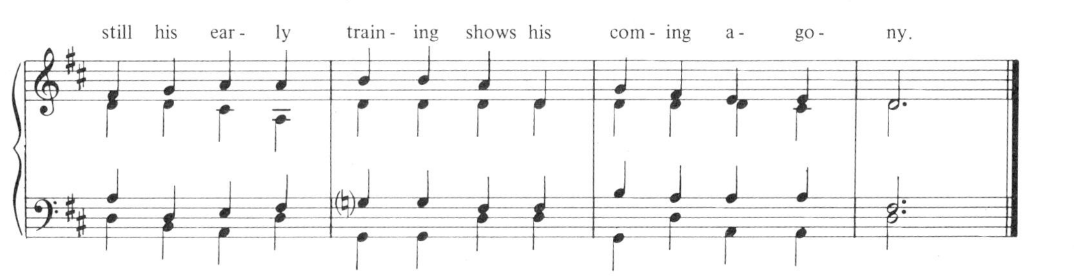

2. The Son of God his glory hides
to dwell with parents poor;
and he who made the heavens abides
in dwelling-place obscure.

3. Those mighty hands that rule the sky
no earthly toil refuse;
the maker of the stars on high
an humble trade pursues.

4. He whom the choirs of angels praise,
bearing each dread decree,
his earthly parents now obeys
in glad humility.

5. For this thy lowliness revealed,
Jesu, we thee adore,
and praise to God the Father yield
and Spirit evermore.

Words: J.B. de Santeuil (1630-97), tr. J. Chandler
Music: Thomas Tallis (1505-85)

495 THE HOLLY AND THE IVY

Verse

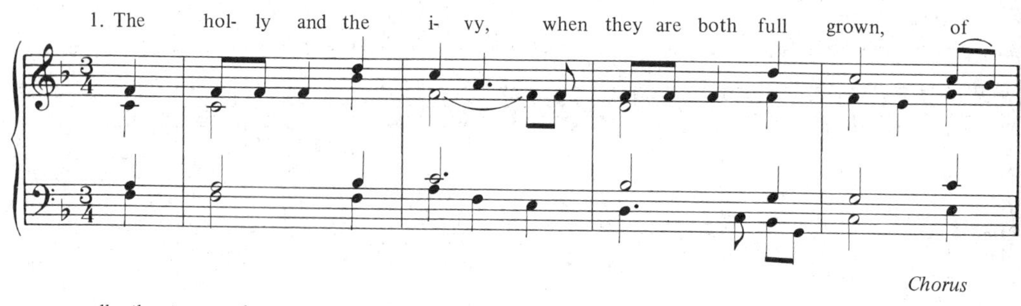

all the trees that are in the wood the hol- ly bears the crown.

Chorus

The

2. The holly bears a blossom,
white as the lily flow'r,
and Mary bore sweet Jesus Christ
to be our sweet Saviour.

3. The holly bears a berry,
as red as any blood,
and Mary bore sweet Jesus Christ
to do poor sinners good.

4. The holly bears a prickle,
as sharp as any thorn,
and Mary bore sweet Jesus Christ
on Christmas day in the morn.

5. The holly bears a bark,
as bitter as any gall,
and Mary bore sweet Jesus Christ
for to redeem us all.

6. The holly and the ivy,
when they are both full grown,
of all the trees that are in the wood
the holly bears the crown.

Words and Music: Traditional English folk carol, arranged by Rachel Hall

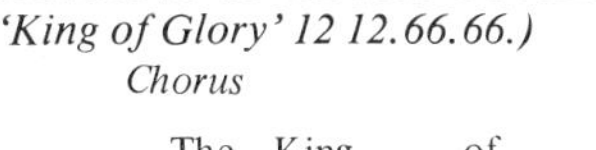

THE KING OF GLORY COMES

('King of Glory' 12 12.66.66.)

496

2. In all of Galilee,
   in city and village,
   he goes among his people,
   curing their illness.

3. Sing then of David's Son,
   our Saviour and brother;
   in all of Galilee
   was never another.

4. He gave his life for us,
   the pledge of salvation.
   He took upon himself
   the sins of the nation.

5. He conquered sin and death;
   he truly has risen.
   And he will share with us
   his heavenly vision.

Words: Willard F. Jabusch
Music: Israeli Folk Song, arranged by John Rombaut

THE KING OF LOVE MY SHEPHERD IS

497

('Dominus regit me' 87.87.) [HARMONY]

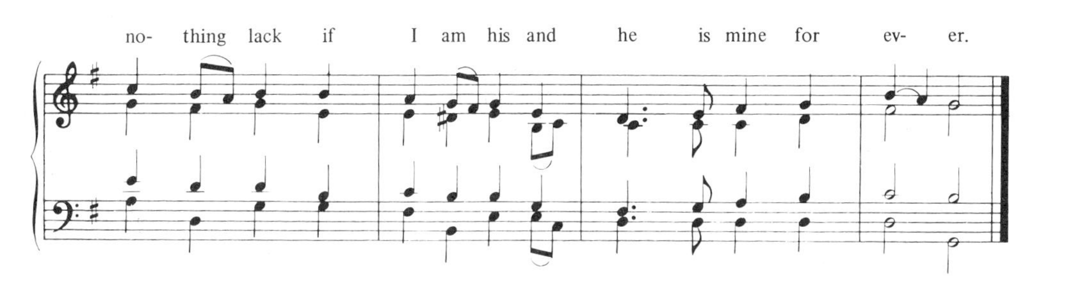

2. Where streams of living water flow
my ransomed soul he leadeth,
and where the verdant pastures grow
with food celestial feedeth.

3. Perverse and foolish oft I strayed,
but yet in love he sought me,
and on his shoulder gently laid,
and home, rejoicing, brought me.

4. In death's dark vale I fear no ill
with thee, dear Lord, beside me;
thy rod and staff my comfort still,
thy cross before to guide me.

5. Thou spread'st a table in my sight,
thy unction grace bestoweth:
and O what transport of delight
from thy pure chalice floweth!

6. And so through all the length of days
thy goodness faileth never;
good Shepherd, may I sing thy praise
within thy house for ever.

Words: Henry Williams Baker (1821-77), based on Psalm 23
Music: John Bacchus Dykes (1823-76)

Chorus
The light of Christ has come in- to the
The light of Christ has come in-
C F Dm

world. The light of Christ has
to the world. The light of Christ
G C

2. God gave up his only Son
   out of love for the world,
   so that all men who believe in him
   will live for ever.

3. The light of God has come to us
   so that we might have salvation;
   from the darkness of our sins we walk
   into glory with Christ Jesus.

Words and Music: Donald Fishel

THE LORD IS KING!
('Niagara' L.M.)

[HARMONY]

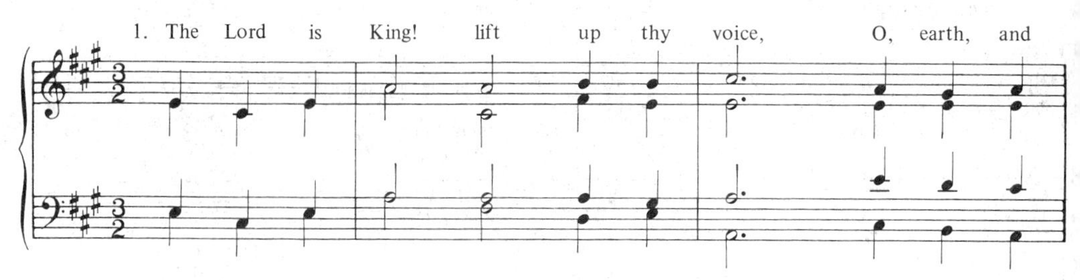

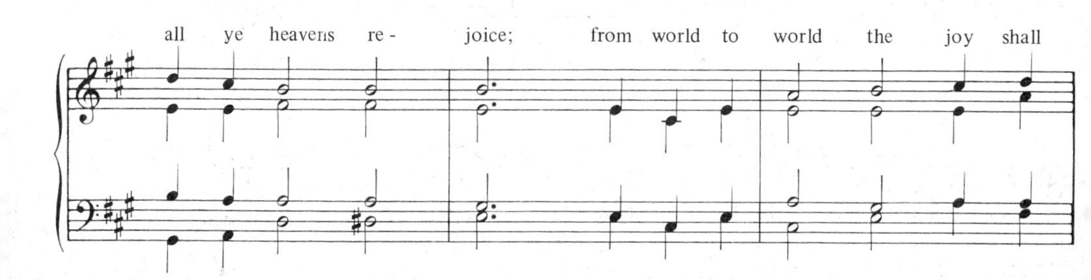

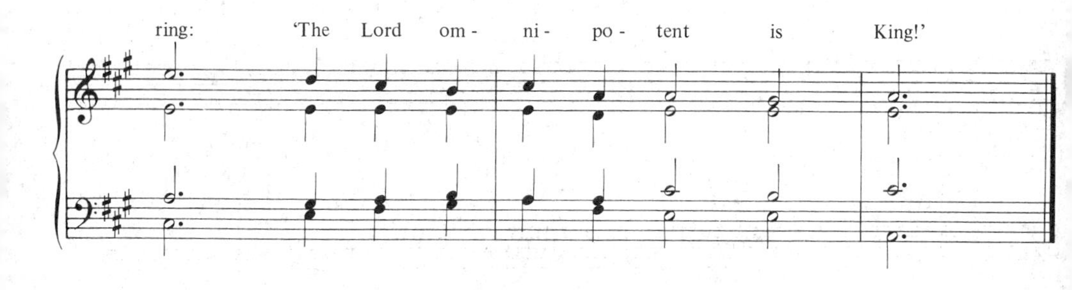

2. The Lord is King! who then shall dare
resist his will, distrust his care,
or murmur at his wise decrees,
or doubt his royal promises?

3. The Lord is King! child of the dust,
the judge of all the earth is just;
holy and true are all his ways:
let every creature speak his praise.

4. He reigns! ye saints, exalt your strains;
your God is King, your Father reigns;
and he is at the Father's side,
the man of love, the crucified.

5. One Lord, one empire, all secures;
he reigns, – and life and death are yours,
through earth and heaven one song shall ring,
'The Lord omnipotent is King!'

Words: Josiah Conder (1789-1855)
Music: R. Jackson (1840-1914)

THE LORD IS MY SHEPHERD

500

The verse (1) may be sung against the Chorus (2) as a round.

2. The Lord guides my footsteps,
   I'll follow him alway;
   the Lord is ever faithful,
   I'll follow him alway.

3. And even in darkness,
   I'll follow him alway;
   no fear of any evil,
   I'll follow him alway.

4. The Lord is my comfort,
   I'll follow him alway;
   he feeds me at his banquet,
   I'll follow him alway.

5. He's kindness and mercy,
   I'll follow him alway;
   with him I'll dwell for ever,
   I'll follow him alway.

Words, based on Psalm 22/23: Verse 1, unknown
Verses 2-5, Robert B. Kelly
Music: Anonymous, arranged by Frances M. Kelly

THE LORD IS RISEN INDEED
('Narenza' S.M.)

[HARMONY]

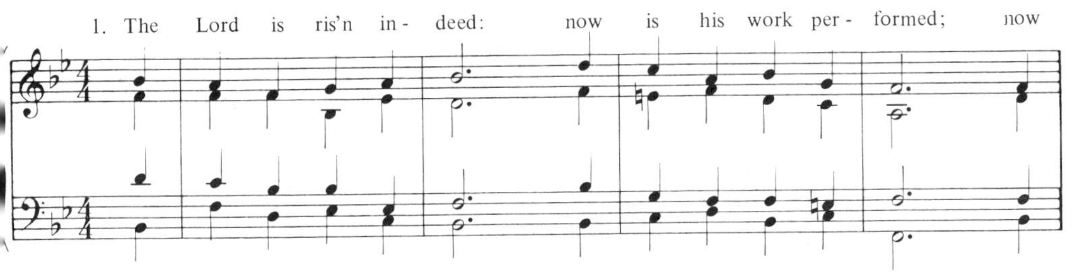

2. The Lord is risen indeed:
then hell has lost his prey;
with him is risen the ransomed seed
to reign in endless day.

3. The Lord is risen indeed:
he lives, to die no more;
he lives, the sinner's cause to plead,
whose curse and shame he bore.

4. The Lord is risen indeed:
attending angels, hear!
up to the courts of heaven with speed
the joyful tidings bear.

5. Then take your golden lyres
and strike each cheerful chord;
join, all ye bright celestial choirs,
to sing our risen Lord.

Words: Thomas Kelly (1769-1855)
Music: adapted from J. Leisentritt's 'Catholicum Hymnologium' (1584)

[HARMONY]

1. The Lord's my shep- herd, I'll not want. He makes me down to
Capo 1:
Em
B7

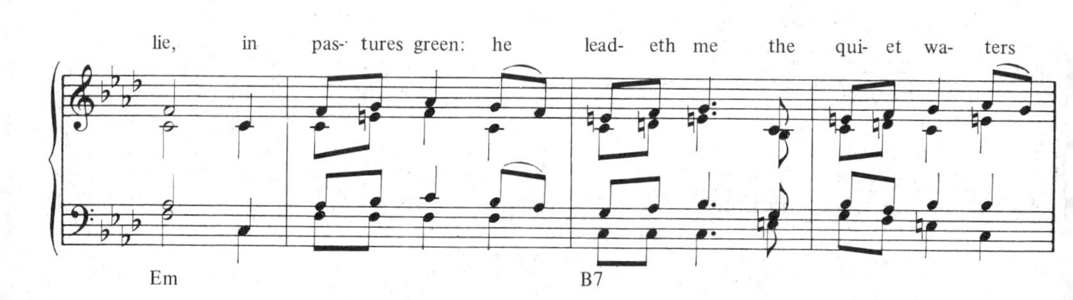
lie, in pas- tures green: he lead- eth me the qui- et wa- ters
Em
B7

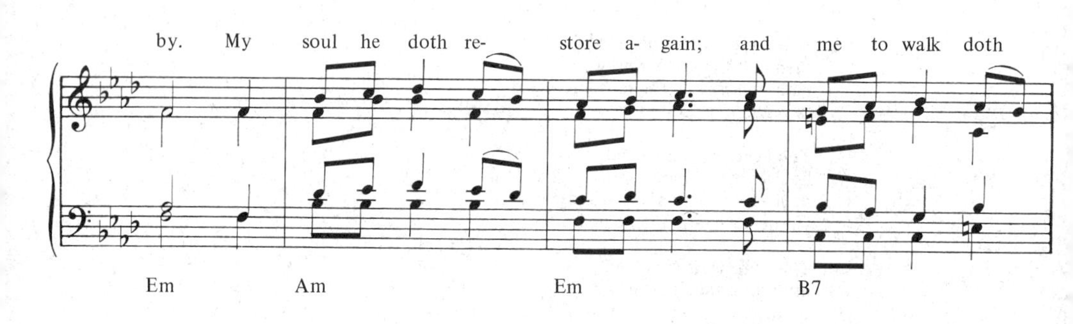
by. My soul he doth re- store a- gain; and me to walk doth
Em
Am
Em
B7

make with- in the paths of right- eous- ness, e'en for his own name's sake.
Em
Am
Em
B7
Em

2. Yea, though I walk in death's dark vale,
yet will I fear none ill:
for thou art with me, and thy rod
and staff me comfort still.
My table thou hast furnishèd
in presence of my foes;
my head thou dost with oil anoint,
and my cup overflows.

3. Goodness and mercy all my life
shall surely follow me;
and in God's house for evermore
my dwelling place shall be.
* Hallelujah, hallelujah,
hallelujah, hallelujah!
Hallelujah, hallelujah,
hallelujah, amen!

* *The 'Hallelujah' refrain may be repeated several times, with acceleration of tempo.*

Words, Psalm 23: The 'Scottish Psalter' (1650)
Music: Merla Watson

503 THE LORD'S MY SHEPHERD

(First tune: 'Crimond' C.M.)

[HARMONY]

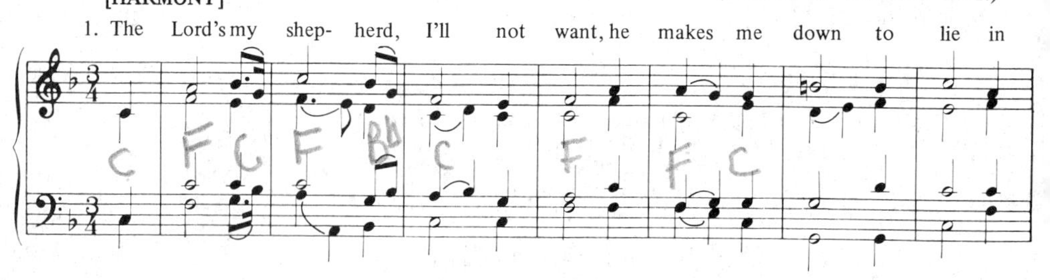

2. My soul he doth restore again,
   and me to walk doth make
   within the paths of righteousness,
   e'en for his own name's sake.

3. Yea, though I walk in death's dark vale,
   yet will I fear none ill.
   For thou art with me, and thy rod
   and staff me comfort still.

4. My table thou hast furnishèd
   in presence of my foes,
   my head thou dost with oil anoint,
   and my cup overflows.

5. Goodness and mercy all my life
   shall surely follow me.
   And in God's house for evermore
   my dwelling-place shall be.

Words: Psalm 23: The 'Scottish Psalter' (1650)
Music: First tune - Jessie Seymour Irvine (1836-87), harmony by T. C. L. Pritchard

THE LORD'S MY SHEPHERD
(Second tune: 'Brother James' Air' C.M.)

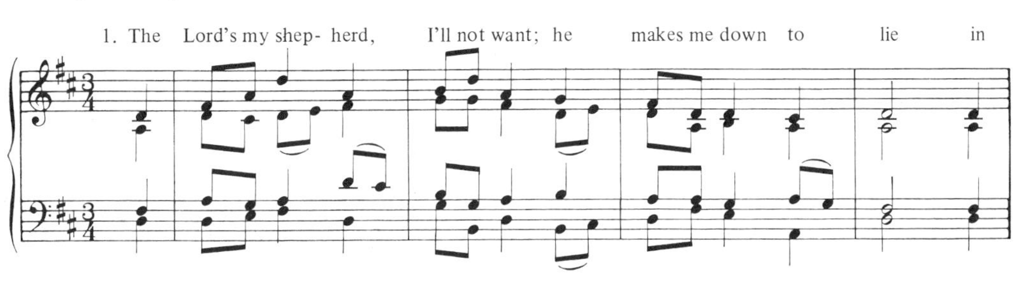

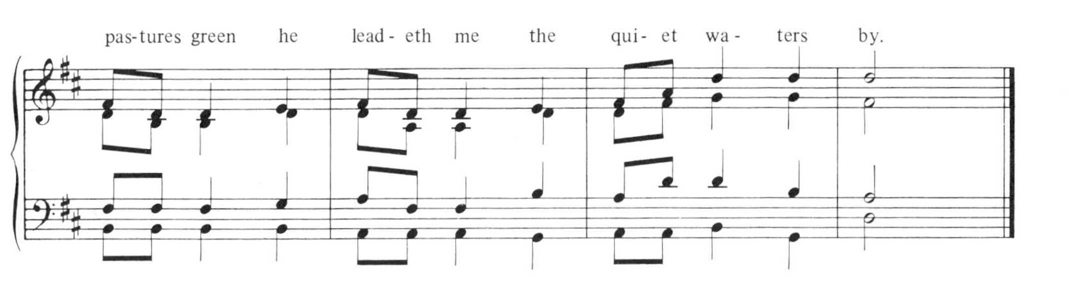

2. My soul he doth restore again;
and me to walk doth make
within the paths of righteousness,
e'en for his own name's sake.

3. Yea, though I walk in death's dark vale,
yet will I fear none ill:
for thou art with me, and thy rod
and staff me comfort still.

4. My table thou hast furnishèd
in presence of my foes;
my head thou dost with oil anoint,
and my cup overflows.

5. Goodness and mercy all my life
shall surely follow me:
and in God's house for evermore
my dwelling-place shall be.

Words: Psalm 23: The 'Scottish Psalter' (1650)
Music: Second tune - J. L. MacBeth Bain, arranged by John Barnard

THE LORD WILL COME AND NOT BE SLOW

('St Stephen' C.M.)

[HARMONY]

2. Truth from the earth, like to a flower
shall bud and blossom then;
and justice, from her heavenly bower
look down on mortal men.

3. Rise, God, judge thou the earth in might,
this wicked earth redress;
for thou art he who shall by right
the nations all possess.

4. The nations all whom thou hast made
shall come, and all shall frame
to bow them low before thee, Lord,
and glorify thy name.

5. For great thou art, and wonders great
by thy strong hand are done:
thou in thy everlasting seat
remainest God alone.

Words, based on Psalms 72, 85-6: John Milton (1608-74)
Music: W. Jones (1726-1800)

THE RACE THAT LONG IN DARKNESS PINED
('Dundee' C.M.)

[HARMONY]

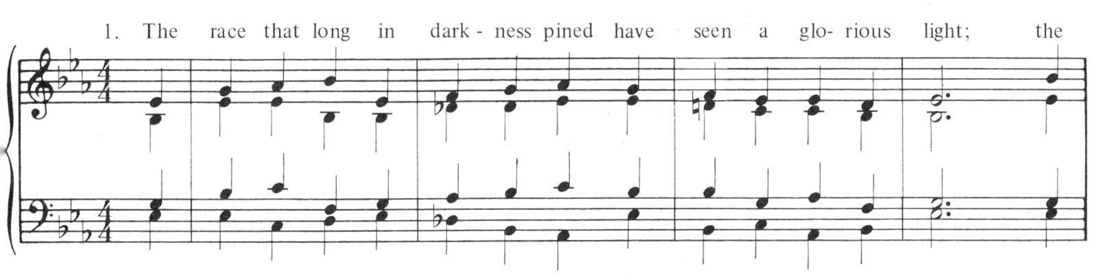

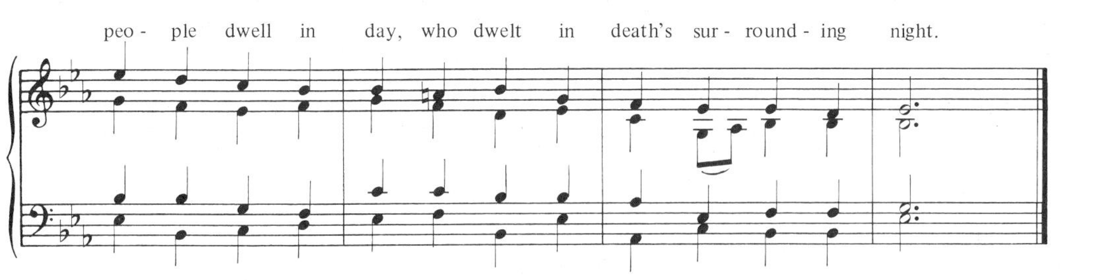

2. To hail thy rise, thou better Sun
the gathering nations come,
joyous as when the reapers bear
the harvest treasures home.

3. To us a child of hope is born:
to us a Son is given;
him shall the tribes of earth obey,
him all the hosts of heaven.

4. His name shall be the Prince of Peace,
for evermore adored,
the Wonderful, the Counsellor,
the great and mighty Lord.

5. His power increasing still shall spread,
his reign no end shall know;
justice shall guard his throne above,
and peace abound below.

Words, paraphrased from Isaiah 9:2-7: John Morrison (1750-98)
Music: Melody from Psalms (Edinburgh, 1615)

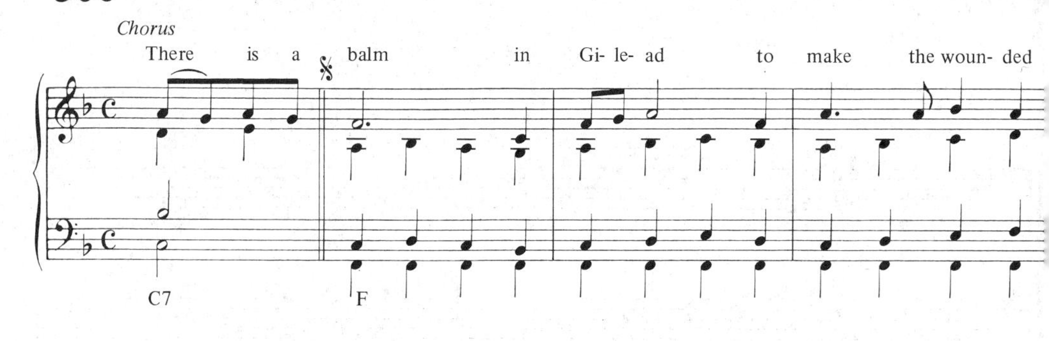

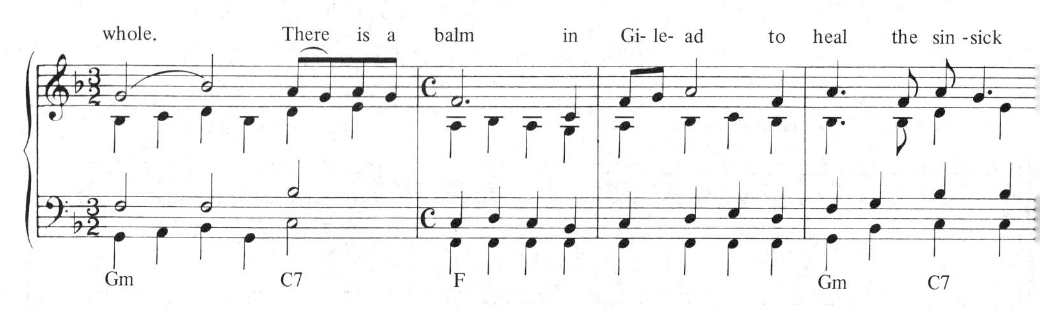

2. If you cannot sing like angels,
if you cannot preach like Paul,
you can tell the love of Jesus
and say he died for all.

Words & Music: North American Spiritual,
arranged by John Rombaut

THERE IS A GREEN HILL FAR AWAY
('Horsley' C.M.)

[HARMONY]

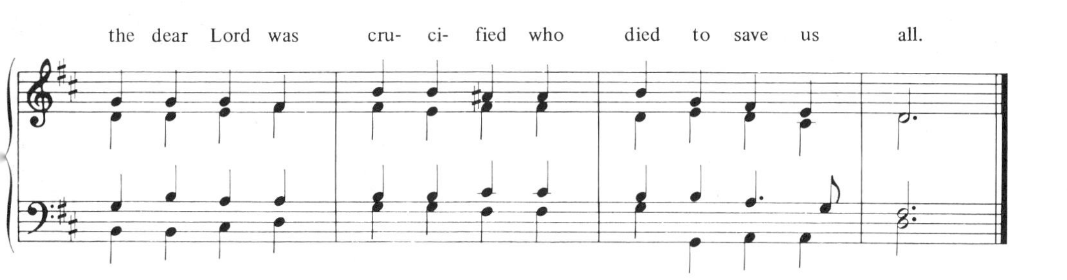

2. We may not know, we cannot tell,
   what pains he had to bear,
   but we believe it was for us
   he hung and suffered there.

3. He died that we might be forgiven,
   he died to make us good;
   that we might go at last to heaven,
   saved by his precious blood.

4. There was no other good enough
   to pay the price of sin;
   he only could unlock the gate
   of heaven, and let us in.

5. O, dearly, dearly has he loved,
   and we must love him too,
   and trust in his redeeming blood,
   and try his works to do.

Words: Cecil Frances Alexander (1818-95)
Music: William Horsley (1774-1858)

508

[HARMONY]

THERE IS A LAND OF PURE DELIGHT
('Mendip' C.M.)

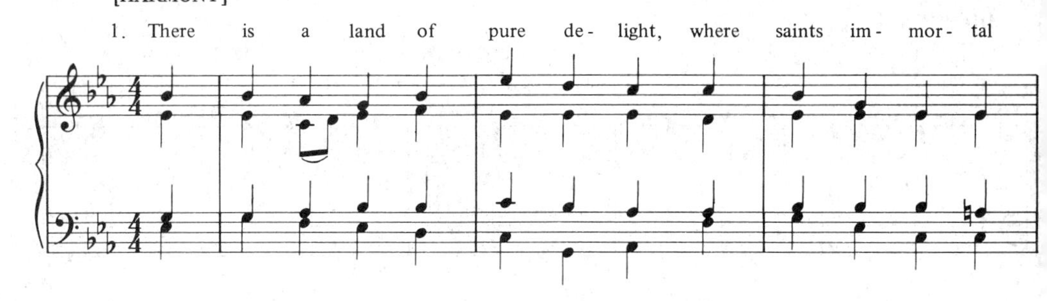

reign; in- fin- ite day ex- cludes the night, and pleas-ures ban- ish pain.

2. There everlasting spring abides,
   and never-withering flowers:
   death, like a narrow sea, divides
   this heavenly land from ours.

3. Sweet fields beyond the swelling flood
   stand dressed in living green;
   so to the Jews old Canaan stood,
   while Jordan rolled between.

4. But timorous mortals start and shrink
   to cross this narrow sea,
   and linger, shivering on the brink,
   and fear to launch away.

5. O could we make our doubts remove –
   those gloomy doubts that rise –
   and see the Canaan that we love,
   with unbeclouded eyes;

6. Could we but climb where Moses stood,
   and view the landscape o'er,
   not Jordan's stream, nor death's cold flood,
   should fright us from the shore.

Words: Isaac Watts (1674-1748)
Music: English traditional melody,
collected and adapted by Cecil J. Sharp (1859-1924)

2. And we know when we're together,
sharing love and understanding,
that our brothers and our sisters
feel the oneness that he brings.
Thank you, thank you, thank you, Jesus,
for the way you love and feed us,
for the many ways you lead us,
thank you, thank you, Lord.

Words and Music: Tedd Smith

THERE'S A WIDENESS IN GOD'S MERCY
('Daily, daily' 87.87.D.)

[HARMONY]

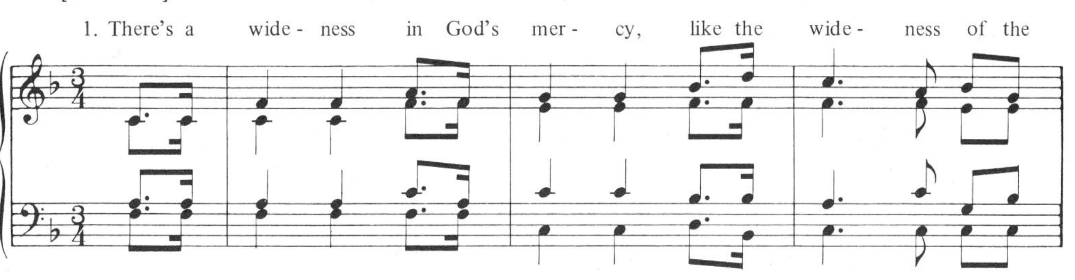

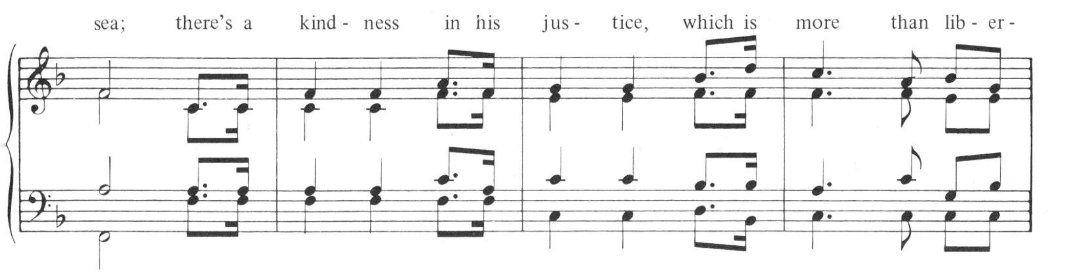

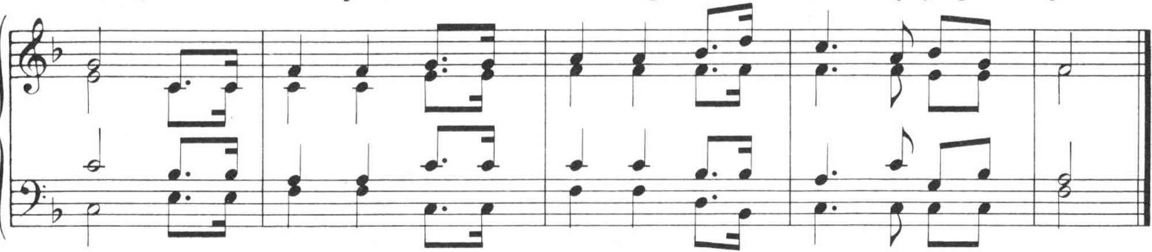

2. There is grace enough for thousands
of new world's as great as this;
there is room for fresh creations
in that upper home of bliss.
For the love of God is broader
than the measures of man's mind,
and the heart of the Eternal
is most wonderfully kind.

3. But we make his love too narrow
by false limits of our own;
and we magnify his strictness
with a zeal he will not own.
There is plentiful redemption
in the blood that has been shed,
there is joy for all the members
in the sorrows of the Head.

4. 'Tis not all we owe to Jesus;
it is something more than all;
greater good because of evil,.
larger mercy through the fall.
If our love were but more simple,
we should take him at his word;
and our lives would be all sunshine
in the sweetness of our Lord.

Words: Frederick William Faber (1814-63)
Music: from the 'Paderborn Gesangbuch' (1765)

511

THERE'S NO GREATER NAME THAN JESUS

('No greater name' 88.85.)

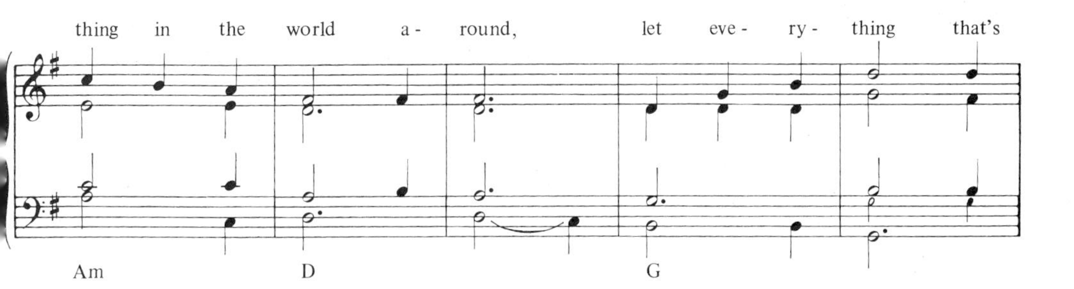

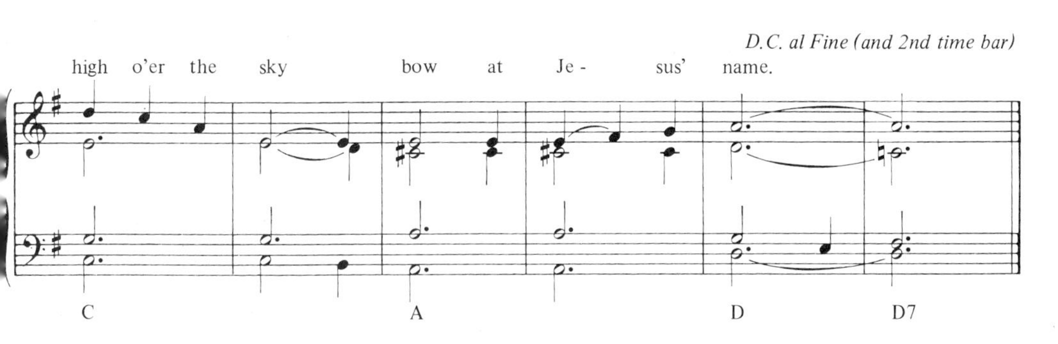

Words and Music: Michael A. Baughen

THE ROYAL BANNERS FORWARD GO
(First tune: 'Vexilla Regis Proper Sarum Melody' L.M.)

2. There whilst he hung, his sacred side
by soldier's spear was opened wide,
to cleanse us in the precious flood
of water mingled with his blood.

3. Fulfilled is now what David told
in true prophetic song of old,
how God the heathen's king should be;
for God is reigning from the tree.

4. O tree of glory, tree most fair,
ordained those holy limbs to bear;
how bright in purple robe it stood,
the purple of a Saviour's blood!

5. Upon its arms, like balance true,
he weighed the price for sinners due,
the price which none but he could pay:
and spoiled the spoiler of his prey.

6. To thee, eternal Three in One,
let homage meet by all be done,
as by the cross thou dost restore,
so rule and guide us evermore. Amen.

Words: Venantius Fortunatus (c. 535-609),
tr. John M. Neale and others
Music: First tune - Mode I, Proper Sarum Melody

THE ROYAL BANNERS FORWARD GO
(Second tune: 'Eisenach' L.M.)

A different harmonisation of this tune may be found at Hymn 371

2. There whilst he hung, his sacred side
by soldier's spear was opened wide,
to cleanse us in the precious flood
of water mingled with his blood.

3. Fulfilled is now what David told
in true prophetic song of old,
how God the heathen's king should be;
for God is reigning from the tree.

4. O tree of glory, tree most fair,
ordained those holy limbs to bear;
how bright in purple robe it stood,
the purple of a Saviour's blood!

5. Upon its arms, like balance true,
he weighed the price for sinners due,
the price which none but he could pay:
and spoiled the spoiler of his prey.

6. To thee, eternal Three in One,
let homage meet by all be done,
as by the cross thou dost restore,
so rule and guide us evermore.

Words: Venantius Fortunatus (c.535-609), tr. John M. Neale and others
Music: Second tune - Johann H. Schein (1586-1630)

THE SON OF GOD PROCLAIM

513

('Mount Ephraim' S.M.)

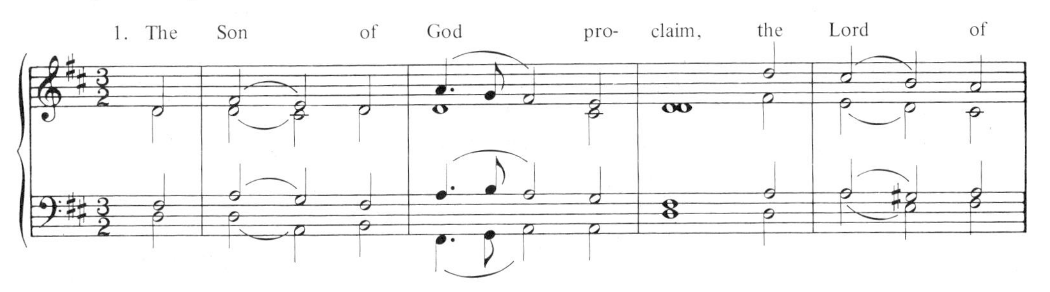

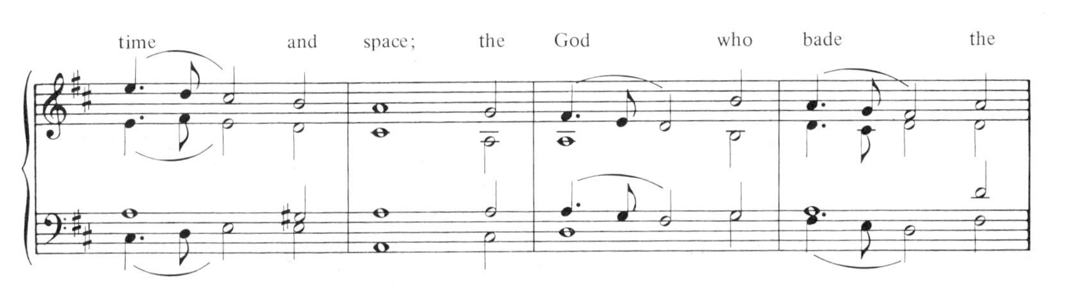

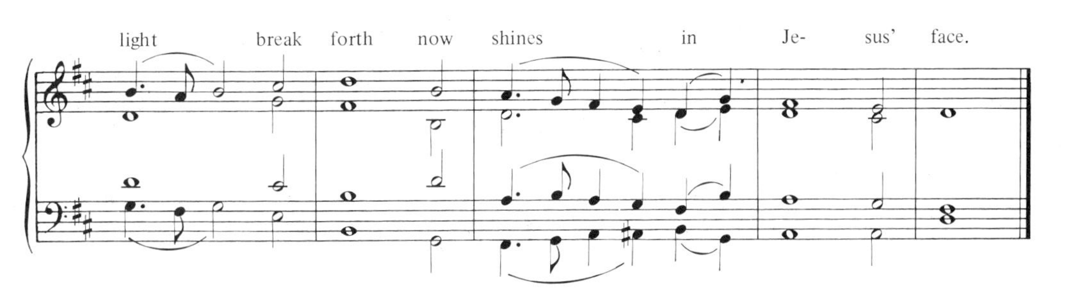

2. He, God's creative Word,
the Church's Lord and Head,
here bids us gather as his friends
and share his wine and bread.

3. The Lord of life and death
with wond'ring praise we sing;
we break the bread at his command
and name him God and King.

4. We take this cup in hope;
for he, who gladly bore
the shameful cross, is risen again
and reigns for evermore.

Words: Basil E. Bridge (b. 1927)
Music: Benjamin Milgrove (1731-1810), harmonised by S. S. Wesley (1810-76)

514

THE SPACIOUS FIRMAMENT ON HIGH

('London (or Addison's)' D.L.M.)

[HARMONY]

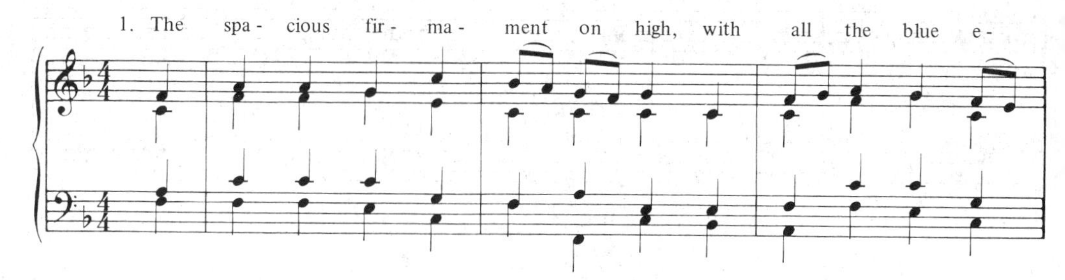

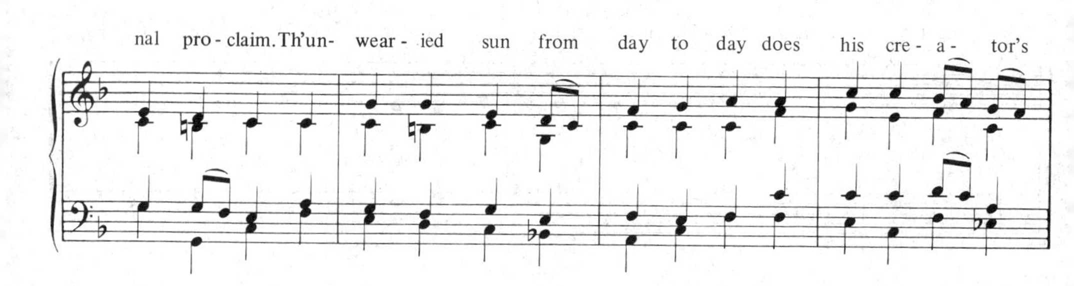

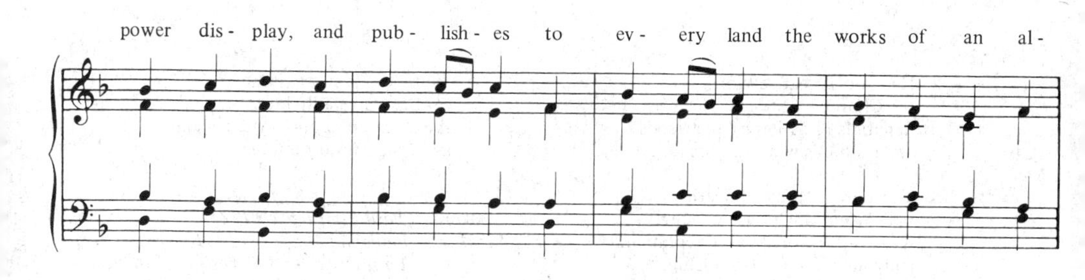

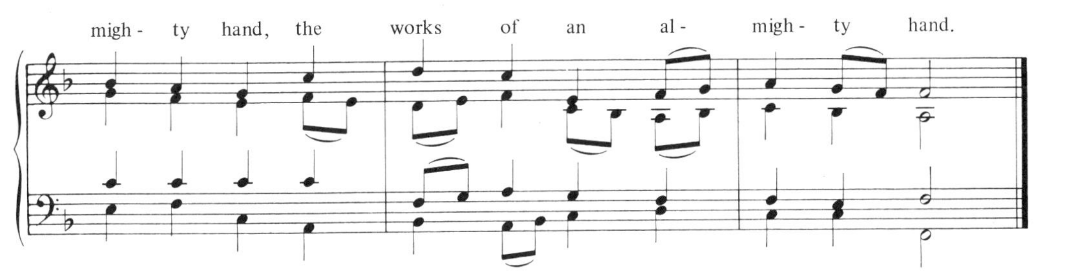

2. Soon as the evening shades prevail
   the moon takes up the wondrous tale,
   and nightly to the listening earth
   repeats the story of her birth;
   whilst all the stars that round her burn
   and all the planets in their turn,
   confirm the tidings as they roll,
   and spread the truth from pole to pole.

3. What though in solemn silence all
   move around the dark terrestrial ball;
   what though nor real voice nor sound
   amid their radiant orbs be found;
   in reason's ear they all rejoice,
   and utter forth a glorious voice;
   for ever singing as they shine,
   'The hand that made us is divine.'

Words: Joseph Addison (1672-1719)
Music: J. Sheeles (1688-1761)

2. Jesus promised life to all,
walk, walk, in the light.
The dead were wakened by his call,
walk, walk in the light.

3. He died in pain on Calvary,
walk, walk in the light,
to save the lost like you and me,
walk, walk in the light.

4. We know his death was not the end,
walk, walk in the light.
He gave his Spirit to be our friend,
walk, walk in the light.

5. By Jesus' love our wounds are healed,
walk, walk in the light.
The Father's kindness is revealed,
walk, walk in the light.

6. The Spirit lives in you and me,
walk, walk in the light.
His light will shine for all to see,
walk, walk in the light.

Words: Damian Lundy
Music: Unknown, arranged by Michael Irwin

THE SPIRIT OF THE LORD IS WITH US
('Chosen')

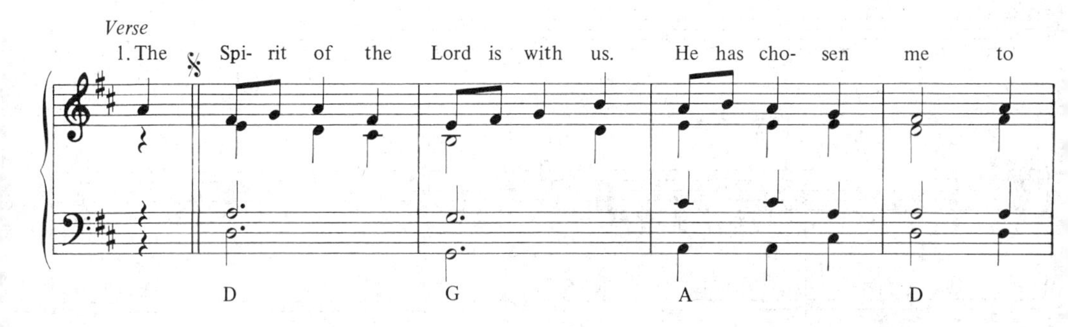

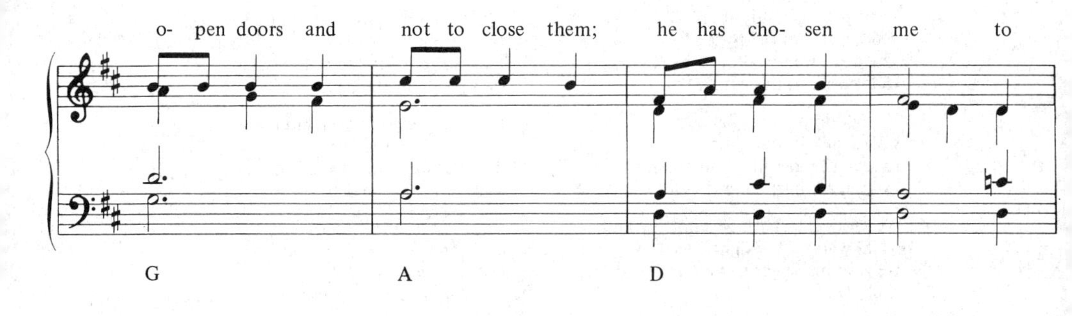

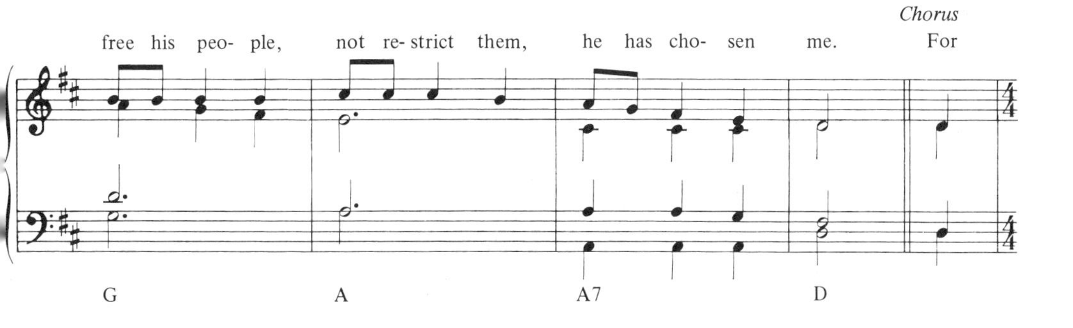

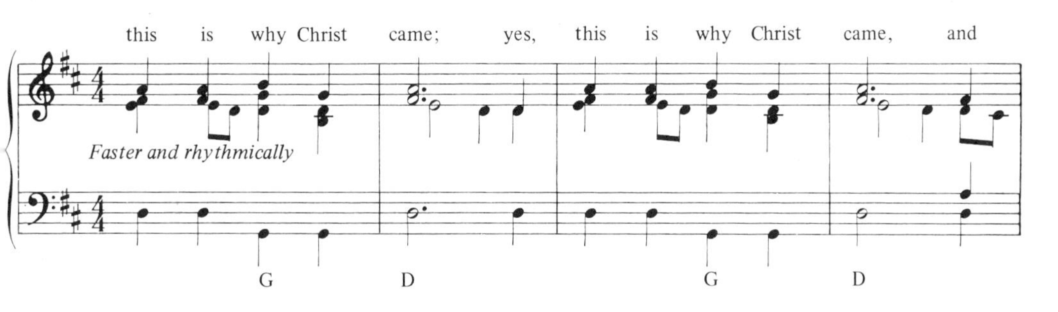

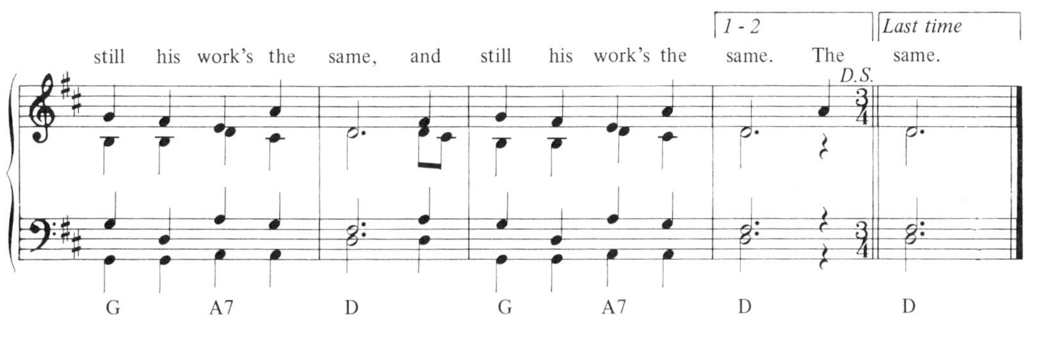

2. The Spirit of the Lord is with us.
He has chosen me
to build up those whose lives have fallen;
he has chosen me
to bring his love to all his children;
he has chosen me
to dry the tears of those in sorrow,
he has chosen me.

3. The Spirit of the Lord is with us.
He has chosen me;
a year of grace his Spirit gives me;
he has chosen me
to bless and comfort all his children;
he has chosen me
to lift and tend the broken-hearted,
he has chosen me.

Words, based on Isaiah 61: 1-2 and Luke 4: 18-19: Graham Jeffery
Music: Kevin Mayhew

THE STEADFAST LOVE OF THE LORD

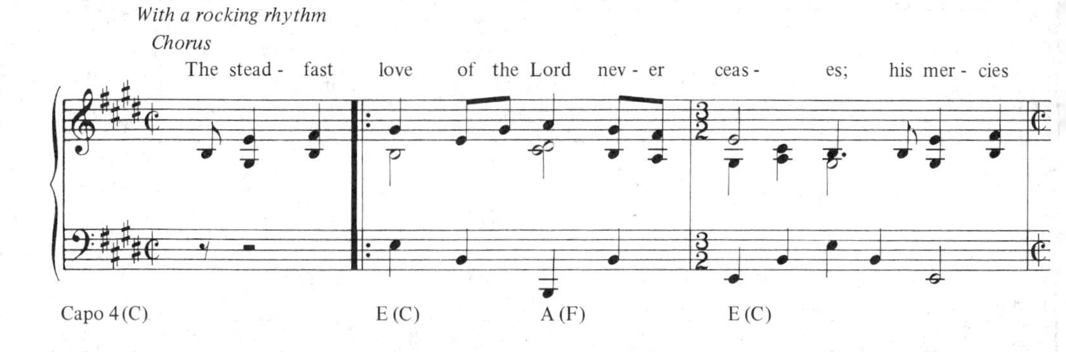

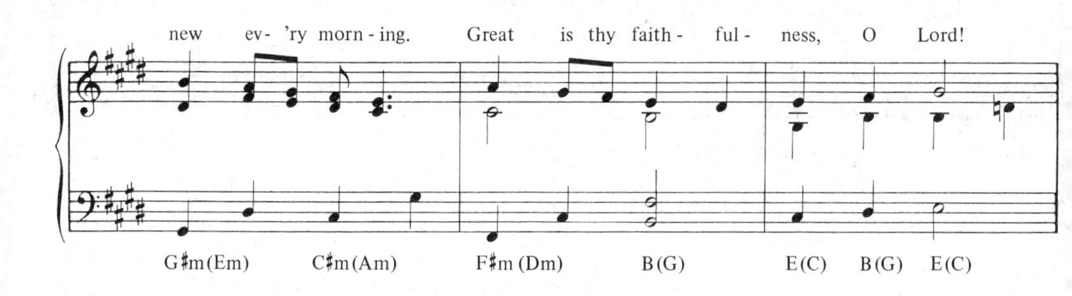

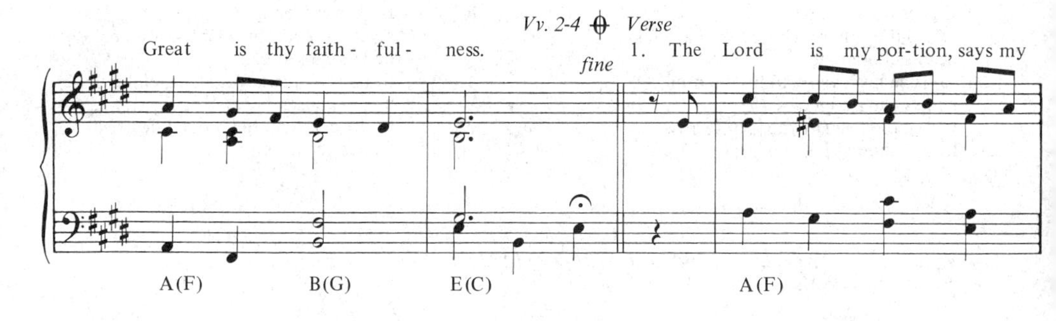

** Guitar chords and piano arrangement not designed to be used together.*

Words and Music: Edith McNeill

THE STRIFE IS O'ER THE BATTLE DONE

518

('Victory' 888 & Alleluias)

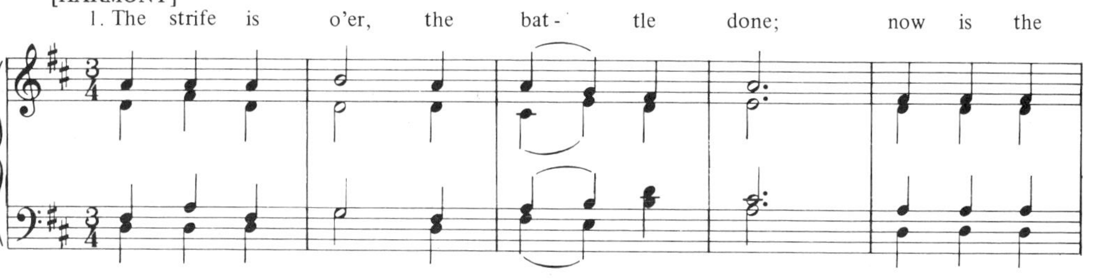

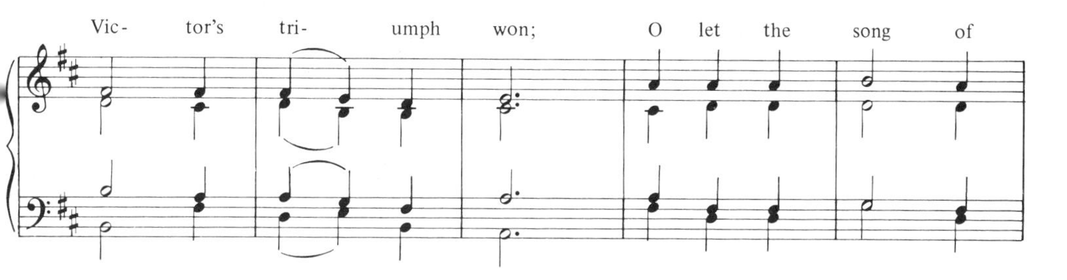

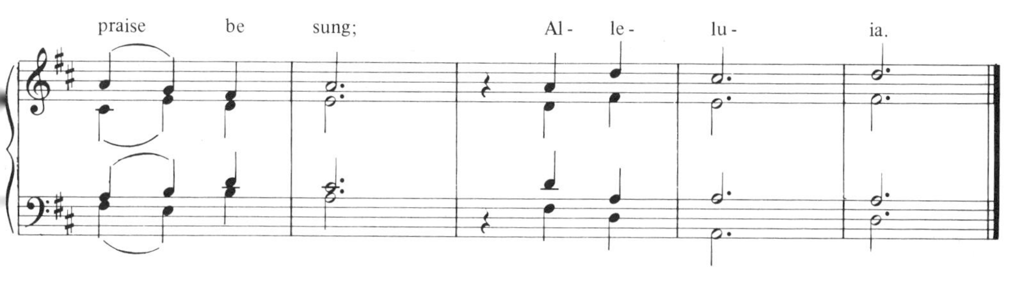

2. Death's mightiest powers have done their worst,
and Jesus hath his foes dispersed;
let shouts of praise and joy outburst:
Alleluia.

3. On the third morn he rose again
glorious in majesty to reign;
O let us swell the joyful strain:
Alleluia.

4. He broke the age-bound chains of hell;
the bars from heaven's high portals fell;
let hymns of praise his triumph tell:
Alleluia.

5. Lord, by the stripes which wounded thee
from death's dread sting thy servants free,
that we may live, and sing to thee
Alleluia.

Words: Latin Hymn (17th/18th century), tr. F. Pott
Music: Giovanni Pierluigi da Palestrina (1525-1594), adapted.

THE VIRGIN MARY HAD A BABY BOY

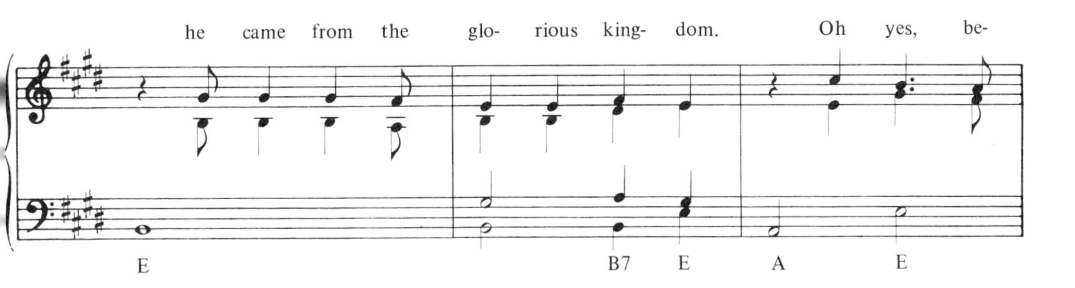

2. The angels sang when the baby was born, *(3)*
   and proclaimed him the Saviour, Jesus.

3. The wise men saw where the baby was born, *(3)*
   and they saw that his name was Jesus.

Words and Music: Traditional West Indian,
arranged by John Rombaut

THE WISE MAY BRING THEIR LEARNING
('Tyrolese Carol' 76.76.D.)

520

[HARMONY]

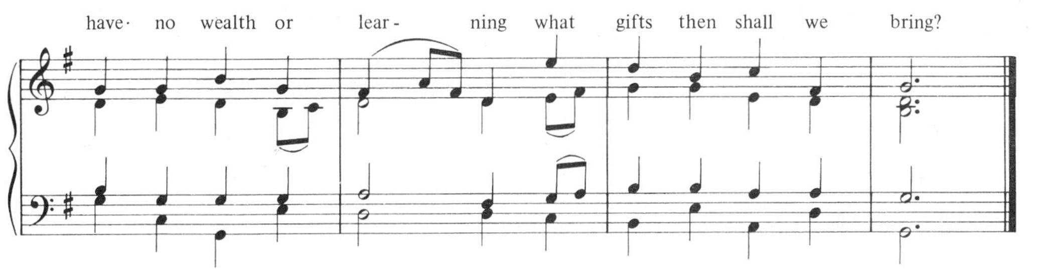

2. We'll bring the many duties
we have to do each day;
we'll try our best to please him,
at home, at school, at play:
and better are these treasures
to offer to the King;
than richest gifts without them;
yet these we all may bring.

3. We'll bring him hearts that love him,
we'll bring him thankful praise,
and lives for ever striving
to follow in his ways:
and these shall be the treasures
we offer to the King,
and these are gifts that ever
our grateful hearts may bring.

Words: from 'Book of Praise for Children' (1881),
adapted for the 'BBC Hymnbook'
Music: Tyrolese Carol,
arranged for the 'BBC Hymnbook'

THEY SHALL HAMMER THEIR SWORDS (**Swords into ploughshares**)

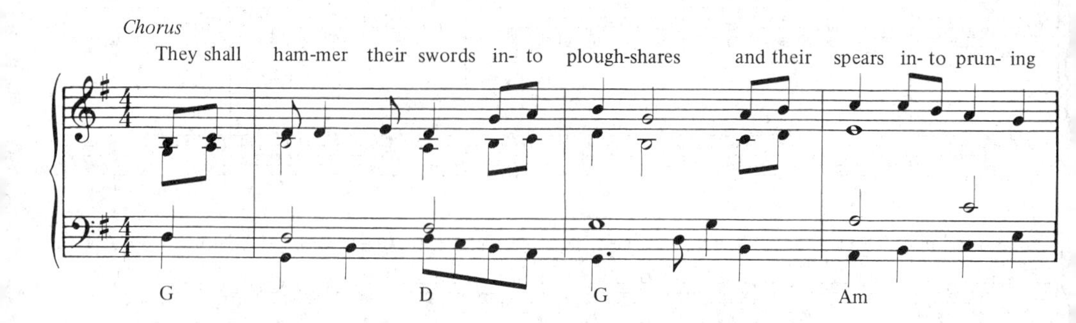

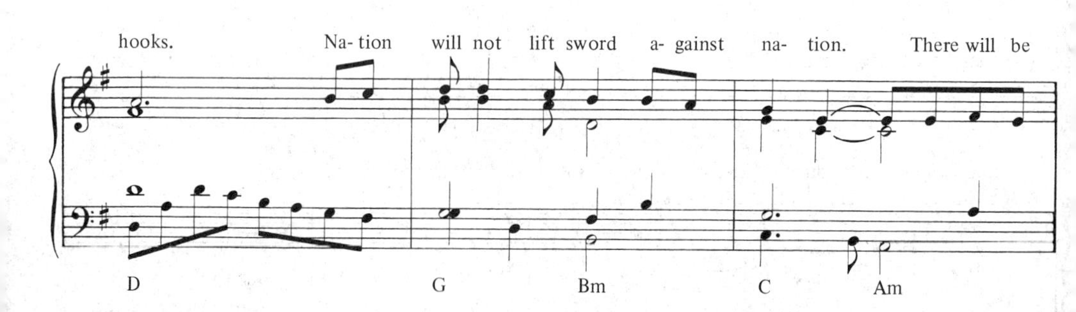

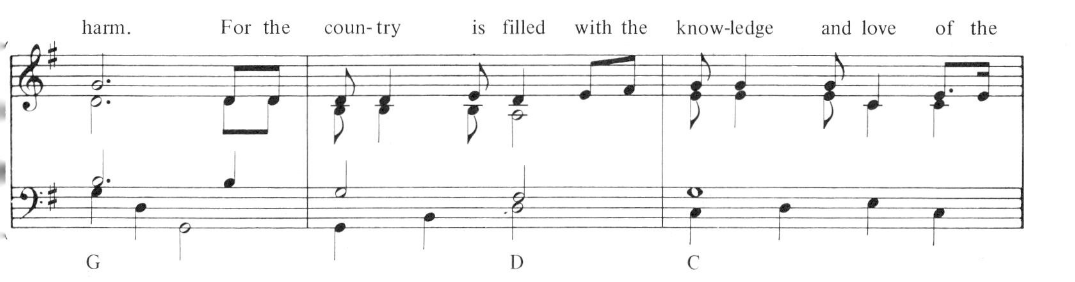

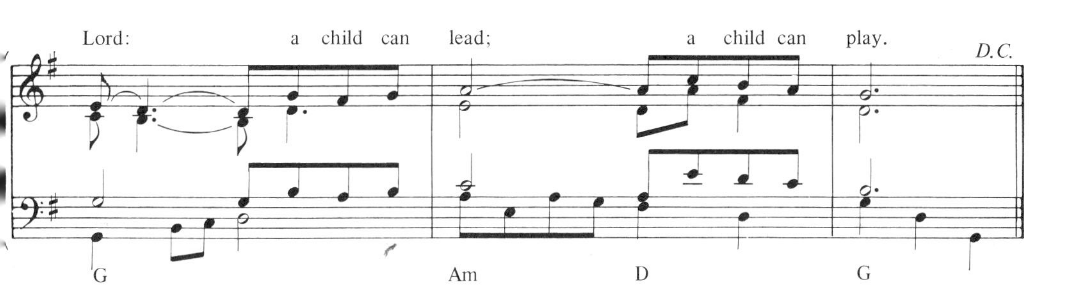

2. The calf feeds with the lion
   and the viper can rest near the young child.
   They do no hurt; they do no harm.
   For the country is filled
   with the knowledge and love of the Lord:
   a child can lead; a child can play.

3. The Spirit of the Lord
   with his wisdom and strong understanding
   transforms the earth; the remnant blooms.
   For the country is filled
   with the knowledge and love of the Lord:
   a child can lead; a child can play.

Words, based on Micah 4 and Isaiah 11, and Music: Noel S. Donnelly,
arranged by Frances M. Kelly

THINE BE THE GLORY
('Maccabaeus' 10 11.11 11 & Chorus)

[HARMONY]

Verse

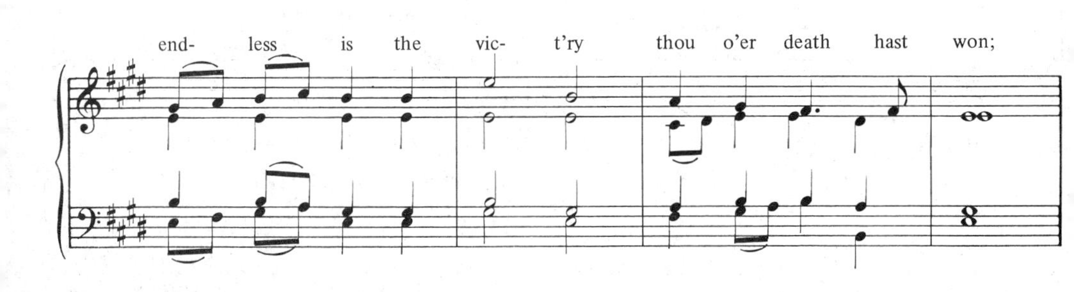

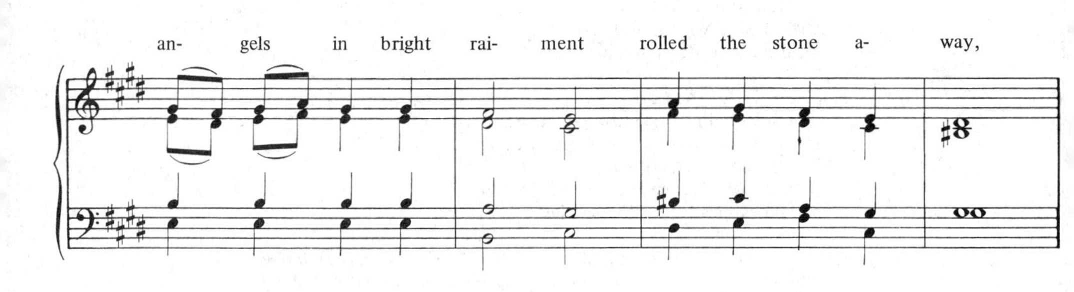

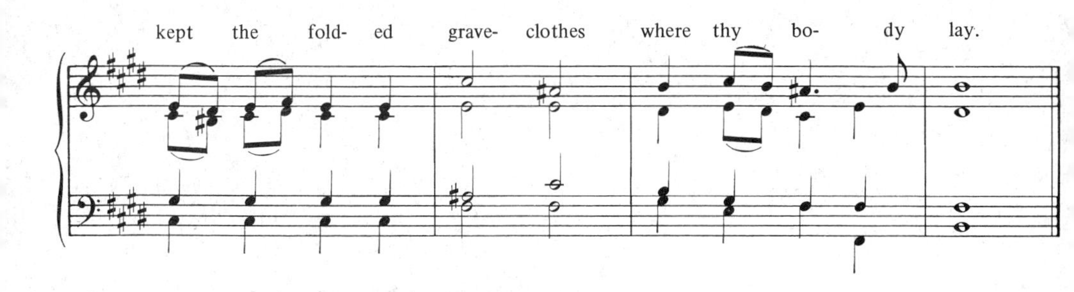

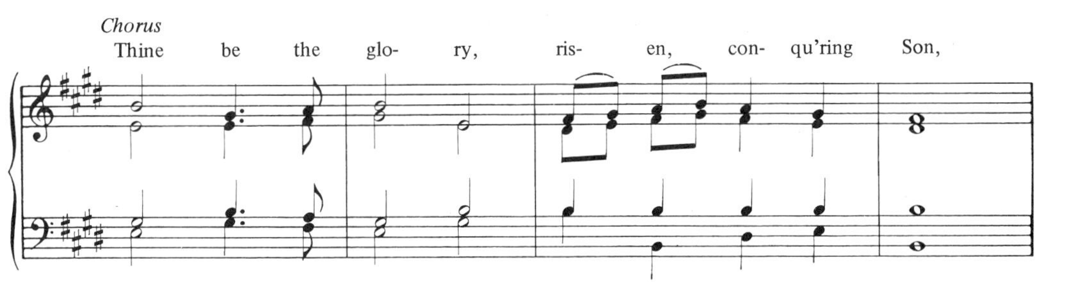

2. Lo! Jesus meets us,
   risen from the tomb;
   lovingly he greets us,
   scatters fear and gloom.
   Let the Church with gladness
   hymns of triumph sing,
   for her Lord now liveth;
   death has lost its sting.

3. No more we doubt thee,
   glorious Prince of life;
   life is nought without thee:
   aid us in our strife.
   Make us more than conqu'rors
   through thy deathless love;
   bring us safe through Jordan
   to thy home above.

Words: E. L. Budry (1854-1932),
tr. R. B. Hoyle
Music: George F. Handel (1685-1759)

523

THINE FOR EVER! GOD OF LOVE
('Newington' 77.77.)

[HARMONY]

2. Thine for ever! Lord of life,
shield us through our earthly strife;
thou the Life, the Truth, the Way,
guide us to the realms of day.

3. Thine for ever! O how blest
they who find in thee their rest!
Saviour, guardian, heavenly friend,
O defend us to the end.

4. Thine for ever! Shepherd, keep
us thy frail and trembling sheep;
safe alone beneath thy care,
let us all thy goodness share.

5. Thine for ever! thou our guide,
all our wants by thee supplied,
all our sins by thee forgiven,
lead us, Lord, from earth to heaven.

Words: Mary Fawler Maude (1819-1913)
Music: William Dalrymple Maclagan (1826-1910)

*As an introduction, use the final four bars (from *)*

2. Think old: a vintage car.
Think older: a full-grown tree.
Think older: a million grains
of the sand beside the surging sea.
Yet old, old, older is God!
And he loves us all!

3. Think strong: a tiger's jaw:
Think stronger: a castle wall.
Think stronger: a hurricane that leaves
little standing there at all.
Yet strong, strong, stronger is God!
And he loves us all!

Words and Music: Susan Sayers,
arranged by Frances M. Kelly

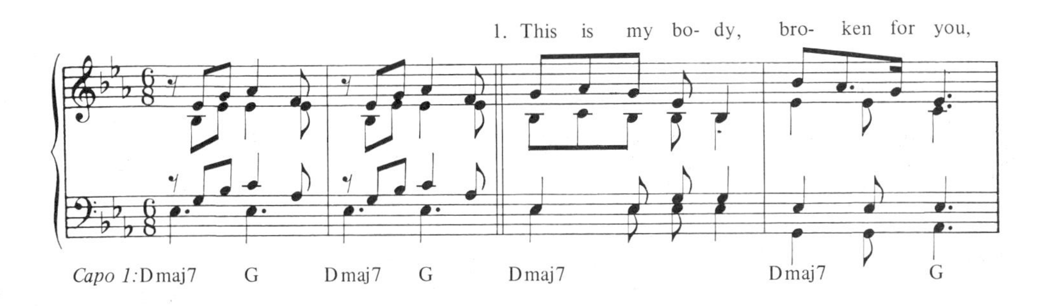

2. This is my blood poured out for you,
bringing forgiveness, making you free.
Take it and drink it, and when you do,
do it in love for me.

3. Back to my Father soon I shall go.
Do not forget me; then you will see
I am still with you, and you will know
you're very close to me.

4. Filled with my Spirit, how you will grow!
You are my branches; I am the tree.
If you are faithful, others will know
you are alive in me.

5. Love one another – I have loved you,
and I have shown you how to be free;
serve one another, and when you do,
do it in love for me.

Words, based on John 14,16: Verses 1 & 2 - Jimmy Owens
Verses 3 - 5 - Damian Lundy
Music: Jimmy Owens

THIS IS MY COMMANDMENT

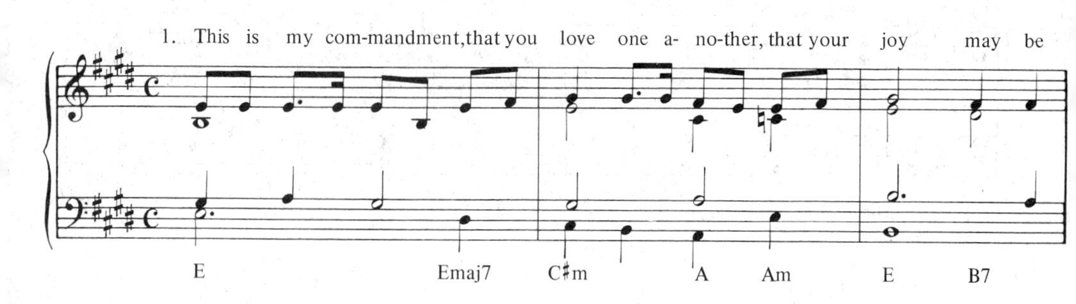

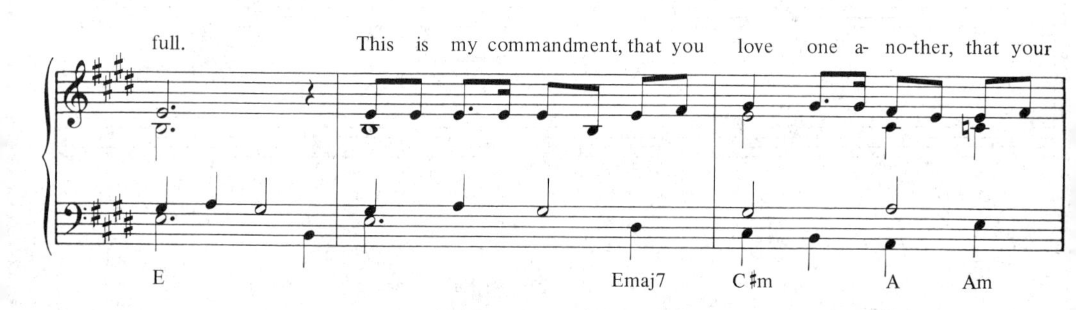

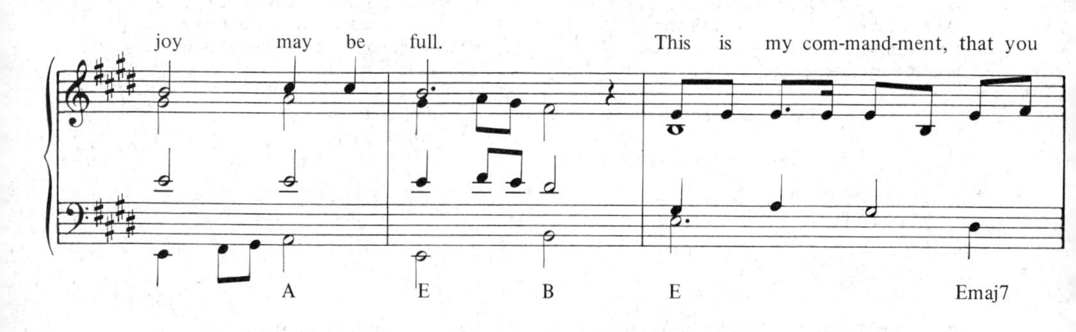

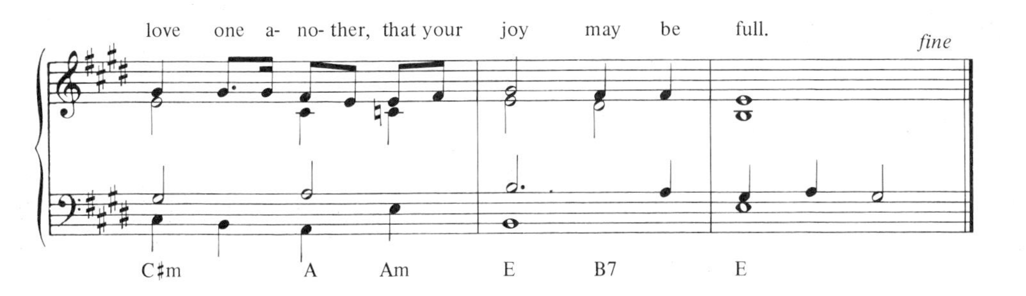

2. This is my commandment
that you serve one another,
that God's Kingdom may come.
This is my commandment
that you serve one another,
that God's Kingdom may come;
that God's Kingdom may come;
that God's Kingdom may come.
This is my commandment
that you serve one another,
that God's Kingdom may come.

Words, based on John 15: Verse 1, unknown
Verse 2, Robert B. Kelly
Music: Anonymous, arranged by Frances M. Kelly

THIS IS MY COMMAND TO YOU
('Commandment')

This may be sung as a round with the second voice entering at the double bar.

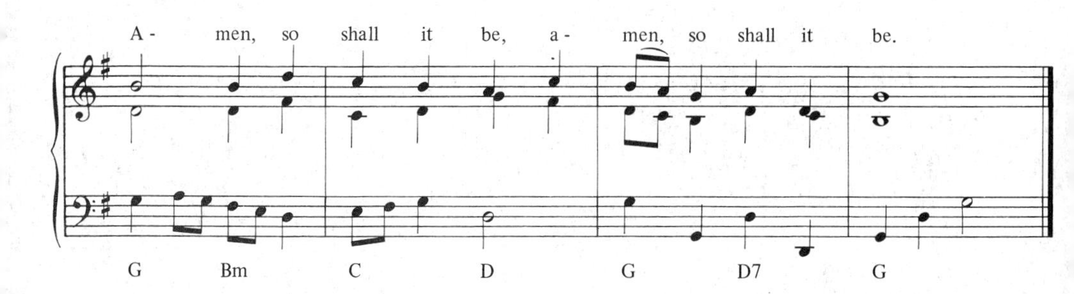

Words and Music: Kevin Mayhew

THIS IS THE DAY OF LIGHT
('Dominica' S.M.)

[HARMONY]

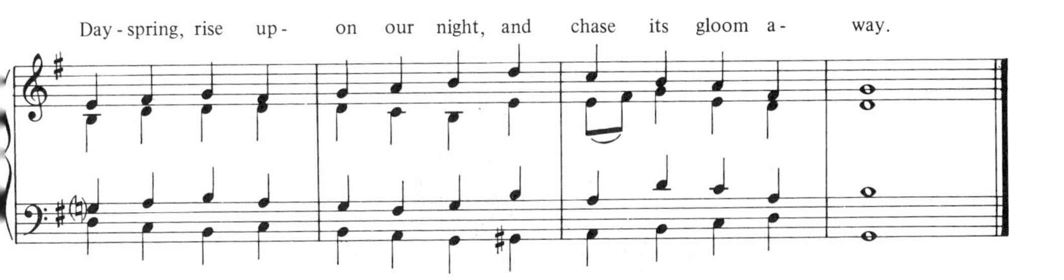

2. This is the day of rest:
our failing strength renew;
on weary brain and troubled breast
shed thou thy freshening dew.

3. This is the day of peace:
thy peace our spirits fill;
bid thou the blasts of discord cease,
the waves of strife be still.

4. This is the day of prayer:
let earth to heaven draw near;
lift up our hearts to seek thee there,
come down to meet us here.

5. This is the first of days:
send forth thy quickening breath,
and wake dead souls to love and praise,
O vanquisher of death.

Words: John Ellerton (1826-93)
Music: Herbert Stanley Oakeley (1830-1903)

529

THIS IS THE DAY THE LORD HATH MADE

('Bishopthorpe' C.M.)

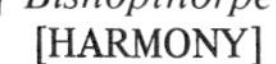

This tune may be found in a lower key at Hymn 228

2. Today he rose and left the dead,
and Satan's empire fell;
today the saints his triumphs spread,
and all his wonders tell.

3. Hosanna to the anointed King,
to David's holy Son!
O help us, Lord, descend and bring
salvation from thy throne.

4. Blest be the Lord, who comes to men
with messages of grace;
who comes, in God his Father's name,
to save our sinful race.

5. Hosanna in the highest strains
the Church on earth can raise;
the highest heavens in which he reigns
shall give him nobler praise.

Words: Isaac Watts (1674-1748)
Music: Jeremiah Clark (1670-1707)

530 THIS IS THE DAY, THIS IS THE DAY

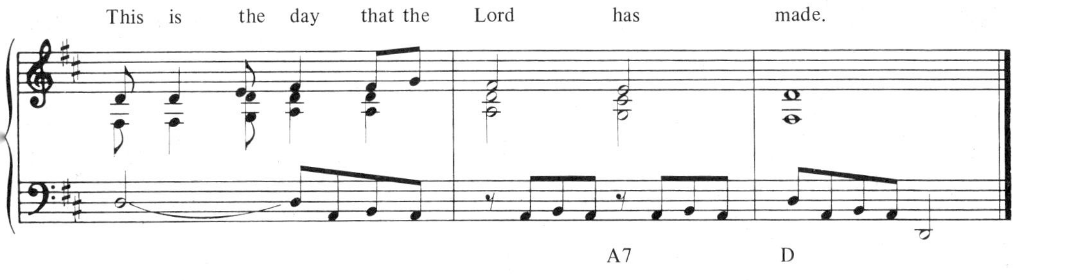

2. This is the day when he rose again . . .

3. This is the day when the Spirit came . . .

Words, based on Psalm 118: 24, and Music: Les Garrett

531 THIS JOYFUL EASTERTIDE

[HARMONY] *('Vruechten' 67.67.D.)*

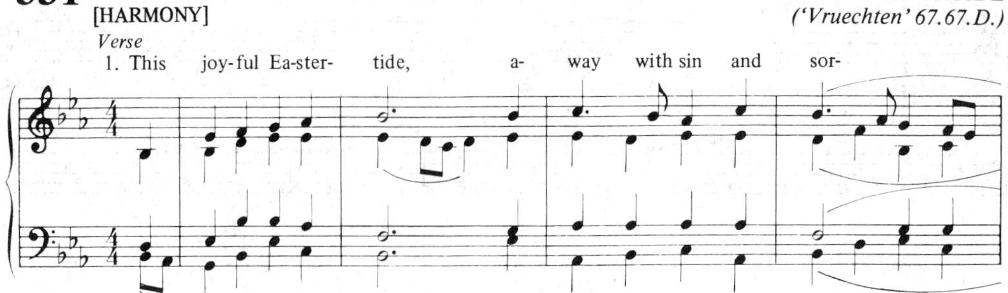

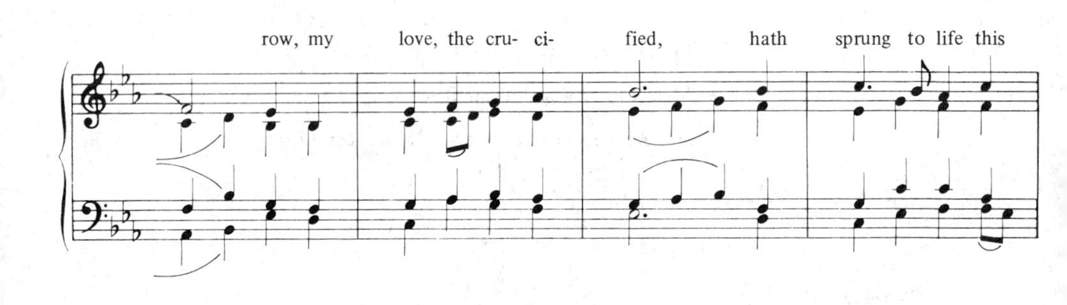

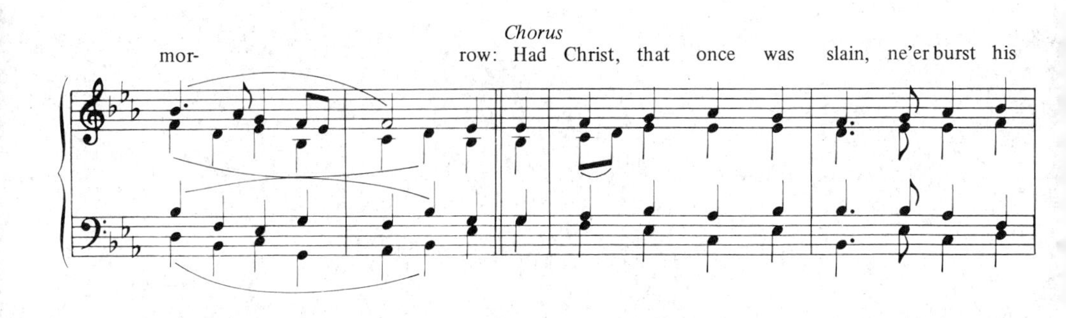

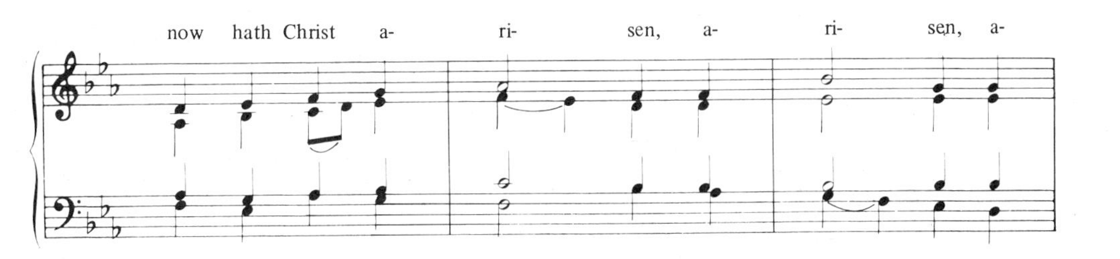

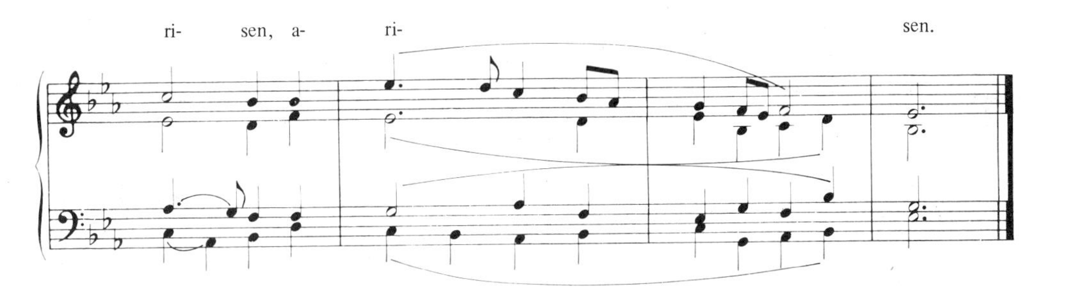

2. My flesh in hope shall rest,
and for a season slumber:
till trump from east to west
shall wake the dead in number:

3. Death's flood hath lost his chill,
since Jesus crossed the river:
lover of souls, from ill
my passing soul deliver:

Words: George Ratcliff Woodward (1849-1934)
Music: 17th century Dutch Melody

Chorus
This lit- tle light of mine, I'm gon- na let it shine,
A
This lit- tle light of mine,
A7
D
I'm gon- na let it shine. This lit- tle light of mine,
I'm gon- na let it shine, let it shine, let it
A7
D
A
shine, let it shine.
Verse
1. The light that shines is the
fine
D
E7
A

2. On Monday he gave me the gift of love,
Tuesday peace came from above.
On Wednesday he told me to have more faith,
on Thursday he gave me a little more grace.
Friday he told me just to watch and pray,
Saturday he told me just what to say,
on Sunday he gave me the power divine
to let my little light shine.

Words and Music: Traditional Spiritual, arranged by John Rombaut

THIS THEN, IS MY PRAYER
('Ephesians 3')

The chorus is not sung after verse 3.

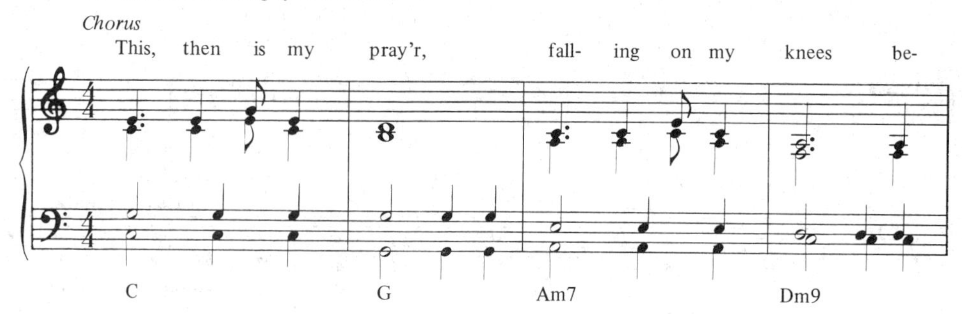

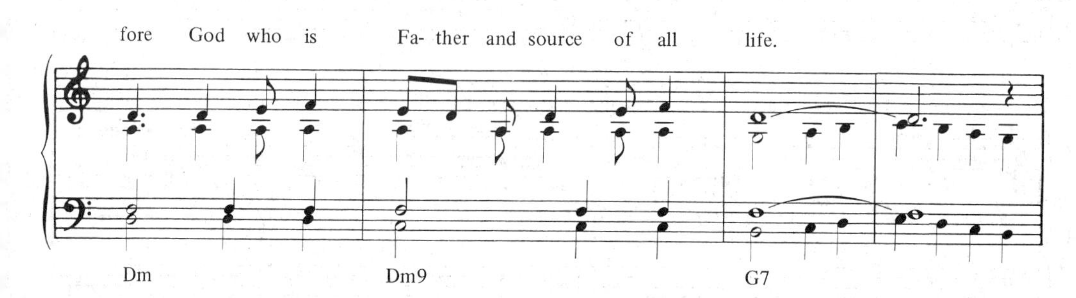

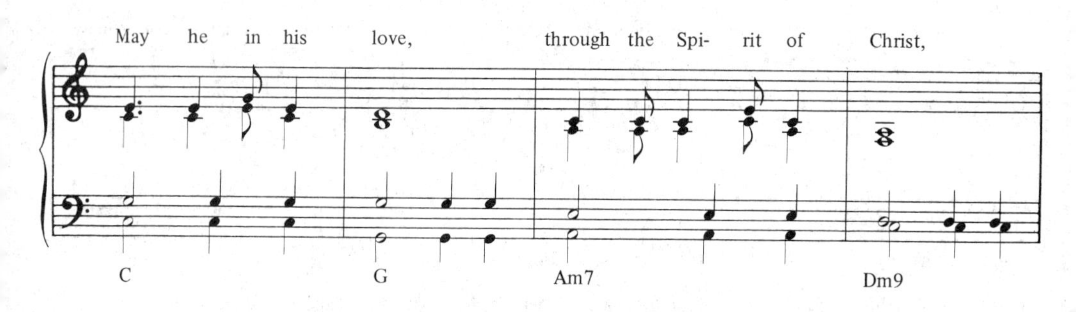

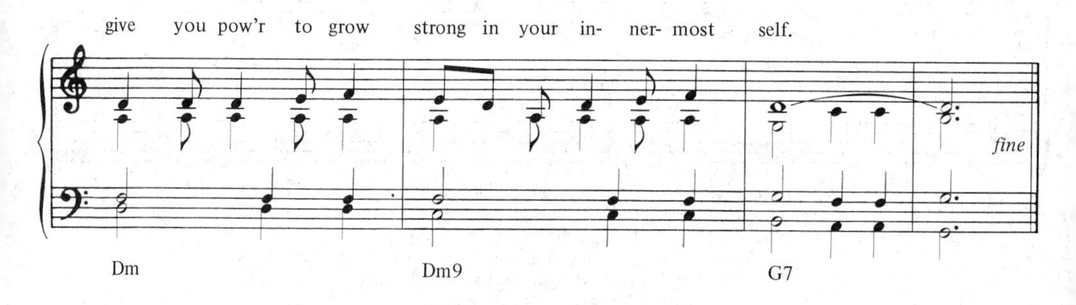

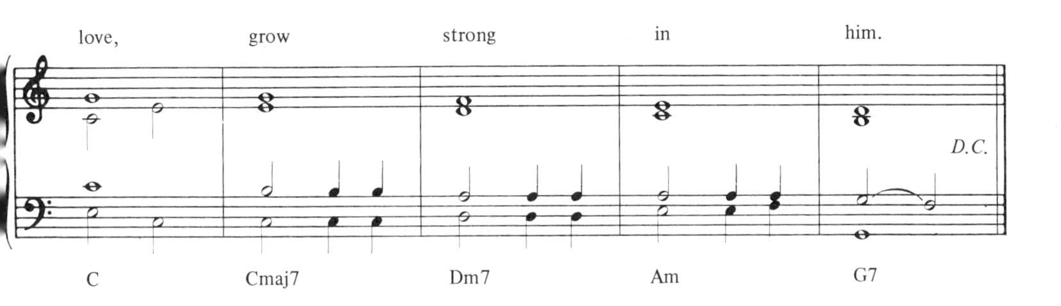

2. May you, with all the saints,
grow in the pow'r to understand
how he loves you!

3. O how can I explain
in all its depth and all its scope
his love, God's love!

The chorus is not sung after verse 3

4. For his love is so full,
it is beyond all we can dream:
his love, in Christ!

5. And so, glory to him
working in us, who can do more
than we can pray!

Words, based on Ephesians 3: 14-21: Damian Lundy
Music: Gerard Markland

THIS WORLD YOU HAVE MADE

('Beautiful world')

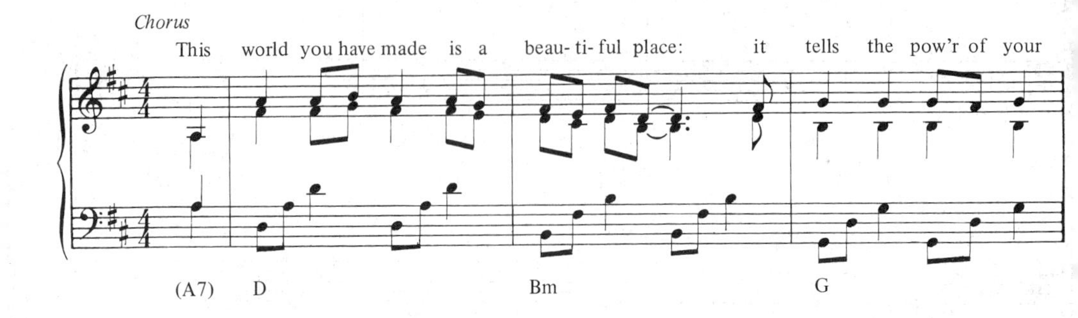

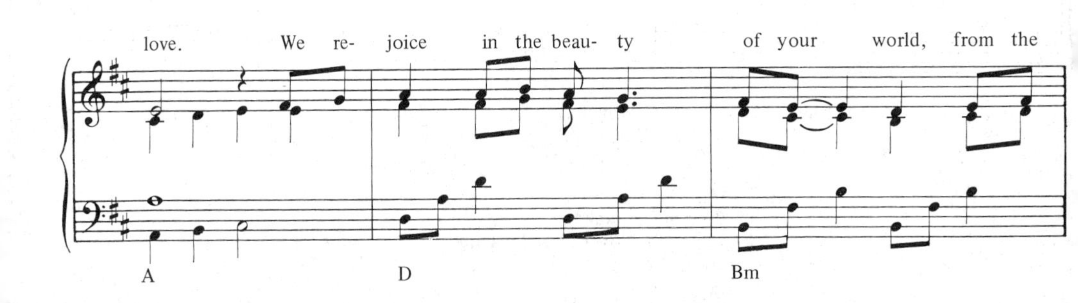

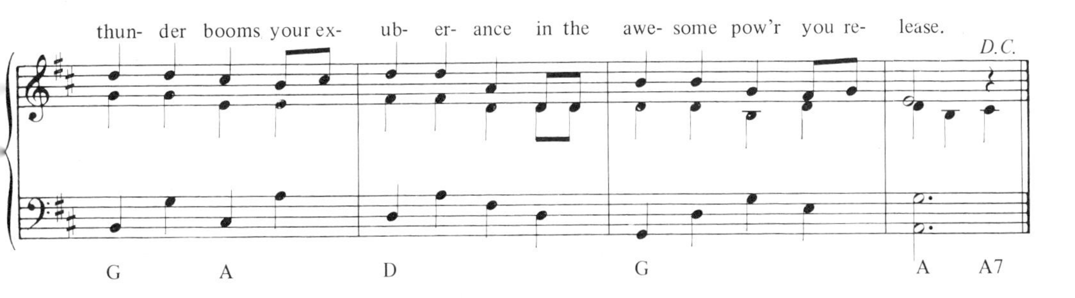

2. The tenderness of a new-born child;
   the gentleness of the rain;
   simplicity in a single cell;
   and complexity in a brain.

3. Your stillness rests in a silent pool;
   infinity drifts in space;
   your grandeur straddles the mountain tops;
   and we see your face in each face.

Words, based on Genesis 1, and Music: Susan Sayers
arranged by John Rombaut

535

THOU ART THE WAY
('St James' C.M.)

[HARMONY]

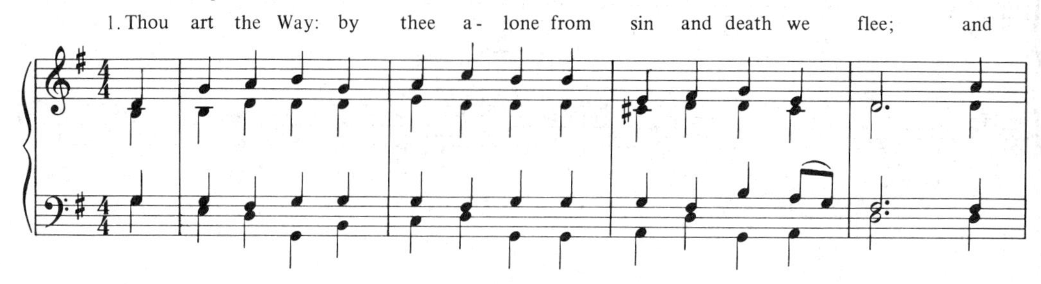

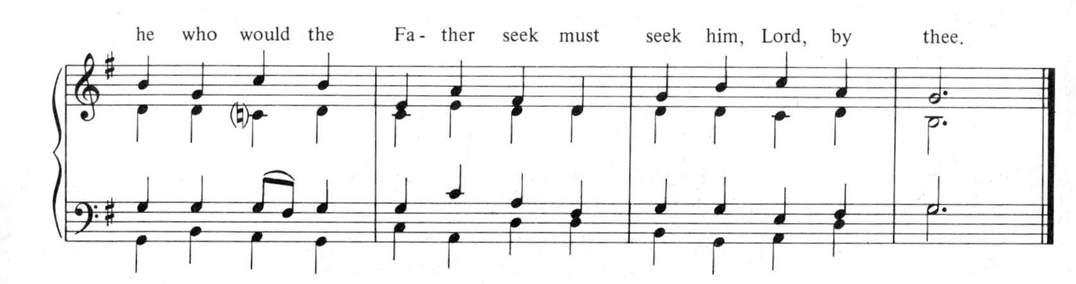

2. Thou art the Truth: thy word alone
   true wisdom can impart;
   thou only canst inform the mind
   and purify the heart.

3. Thou art the Life: the rending tomb
   proclaims thy conquering arm;
   and those who put their trust in thee
   nor death nor hell shall harm.

4. Thou art the Way, the Truth, the Life:
   grant us that Way to know,
   that Truth to keep, that Life to win,
   whose joys eternal flow.

Words, based on John 14:
George Washington Doane (1799-1859)
Music: Raphael Courteville (? - 1772)

Words, based on Revelation 4, and Music: Pauline Michael Mills

THOU DIDST LEAVE THY THRONE

('Margaret' Irregular)

[HARMONY]

Verse

2. Heaven's arches rang when the angels sang,
proclaiming thy royal degree;
but in lowly birth didst thou come to earth,
and in great humility:

3. The foxes found rest, and the bird had its nest
in the shade of the cedar tree;
but thy couch was the sod, O thou Son of God,
in the desert of Galilee:

4. Thou camest, O Lord, with the living word
that should set thy people free;
but with mocking scorn and with crown of thorn
they bore thee to Calvary:

5. When the heavens shall ring, and the angels sing,
at thy coming to victory,
let thy voice call me home, saying, 'Yet there is room,
there is room at my side for thee:'

Words: Emily Elizabeth Steele Elliott (1836-97)
Music: Timothy Richard Matthews (1826-1910)

THOU WHOSE ALMIGHTY WORD

538

('Moscow' 664.666.4.)

[HARMONY]

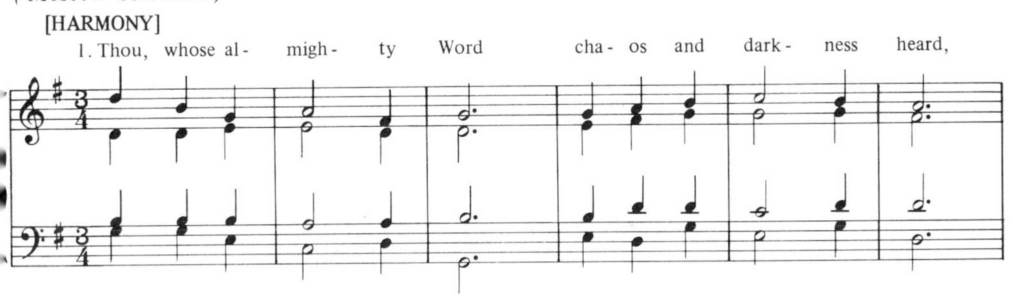

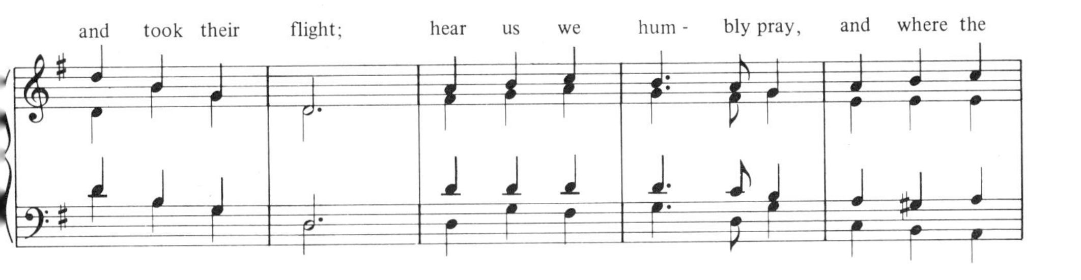

2. Thou, who didst come to bring
   on thy redeeming wing
   healing and sight,
   health to the sick in mind,
   sight to the inly blind,
   ah! now to all mankind
   let there be light!

3. Spirit of truth and love,
   life-giving, holy Dove,
   speed forth thy flight;
   move on the waters' face,
   bearing the lamp of grace,
   and in earth's darkest place
   let there be light!

4. Blessed and holy Three,
   glorious Trinity,
   Wisdom, Love, Might;
   boundless as ocean's tide
   rolling in fullest pride,
   through the world far and wide
   let there be light!

Words: John Marriott (1780-1825)
Music: Felice de Giardini (1716-96)

THOU WILT KEEP HIM IN PERFECT PEACE

2. Marvel not, I say unto you, *(3)*
you must be born again.

3. Though your sins as scarlet be, *(3)*
they shall be white as snow.

4. If the Son shall set you free, *(3)*
you shall be free indeed.

Words, based on Isaiah 26 : 3 and Music:
Anonymous, arranged by John Rombaut

THREE IN ONE, AND ONE IN THREE
('Capetown' 77.75.)

[HARMONY]

2. Light of lights! with morning-shine
lift on us thy light divine;
and let charity benign
breathe on us her balm.

3. Light of lights! when falls the even,
let it sink on sin forgiven;
fold us in the peace of heaven;
shed a vesper calm.

4. Three in One, and One in Three,
darkling here we worship thee;
with the saints hereafter we
hope to bear the palm.

Words: Gilbert Rorison (1821-69)
Music: Friedrich Filitz (1804-76), adapted.

541

THROUGH ALL THE CHANGING SCENES OF LIFE
('Wiltshire' C.M.)

[HARMONY]

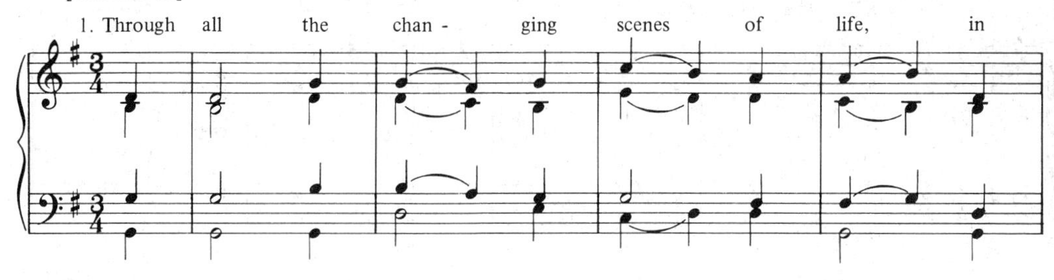

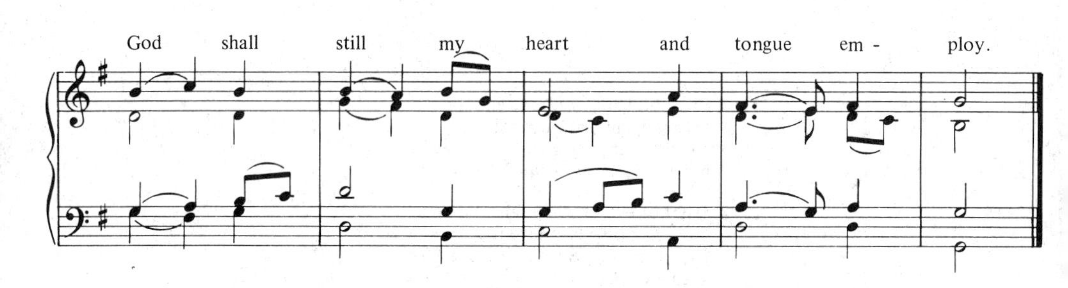

2. O magnify the Lord with me,
with me exalt his name;
when in distress to him I called,
he to my rescue came.

3. The hosts of God encamp around
the dwellings of the just;
deliverance he affords to all
who on his succour trust.

4. O make but trial of his love:
experience will decide
how blest are they, and only they,
who in his truth confide.

5. Fear him, ye saints, and you will then
have nothing else to fear;
make you his service your delight,
your wants shall be his care.

6. To Father, Son, and Holy Ghost,
the God whom we adore,
be glory, as it was, is now,
and shall be evermore.

Words, from Psalm 34: Nahum Tate and Nicholas Brady ('New Version' 1696)
Music: George Thomas Smart (1776-1867)

542

THROUGH THE DAY THY LOVE HAS SPARED US

('Dretzel' 87.87.77.)

[HARMONY]

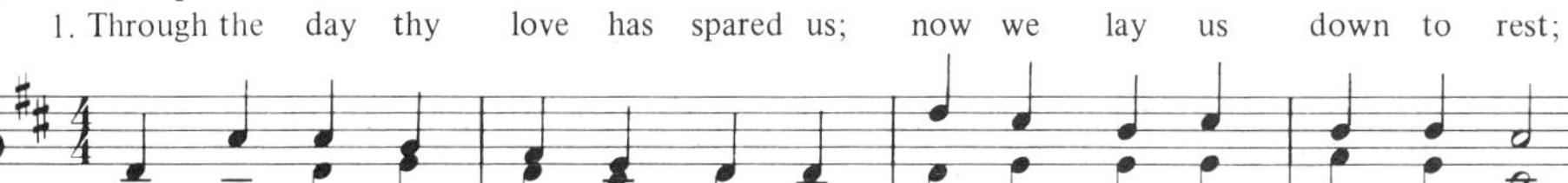

2. Pilgrims here on earth, and strangers,
dwelling in the midst of foes;
us and ours preserve from dangers;
in thine arms may we repose,
and, when life's sad day is past,
rest with thee in heaven at last.

Words: Thomas Kelly (1769-1854)
Music: C.H. Dretzel (1608-1775)

THROUGH THE NIGHT OF DOUBT AND SORROW

(First tune: 'Marching' 87.87.)

[HARMONY]

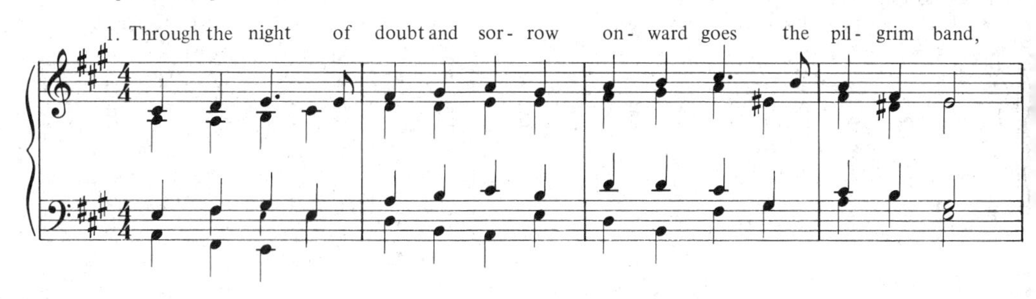

2. Clear before us through the darkness
   gleams and burns the guiding light;
   brother clasps the hand of brother,
   stepping fearless through the night.

3. One the light of God's own presence
   o'er his ransomed people shed,
   chasing far the gloom and terror,
   brightening all the path we tread.

4. One the object of our journey,
   one the faith which never tires,
   one the earnest looking forward,
   one the hope our God inspires.

5. One the strain that lips of thousands
   lift as from the heart of one:
   one the conflict, one the peril,
   one the march in God begun.

6. One the gladness of rejoicing
   on the far eternal shore,
   where the one almighty Father
   reigns in love for evermore.

7. Onward, therefore, pilgrim brothers,
   onward with the Cross our aid;
   bear its shame, and fight its battle,
   till we rest beneath its shade.

8. Soon shall come the great awaking,
   soon the rending of the tomb;
   then the scattering of all shadows,
   and the end of toil and gloom.

Words: Bernhardt S. Ingemann (1789-1862) tr. S. Baring-Gould
Music: First tune – Martin Shaw (1875-1958)

THROUGH THE NIGHT OF DOUBT AND SORROW

(Second tune: 'Rustington' 87.87.)

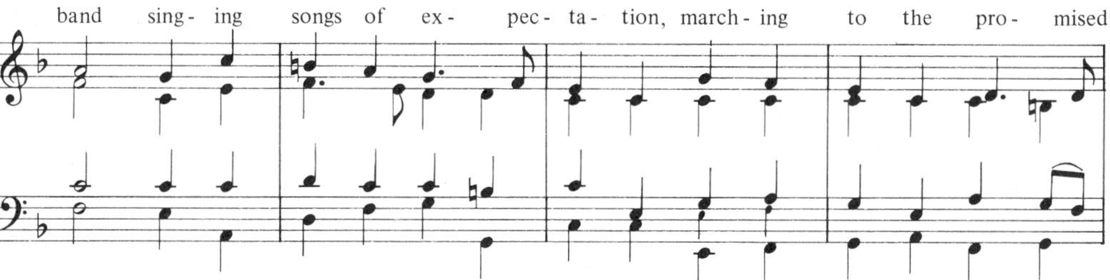

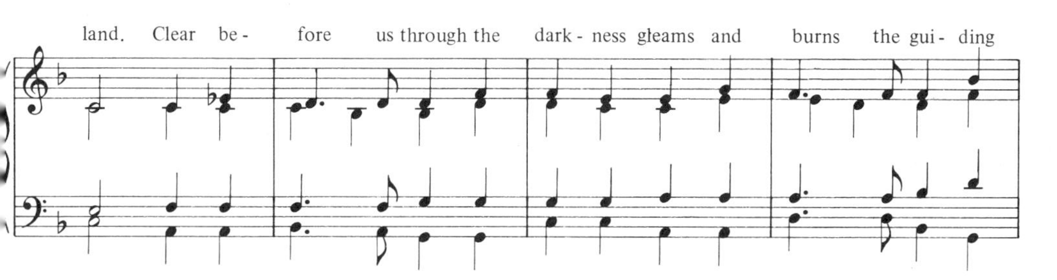

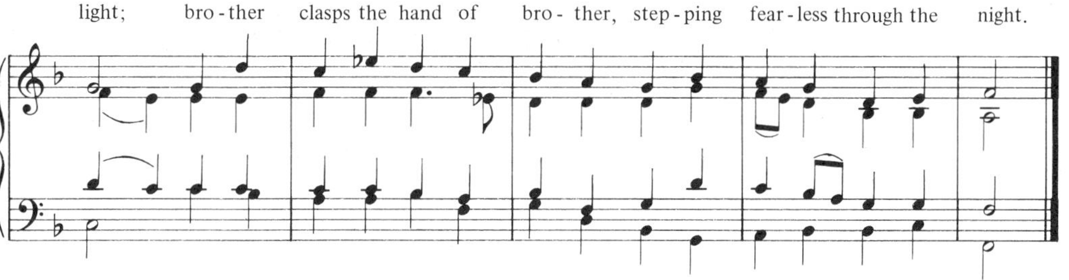

ne the light of God's own presence
'er his ransomed people shed,
hasing far the gloom and terror,
rightening all the path we tread.
ne the object of our journey,
ne the faith which never tires,
ne the earnest looking forward,
ne the hope our God inspires.

3. One the strain that lips of thousands
lift as from the heart of one:
one the conflict, one the peril,
one the march in God begun.
One the gladness of rejoicing
on the far eternal shore,
where the one almighty Father
reigns in love for evermore.

4. Onward, therefore, pilgrim brothers,
onward with the Cross our aid;
bear its shame, and fight its battle,
till we rest beneath its shade.
Soon shall come the great awaking,
soon the rending of the tomb;
then the scattering of all shadows,
and the end of toil and gloom.

Words: Bernhardt S. Ingemann (1789-1862) tr. S. Baring-Gould
Music: Second tune - C. Hubert H. Parry (1848-1918)

1. Thus! says the Lord. Thus! says the Lord. Come, share your bread with the
D F♯m G A7 Bm F♯m

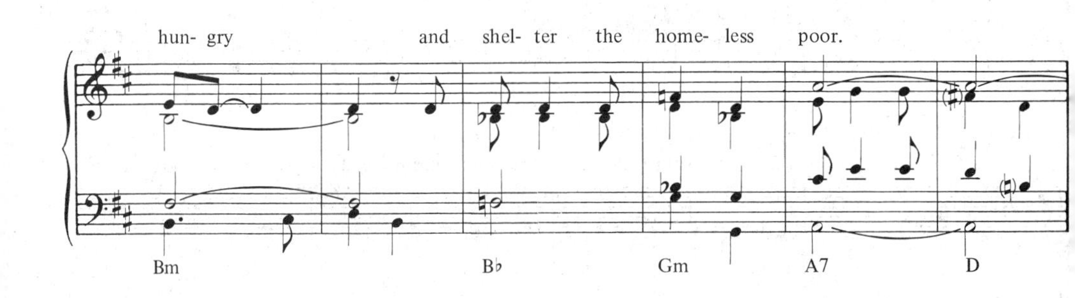
hun- gry and shel- ter the home- less poor.
Bm B♭ Gm A7 D

Thus! says the Lord. Thus! says the Lord.
A7 A D F♯m G A7

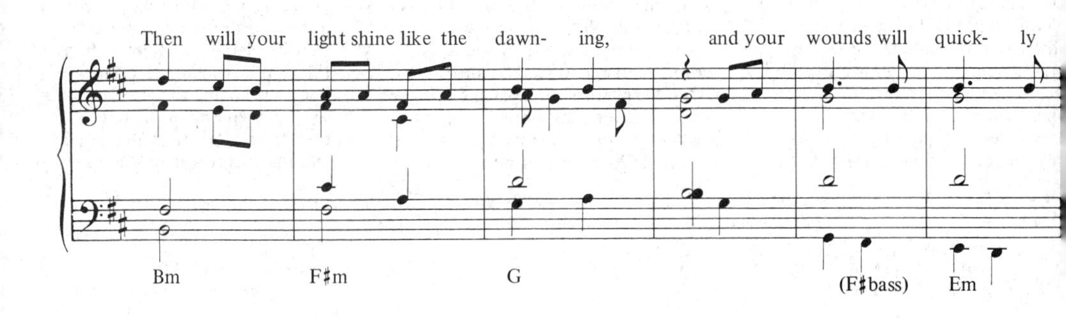
Then will your light shine like the dawn- ing, and your wounds will quick- ly
Bm F♯m G (F♯bass) Em

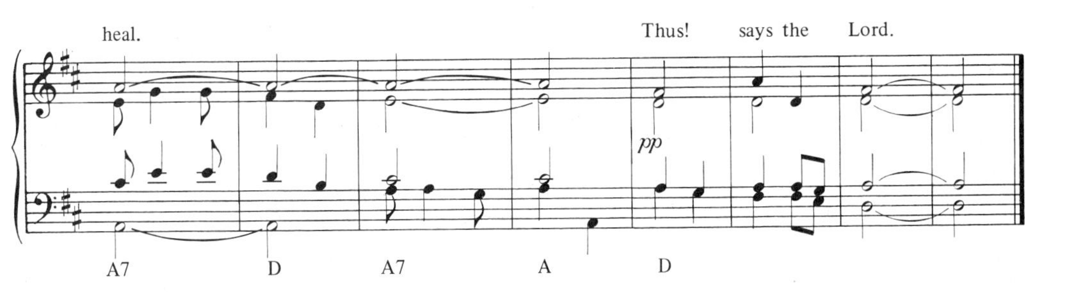

2. Thus! says the Lord. Thus! says the Lord.
   Don't turn your back on your neighbour
   but clothe him and share your love.
   Thus! says the Lord. Thus! says the Lord.
   Then if your justice goes before you
   will my glory come behind.
   Thus! says the Lord.

3. Thus! says the Lord. Thus! says the Lord.
   Loosen the yoke and the fetter,
   and let the oppressed go free.
   Thus! says the Lord. Thus! says the Lord.
   Then will your light rise in the darkness,
   and your shadows be like noon.
   Thus! says the Lord.

Words, based on Isaiah 58: 7-10, and Music: Noel S. Donnelly, arranged by Frances M. Kelly

545

THY HAND, O GOD, HAS GUIDED
('Thornbury' 76.76.D.)

2. Thy heralds brought glad tidings
to greatest, as to least;
they bade men rise, and hasten
to share the great king's feast;
and this was all their teaching,
in every deed and word,
to all alike proclaiming
one Church, one Faith, one Lord.

3. When shadows thick were falling,
and all seemed sunk in night,
thou, Lord, didst send thy servants,
thy chosen sons of light.
On them and on thy people
thy plenteous grace was poured,
and this was still their message:
one Church, one Faith, one Lord.

4. Through many a day of darkness,
through many a scene of strife,
the faithful few fought bravely,
to guard the nation's life.
Their gospel of redemption,
sin pardoned, man restored,
was all in this enfolded:
one Church, one Faith, one Lord.

5. And we, shall we be faithless?
Shall hearts fail, hands hang down?
Shall we evade the conflict,
and cast away our crown?
Not so: in God's deep counsels
some better thing is stored:
we will maintain, unflinching,
one Church, one Faith, one Lord.

6. Thy mercy will not fail us,
nor leave thy work undone;
with thy right hand to help us
the vict'ry shall be won;
and then, by men and angels
thy name shall be adored.
And this shall be their anthem:
one Church, one Faith, one Lord.

Words: E. H. Plumptre (1821-91)
Music: Basil Harwood (1859-1949)

546

THY KINGDOM COME, O GOD
('St Cecilia' 66.66.)

[HARMONY]

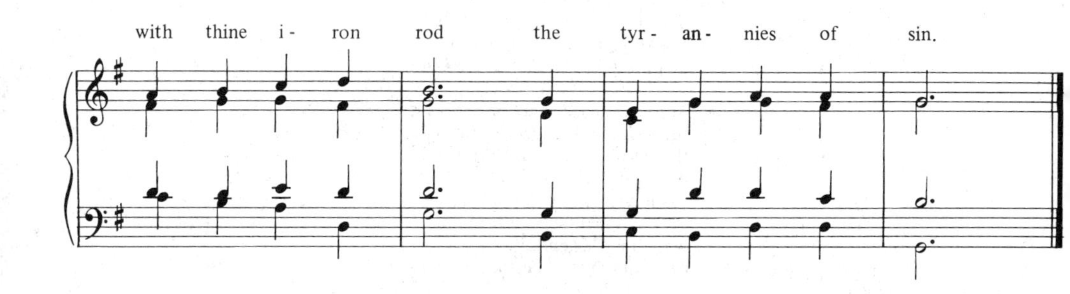

2. Where is thy reign of peace
and purity and love?
When shall all hatred cease,
as in the realms above?

3. When comes the promised time
that war shall be no more,
and lust, oppression, crime
shall flee thy face before?

4. We pray thee, Lord, arise,
and come in thy great might;
revive our longing eyes,
which languish for thy sight.

5. Men scorn thy sacred name,
and wolves devour thy fold;
by many deeds of shame
we learn that love grows cold.

6. O'er heathen lands afar
thick darkness broodeth yet:
arise, O morning star,
arise, and never set.

Words: Lewis Hensley (1824-1905)
Music: Leighton George Hayne (1836-83)

2. As long as life lasts will I bless thee, Lord. *(2)*
My lips shall praise thee, thus will I bless thee.
As long as life lasts will I bless thee, Lord.

3. I raise my hands up to the praise of thy name. *(2)*
My lips shall praise thee, thus will I bless thee.
I raise my hands up to the praise of thy name.

4. My soul is thirsting, I long for thee, Lord. *(2)*
My lips shall praise thee, thus will I bless thee.
My soul is thirsting, I long for thee, Lord.

Words, based on Psalm 63: Verse 1 - traditional
Verses 2-4 - Robert B. Kelly
Music: Unknown, arranged by Frances M. Kelly

548

THY WAY NOT MINE, O LORD
('Ibstone' 66.66.)

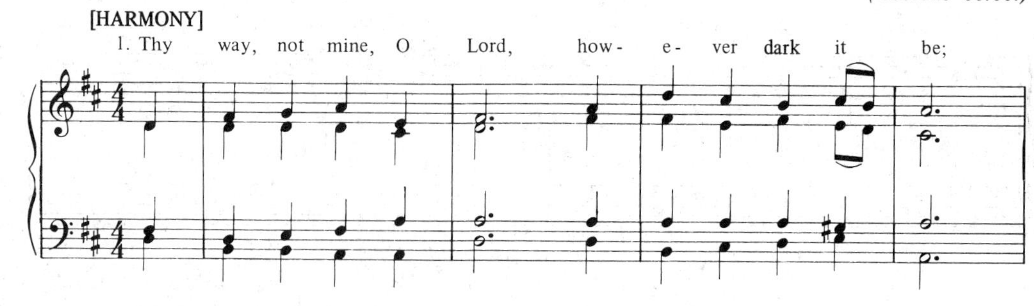

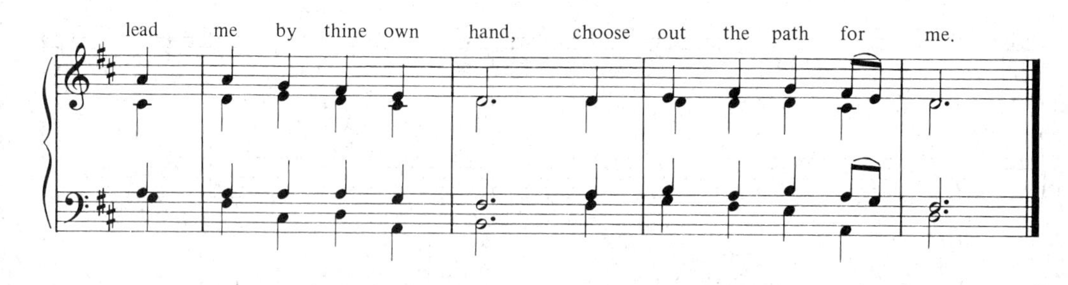

2. Smooth let it be or rough,
it will be still the best;
winding or straight, it leads
right onward to thy rest.

3. I dare not choose my lot;
I would not if I might:
choose thou for me, my God,
so shall I walk aright.

4. The kingdom that I seek
is thine; so let the way
that leads to it be thine,
else I must surely stray.

5. Take thou my cup, and it
with joy or sorrow fill,
as best to thee may seem;
choose thou my good and ill.

6. Choose thou for me my friends,
my sickness or my health;
choose thou my cares for me,
my poverty or wealth.

7. Not mine, not mine, the choice
in things or great or small;
be thou my guide, my strength,
my wisdom, and my all.

Words: Horatio Bonar (1808-89)
Music: Maria Tiddeman (1837-1915)

TIS GOOD, LORD, TO BE HERE
('Carlisle' S.M.)

[HARMONY]

This tune can be found in a lower key at Hymn 428, and in a different harmonisation at Hymn 54

2. 'Tis good, Lord, to be here,
   thy beauty to behold,
   where Moses and Elijah stand,
   thy messengers of old.

3. Fulfiller of the past,
   promise of things to be,
   we hail thy body glorified,
   and our redemption see.

4. Before we taste of death,
   we see thy kingdom come;
   we fain would hold the vision bright,
   and make this hill our home.

5. 'Tis good, Lord, to be here,
   yet we may not remain;
   but since thou bidst us leave the mount,
   come with us to the plain.

Words, based on Luke 9: 28-35: J. Armitage Robinson (1858-1933)
Music: Charles Lockhart (1745-1815)

TO CHRIST THE PRINCE OF PEACE

('St George' S.M.)

[HARMONY]

2. Deep in his heart for us
the wound of love he bore,
that love wherewith he still inflames
the hearts that him adore.

3. O Jesu, victim blest,
what else but love divine
could thee constrain to open thus
that sacred heart of thine?

4. O wondrous fount of love,
O well of waters free,
O heavenly flame, refining fire,
O burning charity!

5. Hide us in thy dear heart,
Jesu, our Saviour blest,
so shall we find thy plenteous grace,
and heaven's eternal rest.

Words: 'Catholicum Hymnologium Germanicum' (1587),
tr. E. Caswall
Music: Henry J. Gauntlett (1805-76)

TO MERCY, PITY, PEACE AND LOVE
('Epsom' C.M.)

[HARMONY]

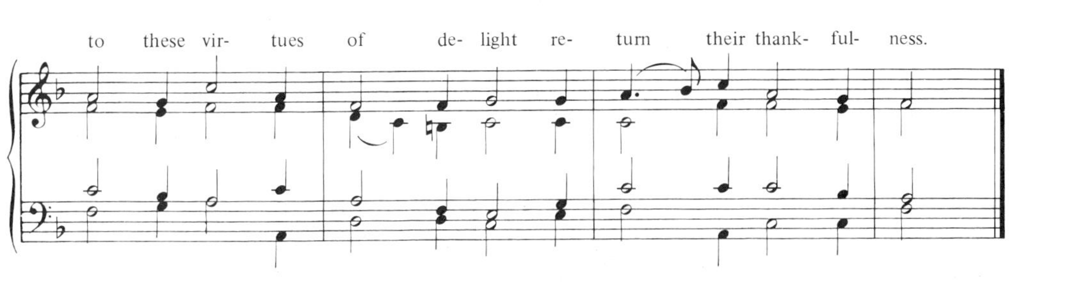

2. For mercy, pity, peace, and love,
   is God our Father dear;
   and mercy, pity, peace, and love,
   is man, his child and care.

3. For mercy has a human heart,
   pity, a human face;
   and love, the human form divine:
   and peace, the human dress.

4. Then every man, of every clime,
   that prays in his distress,
   prays to the human form divine:
   love, mercy, pity, peace.

5. And all must love the human form,
   in heathen, Turk or Jew;
   where mercy, love and pity dwell,
   there God is dwelling too.

Words: William Blake (1757-1827)
Music: from Arnold's 'Complete Psalter' (1756)

552

TO THE NAME THAT BRINGS SALVATION

('Oriel' 87.87.87.)

[HARMONY]

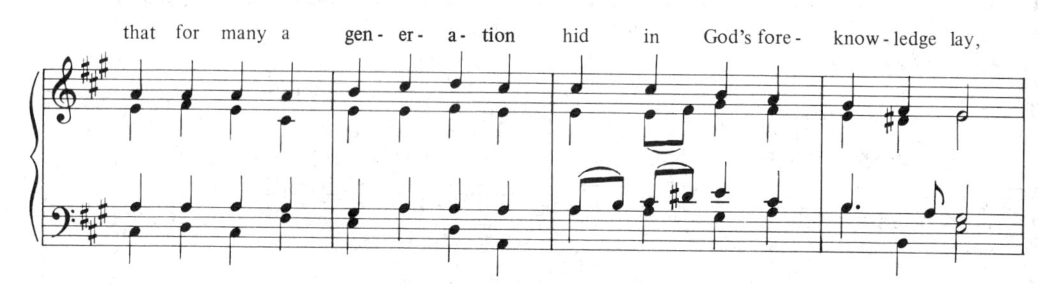

2. Name of gladness, name of pleasure,
   by the tongue ineffable,
   name of sweetness, passing measure,
   to the ear delectable;
   'tis our safeguard and our treasure,
   'tis our help 'gainst sin and hell.

3. 'Tis the name for adoration,
   'tis the name of victory;
   'tis the name for meditation
   in the vale of misery:
   'tis the name for veneration
   by the citizens on high.

4. 'Tis the name that whoso preaches
   finds it music in his ear;
   'tis the name that whoso teaches
   finds more sweet than honey's cheer:
   who its perfect wisdom reaches
   makes his ghostly vision clear.

5. 'Tis the name by right exalted
   over every other name:
   that when we are sore assaulted
   puts our enemies to shame:
   strength to them that else had halted,
   eyes to blind, and feet to lame.

6. Jesu, we thy name adoring,
   long to see thee as thou art:
   of thy clemency imploring
   so to write it in our heart,
   that hereafter, upward soaring,
   we with angels may have part.

Words: 'Gloriosi Salvatoris' (15th century) tr. J.M. Neale
Music: Caspar Ett's 'Cantica Sacra' (1840)

UNTO US IS BORN A SON
('Puer Nobis' 76.76.D.)

2. Christ, from heav'n descending low,
 comes on earth a stranger:
 ox and ass their owner know
 be cradled in a manger. *(2)*

3. This did Herod sore affray,
 and grievously bewilder:
 so he gave the word to slay,
 and slew the little childer. *(2)*

4. Of his love and mercy mild
 this the Christmas story,
 and O that Mary's gentle child
 might lead us up to glory! *(2)*

5. 'O' and 'A', and 'A' and 'O'
 cum cantibus in choro;
 let the merry organ go,
 Benedicamus Domino. *(2)*

Words: 15th c., tr. G. R. Woodward
Music: from 'Piae Cantiones' (1582)

VASTER FAR THAN ANY OCEAN

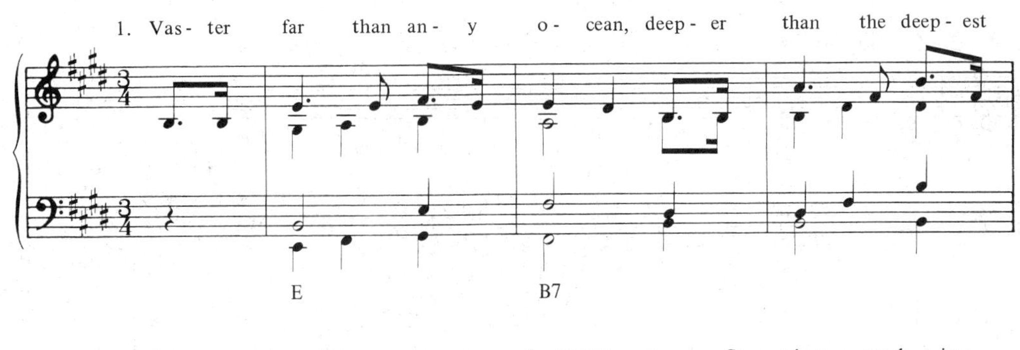

2. But my sins are truly many,
 is God's grace so vast, so deep?
 Yes, there's grace o'er sin abounding,
 grace to pardon, grace to keep.

3. Can he quench my thirst for ever?
 Will his Spirit strength impart?
 Yes, he gives me living water,
 springing up within my heart.

Words: Author unknown
Music: Russian Folk Melody,
arranged by John Rombaut

VIRGIN-BORN, WE BOW BEFORE THEE

('Quem pastores laudavere' 88.87.D.)

[HARMONY]

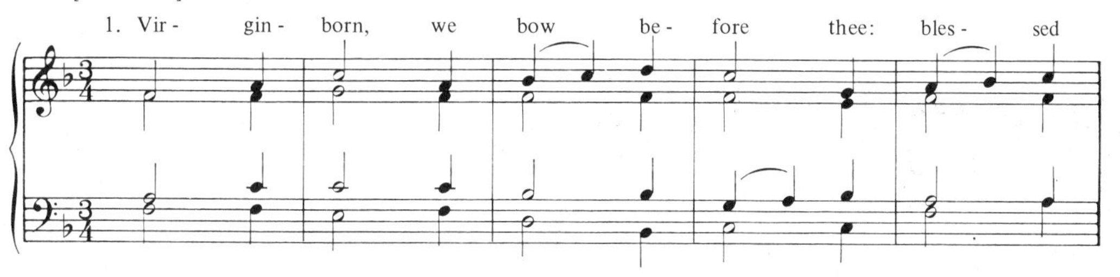

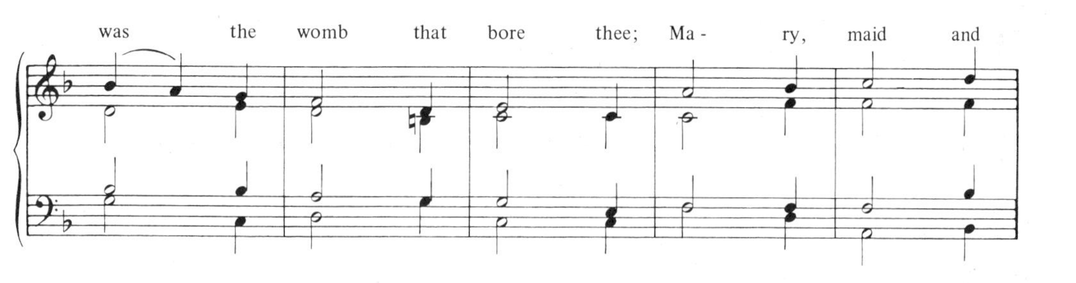

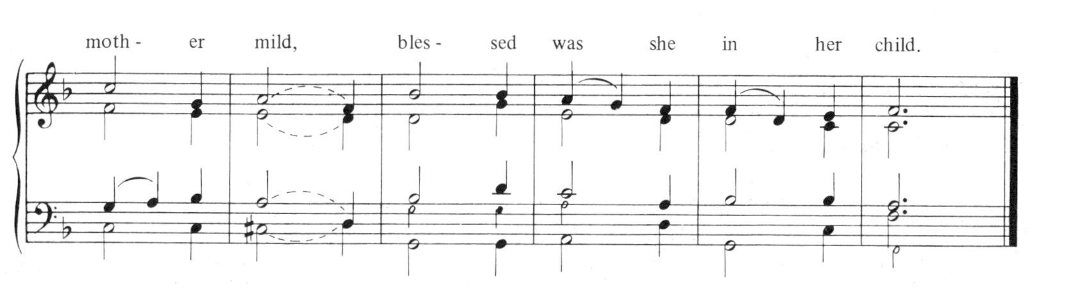

2. Blessèd was the breast that fed thee;
   blessèd was the hand that led thee;
   blessèd was the parent's eye
   that watched thy slumbering infancy.

3. Blessèd she by all creation,
   who brought forth the world's salvation,
   blèssed they for ever blest
   who love thee most and serve thee best.

4. Virgin-born, we bow before thee:
   blessèd was the womb that bore thee;
   Mary, maid and mother mild,
   blessèd was she in her child.

Words: Reginald Heber (1783-1826)
Music: Melody form 14th c. German MS.

WALK WITH ME

Introduction
Chorus
Walk
with me, oh my Lord,
through the dark- est
night and bright- est day.
Be
at my side, oh Lord,
hold my hand and
mf
f
mf
A7
D
D
A7
Em
A7

2. Stones often bar my path
and there are times I fall,
but you are always there
to help me when I call.

3. Just as you calmed the wind
and walked upon the sea,
conquer, my living Lord,
the storms that threaten me.

4. Help me to pierce the mists
that cloud my heart and mind,
so that I shall not fear
the steepest mountain-side.

5. As once you healed the lame
and gave sight to the blind,
help me when I'm downcast
to hold my head up high.

Words and Music: Estelle White

WANDER IN THE SUN

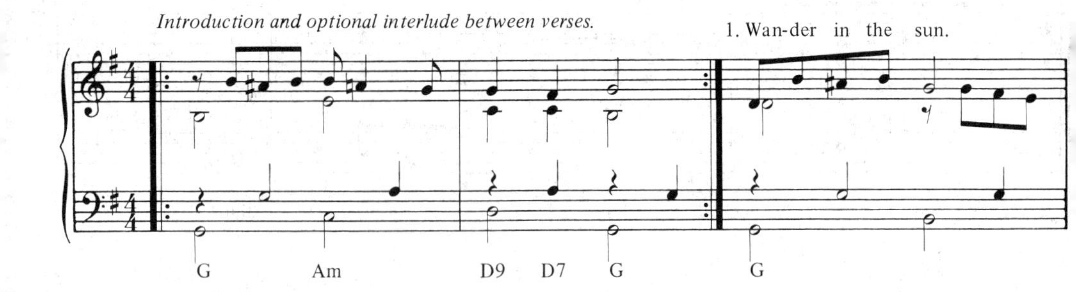

2. Watch a feather fall.
Lay it on your cheek.
Jesus is as gentle
with the frightened and the weak.

3. See the drops of rain,
sparkling as they fall.
Jesus is as gen'rous
with his blessings to us all.

4. Can you hold the sea?
Make a living flower?
Neither can we understand
the greatness of his power.

5. Yet run against the wind –
very soon you'll see –
just as strong and free is
Jesus' love for you and me.

Words and Music: Susan Sayers,
arranged by Gerard P. Fitzpatrick

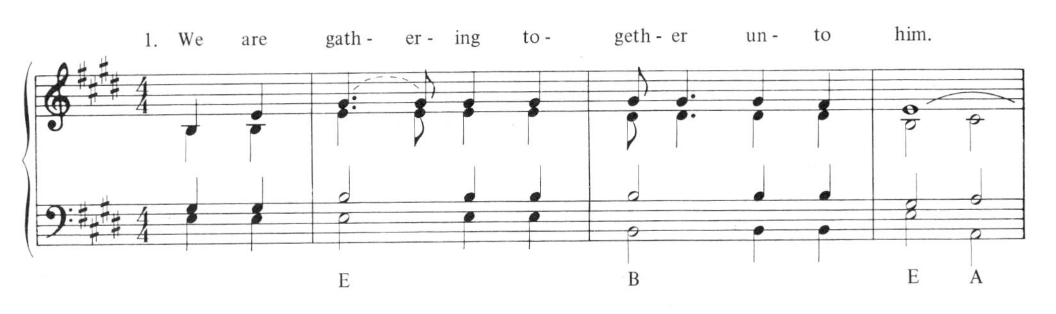

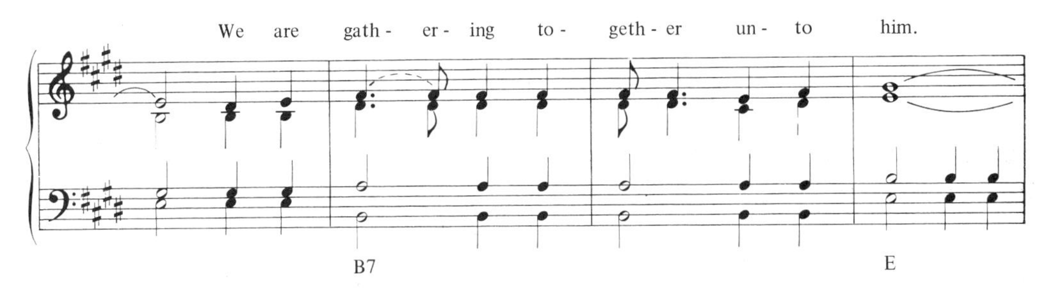

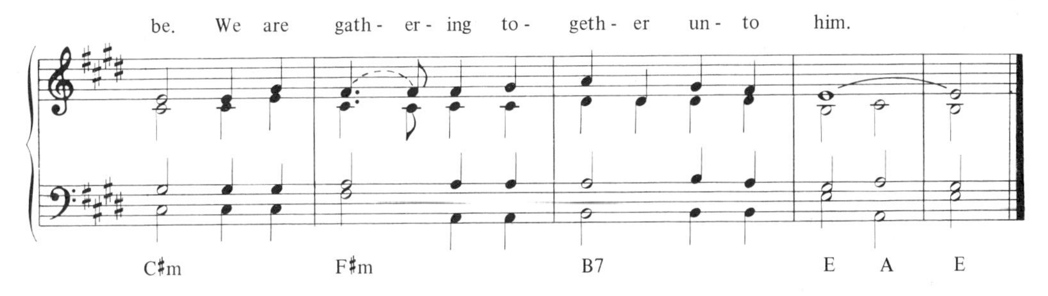

2. We are offering together unto him. *(2)*

3. We are singing together unto him. *(2)*

4. We are praying together unto him. *(2)*

Words and Music: Unknown, arranged by John Rombaut

Refrain descant (preferably for tenors)

Words, based on Matthew 21: 6-9, and Music: Mimi Farra

WE FIND THEE, LORD, IN OTHERS' NEED
('Wilford' 87.87.)

[HARMONY]

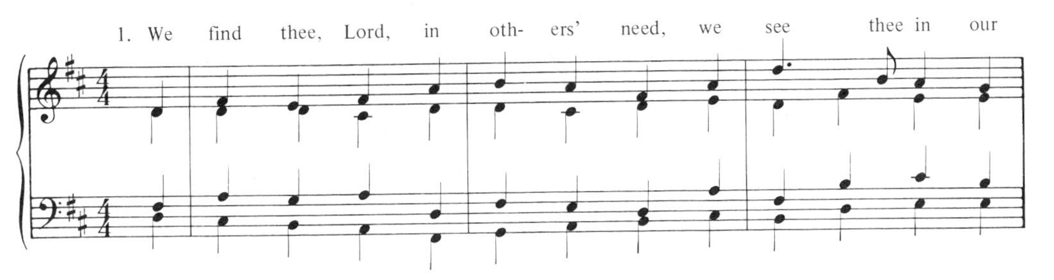

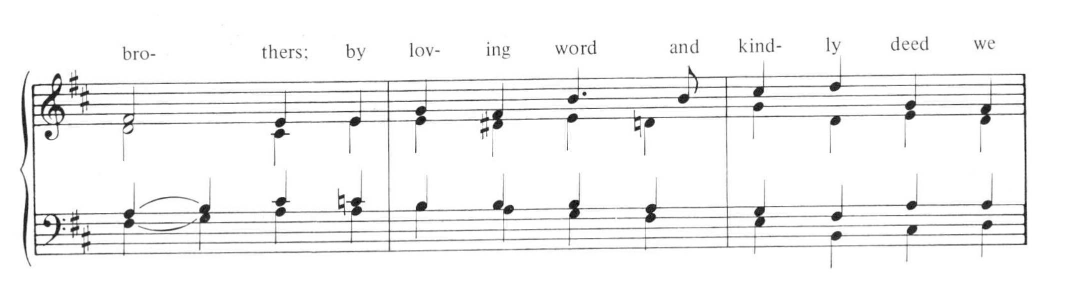

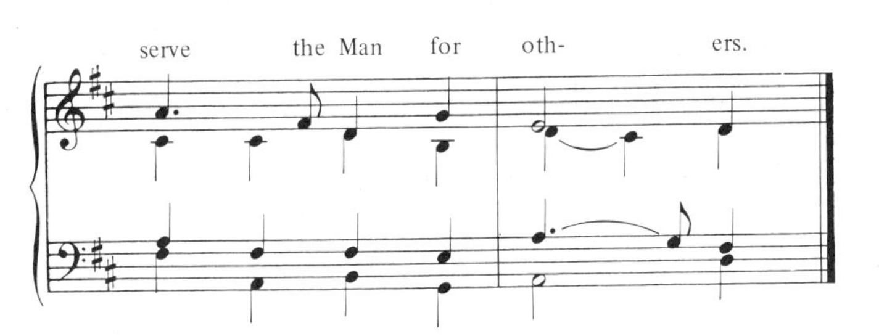

2. We look around and see thy face
disfigured, marred, neglected;
we find thee Lord in every place,
sought for and unexpected.

3. We offer in simplicity
our loving gift and labour;
and what we do, we do to thee,
incarnate in our neighbour.

4. We love since we are loved by thee;
new strength from thee we gather;
and in thy service we shall be
made perfect with each other.

Words: Giles Ambrose
Music: Adapted from a melody by George Gardner (1853-1925)

WE HAVE COME INTO HIS HOUSE

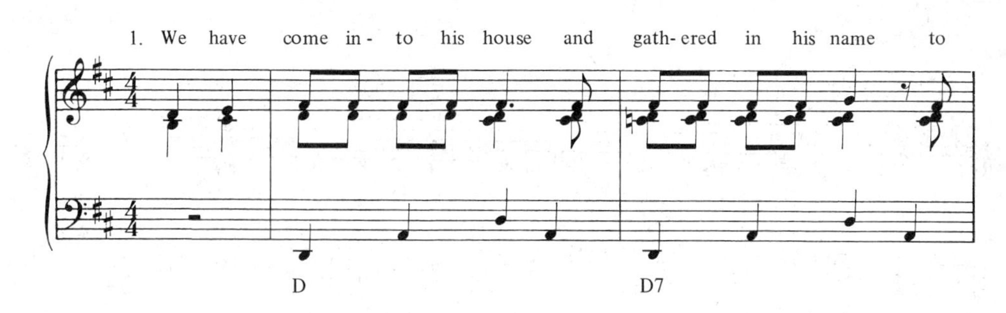

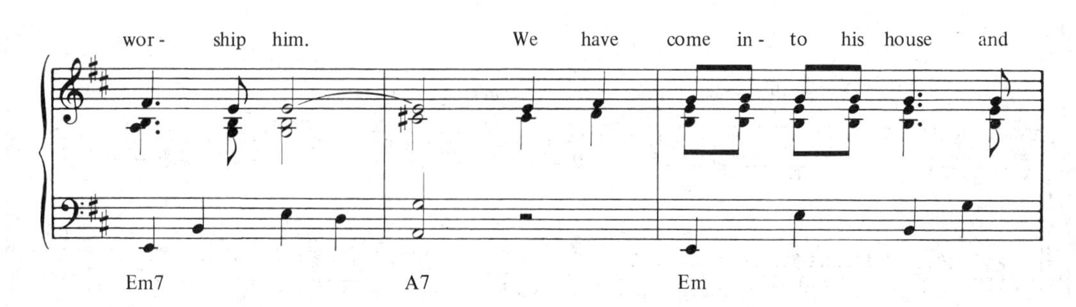

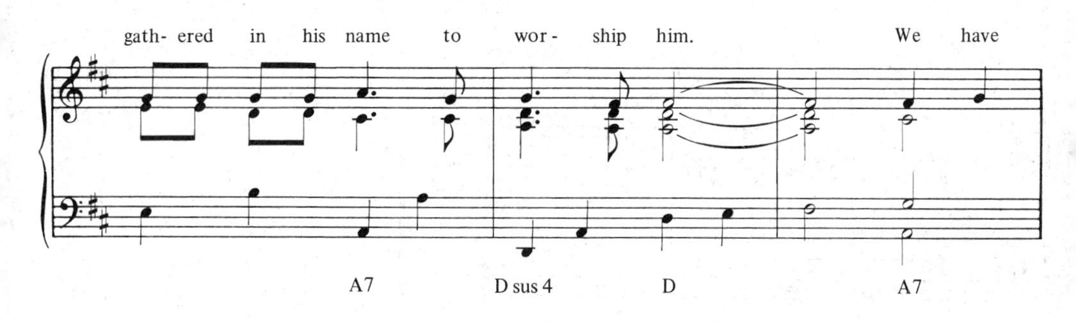

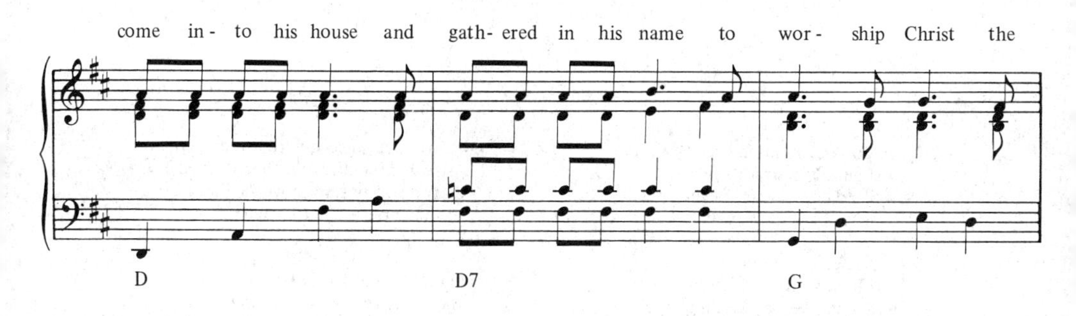

2. So forget about yourself
 and concentrate on him
 and worship him. *(2)*
 So forget about yourself
 and concentrate on him
 and worship Christ the Lord,
 worship him, Christ, the Lord.

3. Let us lift up holy hands
 and magnify his name
 and worship him. *(2)*
 Let us lift up holy hands,
 and magnify his name,
 and worship Christ the Lord,
 worship him, Christ, the Lord.

Words and Music: Bruce Ballinger

562

WELCOME ALL YE NOBLE SAINTS **(God and man at table are sat down)**

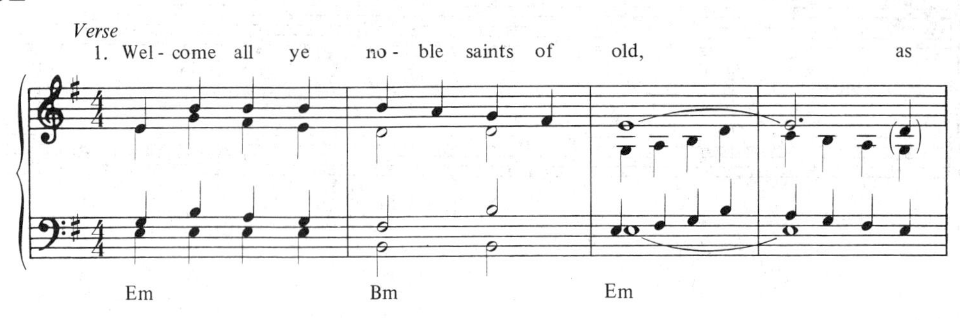

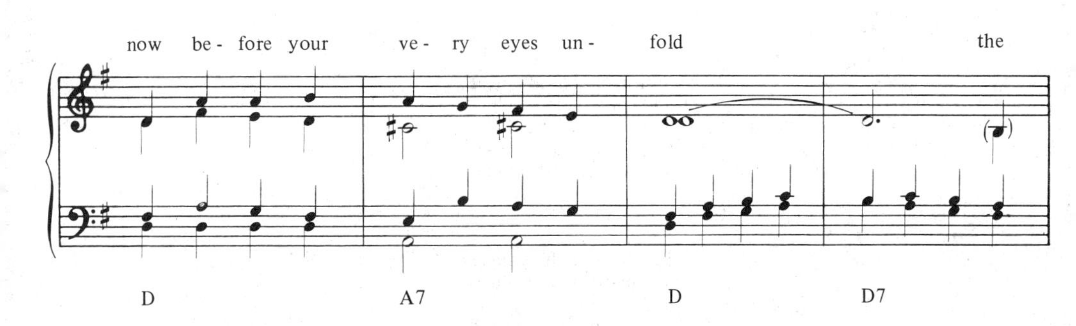

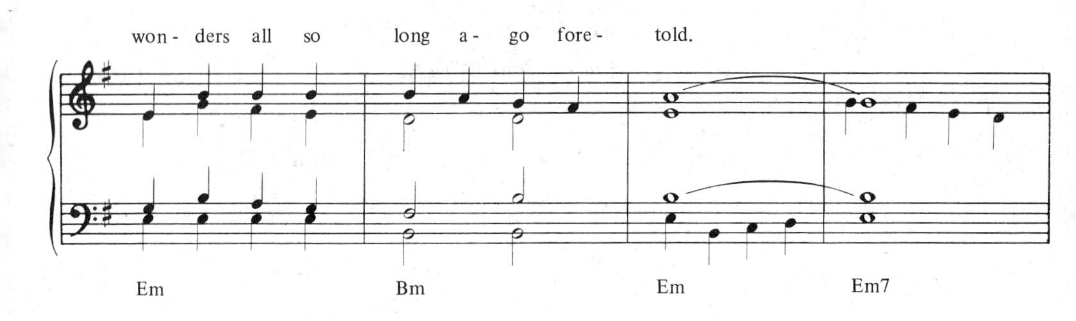

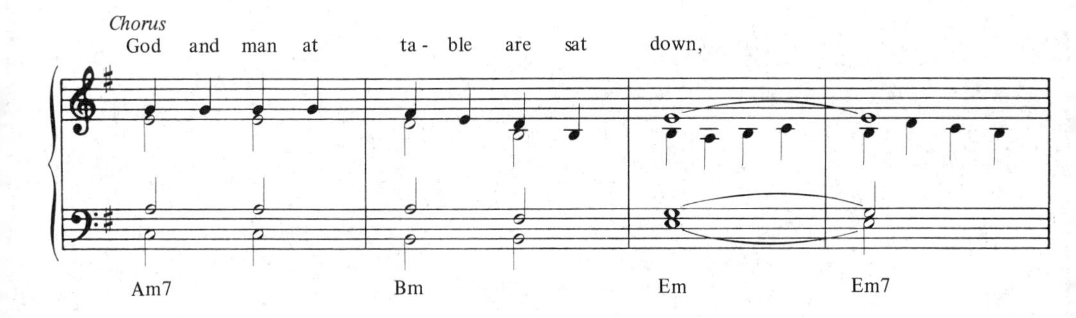

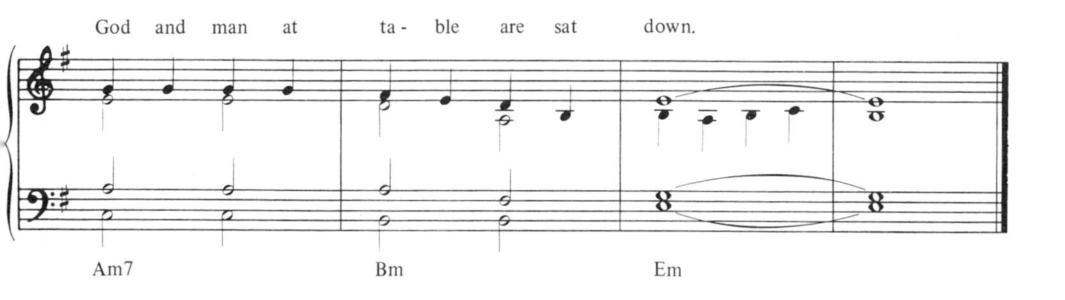

2. Elders, martyrs, all are falling down,
prophets, patriarchs are gath'ring round;
what angels longed to see, now man has found.

3. Who is this who spreads the vict'ry feast?
Who is this who makes our warring cease?
Jesus risen, Saviour, Prince of Peace.

4. Beggars lame, and harlots also here;
repentant publicans are drawing near;
wayward sons come home without a fear.

5. Worship in the presence of the Lord
with joyful songs, and hearts in one accord,
and let our host at table be adored.

6. When at last this earth shall pass away,
when Jesus and his bride are one to stay,
the feast of love is just begun that day.

Words and Music: Robert J. Stamps

WE LOVE THE PLACE, O GOD

('Quam dilecta' 66.66.)

[HARMONY]

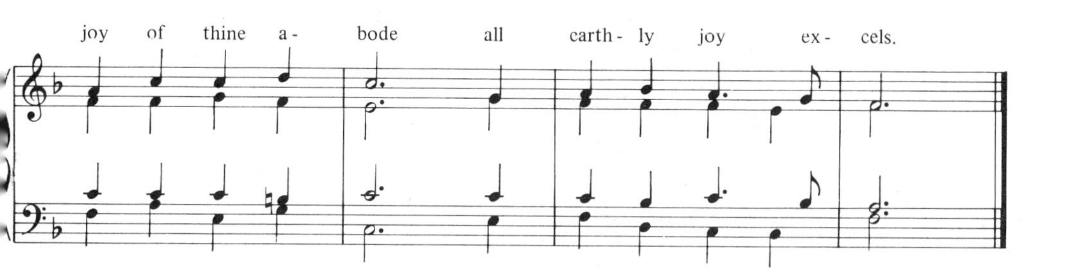

2. We love the house of prayer,
wherein thy servants meet;
and thou, O Lord, art there
thy chosen flock to greet.

3. We love the sacred font;
for there the holy Dove
to pour is ever wont
his blessing from above.

4. We love thine altar, Lord;
O what on earth so dear?
for there, in faith adored,
we find thy presence near.

5. We love the word of life,
the word that tells of peace,
of comfort in the strife,
and joys that never cease.

6. We love to sing below
for mercies freely given;
but O, we long to know
the triumph-song of heaven.

7. Lord Jesus, give us grace
on earth to love thee more,
in heaven to see thy face,
and with thy saints adore.

Words: William Bullock (1798-1874)
and Henry Williams Baker (1821-77)
Music: Henry Lascelles Jenner (1820-98)

564 [HARMONY]

WE PLOUGH THE FIELDS AND SCATTER
('Wir pflügen (Dresden)' 76.76.76.76.66.84.)

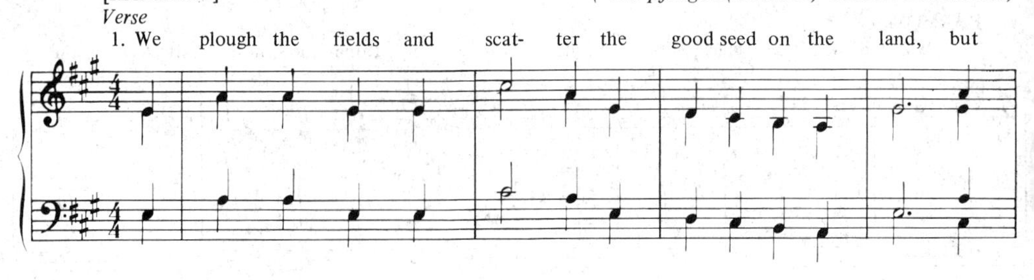

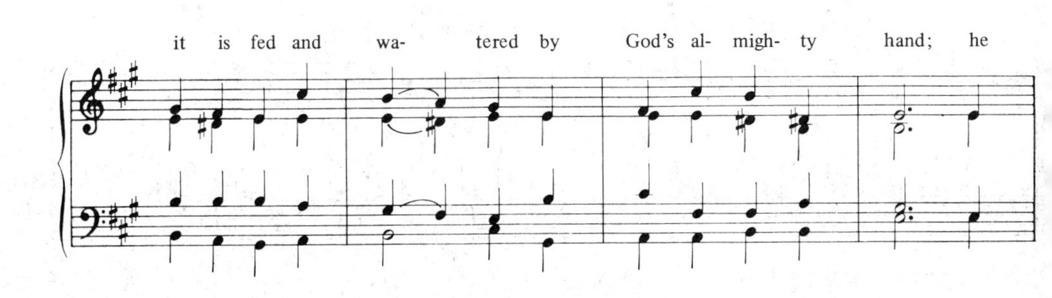

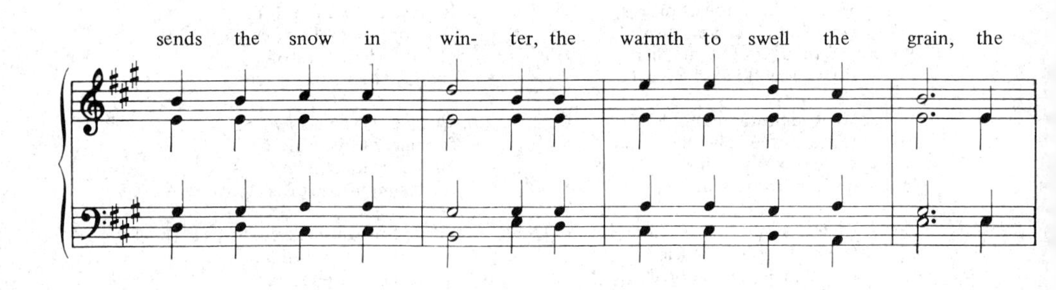

2. He only is the maker
   of all things near and far;
   he paints the wayside flower,
   he lights the evening star.
   The winds and waves obey him,
   by him the birds are fed:
   much more to us his children,
   he gives our daily bread.

3. We thank thee then, O Father,
   for all things bright and good:
   the seed-time and the harvest,
   our life, our health, our food.
   Accept the gifts we offer
   for all thy love imparts,
   and, what thou most desirest,
   our humble, thankful hearts.

Words: M. Claudius (1740-1815),
tr. J. M. Campbell (1817-78)
Music: J. A. P. Schulz (1747-1800)

WE PRAY THEE, HEAVENLY FATHER

('Dies Dominica' 76.76.D.)

2. All that we have we offer,
   for it is all thine own,
   all gifts, by thine appointment,
   in bread and cup are shown;
   one thing alone we bring not,
   the wilfulness of sin,
   and all we bring is nothing
   save that which is within.

3. Within the pure oblation,
   beneath the outward sign,
   by that his operation,
   the Holy Ghost divine,
   lies hid the sacred body,
   lies hid the precious blood,
   once slain, now ever glorious,
   of Christ our Lord and God.

4. Wherefore, though all unworthy
   to offer sacrifice,
   we pray that this our duty
   be pleasing in thine eyes;
   for praise, and thanks and worship,
   for mercy and for aid,
   the catholic oblation
   of Jesus Christ is made.

Words: V. S. S. Coles (1845-1929)
Music: J. B. Dykes (1823-76)

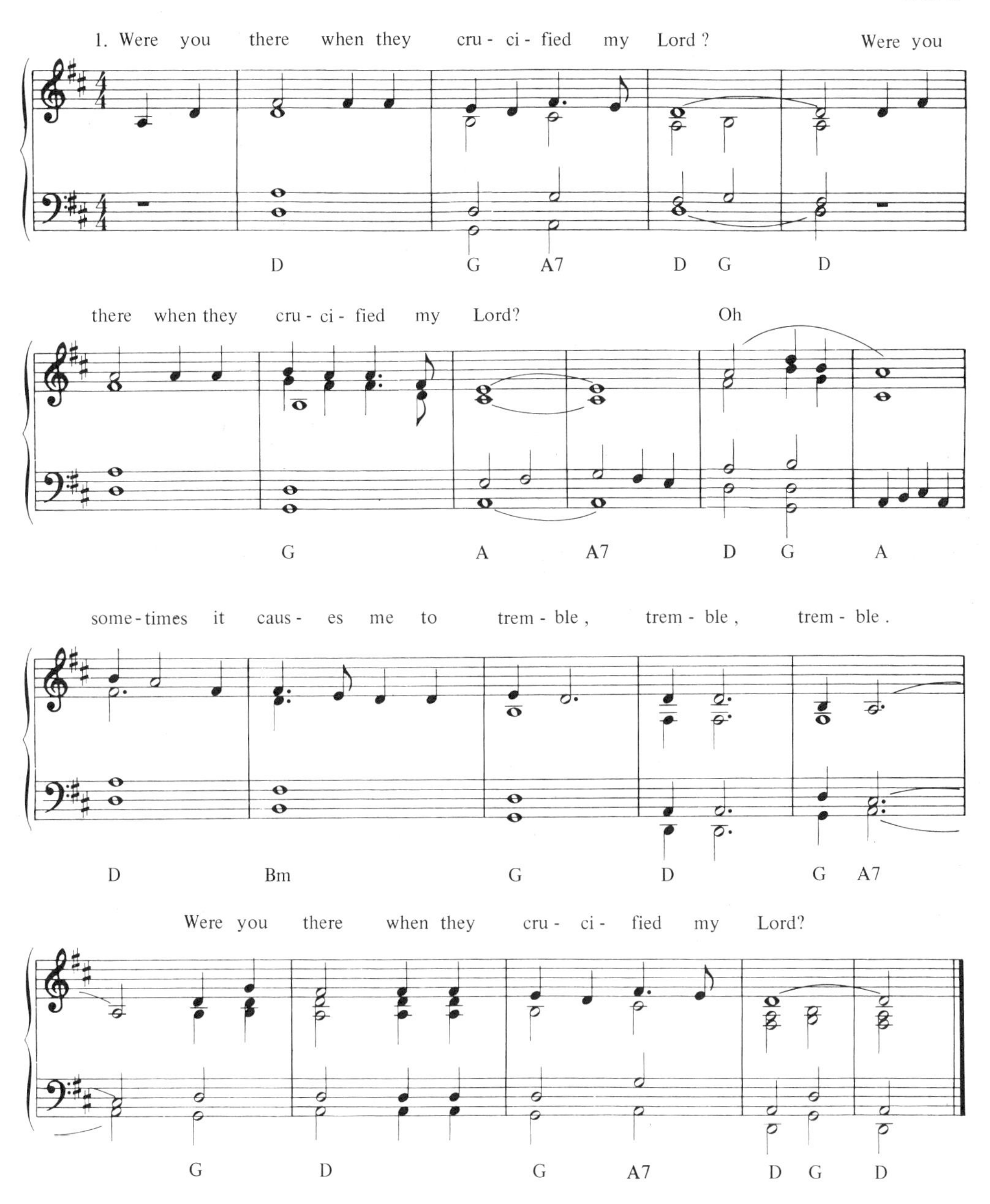

2. Were you there
when they nailed him to a tree? . . .

3. Were you there
when they pierced him in the side? . . .

4. Were you there
when the sun refused to shine? . . .

5. Were you there
when they laid him in the tomb? . . .

6. Were you there
when he rose from out the tomb? . . .

Words and Music: Spiritual,
arranged by John Rombaut

WE SEE THE LORD

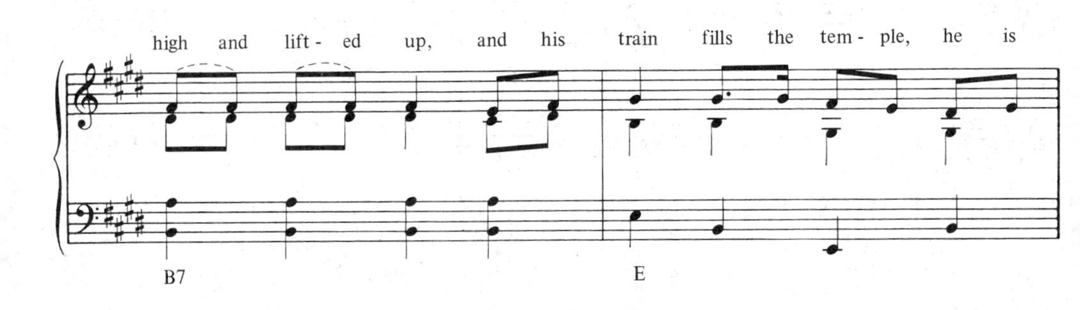

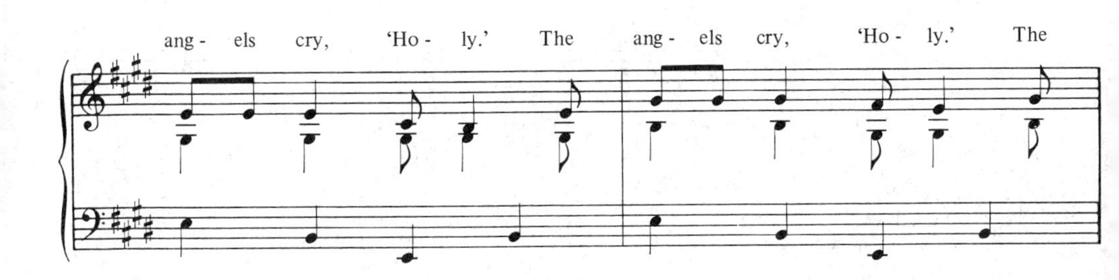

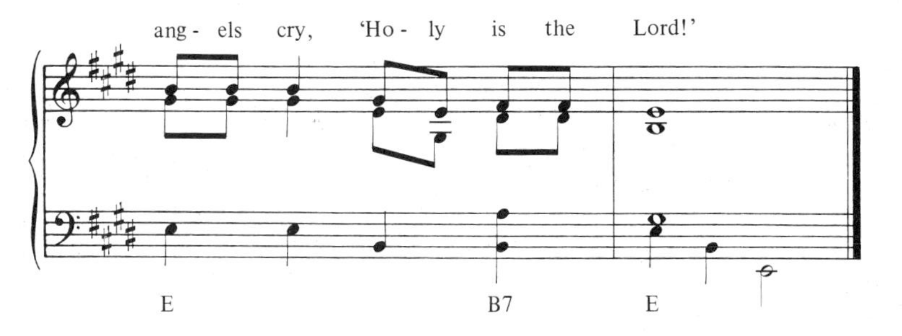

2. We see the Lord, *(2)*
   and his face shines forth
      as a light in the Temple. *(2)*
   The seraphs cry, 'Worthy!' *(2)*
   The seraphs cry, 'Worthy is the Lord!'

3. We hear the Lord, *(2)*
   and his Word issues forth
      and resounds through the temple. *(2)*
   The elders cry, 'Amen!' *(2)*
   The elders cry, 'Amen to the Lord!'

4. We bless the Lord, *(2)*
   and as incense goes up,
      so our prayers fill the temple. *(2)*
   The people cry, 'Glory!' *(2)*
   The people cry, 'Glory to the Lord!'

Words, based on Isaiah 6: 1 & 3, Revelation 4, and Music: Unknown, arranged by John Rombaut

568

WE SING THE GLORIOUS CONQUEST

('Ellacombe' 76.76.D.)

[HARMONY]

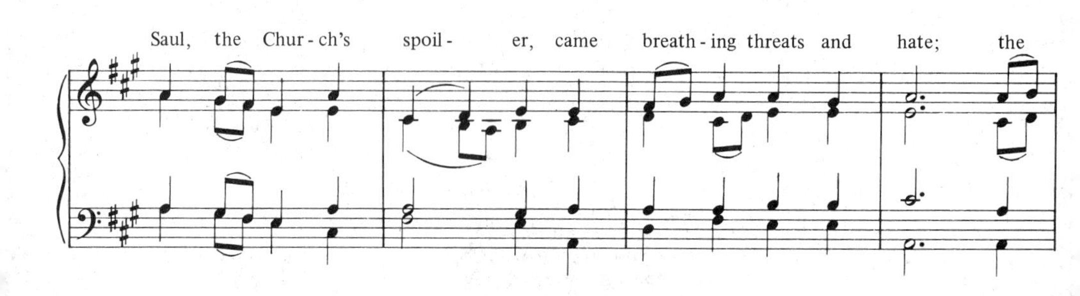

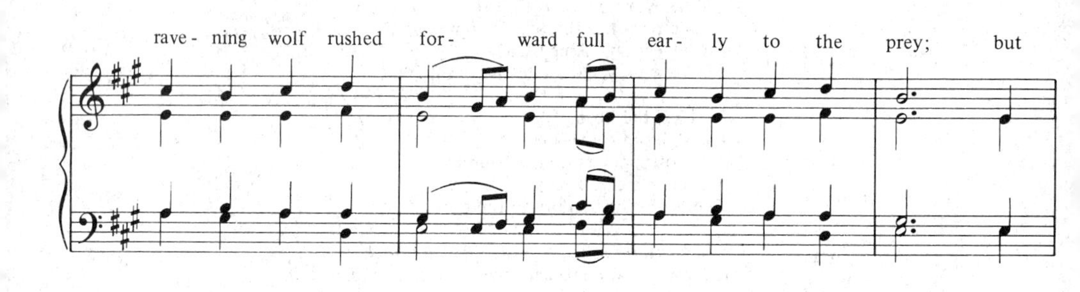

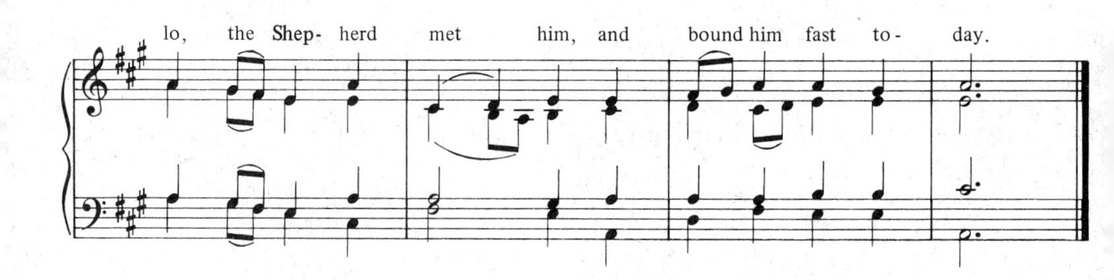

2. O glory most excelling
that smote across his path!
O light that pierced and blinded
the zealot in his wrath!
O voice that spake within him
the calm reproving word!
O love that sought and held him
the bondman of his Lord!

3. O Wisdom, ordering all things
in order strong and sweet,
what nobler spoil was ever
cast at the Victor's feet?
What wiser master-builder
e'er wrought at thine employ
than he, till now so furious
thy building to destroy?

4. Lord, teach thy Church the lesson,
still in her darkest hour
of weakness and of danger
to trust thy hidden power:
thy grace by ways mysterious
the wrath of man can bind,
and in thy boldest foeman
thy chosen saint can find.

Words: John Ellerton (1826-93)
Music: 'Mainz Gesangbuch' (1833)

WE SING THE PRAISE OF HIM WHO DIED

(First tune: 'Calvisius' L.M.)

2. Inscribed upon the cross we see
in shining letters, 'God is love';
he bears our sins upon the Tree;
he brings us mercy from above.

3. The Cross! it takes our guilt away:
it holds the fainting spirit up;
it cheers with hope the gloomy day,
and sweetens every bitter cup.

4. It makes the coward spirit brave,
and nerves the feeble arm for fight;
it takes its terror from the grave,
and gilds the bed of death with light:

5. The balm of life, the cure of woe,
the measure and the pledge of love,
the sinner's refuge here below,
the angels' theme in heaven above.

Words: Thomas Kelly (1769-1855)
Music: First tune - melody by S. Calvisius (1594), harmonised by J. S. Bach

WE SING THE PRAISE OF HIM WHO DIED

(Second tune: 'Bow Brickhill' L.M.)

[HARMONY]

2. Inscribed upon the cross we see
in shining letters, 'God is love';
he bears our sins upon the Tree;
he brings us mercy from above.

3. The Cross! it takes our guilt away:
it holds the fainting spirit up;
it cheers with hope the gloomy day,
and sweetens every bitter cup.

4. It makes the coward spirit brave,
and nerves the feeble arm for fight;
it takes its terror from the grave,
and gilds the bed of death with light:

5. The balm of life, the cure of woe,
the measure and the pledge of love,
the sinner's refuge here below,
the angels' theme in heaven above.

Words: Thomas Kelly (1769-1855)
Music: Second tune - Sydney H. Nicholson (1875-1947)

[HARMONY]

WE THREE KINGS

('We three kings' 88.86. & Chorus)

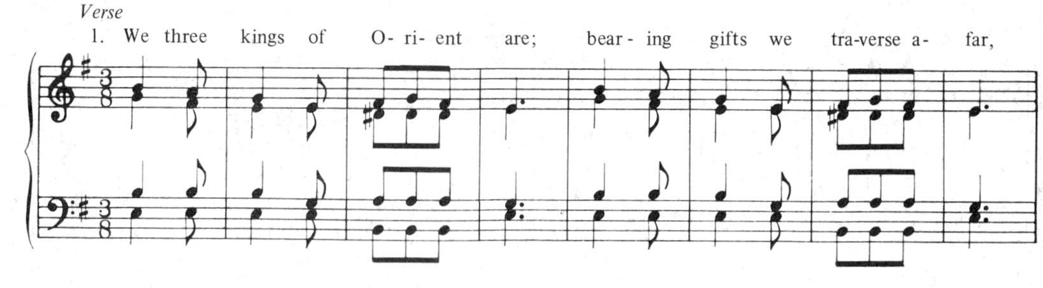

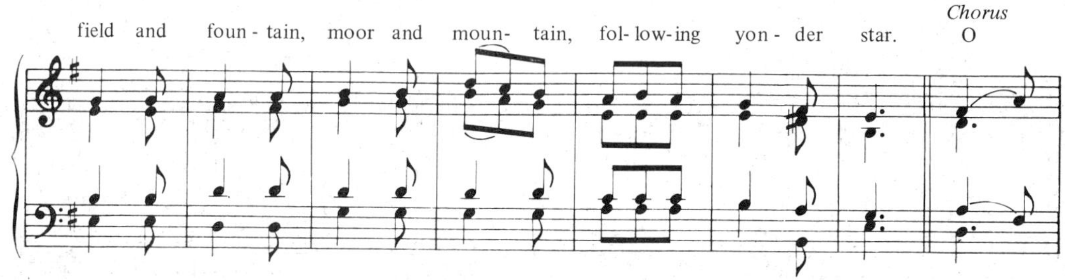

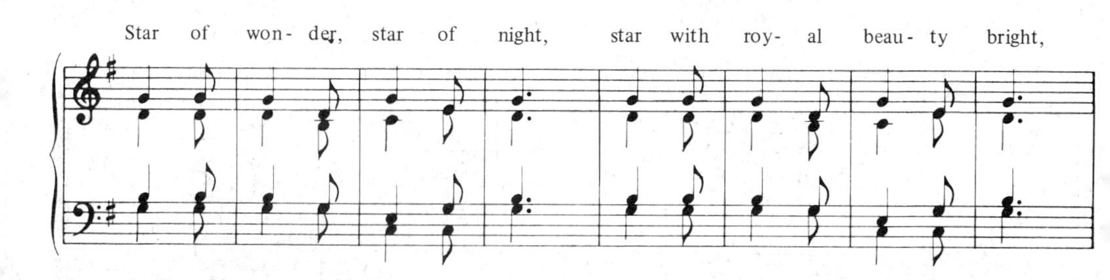

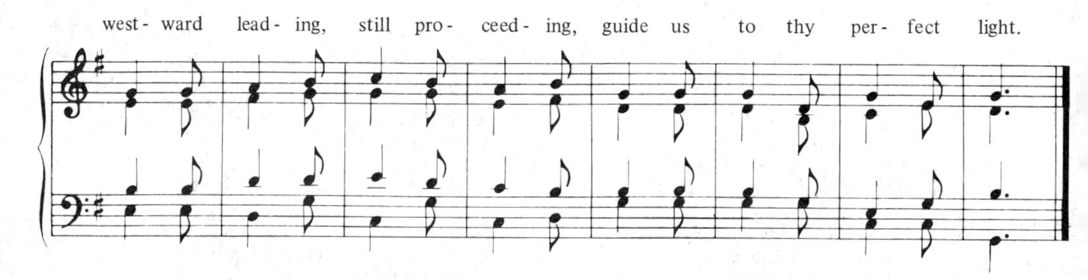

2. Born a King on Bethlehem plain,
gold I bring, to crown him again,
King for ever, ceasing never,
over us all to reign.

3. Frankincense to offer have I,
incense owns a Deity nigh,
prayer and praising, all men raising,
worship him, God most high.

4. Myrrh is mine, its bitter perfume
breathes a life of gathering gloom;
sorrowing, sighing, bleeding, dying,
sealed in the stone-cold tomb.

5. Glorious now behold him arise,
King and God and sacrifice;
alleluia, alleluia,
earth to heaven replies.

Words and Music: J. H. Hopkins (1822-1900)

571

WHAT A FRIEND WE HAVE IN JESUS

('Converse' 87.87.D.)

2. Have we trials and temptations?
Is there trouble anywhere?
We should never be discouraged:
take it to the Lord in prayer!
Can we find a friend so faithful,
who will all our sorrows share?
Jesus knows our every weakness –
take it to the Lord in prayer!

3. Are we weak and heavy-laden,
cumbered with a load of care?
Jesus only is our refuge,
take it to the Lord in prayer!
Do thy friends despise, forsake thee?
Take it to the Lord in prayer!
In his arms he'll take and shield thee,
thou wilt find a solace there.

Words: Joseph Scriven (1819-86)
Music: C. C. Converse (1832-1918)

572

WHAT CHILD IS THIS

('Greensleeves' 87.87.68.67.)

2. Why lies he in such mean estate, where ox and ass are feeding?
Good Christians, fear: for sinners here the silent Word is pleading.
Nails, spear, shall pierce him through,
the cross be borne for me, for you:
hail, hail the Word made flesh, the Babe, the Son of Mary!

3. So bring him incense, gold and myrrh, come peasant, king, to own him.
The King of kings salvation brings, let loving hearts enthrone him.
Raise, raise the song on high,
the Virgin sings her lullaby:
joy, joy for Christ is born, the Babe, the Son of Mary!

Words: W. Chatterton Dix (1837-98)
Music: Traditional English Melody

WHEN A KNIGHT WON HIS SPURS

('Stowey' 12 12.12 12.)

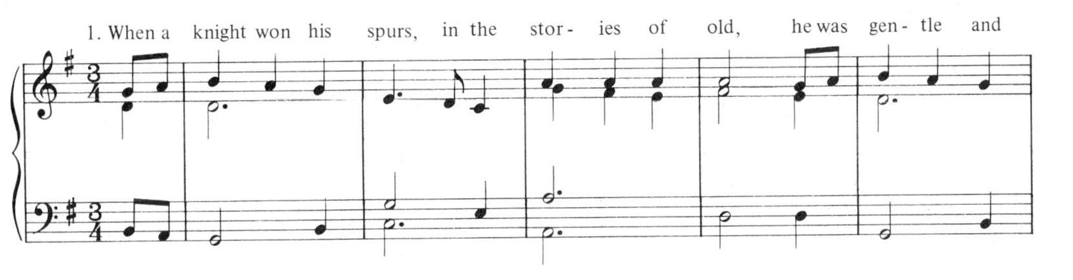

2. No charger have I, and no sword by my side,
yet still to adventure and battle I ride,
though back into storyland giants have fled,
and the knights are no more and the dragons are dead.

3. Let faith be my shield and let joy be my steed
'gainst the dragons of anger, the ogres of greed;
and let me set free, with the sword of my youth,
from the castle of darkness, the power of the truth.

Words: Jan Struther (1901-53)
Music: arranged by R. Vaughan Williams (1872-1958)

574

WHEN ALL THY MERCIES
('Belgrave' C.M.)

[HARMONY]

2. Unnumbered comforts to my soul
thy tender care bestowed,
before my infant heart conceived
from whom those comforts flowed.

3. When in the slippery paths of youth
with heedless steps I ran,
thine arm unseen conveyed me safe,
and led me up to man.

4. When worn with sickness oft hast thou
with health renewed my face;
and when in sins and sorrows sunk,
revived my soul with grace.

5. Through every period of my life
thy goodness I'll pursue,
and after death in distant worlds
the glorious theme renew.

6. Through all eternity to thee
a joyful song I'll raise;
for O! eternity's too short
to utter all thy praise.

Words: Joseph Addison (1672-1719)
Music: William Horsley (1774-1858)

For an alternative version of this tune see From Thee All Skill and Science Flow (137)

WHEN CAME IN FLESH THE INCARNATE WORD

('Winchester Old' C.M.)

[HARMONY]

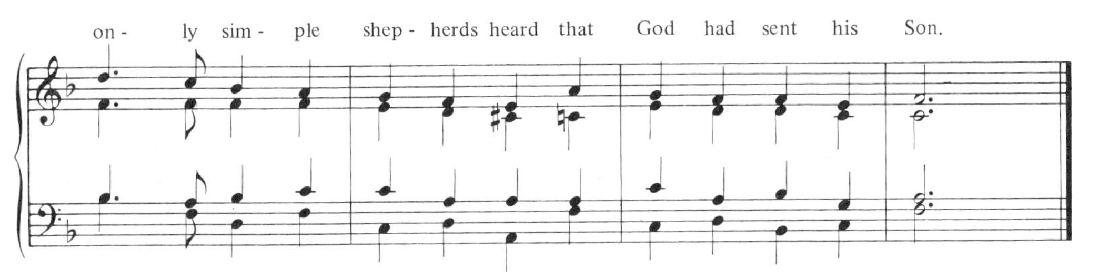

[HARMONY]

Alternative arrangement with the melody in the Tenor, harmonised by Thomas Ravenscroft (1621)

2. When comes the Saviour at the last,
   from east to west shall shine
   the awful pomp and earth aghast
   shall tremble at the sign.

3. Then shall the pure in heart be blest;
   as mild he comes to them,
   as when upon the Virgin's breast
   he lay at Bethlehem.

4. As mild to meek-eyed love and faith,
   only more strong to save;
   strengthened by having bowed to death,
   by having burst the grave.

5. Lord, who could dare see thee descend
   in state, unless he knew
   thou art the sorrowing sinner's friend,
   the gracious and the true?

6. Dwell in our hearts, O Saviour blest;
   so shall thine advent's dawn
   'twixt us and thee, our bosom-guest,
   be but the veil withdrawn.

Words: Joseph Anstice (1808-36)
Music: Melody from T. Este (Psalms, 1592),

WHEN I NEEDED A NEIGHBOUR

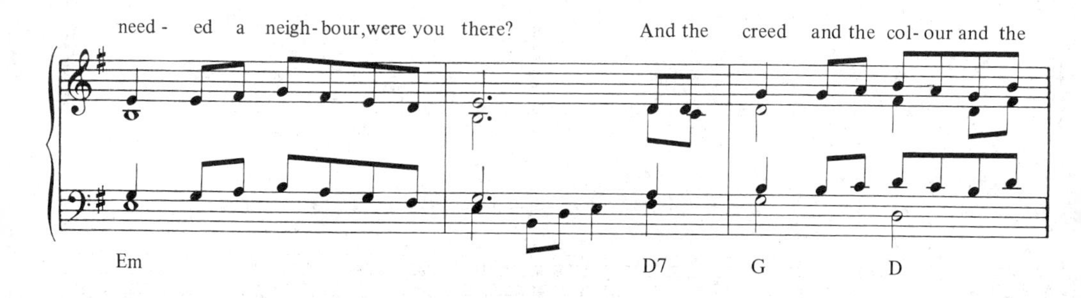

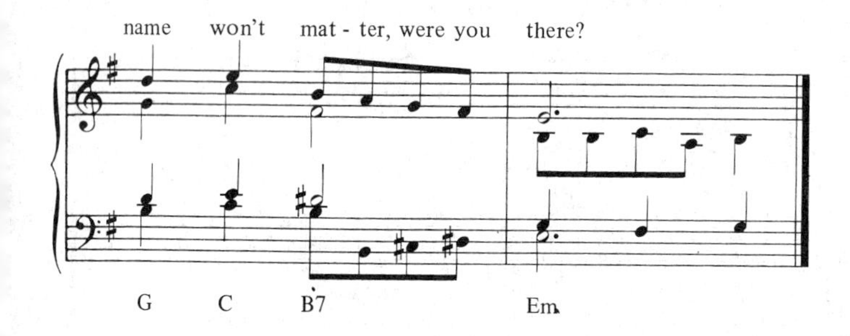

2. I was hungry and thirsty,
   were you there . . .

3. I was cold, I was naked,
   were you there . . .

4. When I needed a shelter,
   were you there . . .

5. When I needed a healer,
   were you there . . .

6. Wherever you travel,
   I'll be there . . .

Words: Sydney Carter
Music: Sydney Carter, arranged by Frances M. Kelly

WHEN ISRAEL WAS IN EGYPT'S LAND **(Go down, Moses)**

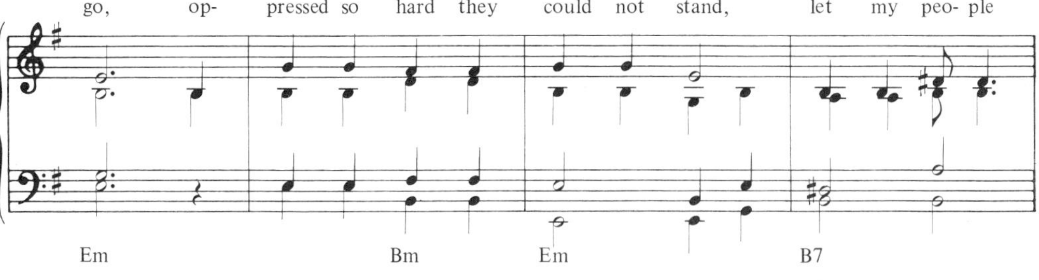

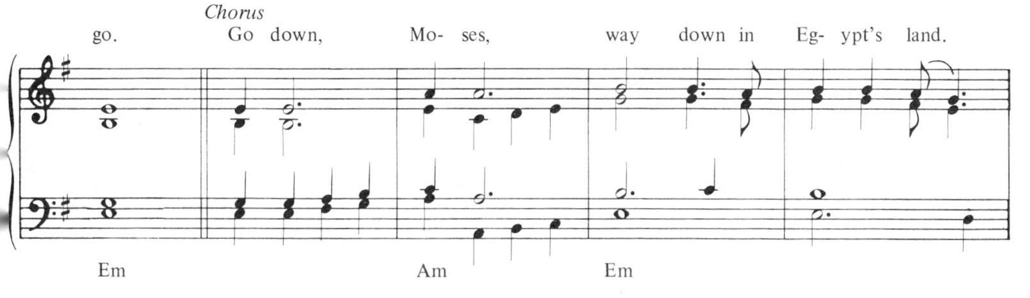

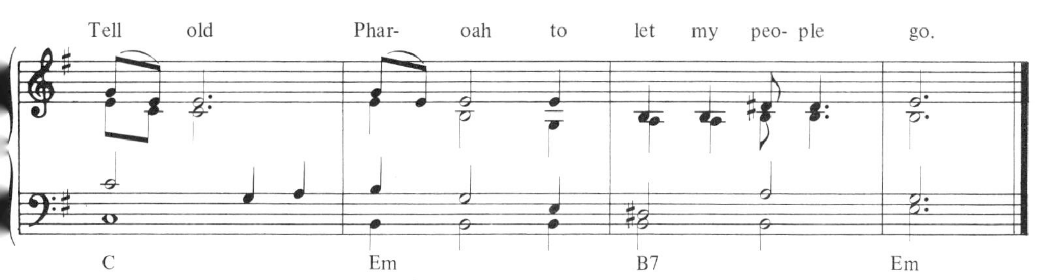

2. The Lord told Moses what to do,
   let my people go,
   to lead the children of Israel through,
   let my people go.

3. Your foes shall not before you stand,
   let my people go,
   and you'll possess fair Canaan's land,
   let my people go.

4. O let us all from bondage flee,
   let my people go,
   and let us all in Christ be free,
   let my people go.

5. I do believe without a doubt,
   let my people go,
   a Christian has a right to shout,
   let my people go.

Words and Music: Spiritual, arranged by John Rombaut

WHEN I SURVEY THE WONDROUS CROSS

('Rockingham' L.M.)

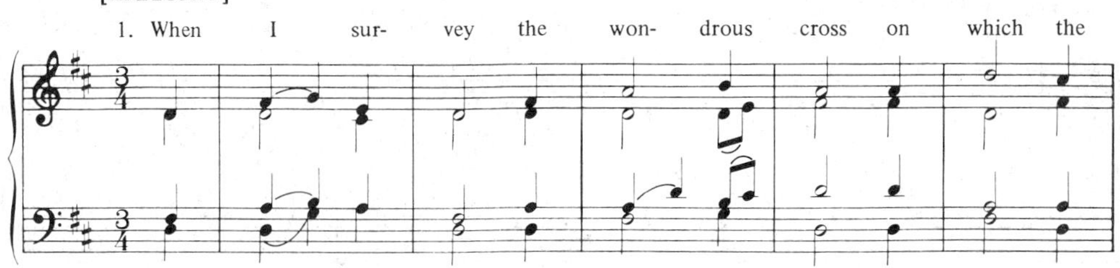

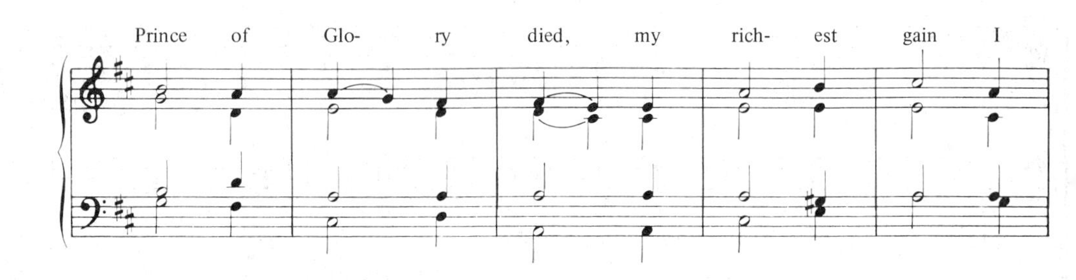

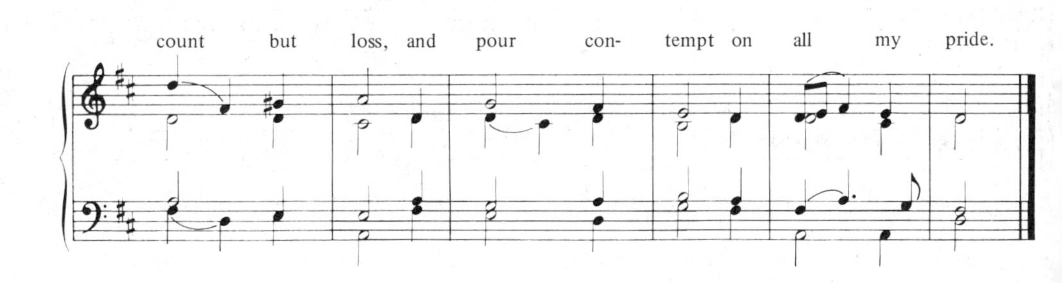

2. Forbid it, Lord, that I should boast,
   save in the death of Christ, my God:
   all the vain things that charm me most,
   I sacrifice them to his blood.

3. See from his head, his hands, his feet,
   sorrow and love flow mingled down:
   did e'er such love and sorrow meet,
   or thorns compose so rich a crown?

4. Were the whole realm of nature mine,
   that were an offering far too small;
   love so amazing, so divine,
   demands my soul, my life, my all.

Words, based on Galatians 6: Isaac Watts (1674-1748)
Music: Edward Miller (1735-1807)

WHEN MORNING GILDS THE SKIES

('Laudes Domini' 66.66.66.)

[HARMONY]

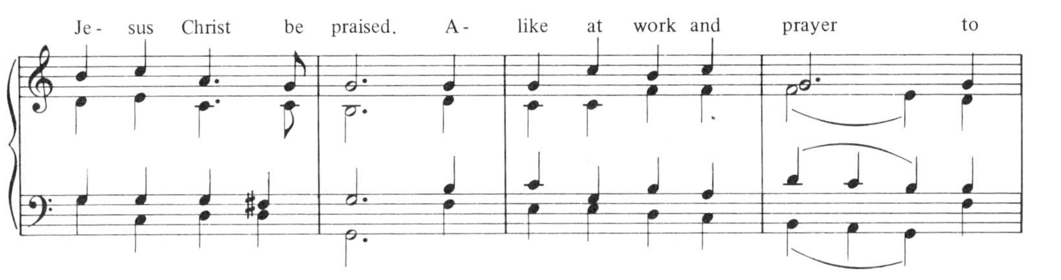

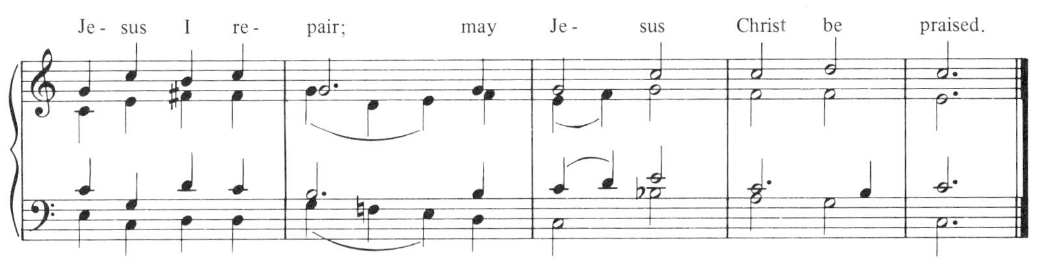

2. The sacred minster bell
it peals o'er hill and dell,
may Jesus Christ be praised.
O hark to what it sings,
as joyously it rings,
may Jesus Christ be praised.

3. My tongue shall never tire
of chanting in the choir,
may Jesus Christ be praised;
the fairest graces spring
in hearts that ever sing,
may Jesus Christ be praised.

4. When sleep her balm denies,
my silent spirit sighs,
may Jesus Christ be praised;
when evil thoughts molest,
with this I shield my breast,
may Jesus Christ be praised.

5. Does sadness fill my mind?
a solace here I find,
may Jesus Christ be praised;
or fades my earthly bliss?
my comfort still is this,
may Jesus Christ be praised.

6. The night becomes as day,
when from the heart we say,
may Jesus Christ be praised;
the powers of darkness fear,
when this sweet chant they hear,
may Jesus Christ be praised.

7. In heaven's eternal bliss
the loveliest strain is this,
may Jesus Christ be praised;
let air, and sea, and sky
from depth to height reply,
may Jesus Christ be praised.

8. Be this, while life is mine,
my canticle divine,
may Jesus Christ be praised;
be this the eternal song
through all the ages on,
may Jesus Christ be praised.

Words: German (19th century), tr. E. Caswall
Music: Joseph Barnby (1838-96)

580

[HARMONY]

WHILE SHEPHERDS WATCHED
('Winchester Old' C.M.)

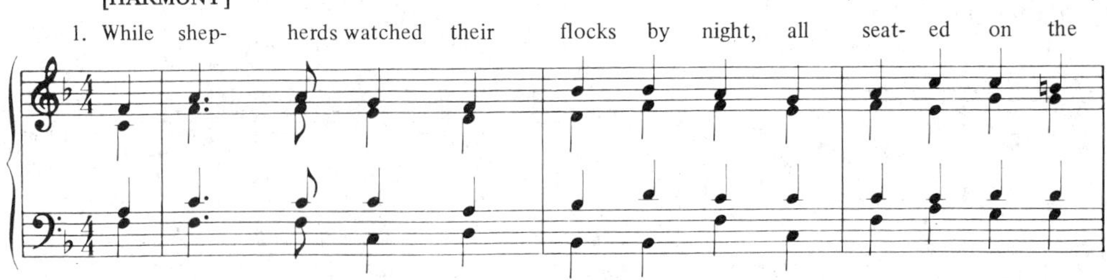

An alternative arrangement of this tune may be found at Hymn 575

2. 'Fear not,' said he, (for mighty dread
had seized their troubled mind)
'Glad tidings of great joy I bring
to you and all mankind.'

3. 'To you in David's town this day
is born of David's line
a Saviour, who is Christ the Lord;
and this shall be the sign:

4. 'The heavenly Babe you there shall find
to human view displayed,
all meanly wrapped in swathing bands,
and in a manger laid.'

5. Thus spake the Seraph; and forthwith
appeared a shining throng
of angels praising God, who thus
addressed their joyful song:

6. 'All glory be to God on high,
and on the earth be peace,
goodwill henceforth from
heaven to men
begin and never cease.'

Words: Nahum Tate (1652-1715)
Music: from 'Este's Psalter' (1592)

WHO ARE THESE, LIKE STARS APPEARING

581

('All Saints' 87.87.77.)

[HARMONY]

2. Who are these in dazzling brightness,
clothed in God's own righteousness,
these, whose robes of purest whiteness
shall their lustre still possess,
still untouched by time's rude hand?
whence came all this glorious band?

3. These are they who have contended
for their Saviour's honour long,
wrestling on till life was ended,
following not the sinful throng;
these, who well the fight sustained,
triumph by the Lamb have gained.

4. These are they whose hearts were riven,
sore with woe and anguish tried,
who in prayer full oft have striven
with the God they glorified;
now, their painful conflict o'er,
God has bid them weep no more.

5. These like priests have watched and waited,
offering up to Christ their will,
soul and body consecrated,
day and night to serve him still:
now, in God's most holy place
blest they stand before his face.

Words, based on Revelation 7: 13:
Heinrich Theobald Schenk (1656-1727), tr. T. E. Cox
Music: 'Darmstadt Gesangbuch' (1698)

Verse
1. Who is this man who makes the sweet- est wine from wa- ter?
2. Who is this man who casts out dev - ils with a ges- ture?
D F♯m Em E A
Who is this man whose touch is gen- tle as a pas- sing breeze?
Who is this man who makes the crippled walk, the blind to see?
D F♯m Em A
V.5 to CODA
Who is this man whose pow'r is ov- er- whelm- ing? Tell me.
Who is this man whose love is ov- er- whelm- ing? Tell me.
G A D
Who is this man? Who can he be?
Who is this man? Who can he
(To verse 2)
G Em A D

Chorus
A. Some say E- li- jah, some say a-
be? (To Chorus) B. Some say E- li- jah, some say a-
D7 G Em7 A A7 D D7
no- ther pro- phet. Some say he's John the Bap-tist raised.
no- ther pro- phet. Some say he's John the Bap-tist raised.
Bm Bm7 G Em A A7 D
Well, all I know is he has the
Well, all I know is he is the
G Em A A7 D D7
pow'r of mi- ra- cles; for this may God a- bove be praised.
One, the sav- ing Lord: for him may God a- bove be praised.
D.C.
Bm Bm7 G Gmaj7 Em A A7

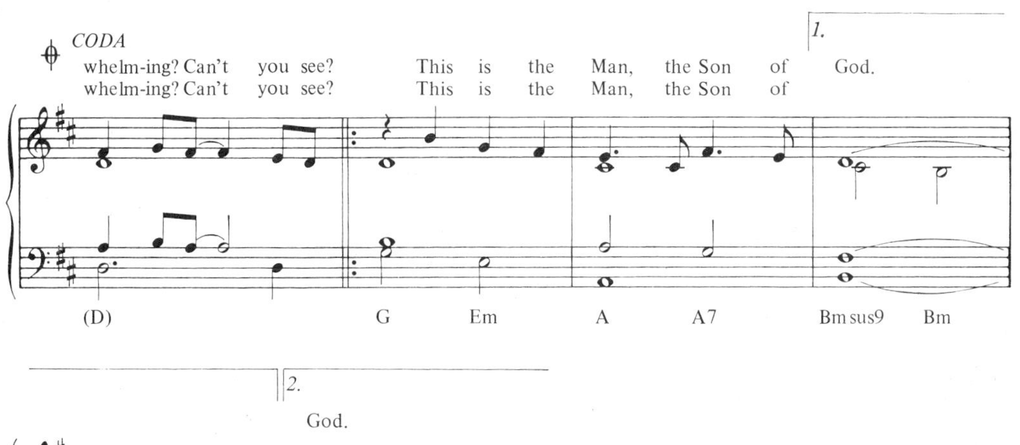

3. Who is this man
who feeds the thousands bread and fishes?
Who is this man
at whose command the world appears to be?
Who is this man
whose care is overwhelming?
Tell me: who is this man, who can he be?

(Straight on to Verse 4)

4. Who is this man
who heals the sick and raises dead men?
Who is this man
that when you touch his cloak you're well again?
Who is this man
whose words are overwhelming?
Tell me: who is this man, who can he be?

Chorus B, as given above accompaniment

5. Who is this man
who calms the wind and walks on water?
Who is this man
that when you meet his eyes your life is changed?
Who is this man
whose voice is overwhelming?

Coda
Can't you see? This is the Man, the Son of God.
This is the Man, the Son of God.

Words and Music: *Anthony Welsh,*
arranged by Frances M. Kelly

WHOM DO YOU SEEK?

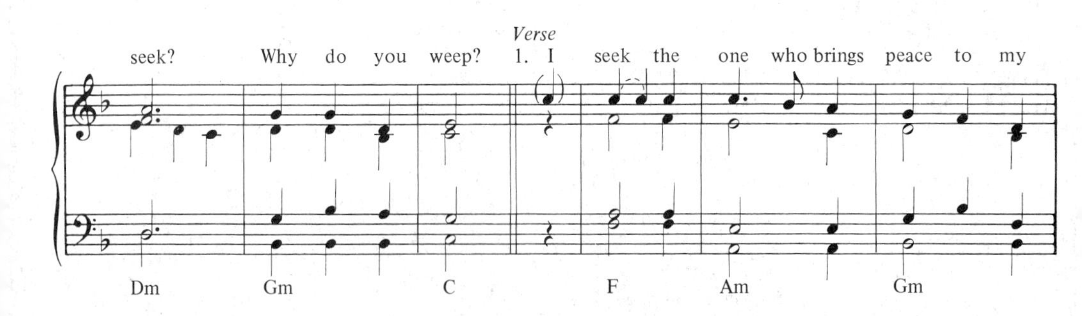

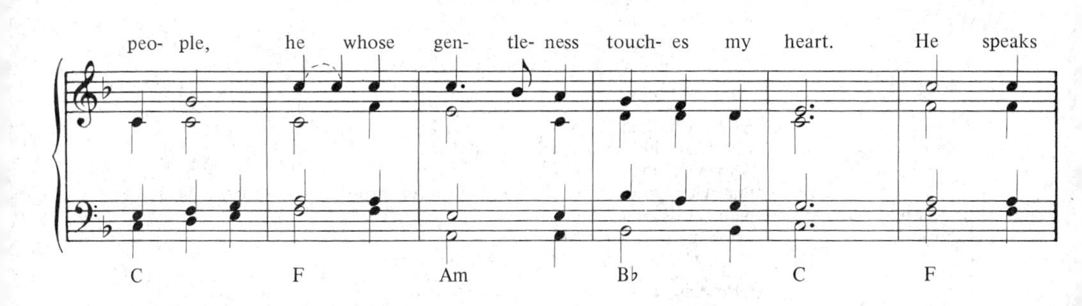

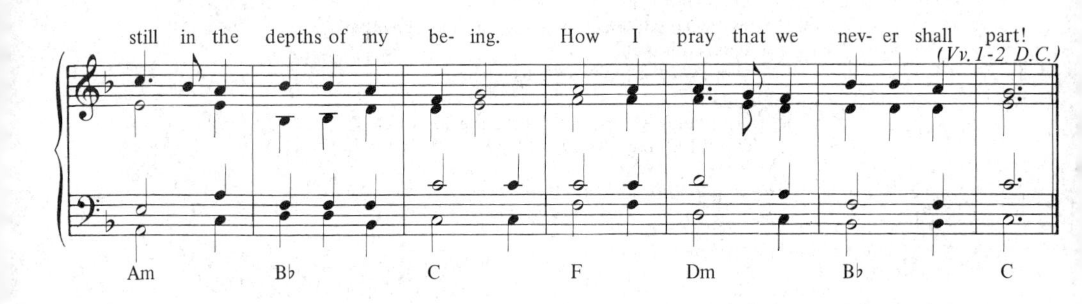

2. I seek the one who shows love for all nations,
heals all suffering, offers us peace.
He has promised a life without ending.
Love and laughter and joy will not cease.

Repeat First Chorus

3. I am the one who brings peace to all nations,
I am the one who brings love to you all.
Come to me and your hearts will be restful.
I have come to bring life to you all.

Use Final Chorus, as below.

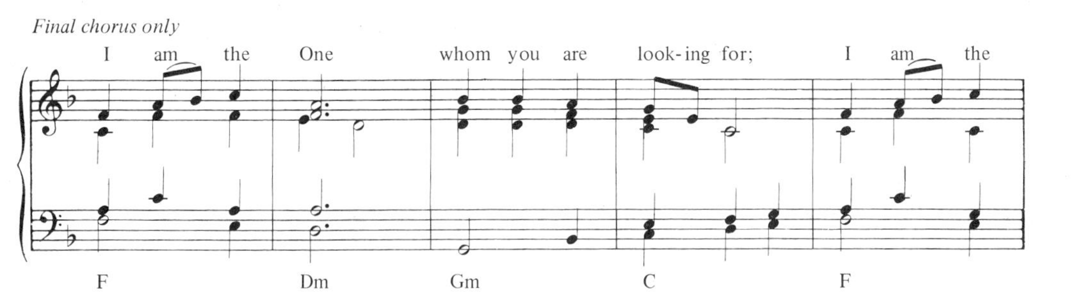

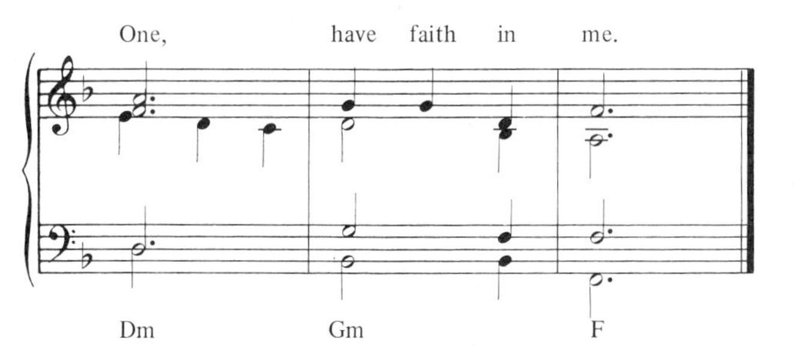

Words and Music: *Francesca Leftley,*
arranged by John Rombaut

WHO PUT THE COLOURS IN THE RAINBOW?

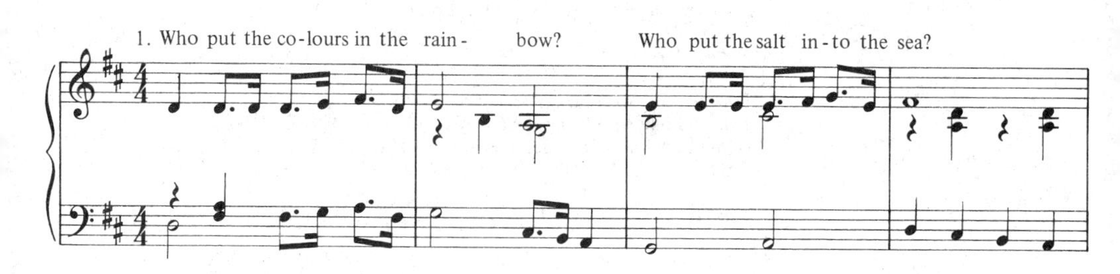

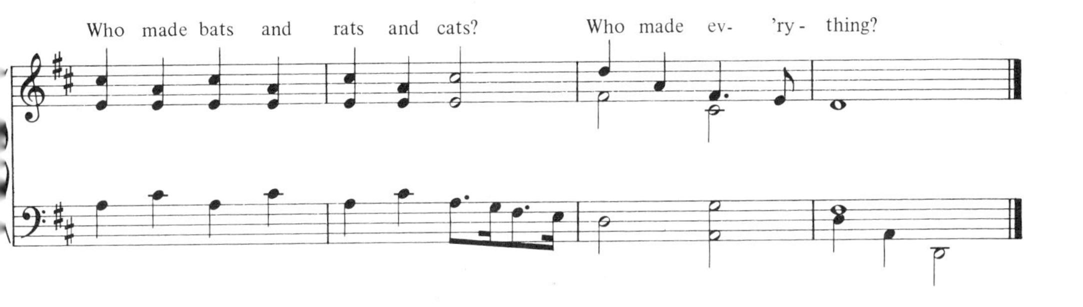

2. Who put the gold into the sunshine?
Who put the sparkle in the stars?
Who put the silver in the moonlight?
Who made Earth and Mars?
Who put the scent into the roses?
Who taught the honey bee to dance?
Who put the tree inside the acorn?
It surely can't be chance!
Who made seas and leaves and trees?
Who made snow and winds that blow?
Who made streams and rivers flow?
God made all of these!

Words and Music: Paul Booth

Words and Music: C. Austin Miles

Chorus
With- out see- ing you, we love you; with- out see- ing, we be-
C
Em7
A7

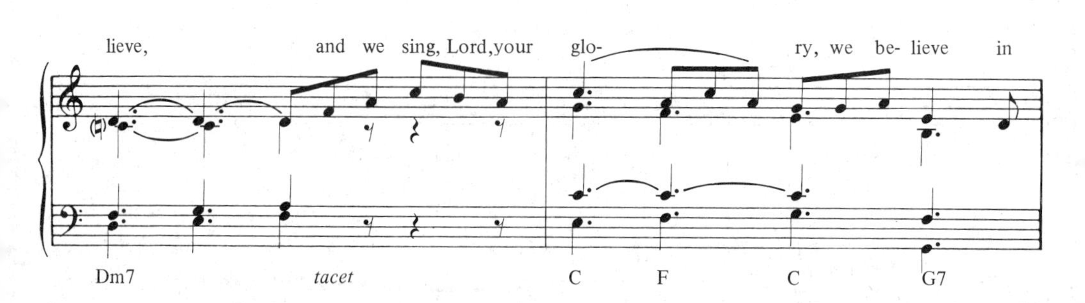
lieve, and we sing, Lord, your glo- ry, we be- lieve in
Dm7
tacet
C
F
C
G7

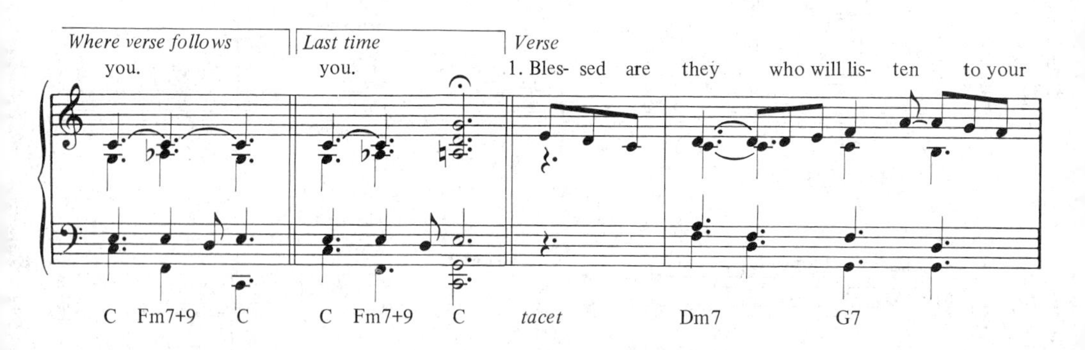
Where verse follows
Last time
Verse
you.
you.
1. Bles- sed are they who will lis- ten to your
C
Fm7+9
C
C
Fm7+9
C
tacet
Dm7
G7

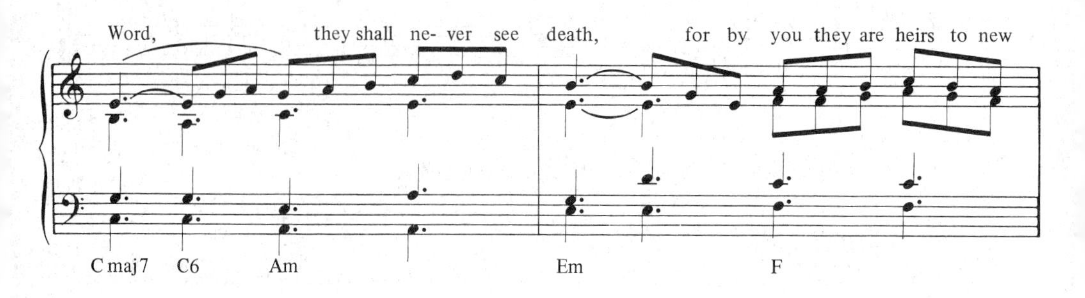
Word, they shall ne- ver see death, for by you they are heirs to new
C maj7
C6
Am
Em
F

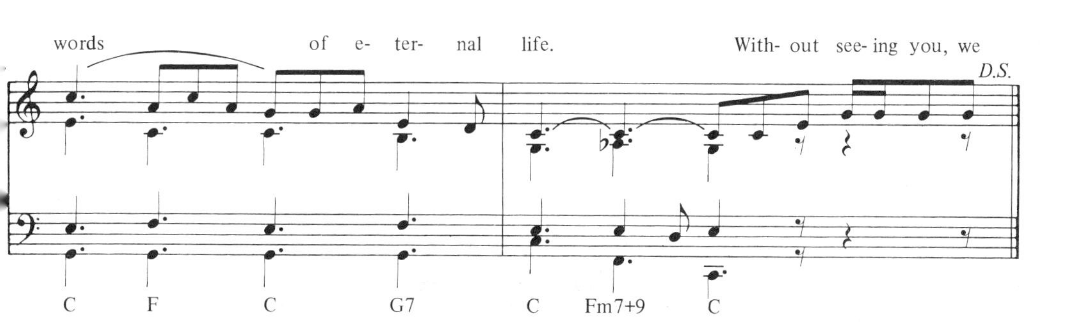

2. If we abide in the Spirit of the Word,
we find true life in you,
and your word of truth will make us free.
Lord, to whom shall we go?
You alone have the words of eternal life.

3. Lord, we believe you abide within our hearts.
Keep us safe in your love.
Give to us all the hope of your pow'r.
Lord, to whom shall we go?
You alone have the words of eternal life.

Words, based on Scripture, adapted from Lucien Deiss, and Music: Aniceto Nazareth,
arranged by John Rombaut

WITH YOU, O GOD (With you I am secure) 587

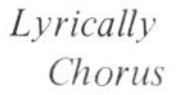

(♩ = 72)

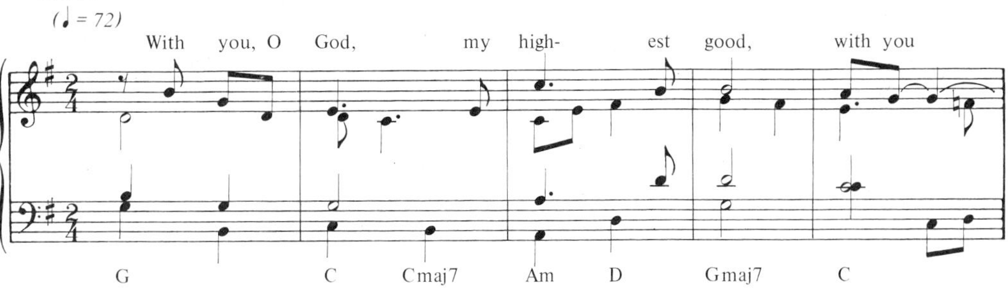

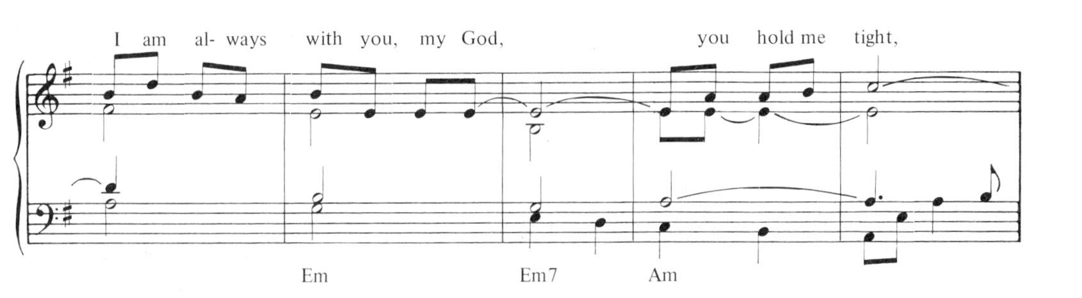

2. All things come to their fulfilment in you;
you lead me on in your good pleasure.

3. Heaven, what is that if you are not there?
And here on earth you are my joy.

4. And when life on earth has come to an end
I have a fu- ture with you, my God.

Words, based on Huub Oosterhuis' version of Psalm 73, and Music: Frances M. Kelly

WORSHIP, GLORY, PRAISE AND HONOUR (Creation's Hymn of Praise)

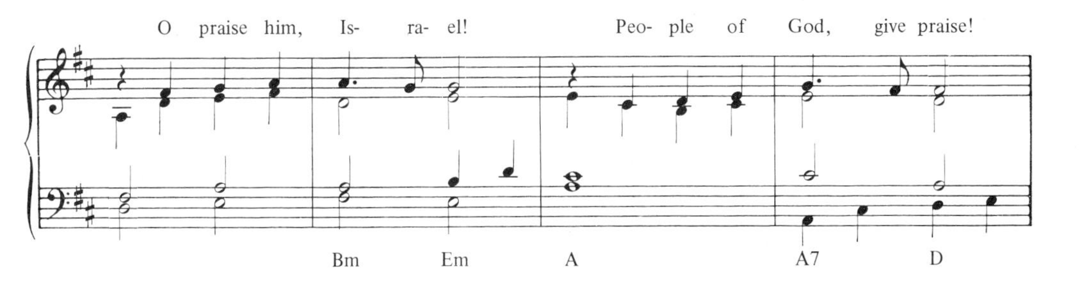

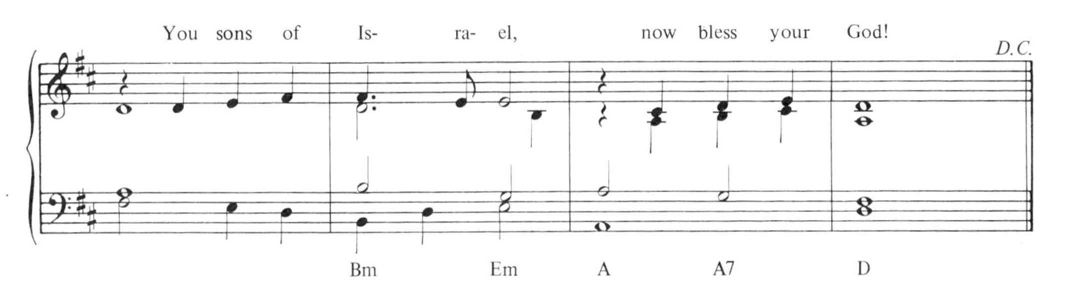

2. Mountains and hills, give praise!
Plants of the earth, give praise!
Darkness and light, give praise!
O bless his glorious name!
Fish of the sea, give praise!
Clouds of the sky, give praise!
Rivers and seas, give praise!
Now bless your God!

3. Birds of the sky, give praise!
Wild beasts and tame, give praise!
Works of the Lord, give praise!
O bless his glorious name!
Angels of God, give praise!
Priests of the Lord, give praise!
Children of God, give praise!
Now bless your God!

4. To God the Father, praise!
To Christ, his Son, give praise!
And Spirit Holy, praise!
We bless his glorious name!
May you be blest, O Lord!
All glory be to you!
Glory to God most high!
We bless our God!

Words, based on Psalm 148 and Music: Alfred Camilleri,
arranged by Frances M. Kelly

589

YE CHOIRS OF NEW JERUSALEM
('St Fulbert' C.M.)

[HARMONY]

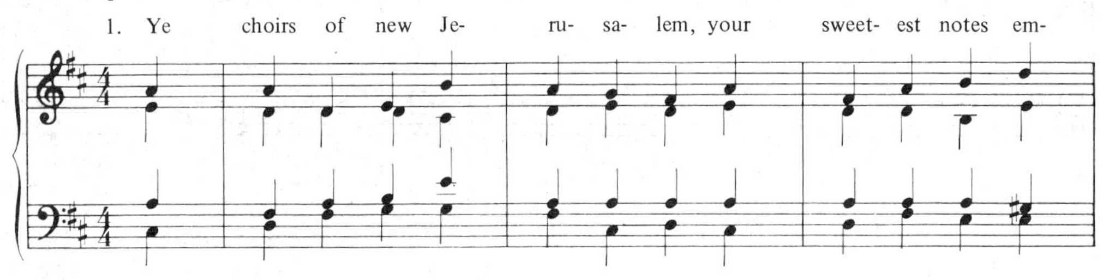

2. How Judah's Lion burst his chains,
and crushed the serpent's head;
and brought with him, from death's domain,
the long-imprisoned dead.

3. From hell's devouring jaws the prey
alone our leader bore;
his ransomed hosts pursue their way
where he hath gone before.

4. Triumphant in his glory now
his sceptre ruleth all:
earth, heaven, and hell before him bow
and at his footstool fall.

5. While joyful thus his praise we sing,
his mercy we implore,
into his palace bright to bring,
and keep us evermore.

6. All glory to the Father be,
all glory to the Son,
all glory, Holy Ghost, to thee,
while endless ages run.

Words: St Fulbert of Chartres (c. 1000),
translated by R. Campbell
Music: Henry J. Gauntlett (1805-76)

YE HOLY ANGELS BRIGHT

('Darwall's 148th' 66.66.44.44.)

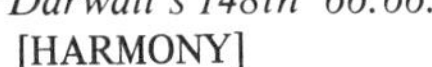

[HARMONY]

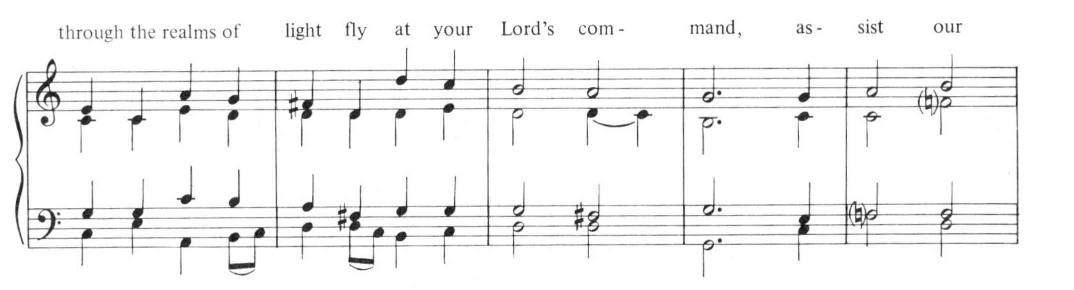

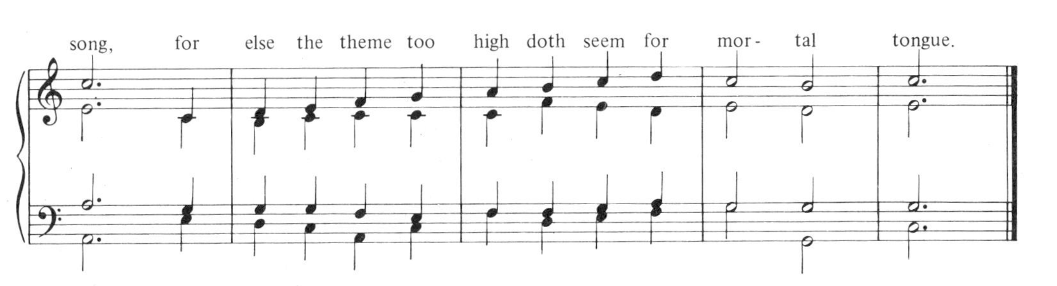

2. Ye blessèd souls at rest,
who ran this earthly race,
and now, from sin released,
behold the Saviour's face,
his praises sound,
as in his light
with sweet delight
ye do abound.

3. Ye saints, who toil below,
adore your heavenly King,
and onward as ye go
some joyful anthem sing;
take what he gives
and praise him still,
through good and ill,
who ever lives.

4. My soul, bear thou thy part,
triumph in God above,
and with a well-tuned heart
sing thou the songs of love;
let all thy days
till life shall end,
what'er he send,
be filled with praise.

Words: Richard Baxter (1615-91)
and John Hampden Gurney (1802-62)
Music: John Darwall (1731-89)

YE SERVANTS OF GOD
('Paderborn' 10 10.11 11.)

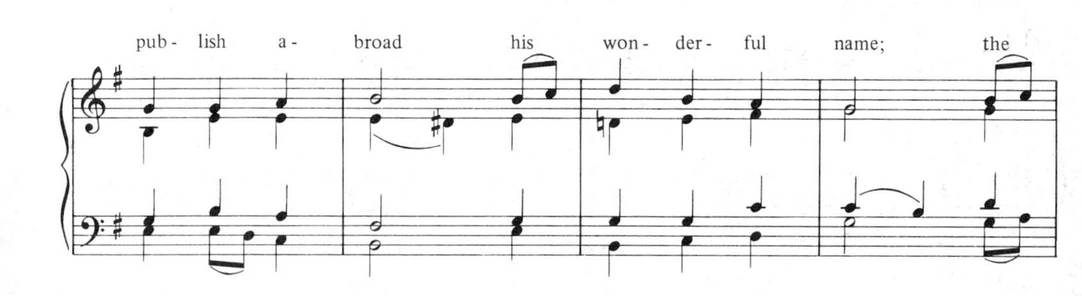

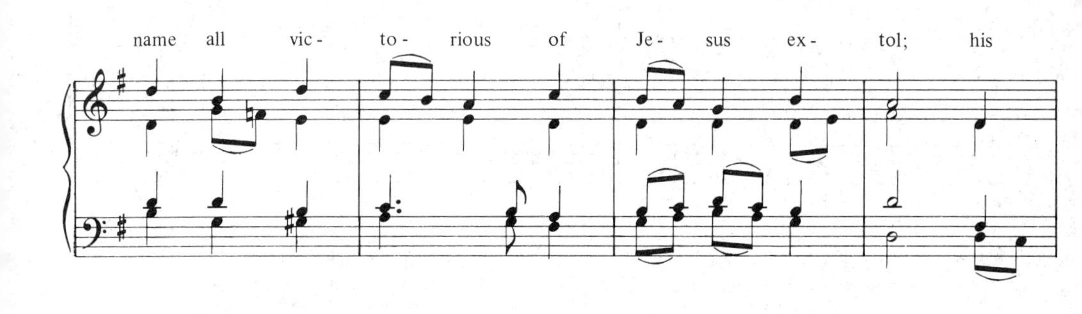

2. God ruleth on high, almighty to save;
and still he is nigh: his presence we have;
the great congregation his triumph shall sing,
ascribing salvation to Jesus our King.

3. Salvation to God who sits on the throne!
let all cry aloud, and honour the Son.
The praises of Jesus the angels proclaim,
fall down on their faces, and worship the Lamb.

4. Then let us adore, and give him his right:
all glory and power, all wisdom and might,
and honour and blessing, with angels above,
and thanks never-ceasing, and infinite love.

Words: Charles Wesley (1707-88)
Music: 'Paderborn Gesangbuch' (1765)

592

YE THAT KNOW THE LORD IS GRACIOUS

('Hyfrydol' 87.87.D.)

[HARMONY]

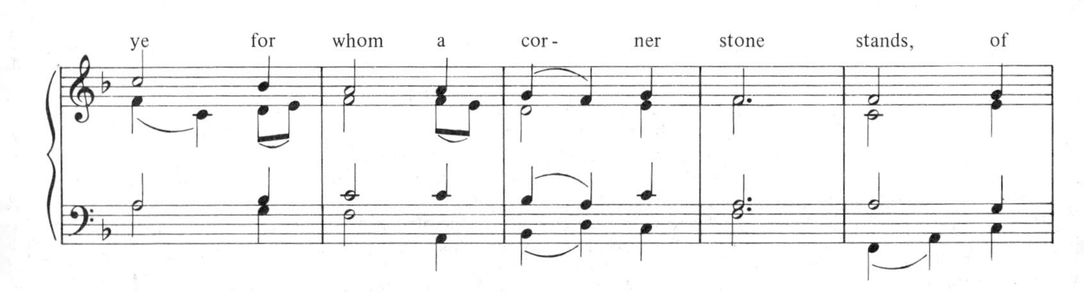

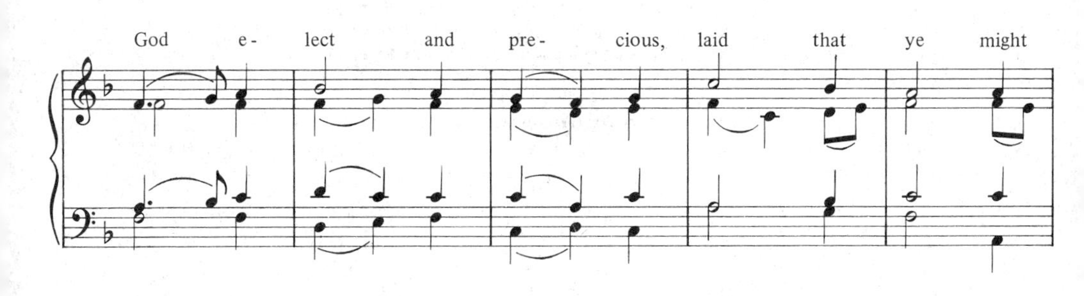

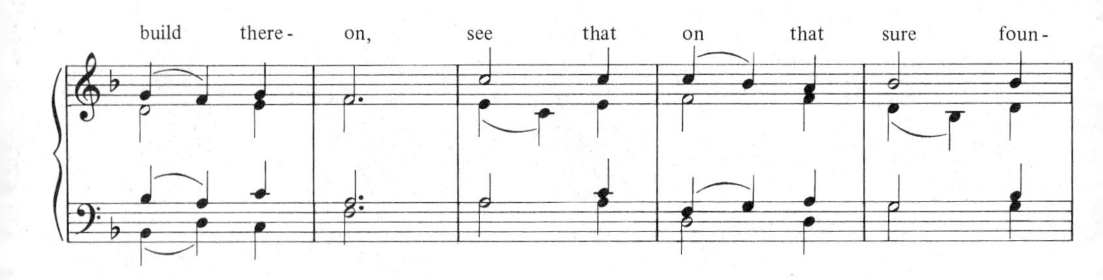

2. Living stones, by God appointed
each to his allotted place,
kings and priests, by God anointed,
shall ye not declare his grace?
Ye, a royal generation,
tell the tidings of your birth,
tidings of a new creation
to an old and weary earth.

3. Tell the praise of him who called you
out of darkness into light,
broke the fetters that enthralled you,
gave you freedom, peace and sight:
tell the tale of sins forgiven,
strength renewed and hope restored,
till the earth, in tune with heaven,
praise and magnify the Lord!

Words: Cyril A. Alington (1872-1955)
Music: Rowland H. Prichard (1811-87)

A different harmonisation of this tune may be found at Hymn 251

593

YE WHO OWN THE FAITH OF JESUS

('Daily, daily' 87.87.D.)

[HARMONY]

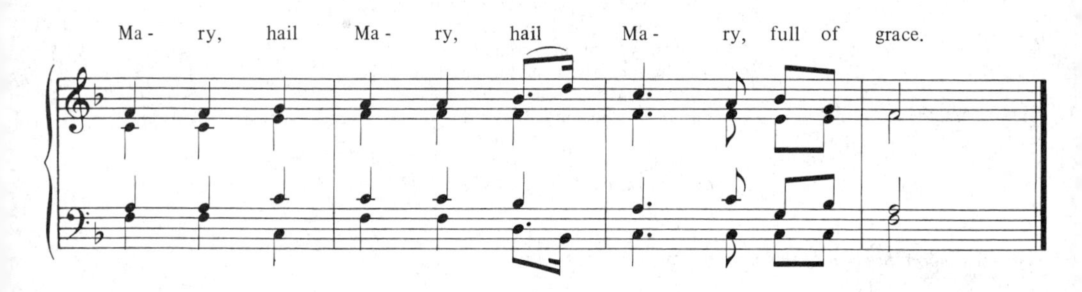

2. Blessed were the chosen people
out of whom the Lord did come,
blessed was the land of promise
fashioned for his earthly home;
but more blessed far the mother,
she who bore him in her womb.

3. Wherefore let all faithful people
tell the honour of her name,
let the church in her foreshadowed
part in her thanksgiving claim;
what Christ's mother sang in gladness,
let Christ's people sing the same.

4. May the mother's intercessions
on our homes a blessing win,
that the children all be prospered
strong and fair and pure within,
following our Lord's own footsteps,
firm in faith and free from sin.

5. For the sick and for the aged,
for our dear ones far away,
for the hearts that mourn in secret,
all who need our prayers today,
for the faithful gone before us,
may the Holy Virgin pray.

6. Praise, O Mary, praise the Father,
praise thy Saviour and thy Son,
praise the everlasting Spirit,
who hath made thee ark and throne.
O'er all creatures high exalted,
lowly praise the Three in One.

Words: V. S. S. Coles (1845-1929)
Music: From 'Paderborn Gesangbuch' (1765)

Introduction
1. You can't stop rain from fall- ing down, pre-
C
C7

vent the sun from shin- ing. You can't stop Spring from com- ing in, or
F
C7

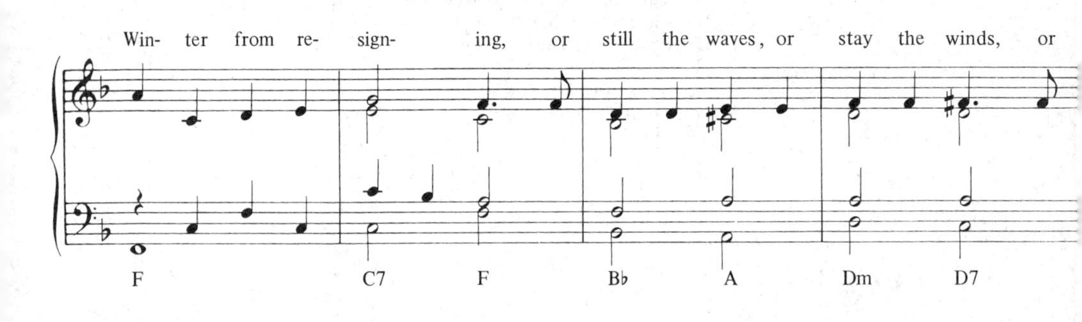
Win- ter from re- sign- ing, or still the waves, or stay the winds, or
F C7 F B♭ A Dm D7

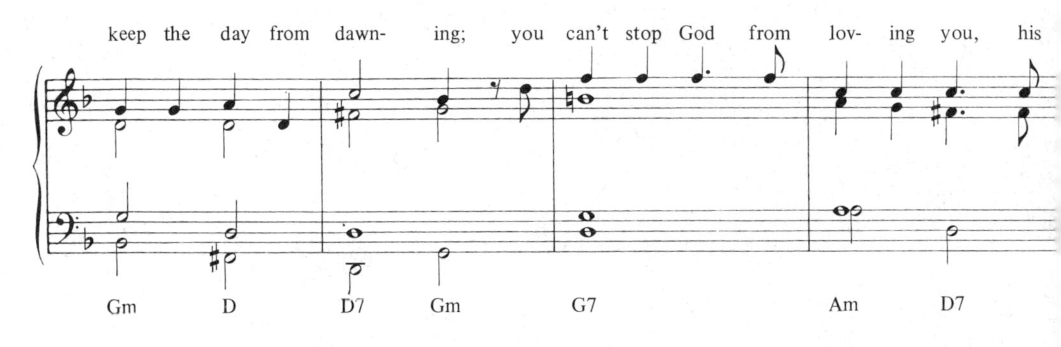
keep the day from dawn- ing; you can't stop God from lov- ing you, his
Gm D D7 Gm G7 Am D7

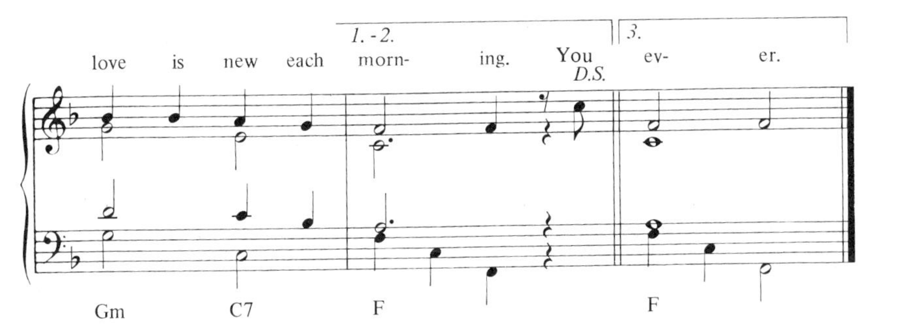

2. You can't stop ice from being cold,
you can't stop fire from burning,
or hold the tide that's going out,
delay its sure returning,
or halt the progress of the years,
the flight of fame and fashion;
you can't stop God from loving you,
his nature is compassion.

3. You can't stop God from loving you,
though you may disobey him,
you can't stop God from loving you,
however you betray him;
from love like this no pow'r on earth
the human heart can sever,
you can't stop God from loving you,
not God, not now, nor ever.

Words, based on Lamentations 3: 23: John Gowans
Music: John Larsson,
arranged by Frances M. Kelly

YOU SHALL GO OUT WITH JOY **(Trees of the field)**

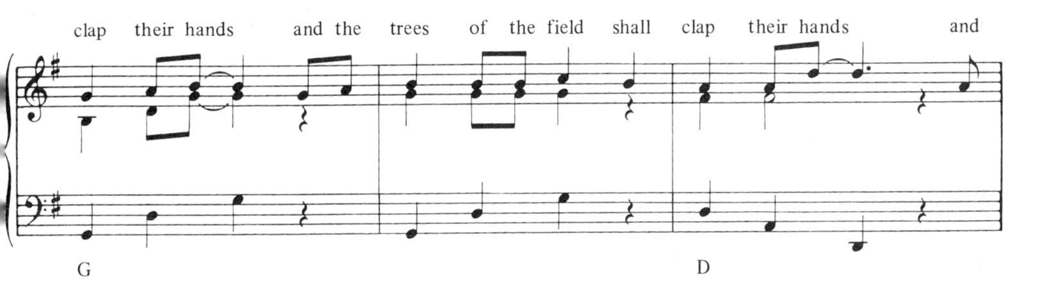

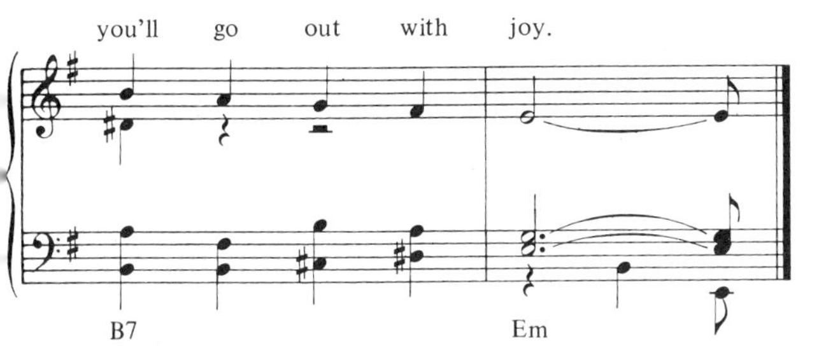

Words: S. Dauermann
Music: S. Dauermann, arranged by Roland Fudge

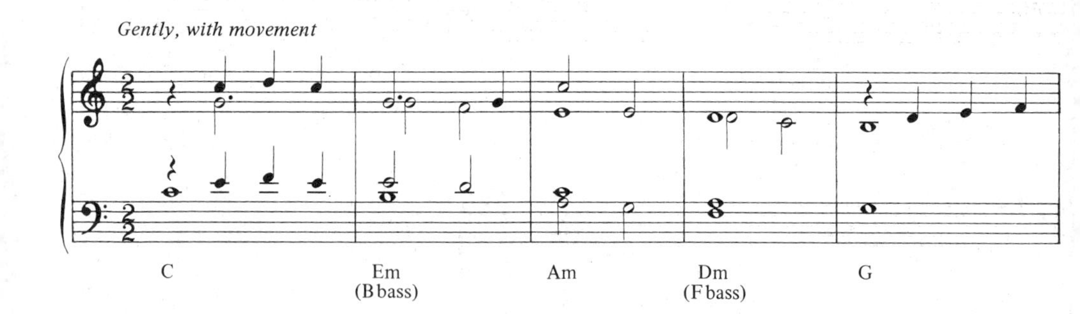
Gently, with movement
C
Em
(B bass)
Am
Dm
(F bass)
G

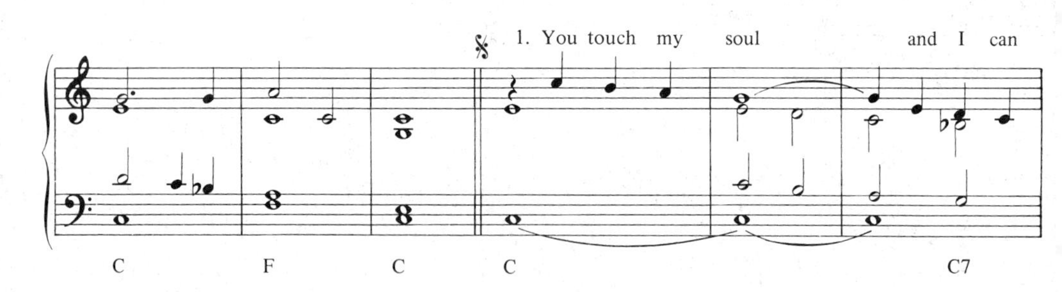
1. You touch my soul and I can
C
F
C
C
C7

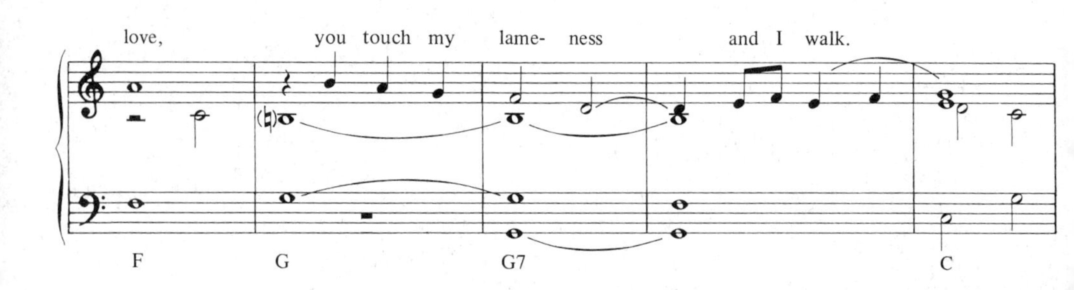
love, you touch my lame- ness and I walk.
F
G
G7
C

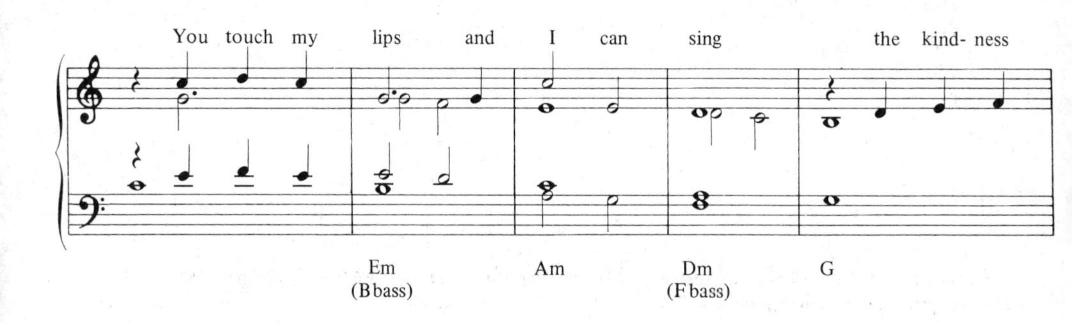
You touch my lips and I can sing the kind- ness
Em
(B bass)
Am
Dm
(F bass)
G

2. You touch my hands
   and I can bless,
   you touch my hardness,
   make it less.
   You touch my ears
   and I can hear
   the kindness of your love
   for me.

3. You touch my heart
   and I can feel,
   you touch my life and
   make it real.
   You touch my soul
   and I receive
   the Spirit that you give
   to me.

Words: Graham Jeffery
Music: Kevin Mayhew

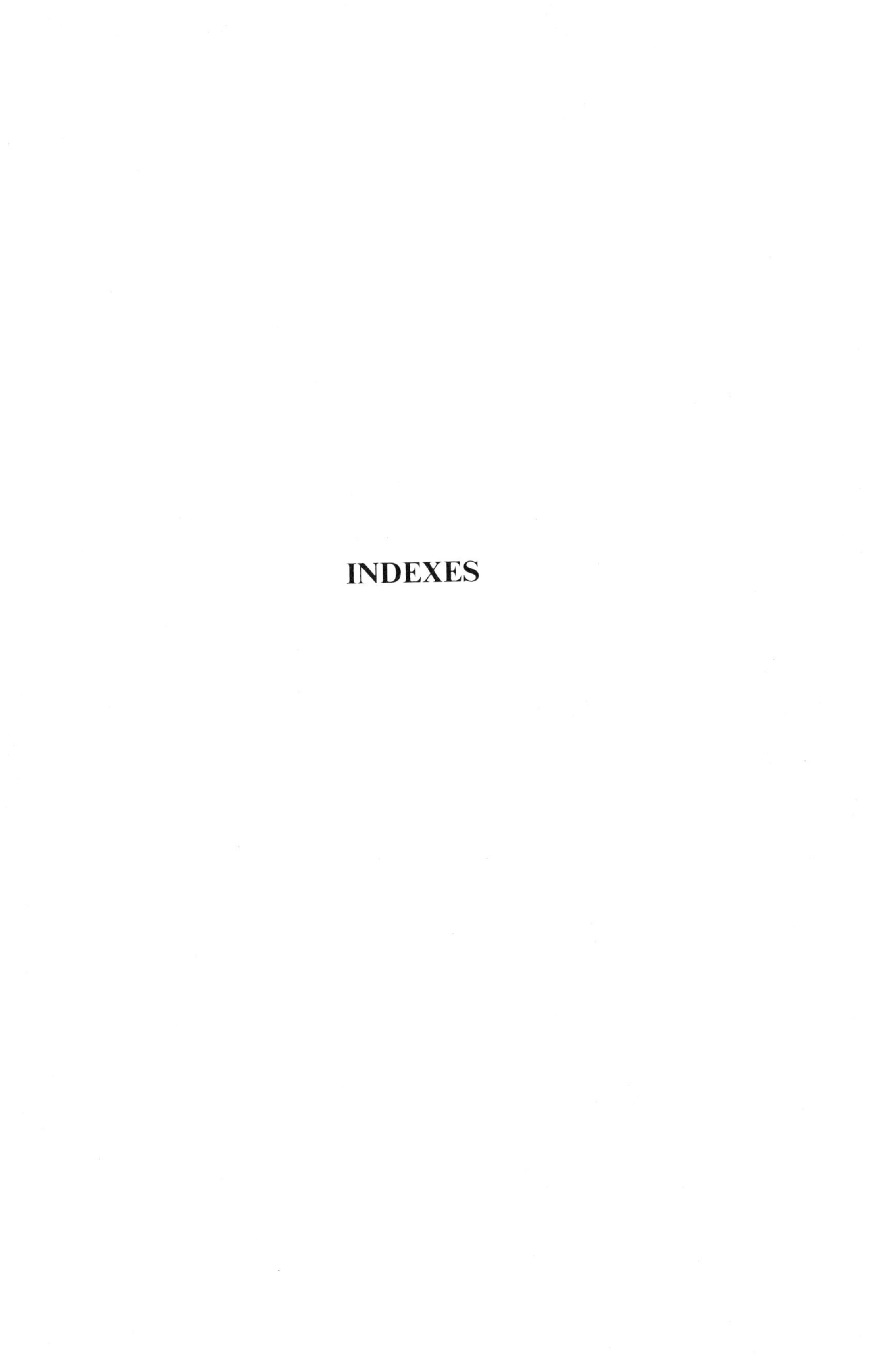

INDEXES

INDEX OF USES

MORNING

EVENING

HOLY COMMUNION

ENTRY

OFFERTORY

COMMUNION

DISMISSAL

THE SACRAMENTS

BAPTISM

CONFIRMATION

MARRIAGE

FUNERALS

ORDINATION

THE CHURCH'S YEAR

9th BEFORE CHRISTMAS

8th BEFORE CHRISTMAS

7th BEFORE CHRISTMAS

6th BEFORE CHRISTMAS

5th BEFORE CHRISTMAS

ADVENT SUNDAY

ADVENT 2

ADVENT 3

ADVENT 4

CHRISTMAS

SUNDAY AFTER CHRISTMAS DAY

CHRISTMAS 2

EPIPHANY

EPIPHANY 1

EPIPHANY 2

EPIPHANY 3

EPIPHANY 4

EPIPHANY 5

EPIPHANY 6

9th BEFORE EASTER

8th BEFORE EASTER

7th BEFORE EASTER

ASH WEDNESDAY

LENT 1

LENT 2

LENT 3

LENT 4

LENT 5

PALM SUNDAY

MAUNDY THURSDAY

GOOD FRIDAY

EASTER EVE

EASTER

EASTER 1

EASTER 2

Breaking of Bread

Good Shepherd

EASTER 3

EASTER 4

EASTER 5

ASCENSION

PENTECOST

TRINITY

PENTECOST 2

PENTECOST 3

PENTECOST 4

PENTECOST 5

PENTECOST 6

PENTECOST 7

PENTECOST 8

PENTECOST 9

PENTECOST 10

PENTECOST 11

PENTECOST 12

PENTECOST 13

PENTECOST 14

PENTECOST 15

PENTECOST 16

PENTECOST 17

PENTECOST 18

PENTECOST 19

PENTECOST 20

PENTECOST 21

PENTECOST 22

LAST SUNDAY AFTER PENTECOST

NAMING OF JESUS

CONVERSION OF PAUL

PRESENTATION OF CHRIST

ST. JOSEPH

ANNUNCIATION

VISITATION

ST. PETER

ST. THOMAS

ST. MARY MAGDALEN

TRANSFIGURATION

THE BLESSED VIRGIN MARY

ST. MICHAEL AND ALL ANGELS

ST. ANDREW

ST. STEPHEN

OTHER SPECIAL USES

SUITABLE FOR CHILDREN

CIVIC AND NATIONAL

METRICAL INDEX OF TUNES

ALPHABETICAL INDEX OF TUNES

COMPOSERS, ARRANGERS AND SOURCES OF MUSIC

Spirituals

AUTHORS, TRANSLATORS AND SOURCES OF WORDS

SCRIPTURAL INDEX

INDEX OF FIRST LINES AND TITLES

This index gives the first line of each hymn. If a hymn is known also by a title (e.g. In love for me) this is given as well, in italic and indented.